FUSED PYRIMIDINES
Part I: QUINAZOLINES

This is the twenty-fourth volume (Part I) in the series

THE CHEMISTRY OF HETEROCYCLIC COMPOUNDS

THE CHEMISTRY OF HETEROCYCLIC COMPOUNDS

A SERIES OF MONOGRAPHS

ARNOLD WEISSBERGER, *Editor*

FUSED PYRIMIDINES

Edited by
D. J. Brown

Part I

QUINAZOLINES

W. L. F. Armarego
Department of Medical Chemistry,
The John Curtin School of Medical Research,
The Australian National University, Canberra

With collaboration in part by
GEORGE H. HITCHINGS and GERTRUDE B. ELION
Wellcome Research Laboratories, Tuckahoe, N.Y.

1967
INTERSCIENCE PUBLISHERS
a division of John Wiley & Sons
New York - London - Sydney

First published 1967 by John Wiley & Sons, Ltd.

All Rights Reserved

Library of Congress Catalog Card Number 67-27306

MADE AND PRINTED IN GREAT BRITAIN BY
WILLIAM CLOWES AND SONS, LIMITED, LONDON AND BECCLES

The Chemistry of Heterocyclic Compounds

The Chemistry of heterocyclic compounds is one of the most complex branches of organic chemistry. It is equally interesting for its theoretical implications, for the diversity of its synthetic procedures, and for the physiological and industrial significance of heterocyclic compounds.

A field of such importance and intrinsic difficulty should be made as readily accessible as possible, and the lack of a modern detailed and comprehensive presentation of heterocyclic chemistry is therefore keenly felt. It is the intention of the present series to fill this gap by expert presentations of the various branches of heterocyclic chemistry. The subdivisions have been designed to cover the field in its entirety by monographs which reflect the importance and the interrelations of the various compounds and accommodate the specific interests of the authors.

ARNOLD WEISSBERGER

Research Laboratories
Eastman Kodak Company
Rochester, New York

Foreword to The Fused Pyrimidines

Originally it was intended to present all the fused pyrimidine systems in one volume of this series. Resurgence of interest in purines and quinazolines, the development of pteridine chemistry, and the wide exploration of a great many new fused systems embracing the pyrimidine ring, have made the task impossible.

The fused pyrimidines will now be covered in four parts, of which Dr. Armarego's *Quinazolines* is the first. Others, dealing with *Purines, Pteridines,* and *Miscellaneous Fused Pyrimidines* respectively, are in active preparation. Eventually, this bracket of volumes will bring to the series the expertise of six enthusiastic authors with wide and diverse experience in the field.

It is a privilege to assist Dr. Weissberger and the authors in organizing this project and in maintaining a measure of uniformity and balance in its parts.

D. J. BROWN

The Australian National University
Canberra, Australia

Preface

The presence of the benzene ring in quinazoline modifies the chemistry of the pyrimidine ring in a number of ways. The modifications are so diverse that a description of the chemistry of quinazolines merits a separate monograph. Quinazolines were originally prepared for academic interest, and a considerable variety were made because many synthetic approaches were possible. In the last two decades several naturally occurring quinazolines were discovered, and many quinazolines were synthesized for biological testing. The antimalarial activity of the alkaloid febrifugine, for example, led to the preparation of a large number of different quinazoline derivatives. The neurotoxic activity of the recently discovered tetrodotoxin, a perhydroiminoquinazoline, will undoubtedly stimulate research in this previously unknown class of quinazolines.

This monograph is intended as a critical review of quinazoline chemistry as well as a compilation of the melting points of quinazolines. Condensed quinazolines are excluded, with the exception of the thiazoloquinazolines (thiopegenes) because the chemistry of these is closely related to that of the thioquinazolines. The literature is covered completely from the preparation of the first quinazoline in 1869 to the middle of 1965, and incompletely until mid-1966.

I am grateful to the many people who helped me during the months of writing. Drs. G. H. Hitchings and G. B. Elion loaned me a preliminary account of the chemistry of quinazolines based essentially on synthetic methods. Dr. D. J. Brown has unselfishly guided and inspired me, particularly through the most difficult sections, and to him I owe a great debt of gratitude. Professor Adrien Albert carefully read several chapters and made constructive criticisms. The following were of considerable help in discussions, in making available to me information prior to publication, and in allowing me to reproduce some of their published data: Professors R. D. Brown, A. R. Katritzky, K. S. Narang, Drs. G. B. Barlin, T. J. Batterham, M. E. C. Biffin, J. W. Bunting, Gordon Catterall, M. L. Heffernan, D. D. Perrin, N. K. Ralhan, J. I. C. Smith, and Mr. H. Yamamoto. My wife (who is also an organic chemist) assisted in making the tables, compiling the index, and in reading the whole manuscript. Finally, grateful thanks are due to Miss P. Cope who carried out the tedious task of typing the manuscript and to Mrs. D. McLeod for library facilities.

W. L. F. ARMAREGO

The Australian National University, Canberra
June 1966

Contents

I. **Introduction** 1
  1. History 1
  2. Nomenclature 2
  3. The Dual Character of Quinazolines. 3
  4. General Summary of Quinazoline Chemistry 4
    A. Syntheses 4
      a. Primary Syntheses 4
      b. Secondary Syntheses 6
    B. The Heightened Reactivity of 2- and 4-Alkyl Groups . . 6
    C. Addition and Substitution Reactions, and Nucleophilic Meta-
      thesis 6
    D. N-Oxides 7
    E. Tautomerism 7
    F. Oxidation and Reduction 8
    G. Rearrangements 8
    H. Biological Activity in Quinazolines 9
  5. Tables 9
  6. References 10

II. **Quinazoline** 11
  1. Synthesis of Quinazoline 11
  2. Physical Properties 13
    A. Theoretical Aspects 14
    B. Spectra 14
      a. Ultraviolet Spectra 14
      b. Phosphorescence Spectra 15
      c. Infrared Spectra 15
      d. Proton Magnetic Resonance Spectra 16
      e. Mass Spectra 18
    C. Covalent Hydration 19
      a. Covalent Hydration in Quinazoline. 19
      b. Effect of Substituents in the Pyrimidine Ring on Covalent
        Hydration 27
        (i) Effect of substituents in position 4 . . . 27
        (ii) Effect of substituents in position 2 28

    c. Effect of Substituents in the Benzene Ring on Covalent
       Hydration   29
    D. Polarography   32
  3. Chemical Reactivity of Quinazoline   33
    A. Hydrolysis, Oxidation, and Reduction   33
    B. Electrophilic and Nucleophilic Substitution, and Alkylation . 34
    C. Addition Reactions   35
  4. References   36

III. *C*-Alkyl- and *C*-Arylquinazolines   39
  1. Methods of Preparation   39
    A. Bischler's Synthesis   39
    B. Oxidation of 3,4-Dihydroquinazolines   41
    C. Decarboxylation of Acids   42
    D. From N′-Toluene-p-sulphonylhydrazino Derivatives . .   42
    E. From Imidoyl Chlorides and Nitriles   42
    F. From Aryl Diazonium Salts and Nitriles   43
    G. From 4-Chloro or 4-Cyanoquinazolines and Grignard Reagents   44
    H. From Chloro- or Cyanoquinazolines and Substances with an
       Active Methylene Group   45
    I. Reidel's Synthesis   48
    J. Miscellaneous   48
  2. Properties   49
    A. Physical Properties   49
    B. Chemical Properties   50
      a. The Heightened Reactivity of 2- and 4-Methyl Groups .   50
      b. Oxidation and Reduction   54
      c. Electrophilic Substitution.   55
      d. Alkylation   56
      e. Reactivity of the Substituted Carbon Atoms Attached to
         $C_{(2)}$ and $C_{(4)}$ 58
  3. Tables   60
  4. References   67

IV. Oxoquinazolines and 5-, 6-, 7-, and 8-Hydroxyquinazolines .   69
  1. 2-Oxoquinazolines   69
    A. Preparation   69
    B. Properties   72
  2. 3,4- and 1,4-Dihydro-4-oxoquinazolines   74
    A. Preparation of 3,4-Dihydro-4-oxoquinazolines . . .   74
      a. Niementowski's Synthesis   74
      b. Cyclization of o-Amidobenzamides   78
      c. From o-Aminobenzonitriles   80
      d. From Anthranilic Acid Derivatives and Nitriles . .   81
      e. From 3,1,4-Benzoxazones (Acylanthranils) and Amines .   83
      f. From Isatoic Anhydrides   87
      g. From Anthranilic Acids or Esters and Imidoyl Chlorides .   88
      h. From Anthranilic Acids or Esters and Imidates . .   91
      i. Grimmel, Guenther, and Morgan's Synthesis . . .   93
      j. Sen and Ray's Synthesis   94

k. Oxidation of Reduced Quinazolines 96
l. From Indoles and Related Compounds 96
m. Miscellaneous 98
B. Preparation of 1,4-Dihydro-4-oxoquinazolines . . . 99
C. Properties of 4-Oxoquinazolines 102
   a. Physical Properties 102
   b. Chemical Properties 104
      (i) Alkylation and acylation 104
      (ii) The heightened reactivity of the 2-methyl group . 107
      (iii) Oxidation, reduction, and hydrolysis . . . 109
      (iv) Electrophilic substitution 111
      (v) Substitution reactions involving ring opening . . 112
      (vi) Reaction with Grignard reagents 113
      (vii) Mannich reactions 114
      (viii) Miscellaneous 115
3. 2,4-Dioxoquinazolines 116
  A. Preparation of 1,2,3,4-Tetrahydro-2,4-dioxoquinazolines . 116
   a. From Anthranilic Acid (or Derivatives) and Cyano Compounds 116
   b. From Anthranilic Acid (or Derivatives) and Ureas . . 119
   c. Cyclization of o-Ureidobenzoic Acids and Derivatives . 120
   d. From o-Ethoxycarbonylaminobenzoic Esters or Amides . 122
   e. From Phthalic Acid Derivatives 123
   f. From Isatins 125
   g. From Anilines and Related Compounds 125
   h. Miscellaneous 127
  B. Properties of 1,2,3,4-Tetrahydro-2,4-dioxoquinazolines . . 128
   a. Physical Properties 128
   b. Chemical Properties 130
4. Quinazolines with Hydroxy Groups in the Benzene Ring . . 133
  A. Preparation 133
  B. Properties 134
5. Tables 136
6. References 206

V. Halogenoquinazolines and Quinazolinyl Ethers . . . 219
1. Halogenoquinazolines 219
  A. Preparation of 2-Halogenoquinazolines 219
  B. Preparation of 4-Halogenoquinazolines 222
  C. Preparation of 2,4-Dihalogenoquinazolines 225
  D. Preparation of Quinazolines Substituted with Halogen in the Benzene Ring or in the Side Chain 226
  E. Properties of Halogenoquinazolines 227
   a. Physical Properties 227
   b. Chemical Properties 227
      (i) Reactivity of halogens in the side chain or in the benzene ring 227
      (ii) Reactivity of the 2- and 4-halogen atoms . . 227
      (iii) Metathesis 230

(iv) Reduction 231
(v) Dehalogenation 233
(vi) Miscellaneous 234
2. Quinazolinyl Ethers 235
A. Preparation of 2-Quinazolinyl Ethers 235
B. Preparation of 4-Quinazolinyl Ethers 236
  a. Alkylation of 3,4-Dihydro-4-oxoquinazolines . . . 236
  b. Nucleophilic Displacement at Position 4 237
  c. From o-Aminobenzonitrile Derivatives 238
  d. Miscellaneous 239
C. Preparation of 2,4-Quinazolinyl Diethers 239
D. Preparation of Quinazolines with Alkoxy Groups in the Benzene
  Ring 240
E. Properties of Quinazolinyl Ethers 241
  a. Physical Properties 241
  b. Chemical Properties 241
    (i) Hydrolysis 241
    (ii) Alkylation 242
    (iii) Metathesis 243
    (iv) Rearrangements 243
3. Tables 245
4. References 264

VI. Thio- and Oxothioquinazolines 270
1. 2-Thioquinazolines 270
A. 1,2-Dihydro-2-thioquinazolines 270
B. 3-Substituted 2,3-Dihydro- and 1,2,3,4-Tetrahydro- 2-Thio-
  quinazolines 271
2. 4-Thioquinazolines 277
A. 1,4- and 3,4-Dihydro-4-thioquinazolines 277
B. 4-Alkylthio- and Arylthioquinazolines 280
C. 1,2,3,4-Tetrahydro-4-thioquinazolines 281
D. Properties of 4-Thioquinazolines 282
3. 2,4-Dithioquinazolines 284
4. 1,2,3,4-Tetrahydro-4-oxo-2-thioquinazolines 285
5. Quinazolines Substituted with Thio Groups in the Benzene Ring . 287
6. Thiazoloquinazolines (Thiopegenes) 288
7. Tables 292
8. References 317

VII. Aminoquinazolines (including Aminooxo- and Aminothioquinazolines) 322
1. 2- and 4-Amino-, and 2,4-Diaminoquinazolines . . . 322
A. Preparation of 2-Aminoquinazolines and 2-Amino-3,4-dihydro-
  4-oxoquinazolines 322
  a. By Nucleophilic Displacement with Amines . . . 322
  b. Syntheses involving Guanidines, Cyanamides, Ureas, and
    Related Compounds 324
  c. Miscellaneous 327

  B. Preparation of 4-Aminoquinazolines, 4-Amino-1,2-dihydro-2-
     oxo- and 4-Amino-1,2-dihydro-2-thioquinazolines   .   . 327
     a. By Nucleophilic Displacement with Amines   .   .   . 327
     b. From o-Aminobenzonitriles 328
     c. Miscellaneous   330
  C. Preparation of 2,4-Diaminoquinazolines   330
     a. By Nucleophilic Displacement with Amines   .   .   . 330
     b. From Guanidines 331
     c. From o-Aminobenzonitriles   332
  D. Properties of 2- and 4-Amino-, and 2,4-Diaminoquinazolines.   332
  E. Reactions of 2- and 4-Amino-, and 2,4-Diaminoquinazolines.   333
     a. Hydrolysis   333
     b. Acylation, Methylation, and Chlorination   .   .   . 334
     c. Transamination and Molecular Rearrangements   .   . 335
     d. Reactions of Hydrazinoquinazolines   336
  2. 3-Aminooxo- and 3-Aminothioquinazolines   337
  A. Preparation of 3-Amino-3,4-dihydro-4-oxo- (and 4-thio-) and
     3-Amino-1,2,3,4-tetrahydro-2,4-dioxoquinazolines   .   . 337
     a. Syntheses from Anthranilic Acid Derivatives .   .   . 337
     b. From 3,1,4-Benzoxazones and Related Thio Compounds .   338
     c. From 3,4-Dihydro-4-oxoquinazolines and Hydrazines   . 339
     d. Miscellaneous   339
  B. Reactions of 3-Aminooxoquinazolines   340
  3. Aminoquinazolines with Amino Groups in the Benzene Ring   . 340
  A. Preparation of 5-,6-,7-, and 8-Amino- and Aminooxoquina-
     zolines   340
  B. Properties of 5-,6-,7-, and 8-Amino- and Aminooxoquina-
     zolines   341
  4. Tables   342
  5. References 384

VIII. The Reduced Quinazolines 391
  1. Preparation of 1,2-Dihydroquinazolines 391
  A. By the Reaction of o-Aminobenzaldehyde with Amines and
     Formaldehyde   391
  B. From Anthranilamides and Aldehydes, Ketones, or Related
     Compounds   392
  C. By Reduction of 3,4-Dihydro-4-oxoquinazolines and Related
     Compounds   393
  2. Preparation of 1,4-Dihydroquinazolines 394
  3. Preparation of 2,3-Dihydroquinazolines 395
  4. Preparation of 3,4-Dihydroquinazolines 395
  A. From o-Aminobenzylamines or o-Aminobenzyl Alcohols   . 395
  B. From Anilines and Formaldehyde   396
  C. By Nucleophilic Addition or Displacement Reactions .   . 398
  D. By Reduction of Quinazolines 398
  E. From o-Aminobenzyl Chloride and Nitriles.   .   .   . 399
  F. Miscellaneous 400
  5. Preparation of 1,2,3,4-Tetrahydroquinazolines   .   .   . 400

A. From Anilines and Formaldehyde 400
B. From o-Aminobenzylamines and Aldehydes . . . 401
C. By Reduction of 3,4-Dihydroquinazolines (including their
   4-Oxo Derivatives) 401
   a. Chemical Reductions 401
   b. Catalytic and Electrolytic Reductions 402
6. Physical and Chemical Properties of 1,2-, 1,4-, and 3,4-Dihydro-,
   and 1,2,3,4-Tetrahydroquinazolines 402
7. Tröger's Base and Related Compounds 406
8. 5,6,7,8-Tetrahydroquinazolines 409
   A. Preparation of 5,6,7,8-Tetrahydroquinazolines . . . 409
      a. From Cyclohexanones 409
      b. From 2-Ethoxycarbonylcyclohexanones. . . . 410
      c. From 2-Formyl-(or Acetyl-)cyclohexanones . . . 410
      d. From Cyclohexenes 411
   B. Properties of 5,6,7,8-Tetrahydroquinazolines . . . 412
9. Miscellaneous Reduced Quinazolines 413
10. Tables 415
11. References 440

IX. Quinazoline N-oxides (including 1- and 3-Hydroxyquinazolines) . 446
1. Quinazoline-1-oxides 446
2. Quinazoline-3-oxides 450
   A. Preparation and Structure of Quinazoline-3-oxides . . 450
   B. Physical Properties of Quinazoline-3-oxides 452
   C. Reactions of Quinazoline-3-oxides 455
3. 1,2-Dihydroquinazoline-3-oxides 456
4. 1- and 3-Hydroxyoxoquinazolines 457
5. Tables 461
6. References 471

X. Quinazoline Carboxylic and Sulphonic Acids, and Related Compounds 473
1. Cyano- and Carbamoylquinazolines 473
2. Carboxyquinazolines 475
   A. 2-Carboxyquinazolines 475
   B. 4-Carboxyquinazolines 478
   C. Quinazolines with Carboxy Groups in the Benzene Ring . 479
3. Formyl- and Acetylquinazolines 480
4. Sulphoquinazolines and Related Compounds 480
5. Tables 481
6. References 488

XI. Naturally Occurring and Biologically Active Quinazolines . 490
1. Naturally Occurring Quinazolines 490
   A. Arborine, Glycosmicine, Glycorine, and Glycosminine . . 490
   B. Vasicine and Related Alkaloids 492
   C. Febrifugine and Isofebrifugine 496
   D. Evodiamine, Rutaecarpine, Hortiamine, and Rhetsinine . 500
   E. Tetrodotoxin 503
2. Biologically Active Synthetic Quinazolines 508
3. References 513

Subject Index 519

Tables

Introduction 9
II.1. Quinazoline and 3-Alkyl Derivatives 13
II.2. Electronic Effects and Hydration in 2-Substituted Quinazoline Cations 29
II.3. Ionization and Covalent Hydration of Quinazolines in Water at 20° 30
II.4. Ionization Constants of Substituted Quinazolines in Water at 20° 31

III.1. 2-Alkyl- and Aryl- (including Heteroaryl-) quinazolines . . 60
III.2. 4-Alkyl- and Aryl- (including Heteroaryl-) quinazolines . . 61
III.3. 2,4-Disubstituted Alkyl- and Arylquinazolines 63
III.4. Alkylquinazolines Substituted in the Benzene Ring . . . 64
III.5. Alkyl- and Arylquinazolines Substituted in Both Rings . . 65
III.6. Miscellaneous Alkyl- and Arylquinazolines (including Quinazolinium Salts) 66

IV.1. 1,2-Dihydro-2-oxoquinazolines 136
IV.2. 1,4-Dihydro-4-oxoquinazolines 137
IV.3. 2-Alkyl-3,4-dihydro-4-oxoquinazolines 139
IV.4. 2-Aryl-(and Heteroaryl-)3,4-dihydro-4-oxoquinazolines . . 142
IV.5. 3,4-Dihydro-4-oxoquinazolines with Alkoxy, Aryloxy, or Chloro Substituents in Position 2 143
IV.6. 3-Alkyl- (other than Oxygen-containing Alkyl) 3,4-dihydro-4-oxoquinazolines 144
IV.7. 3-Alkyl- (with Oxygen-containing Side Chain other than Acetonyl) 3,4-dihydro-4-oxoquinazolines 146
IV.8. 3-Acetonyl-3,4-dihydro-4-oxoquinazolines 149
IV.9. 3-Aryl-3,4-dihydro-4-oxoquinazolines 152
IV.10. 3,4-Dihydro-4-oxoquinazolines with a Heterocyclic Group in Position 3 153
IV.11. 3,4-Dihydro-4-oxoquinazoline and Derivatives with Substituents in the Benzene Ring 153
IV.12. 3-Alkyl- (other than Oxygen-containing Alkyl) 3,4-dihydro-2-methyl-4-oxoquinazolines 156

IV.13. 3-Alkyl- (with Oxygen-containing Side Chain) 3,4-dihydro-2-methyl-4-oxoquinazolines 157

IV.14. 3-Aryl-3,4-dihydro-2-methyl-4-oxoquinazolines . . . 158

IV.15. 3,4-Dihydro-2-methyl-4-oxoquinazolines with a Heterocyclic Group in Position 3 163

IV.16. 3-Substituted 2-Ethyl-3,4-dihydro-4-oxoquinazolines. . . 164

IV.17. 3-Substituted 3,4-Dihydro-4-oxo-2-propyl- (and isopropyl-) quinazolines 165

IV.18. 3-Substituted 2-Ethenyl-3,4-dihydro-4-oxoquinazolines . . 166

IV.19. 2-Alkyl- (other than Methyl, Ethyl, Propyl, or Ethenyl) 3-Substituted 3,4-Dihydro-4-oxoquinazolines 168

IV.20. 3-Substituted 2-Aryl-3,4-dihydro-4-oxoquinazolines . . . 170

IV.21. 3-Aryl-3,4-dihydro-4-oxoquinazolines with a Heterocyclic Group in Position 2 171

IV.22. 3-Substituted 3,4-Dihydro-4-oxoquinazolines with Halogeno, Alkoxy, or Aryloxy Substituents in Position 2 172

IV.23. 3,4-Dihydro-2-methyl-4-oxoquinazolines Substituted in the Benzene Ring 173

IV.24. 2-Alkyl- (other than Methyl) 3,4-dihydro-4-oxoquinazolines with Substituents in the Benzene Ring 174

IV.25. 2-Aryl-3,4-dihydro-4-oxoquinazolines with Substituents in the Benzene Ring 176

IV.26. 3,4-Dihydro-3-methyl-4-oxoquinazolines with Substituents in the Benzene Ring 177

IV.27. 3-Alkyl- (other than Methyl) 3,4-dihydro-4-oxoquinazolines with Substituents in the Benzene Ring 177

IV.28. 3-Aryl-3,4-dihydro-4-oxoquinazolines with Substituents in the Benzene Ring 180

IV.29. 3-Alkyl-3,4-dihydro-2-methyl-4-oxoquinazolines with Substituents in the Benzene Ring 180

IV.30. 3-Aryl- (and Heteroaryl-) 3,4-dihydro-2-methyl-4-oxoquinazolines with Substituents in the Benzene Ring 182

IV.31. 2-Ethyl-3,4-dihydro-4-oxoquinazolines with Substituents in the Benzene Ring and in Position 3 186

IV.32. 2-Alkyl- (other than Methyl or Ethyl) 3,4-dihydro-4-oxoquinazolines with Substituents in the Benzene Ring and in Position 3 . 188

IV.33. 3,4-Dihydro-4-oxo-2-phenylquinazolines with Substituents in the Benzene Ring and in Position 3 189

IV.34. 3,4-Dihydro-3-(3'-(3-hydroxy-2-piperidyl)-2'-oxo)propyl-4-oxoquinazolines with Substituents in the Benzene Ring . . . 190

IV.35. 3-(3'-(1-Ethoxycarbonyl-3-methoxy-2-piperidyl)-2'-oxo)propyl-4-oxoquinazolines with Substituents in the Benzene Ring . 192

IV.36. 3-(3'-(3-Methoxy-2-piperidyl)-2'-oxo)propyl-4-oxoquinazolines with Substituents in the Benzene Ring 193

IV.37. Miscellaneous 3,4-Dihydro-4-oxo-3-(2'-oxo-3'-(2-piperidyl))propylquinazolines 195

IV.38. 3,4-Dihydro-4-oxo-3-(2'-oxo-3'-(pyrrolidin-2-yl))propylquinazolines 196

IV.39. Quinazolines with Hydroxy Groups in the Benzene Ring . . 197

IV.40. 3,4-Dihydro-4-oxoquinazolines with Hydroxy Groups in the
        Benzene Ring   198
IV.41. 1-Substituted (and Unsubstituted) 1,2,3,4-Tetrahydro-2,4-dioxo-
        quinazolines   199
IV.42. 3-Substituted 1,2,3,4-Tetrahydro-2,4-dioxoquinazolines . . 199
IV.43. 1,2,3,4-Tetrahydro-2,4-dioxoquinazolines with Substituents in the
        Benzene Ring   202
IV.44. 3-Substituted (and Unsubstituted) 1,2,3,4-Tetrahydro-2,4-dioxo-
        quinazolines with Halogens in the Benzene Ring . . . 202
IV.45. 3-Substituted (and Unsubstituted) 1,2,3,4-Tetrahydro-2,4-dioxo-
        quinazolines with Hydroxy or Alkoxy Groups in the Benzene
        Ring   204
IV.46. 1,3-Disubstituted 1,2,3,4-Tetrahydro-2,4-dioxoquinazolines. . 204
IV.47. 3- and 1,3-Substituted 1,2,3,4-Tetrahydro-2,4-dioxoquinazolines
        with Substituents in the Benzene Ring 206

V.1.   Replacement of Chlorine in 2- and 4-Chloroquinazolines by Piperi-
        dine in Ethanol   228
V.2.   Quinazolines Prepared from 4-N'-Toluene-p-sulphonylhydrazino-
        quinazoline Derivatives in Ethylene Glycol–Water (7:3) . . 235
V.3.   2-Chloroquinazolines 245
V.4.   4-Chloroquinazolines 247
V.5.   2,4-Dichloroquinazolines 248
V.6.   Chloroquinazolines with Chloro Substituents in the Benzene Ring 249
V.7.   Chloroquinazolines with Chloro Substituents in Both Rings . 251
V.8.   Miscellaneous Halogenoquinazolines 252
V.9.   2-Quinazolinyl Ethers 253
V.10.   4-Quinazolinyl Ethers 254
V.11.   4-Quinazolinyl Ethers with a Substituent in Position 2 . . 255
V.12.   4-Quinazolinyl Ethers with Substituents in the Benzene Ring . 258
V.13.   4-Quinazolinyl Ethers with Substituents in Both Rings . . 258
V.14.   2,4-Quinazolinyl Diethers 259
V.15.   Quinazolinyl Ethers with Ether Groups in the Benzene Ring . 260
V.16.   Chloroquinazolinyl Ethers with Chloro and Ether Groups in the
        Pyrimidine Ring   263
V.17.   Chloroquinazolinyl Ethers with Chloro and Ether Groups in
        Separate Rings   263

VI.1.   1,2- and 2,3-Dihydro-2-thioquinazolines, and 2-Alkylthio- and
        2-Arylthioquinazolines   292
VI.2.   1,2,3,4-Tetrahydro-2-thioquinazolines 293
VI.3.   4-Substituted 1,2,3,4-Tetrahydro-2-thioquinazolines . . . 294
VI.4.   3,4-Dihydro-4-thioquinazolines without Substituents on $N_{(3)}$. 296
VI.5.   3,4-Dihydro-4-thioquinazolines Substituted on $N_{(3)}$ . . 297
VI.6.   4-Alkylthio- and 4-Arylthioquinazolines 298
VI.7.   4-Arylsulphonylquinazolines and 1,2- and 1,4-Dihydro-4-thio-
        quinazolines.   301
VI.8.   2,4-Dithioquinazolines 302
VI.9.   2-Alkylthio-3,4-dihydro-4-oxoquinazolines 303

VI.10. 3-Substituted 2-Alkylthio-3,4-dihydro-4-oxoquinazolines   .   .   304
VI.11. 3-Substituted (and 3-Unsubstituted) 1,2,3,4-Tetrahydro-4-oxo-
        2-thioquinazolines   306
VI.12. 1- and 1,3-Substituted 1,2,3,4-Tetrahydro-4-oxo-2-thioquinazo-
        lines   308
VI.13. 3-Substituted (and 3-Unsubstituted) 1,2,3,4-Tetrahydro-4-oxo-
        2-thioquinazolines with Substituents in the Benzene Ring .   .   309
VI.14. 3,4-Dihydro-4-oxoquinazolines with Thio or Sulphonyl Groups in
        the Benzene Ring.   310
VI.15. Aminothioquinazolines   310
VI.16. Thiazolo(2,3-b)quinazolin-5-ones   311
VI.17. 2,3-Dihydrothiazolo(2,3-b)quinazolin-5-ones   314
VI.18. Thiazolo(3,2-a)quinazolin-5-ones   315
VI.19. 3-H-1,3-Thiazino(3,2-a)quinazolin-6-ones   316
VI.20. 11-H-Thiazolo(3,2-c)quinazolines   317

VII.1. 2-Amino- and 2-Substituted-aminoquinazolines   .   .   .   342
VII.2. 2-Guanidinoquinazolines   343
VII.3. 4-Aminoquinazolines   344
VII.4. 4-Substituted-aminoquinazolines   345
VII.5. 4-Substituted-aminoquinazolines with a Substituent in Position 2   348
VII.6. 4-Substituted-aminoquinazolines with Substituents in the Benzene
        Ring   351
VII.7. 4-Substituted-aminoquinazolines with Substituents in Both
        Rings.   353
VII.8. 2,4-Diaminoquinazolines with Substituents in the Benzene Ring.   354
VII.9. 2,4-Bis Substituted-aminoquinazolines   355
VII.10. 4-Substituted-amino-2-p-chloroanilinoquinazolines   .   .   359
VII.11. 2,4-Diamino- (and Substituted-amino-) quinazolines with Substi-
        tuents in the Benzene Ring   361
VII.12. Quinazolines with an Amino or Substituted-amino Group in the
        Benzene Ring   362
VII.13. 4-Alkylamino-2-p-chloroanilinoquinazolines with Substituents (in-
        cluding Amino Groups) in the Benzene Ring   362
VII.14. 4-Amino- (and Substituted-amino-) quinazolines with an Amino
        (and Substituted-amino) Group in the Benzene Ring   .   .   363
VII.15. 2-Amino (and Substituted-amino)-3,4-dihydro-4-oxoquinazolines
        (including its 3-Amino Derivatives).   364
VII.16. 4-Amino (and Substituted-amino)-1,2-dihydro-2-oxoquinazolines.   366
VII.17. 4-Amino (and Substituted-amino)-1,2-dihydro-2-thioquinazolines   367
VII.18. 3,4-Dihydro-4-oxoquinazolines with Amino (and Substituted-
        amino) Groups in Positions 5 or 6   367
VII.19. 3,4-Dihydro-4-oxoquinazolines with Amino (and Substituted-
        amino) Groups in Positions 7 or 8   369
VII.20. 3-Amino-3,4-dihydro-4-oxoquinazoline and 2-Substituted Deriva-
        tives   371
VII.21. 3-Substituted-amino-3,4-dihydro-4-oxoquinazolines with a Sub-
        stituent in Position 2   372
VII.22. 3-Amino (and Substituted-amino)-3,4-dihydro-4-oxoquinazolines
        Substituted (and Unsubstituted) in the Benzene Ring   .   .   374

VII.23. 3-Amino-3,4-dihydro-4-oxoquinazolines with Substituents in
Position 2 and in the Benzene Ring 375
VII.24. 3-Substituted-amino-3,4-dihydro-4-oxoquinazolines with Substi-
tuents in Position 2 and in the Benzene Ring 377
VII.25. 3-Amino (and Substituted-amino)-3,4-dihydro-4-oxoquinazolines
Substituted (and Unsubstituted) in Position 2, with Amino (and
Substituted-amino) Groups in the Benzene Ring . . . 380
VII.26. 3-Amino (and Substituted-amino)-3,4-dihydro-4-thioquinazolines 381
VII.27. 3-Amino (and Substituted-amino)-1,2,3,4-tetrahydro-2,4-dioxo-
quinazolines 382
VII.28. 1,2,3,4-Tetrahydro-2,4-dioxoquinazolines with Amino (and Sub-
stituted-amino) Groups in the Benzene Ring 383
VII.29. Hydrazinoquinazolines with Hydrazino Groups in the Pyrimidine
Ring 383

VIII.1. Ionization Constants of Reduced Quinazolines in Water . . 404
VIII.2. 1,2-Dihydroquinazolines 415
VIII.3. 1,2,3,4-Tetrahydro-4-oxoquinazolines 415
VIII.4. 1,4- and 2,3-Dihydroquinazolines 418
VIII.5. 3,4-Dihydroquinazolines Unsubstituted in Positions 3 and 4 . 419
VIII.6. 3-Substituted 3,4-Dihydroquinazolines 420
VIII.7. 4-Substituted 3,4-Dihydroquinazolines 423
VIII.8. 1,2,3,4-Tetrahydro-2-oxo-(and thio-)quinazolines . . . 425
VIII.9. 1,2,3,4-Tetrahydroquinazolines (Unsubstituted in Position 2) . 427
VIII.10. 2-Substituted 1,2,3,4-Tetrahydroquinazolines 428
VIII.11. 5,11-Methano-6H,12H-dibenzo[b,f][1,5]diazocines . . . 430
VIII.12. 5,6,7,8-Tetrahydroquinazolines 430
VIII.13. 3,4,5,6,7,8-Hexahydro-4-oxoquinazolines 434
VIII.14. 1,2-Disubstituted 1,4,5,6,7,8-Hexahydro-4-oxo- (and thio-)quina-
zolines 437
VIII.15. 1,2,3,4,5,6,7,8-Octahydro-2,4-dioxoquinazolines . . . 438
VIII.16. 1,2,3,4,5,6,7,8-Octahydro-2,4-dithio- (and oxothio-)quinazolines 439
VIII.17. Miscellaneous Reduced Quinazolines 440

IX.1. Ionization Constants of Quinazoline-3-oxides (H$_2$O, 20°) . . 454
IX.2. Quinazoline-1-oxides 461
IX.3. Quinazoline-3-oxides 462
IX.4. 1,2-Dihydro-4-methylquinazoline-3-oxides 465
IX.5. 1-Hydroxy- and 3-Oxo- 1,2-Dihydro-2-oxoquinazolines . . 466
IX.6. 3,4-Dihydro-4-oxoquinazoline-1-oxides 466
IX.7. 3,4-Dihydro-3-hydroxy-4-oxoquinazolines 467
IX.8. 3,4-Dihydro-3-hydroxy-4-thioquinazolines 468
IX.9. 3-Alkoxy- and 3-Aryloxy- 3,4-Dihydro-4-oxoquinazolines . . 469
IX.10. N-Hydroxy-1,2,3,4-tetrahydro-2,4-dioxoquinazolines and Deriva-
tives 470

X.1. Cyanoquinazolines 481
X.2. Carbamoyl- and Hydrazinocarbonylquinazolines . . . 481
X.3. Quinazolines with Carboxy (and Ester) Groups in Positions 2 and 4 482
X.4. 3,4-Dihydro-4-oxo- and 1,2-Dihydro-2-oxoquinazolines with a
Carboxy (or Ester) Group in the Pyrimidine Ring . . . 483

X.5.   3,4-Dihydro-4-oxoquinazolines with a Carboxy (or Ester) Group
       in the Benzene Ring   484
X.6.   1,2,3,4-Tetrahydro-2,4-dioxoquinazolines with a Carboxy (or
       Related) Group in the Benzene Ring   485
X.7.   Quinazolines with Formyl or Acyl Substituents.   .   .   .   486
X.8.   3,4-Dihydro-4-oxoquinazolines with a Sulpho (or Related) Group
       in the Benzene Ring   486
X.9.   Unsubstituted Nitroquinazolines and 3,4-Dihydro-4-oxoquinazo-
       lines with an Arsono Group in the Benzene Ring   .   .   .   487

CHAPTER I

Introduction

1. History

In 1869 Griess[1] prepared the first quinazoline derivative, 2-cyano-3,4-dihydro-4-oxoquinazoline, by the reaction of cyanogen with anthranilic acid. Griess apparently recognized the bicyclic nature of the product, which he called bicyanoamidobenzoyl and used this name until 1885[2] when the structure 1 was known with some certainty.

Weddige[3,4] carried out systematic quinazoline syntheses following the observation that the formyl and acetyl derivatives of anthranilamide lost water on heating. He correctly interpreted this as a cyclization reaction and was the first to realize the possibility of tautomerism in the oxoquinazolines. The preparation of the parent quinazoline came many years later when Bischler and Lang[5] obtained it by decarboxylation of the 2-carboxy derivative. A more satisfactory synthesis of quinazoline was subsequently devised by Gabriel[6] who studied its properties and those of its derivatives in greater detail. A large number and variety of quinazolines were synthesized in an intensive research programme by Bogert and his collaborators at Columbia University, U.S.A. The earlier part of this research was reviewed in 1910.[7] The published papers on quinazoline chemistry grew steadily until about 1939 when the annual output until about 1945 was constant. After the second world war the number of papers rose rapidly for a few years, then was steady until about 1959, and has been increasing rapidly since then.

The discovery in 1956,[8] that quinazoline exists mainly as a hydrated molecule in aqueous acid and the confirmation of the structure of the hydrated cation in 1961,[9] has thrown much light on the understanding of the properties and reactions of quinazolines. A knowledge of the effects of substituents on the hydration pattern in substituted quinazolines is very useful in devising new experiments and in understanding already known properties. The chemistry of quinazolines was

1

reviewed by Williamson[10] in 1957, then by Landquist[11] in 1959, and was brought up to date by Armarego[12] in 1963.

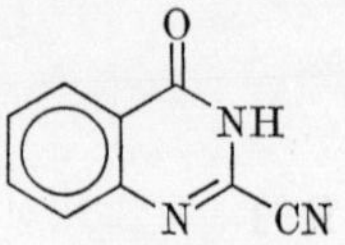

(1)

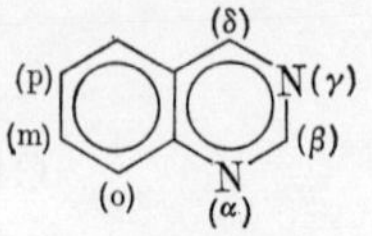

(2)

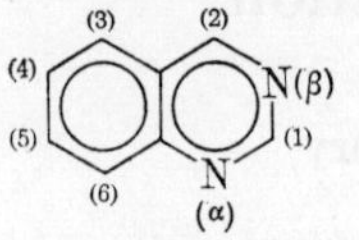

(3)

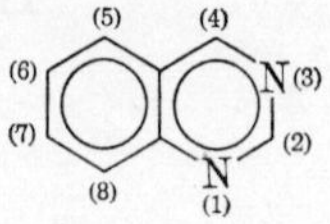

(4)

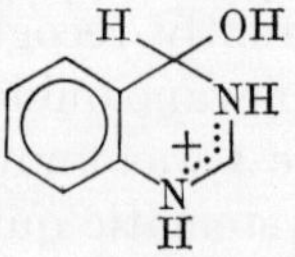

(5)

2. Nomenclature

Quinazoline has also been called phenmiazine, benzyleneamidine, benzo-1,3-diazine, 5,6-benzopyrimidine, and 1,3-diazanaphthalene. The term phenmiazine was used by Widman[13] and later by Bischler,[5] and the positions in the pyrimidine ring were designated by α, β, γ, and δ (**2**). A second system of numbering is shown in **3**. The name quinazoline (German: chinazoline), which is now universally adopted, was first proposed by Weddige[3] because he observed that his compounds were isomeric with the then known cinnoline and quinoxaline. It probably arose from the fact that it was an aza derivative of quinoline, hence quinazoline. The numbering shown in **4** was suggested by Paal and Busch[14] and is the one in current use.[15] The above names and numbering must be remembered particularly when reading through the earlier literature.

The nomenclature used in this volume is essentially, though not entirely, in accordance with the *Handbook for Chemical Society Authors*[16] published by the Chemical Society of London in 1960. The nomenclature rules used are known as the I.U.P.A.C. 1957 rules. The substitutive naming system is adopted because in this way it is much easier to find a particular compound from the index and the tables; e.g.

2-ethoxycarbonylquinazoline and not ethyl 2-quinazolinylcarboxylate. The names of radicals given in the handbook are used, with the exception of ureylene for the radical RNHCONH—, which is here referred to as an N'-substituted ureido radical. Radicals which are not listed, e.g. thioureido, were made up by analogy, or the respective literature naming was adopted. In polysubstituted quinazolines the substituents are written alphabetically irrespective of the position of substitution, e.g. 4-amino-2-chloroquinazoline and not 2-chloro-4-aminoquinazoline. For branched alkyl groups the following order is used: butyl, ethyl, isobutyl, methyl, neopentyl, pentyl, s-butyl, t-butyl, although this is not universally accepted. Bisethylamino and dimethyl are listed alphabetically under E and M, respectively, if the substituents are directly attached to the quinazoline ring system, but not if they are part of a substituent, e.g. 4-dimethylamino is listed under D. These points must be borne in mind particularly when using the tables (see Sect. 5).

The naming of oxo- and thioquinazolines is confusing, as it is indeed with most heterocyclic compounds with oxo (hydroxy) or thio (thiol) groups α or γ to the heterocyclic nitrogen atom. Throughout this work the 2- and 4-hydroxy-, and 2,4-dihydroxyquinazolines are named after their most likely tautomeric forms which require the dihydrooxo nomenclature after the related parent (hypothetical or not) hydro compound. Thus 4-hydroxyquinazolines are always referred to as 3,4-dihydro-4-oxoquinazolines. This becomes even more confusing when classifying reduced quinazolines where part of the molecule is reduced and the other part is 'derived' (at least by name) from a reduced system; e.g. 3,4,5,6-tetrahydro-4-oxoquinazoline is a 5,6-dihydro compound. This system of nomenclature, however, is used for convenience and to avoid ambiguity. The names 'quinazolinone' and 'quinazolinthione' are avoided deliberately. Details of the nomenclature used in these compounds are given at the beginning of the relevant chapters (see Chs. IV, VI, and VIII).

3. The Dual Character of Quinazolines

Quinazolines can be divided into two main groups according to their characteristic properties. The first group includes all the quinazolines in which the two rings are fully aromatic. These do not behave entirely as pyrimidines. The benzene ring has a profound effect on the properties of the pyrimidine ring: it delocalizes the π electrons of the 3,4-double bond making its reactivity like that of an isolated double

bond. As a consequence of this, quinazoline is very reactive towards
nucleophiles which readily add across the 3,4-double bond (Ch. II,
Sect. 3.C.). The cation in water has the structure 5,[9,17] which makes it a
cyclic carbinolamine. The energy required to form the hydrated cation
is such that the electronic effects of substituents in position 2[18] and in
the benzene ring[19] have a direct influence on the extent of hydration,
and consequently the reactivity of the 3,4-double bond (Ch. II, Sect.
2.C.). The quinazoline-3-oxides behave in a similar way (Ch. IX,
Sect. 2.C.). The high polarization of the 3,4-double bond also shows up
in the relative reactivity of substituents in positions 2 and 4. The
hydrolysis of 4-substituted quinazolines, e.g. chloro and alkoxy (Ch. V,
Sects. 1.E.b.(ii) and 2.E.b.(i)), amino (Ch. VII, Sect. 1.E.a.), and
α,α-diethoxycarbonylmethyl (Ch. III, Sect. 2.B.e.), to 3,4-dihydro-4-
oxoquinazoline is thus more clearly understood.

The second group includes the quinazolines which lack the full
complement of six π electrons in either the pyrimidine or the benzene
ring. These compounds can be divided into the quinazolines with
tautomeric groups in the pyrimidine ring, and the reduced quinazolines.
The derivatives in this group show the characteristic reactions of
pyrimidines and the following are a few examples to show the similarity.
2- and 4-Hydroxyquinazoline exist largely in the oxo form, they can be
converted to chloroquinazolines (Ch. V, Sect. 1.) and are alkylated
(Ch. IV, Sect. 2.C.b.(i)) in the usual way. Rearrangements of the
Dimroth type, which were studied in detail in the pyrimidine series,[20]
are also known in aminooxo- and aminothioquinazolines (Ch. VII,
Sect. 1.E.c.). 5,6,7,8-Tetrahydroquinazolines are indeed 4,5-tetra-
methylenepyrimidines (Ch. VIII, Sect. 8.), and the dihydro- and
1,2,3,4-tetrahydroquinazolines have reactivities of the type observed
in reduced pyrimidines,[21] although the fused benzene ring confers on
them slightly greater stability, and certainly makes them more easy to
isolate.

4. General Summary of Quinazoline Chemistry

A. Syntheses

The preparation of quinazolines can be divided into primary and
secondary syntheses.

a. Primary Syntheses

In the primary syntheses use is made of the intact carbocyclic ring
and the quinazoline system is built up in many ways; e.g. 6, 7, 8, 9, 10.
11, and 12. The primary syntheses described in this work are not

classified according to this system but these seven types of ring closure can be easily recognized.

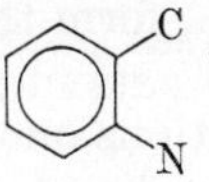

(6) 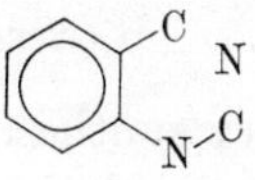   (7)

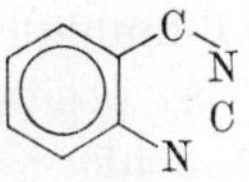

(8) 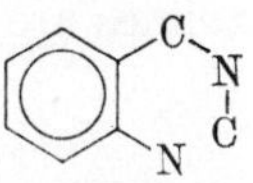   (9)

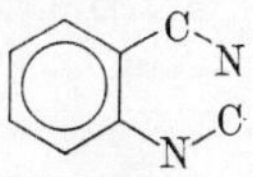

(10) 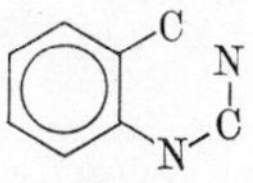   (11)

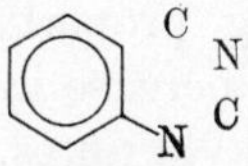

(12)

The following are only a few examples for these types of ring closures. The first, **6**, is exemplified by Niementowski's synthesis in which *o*-aminobenzoic acids (or related compounds) yield 3,4-dihydro-4-oxoquinazolines with amides (Ch. IV, Sect. 2.A.a.). Bischler's synthesis is of the type **7** in which quinazolines are formed by reacting *o*-amido-benzaldehydes (or related compounds) with ammonia (Ch. III, Sect. 1.A.). The type **8** is disguised in several ways which include the formation of 1,2,3,4-tetrahydroquinazolines from *o*-aminobenzylamines and aldehydes (Ch. VIII, Sect. 5.B.) and the preparation of quinazoline-3-oxides from *o*-aminobenzaldehyde or *o*-aminophenyl ketone oximes and ethyl orthoformate (Ch. IX, Sect. 2.A.) among others. Reductive cyclization of bisamido-*o*-nitrobenzaldehydes (Riedel's synthesis, Ch. III, Sect. 1.I.), and *o*-amidomethylnitrobenzenes (Ch. VIII, Sect. 4.A.) are examples of the type **9**. The fifth type **10** is also commonly used, and the cyclization of *o*-amidobenzonitriles with alkaline hydrogen peroxide (Ch. IV, Sect. 2.A.c.) and *o*-amidoacetophenoneoximes by mineral acids (Ch. IX, Sect. 2.A.) to give, respectively, 3,4-dihydro-4-oxoquinazolines and quinazoline-3-oxides, are typical examples. The preparation of 1,2,3,4-tetrahydro-2-oxoquinazolines from *o*-ureido-benzyl alcohols (Ch. VIII, Sect. 4.A.) and 3,4-dihydroquinazolines from anilines and formaldehyde (Ch. VIII, Sect. 4.B.), are examples of type **11** and **12**, respectively.

b. *Secondary Syntheses*

In the secondary syntheses transformations on the intact skeleton **13** are made. Thus oxidation, reduction, metathesis, addition, and substitution reactions (also reactions involving side chains) which are performed on quinazolines are among the more important examples.

(13)

B. The Heightened Reactivity of 2- and 4-Alkyl Groups

The electron-withdrawing property of the pyrimidine ring in quinazoline is reflected in an increase in the acidity of protons on the α-carbon atoms of 2- and 4-alkyl groups. Many examples are known in which the 2-methyl group (and to a smaller extent the 4-methyl group) react in much the same way as 'active methylene' groups adjacent to a strong electron-withdrawing group, e.g. carbonyl. For example, condensation products are formed by reaction with aldehydes and nucleophiles, e.g. $^-CHRCO_2R$, and they undergo Mannich reactions. The alkyl groups are not only reactive in alkylquinazolines in which the two rings of the quinazoline nucleus are aromatic (Ch. III, Sect. 2.B.a.), but also in 2-alkyl-3,4-dihydro-4-oxoquinazolines (Ch. IV, Sect. 2.C.b.(ii)); and the reactivity is enhanced by quaternization of the ring nitrogen atoms.

C. Addition and Substitution Reactions, and Nucleophilic Metathesis

Addition of nucleophilic reagents takes place readily across the 3,4-double bond of quinazolines in which the two rings are fully aromatic, and the nucleophile bonds with $C_{(4)}$. Hence substituents on $C_{(4)}$ can easily hinder these reactions (Ch. II, Sect. 3.C.). Quinazoline-3-oxides behave similarly (Ch. IX, Sect. 2.C.). Quinazoline is a π-electron deficient system,[22] hence electrophilic substitution occurs with difficulty. Quinazoline (Ch. II, Sect. 3.B.), 3,4-dihydro-4-oxo- (Ch. IV, Sect. 2.C.b.(iv)), and 1,2,3,4-tetrahydro-2,4-dioxoquinazoline (Ch. IV,

Sect. 3.B.b.) have been nitrated, and the nitro group first enters position 6. Sulphonation and chlorosulphonation of 3,4-dihydro-4-oxoquinazoline also takes place in position 6 (Ch. IV, Sect. 2.C.b.(iv)).

Nucleophilic metathesis of 2- and 4-chlorine atoms in chloroquinazolines takes place readily and is used in the preparation of alkoxy- and aryloxy- (Ch. V, Sects. 2.A., 2.B.b., and 2.C.), thio- (Ch. VI, Sects. 1.A., 2.B., and 3.), and aminoquinazolines (Ch. VII, Sects. 1.A.a., 1.B.a., and 1.C.a.) by displacement with the appropriate nucleophile. The much greater reactivity of the 4-chlorine atom compared with the 2-chlorine atom makes it possible to prepare a variety of disubstituted quinazolines from 2,4-dichloroquinazolines. 4-Alkylthio groups are displaced by amines (Ch. VII, Sect. 1.B.a.) and alkoxides (Ch. VI, Sect. 2.B.) and 4-alkoxy groups can be displaced by alkoxide ions (Ch. V, Sect. 2.E.b.(iii)). The 2- and 4-chlorine atoms of chloroquinazolines cannot be displaced by cyanide ions, but are displaced by nucleophiles such as $^-CHRCO_2Et$ and less readily by Grignard reagents. These displacements in the cyanoquinazolines take place more satisfactorily, and also occur in aqueous media (Ch. III, Sects. 1.G and H; Ch. X, Sect. 1.).

D. N-Oxides (see Ch. IX)

Quinazoline-3-oxides were first prepared[23] in 1891 but were recognized as quinazoline-3-oxides only as recently as 1960.[24] Although quinazoline-1-oxide is as yet unknown, several of its derivatives have been prepared. The reactions of the N-oxides are in many ways similar to those of the corresponding quinazolines, but in addition, give reactions characteristic of the N-oxide function.

E. Tautomerism

Quinazolines with oxo groups adjacent to the nitrogen atoms are capable of tautomerism between lactim (—C(OH)=N—) and lactam (—C(=O)NH—) forms. This tautomerism is also possible in the thio derivatives (thiol —C(SH)=N— and thione —C(=S)NH—), the oxothio, and in oxo or thio derivatives of N-oxides

$$(-C(OH)=N(\rightarrow O)- \; \rightleftharpoons \; -C(=O)-N(OH)-).$$

Because quinazoline has two nitrogen atoms in a 1,3 relationship the number of possible tautomers is increased. For 2- and 4-hydroxyquinazolines there are three possible tautomers, and for 2,4-dihydroxyquinazoline there are six possible tautomers. These forms are possible also in the thio, thiooxo, oxo-N-oxides, thio-N-oxides, and oxothio-N-oxides. All evidence so far indicates that these exist predominantly in the lactam or thiolactam forms (which could further have two or more tautomers), that is why the oxo and thio compounds described in the respective chapters are drawn and named after the most probably predominant tautomer. Tautomerism in 4-hydroxyquinazoline was examined in some detail[25] but a systematic study of tautomerism in the quinazoline series using modern techniques would be most desirable. Tautomerism is discussed in chapters IV, Sects. 1.B., 2.C.a., 3.B.a., and 4.B.; VI, Sects. 1.A. and 2.D., and IX, Sect. 4.

F. Oxidation and Reduction

Oxidation of quinazolines in acid solution normally yields 3,4-dihydro-4-oxoquinazolines because indeed it is the hydrated cation **5** that is oxidized. On the other hand, in neutral solution (in which the anhydrous neutral species are predominant) 4,5-dicarboxypyrimidine is formed (Ch. II, Sect. 3.A.). Reduced quinazolines are prepared by reduction and by syntheses which lead to a reduced compound. Reduction of the 3,4-double bond to form 3,4-dihydroquinazolines take place without much difficulty, especially when the quinazoline is not substituted on $C_{(4)}$. Further reduction to 1,2,3,4-tetrahydroquinazolines requires stronger conditions. Quinazolines in which the benzene ring is partially reduced are obtained by typical pyrimidine syntheses using a cyclohexane derivative. Oxidation of reduced quinazolines, e.g. 3,4-dihydroquinazoline, may lead to the fully aromatic system, or (as in the case of 3,4-dihydro-3-methylquinazoline) to an oxo compound, depending on the reduced compound (see Ch. VIII).

G. Rearrangements

Three main types of rearrangements have been observed in the quinazoline series. The first is the rearrangement of 2- and 4-alkyl ethers to the corresponding N-alkyl-oxo isomers (Ch. V, Sect. 2.E.b.(iv)). The second is the Dimroth rearrangement, where 2-amino-3-alkyl (or aryl)-3,4-dihydro-4-oxoquinazolines are converted to 2-alkyl (or aryl)amino-3,4-dihydro-4-oxoquinazolines under the influence of base (Ch. VII, Sect. 1.E.c.). The third rearrangement is the ring enlargement of the intermediate 2-aminomethyl-4-phenylquinazoline-3-oxides (obtained from the respective 2-chloromethyl derivative and primary amines) to 2-methylamino-5-phenyl-3(H),1,4-benzodiazepine-4-oxides (Ch. IX, Sect. 2.C.).

H. Biological Activity in Quinazolines (see Ch. XI)

There is only a small number of alkaloids which possess the quinazoline nucleus and some are physiologically active. However, the biological activity was not of the extent which warranted clinical application. The vasicine group has bronchodilator activity, the evodiamine type exhibits hypotensive action, and the febrifugines have high antimalarial activity but their therapeutic index is low. The most active quinazoline known is the 2-iminoperhydroquinazoline, tetrodotoxin, which is one of the most potent non-protein neurotoxins known. Many synthetic quinazolines were tested for various biological activities and some were found to have some specific activity. Of the synthetic quinazolines, the hypnotic 3,4-dihydro-2-methyl-4-oxo-3-o-tolylquinazoline and the oral diuretic 7-chloro-2-ethyl-1,2,3,4-tetrahydro-4-oxo-6-sulphamoylquinazoline are marketed as methaqualone and quinethazone, respectively (among other names), and are being used clinically with considerable success.

5. Tables

Systematic tables of quinazolines will be found at the end of the chapters. The tables cover the literature of non-condensed quinazolines almost completely up to the middle of 1965 and incompletely up to June 1966. Any omissions are purely accidental. In order to facilitate the tedious job of looking for particular compounds, the groups of compounds have been subdivided as much as possible. For example, many tables are given for substituted 3,4-dihydro-4-oxoquinazolines. The general formula is placed at the head of each table wherever possible. The tables contain compounds discussed in the respective chapter. However, it is not possible to do this thoroughly with examples which have several different functional groups without duplicating the entries. Hence the tables at the end of each chapter need not necessarily contain all the compounds discussed in the chapter. The tables in chapter III, for instance, contain all the alkyl- and arylquinazolines which bear no other functional group directly attached to the quinazoline nucleus, but the tables in chapter IV include alkyl- and aryloxoquinazolines. Also, chapter IV does not contain oxoquinazolines with thio, N-hydroxy, or amino substituents, or reduced derivatives because these will be found in chapters VI, IX, VII, and VIII, respectively. For complete coverage of the quinazolines with several functional groups the reader will have to look through the respective tables in all the chapters which discuss the various derivatives.

Important Note

A deliberate attempt is made to keep the order of the compounds in the tables similar to the order in which the chemical names are constructed (see Sect. 2). For example, the following sequence is used for 3,4-dihydro-4-oxoquinazolines: 6-bromo-, 6,8-dibromo-, 5-chloro, 6,8-dichloro-, 8-methyl, 6,8-dimethyl-, 5,6,8-trimethyl-, 6,7-methylene-dioxy-. This is alphabetical according to the types (not number) of substituents, and has the advantage of placing compounds with similar groups close together.

6. References

1. Griess, *Ber. Deut. Chem. Ges.*, **2**, 415 (1869).
2. Griess, *Ber. Deut. Chem. Ges.*, **18**, 2410 (1885).
3. Weddige, *J. Prakt. Chem.*, **36**, (2) 141 (1887).
4. Weddige, *J. Prakt. Chem.*, **31**, (2) 124 (1885).
5. Bischler and Lang, *Ber. Deut. Chem. Ges.*, **28**, 279 (1895).
6. Gabriel, *Ber. Deut. Chem. Ges.*, **36**, 800 (1903).
7. Bogert, *J. Am. Chem. Soc.*, **32**, 784 (1910).
8. Osborn, Schofield, and Short, *J. Chem. Soc.*, **1956**, 4191; see also Albert, *Chem. Soc. Spec. Publ.* (3) 138 (1955).
9. Albert, Armarego, and Spinner, *J. Chem. Soc.*, **1961**, 2689, 5267.
10. Williamson in *Heterocyclic Compounds* (Ed. Elderfield), Wiley, New York, 1957, Vol. 6, Chap. 8, p. 324.
11. Landquist in *Chemistry of Carbon Compounds. IV.B, Heterocyclic Compounds* (Ed. Rodd), Elsevier, Amsterdam, 1959, Chap. XV, p. 1299.
12. Armarego, *Advan. Heterocyclic Chem.*, **1**, 253 (1963).
13. Widman, *J. Prakt. Chem.*, **38**, (2) 185 (1888).
14. Paal and Busch, *Ber. Deut. Chem. Ges.*, **22**, 2683 (1889).
15. *I.U.P.A.C.*, *Nomenclature of Organic Chemistry*, B-2. 11, p. 57, Butterworths, London, 1957; Patterson, Capell, and Walker, *The Ring Index*, 2nd ed., American Chemical Society, RRI 1626, 1959, p. 210.
16. *Handbook for Chemical Society Authors*, London, The Chemical Society, Burlington House, W.1, 1960.
17. Albert and Armarego, *Advan. Heterocyclic Chem.*, **4**, 1 (1965).
18. Armarego and Smith, *J. Chem. Soc.* (*C*), **1966**, 234.
19. Armarego, *J. Chem. Soc.*, **1962**, 561.
20. Brown, England, and Harper, *J. Chem. Soc.* (C), **1966**, 1165; and earlier papers.
21. Brown, *The Pyrimidines*, Interscience, 1962, Ch. XII, 430.
22. Albert, *Heterocyclic Chemistry*, Athlone Press, 1959, p. 39.
23. Auwers and Meyenburg, *Ber. Deut. Chem. Ges.*, **24**, 2370 (1891).
24. Sternbach, Kaiser, and Reeder, *J. Am. Chem. Soc.*, **82**, 475 (1960).
25. Hearn, Morton, and Simpson, *J. Chem. Soc.*, **1951**, 3318.

CHAPTER II

Quinazoline

Quinazolines with substituents (other than those that are capable of tautomerism, e.g. hydroxy and thiol) in positions 2 and 4 show the general reactions and properties typical of quinazoline. This is because the two rings have the full complement of π electrons to make them aromatic. The π electrons of the 3,4-double bond in quinazoline are highly delocalized and confer on it an enhanced reactivity towards nucleophilic reagents. It is the purpose of this chapter to discuss the chemistry of quinazoline together with the effect of substituents, placed in various positions, on its physical and chemical properties.

1. Synthesis of Quinazoline

In 1895 Bischler and Lang[1] prepared quinazoline for the first time by heating 2-carboxyquinazoline with calcium oxide (compare Ch. III, Sect. 1.C.). Eight years later Gabriel[2] obtained quinazoline in good yield by oxidation of 3,4-dihydroquinazoline with alkaline potassium ferricyanide (compare Ch. III, Sect. 1.B.). In a patent,[3] Riedel showed that quinazoline can be prepared by the reductive cyclization of bisformamido-o-nitrobenzaldehyde with zinc and acetic acid. Although iron and hydrochloric acid[4] was claimed to be a better reagent, the yields with the former reagent were higher than 70%.[5,6] A drawback to this preparation was the availability of o-nitrobenzaldehyde. The catalytic reduction of 4-chloroquinazoline was therefore studied by several workers,[7,8,9] and was used to prepare fifty-gram quantities of quinazoline[10] (Ch. V, Sect. 1.E.(iv)).

The decomposition of 4-N'-toluene-p-sulphonylhydrazinoquinazoline hydrochloride to quinazoline by aqueous alkali has many advantages over the above methods because of the ease in preparing the starting material and the simplicity of the apparatus used (Ch. V, Sect. 1.E.b.(v)).

Quinazoline can thus be obtained in 60% yield and in large quantities.[11] This reaction is very useful for the preparation of many quinazolines and other heterocyclic compounds (Ch. V, Sect. 1.E.b.(v)). The formation of an intermediate diimide in the reaction has been suggested.[12] Alkali is necessary for this reaction and nitrogen and toluene-p-sulphinic acid are liberated. The reaction can apparently proceed by the removal of a proton from the hydrazino nitrogen atom attached to the tosyl group, followed by the release of the quinazoline anion. The anion then takes up a proton from the medium to give quinazoline (Reaction 1). The unstable tosyldiimide then decomposes either thermally or by further ionization of the imino proton, followed by release of toluene-p-sulphinic acid and formation of nitrogen (Reaction 2). Alternatively the proton is removed from the hydrazino nitrogen

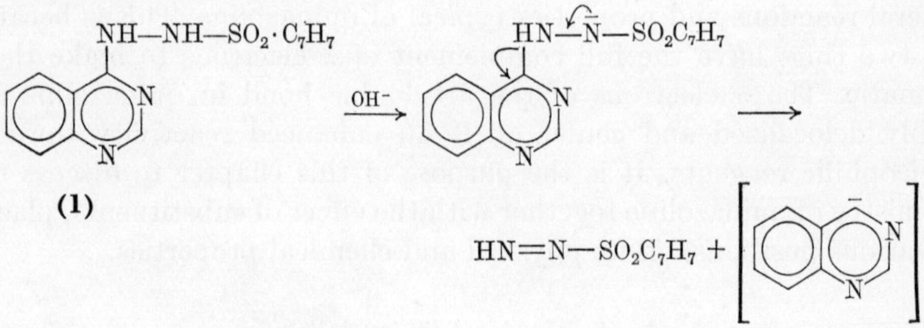

(1)

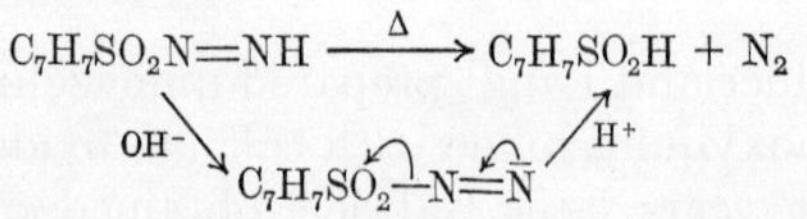

(2)

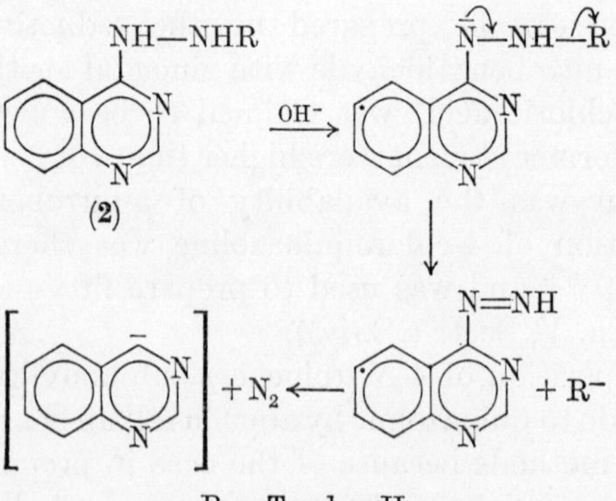

R = Tosyl or H

atom attached to the heterocyclic ring (Reaction 3), and the hetero-cyclic diimide is formed which breaks down thermally or by an anion mechanism as in (2). By decomposing the tosyl derivative (1) with sodium deuteroxide in deuterium oxide, 4-deuteroquinazoline was prepared with almost 100% labelling.[13] 4-Hydrazinoquinazoline (2, R = H) decomposes in ethanolic sodium hydroxide at 25° to give a 60% yield of quinazoline,[14] but with copper sulphate or manganese dioxide the yields are very poor (Ch. V, Sect. 1.E.b.(v)).

Quinazoline was also prepared successfully by the Bischler synthesis (Ch. III, Sect. 1.A.) from o-formamidobenzaldehyde and ethanolic ammonia.[15] All these syntheses have been used for the preparation of substituted quinazolines and are described in the references to other chapters cited above.

2. Physical Properties

Quinazoline is a low-melting solid which can be distilled without decomposition.[2,3,10] It is steam volatile,[1] sublimes readily under vacuum, and crystallizes from light petroleum. When pure it has a characteristic pleasant odour and a bitter taste. It is soluble in organic solvents and in water it gives an alkaline reaction.[2] It gives a blood red colour, in acidic and basic media, in Legal's colour reaction.[16]

TABLE II.1. Quinazoline and 3-Alkyl Derivatives.

Quinazoline	M.p. (°c)	References
Unsubstituted	48–48.5°, 243°/772.5 mm, 241°/764 mm, 120–121°/17–18 mm	2, 3, 10
Hydrochloride	H_2O 127–128°	22
Picrate	188–190°	2
Aurichloride	185°	2
Chloroplatinate	> 250°	2
3-Methiodide	165°	67
3-Allyl-4-ethoxy-3,4-dihydro-	hydroiodide 104–107°	64
3-Allyl-3,4-dihydro-4-hydroxy-[a]	130–131°	63, 64, 65
3-Benzyl-3,4-dihydro-4-hydroxy-[a]	160–161°	66
3-Ethyl-3,4-dihydro-4-hydroxy-[a]	145–146°; hydrochloride 150–151	62 62
3,4-Dihydro-4-hydroxy-3-methyl-[a]	158°, 162–163°, 167–168°; hydrochloride 171–172°; hydrobromide 150–152°	39, 56, 67 56, 62 62

[a] These are pseudo bases.

A. Theoretical Aspects

Theoretical treatment of quinazoline by Longuet-Higgins and Coulson[17] gave the net charges shown in **3**. A more recent calculation[18] based on a set of self-consistent molecular orbitals (SCF-MO's) gave values of charge densities as in **4**, which were slightly different from the values obtained by the former authors. Further calculations by Brown,[19] however, using uniform parameters in the molecular orbital calculations, led to the electron density diagram **5**. These values are smaller than the ones previously calculated but are self consistent and give dipole moments in agreement with experiment.

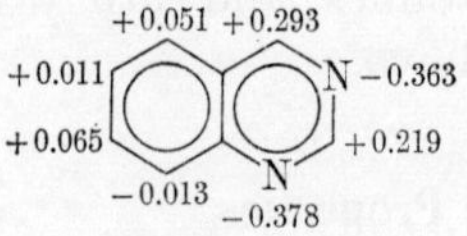

Longuet-Higgins and Coulson

(3)

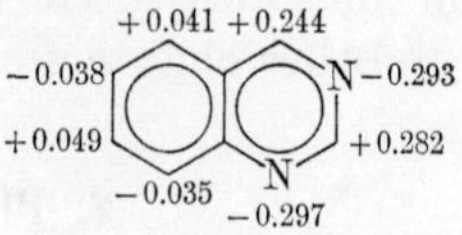

Gawer and Dailey

(4)

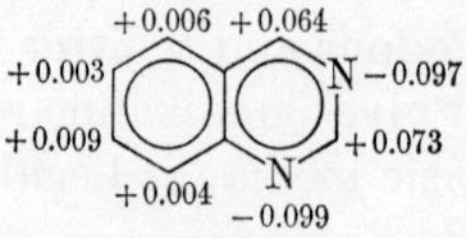

Brown

(5)

The calculated ionization potential of quinazoline was found to fall on a plot of the calculated ionization potentials against pK_a values of a number of heterocyclic molecules.[20] We now know that the pK_a value (3.51) used in the plot is a complex figure (Sect. 2.C.a.) and when it is replaced by the true pK_a value (1.95) the point for quinazoline falls well out of the above plot.

B. Spectra

a. *Ultraviolet Spectra*

The ultraviolet spectrum of the neutral species of quinazoline in water consists of three main bands and is not unlike the spectrum of naphthalene. These bands are at 222, 271, and 305 mμ (see Fig. 2).[21-23] The spectrum in ethanol[24] is very similar to the one in water, but in hexane[25] and heptane[24] there is more fine structure in the two bands at longer wavelengths. The bands at 220, 267, and 311 mμ in cyclohexane have extinction coefficients of 41,000, 2810, and 2100, respectively and have been ascribed to $\pi \to \pi^*$ transitions. In addition, the long wavelength band has a characteristic inflexion at 330 mμ with a low extinction coefficient (200) which is due to an $n \to \pi^*$ transition.[26] The spectra of 2-, 4-, and 6-chloroquinazoline in isooctane also have bands with more fine structure, when compared with the spectra in methanol, but the fine structure for the $n \to \pi^*$ transition is most probably hidden under the first $\pi \to \pi^*$ transition band.[27]

Substituents that are transparent in the ultraviolet light, e.g. methyl and chloro, do not alter the general shape of the spectrum of quinazoline in water, but the band at 305 mμ moves to longer wavelengths. Hydroxy and methoxy groups in the benzene ring make the two bands at longer wavelengths converge into one broad band. The spectra of 5-, 6-, 7-, and 8-nitroquinazoline in water do not resemble that of the parent because of the strong absorbing properties of the nitro group.[23] For the spectra of quinazoline cations see section 2.C.

b. *Phosphorescence Spectra*

The phosphorescence,[24,28] phosphorescence–polarization, and the absorption–polarization (related to the phosphorescence) spectra of quinazoline have been measured.[28] The $\pi \to \pi^*$ phosphorescence of quinazoline is polarized through a $n \to \pi^*$ band on excitation. Excitation through a $\pi \to \pi^*$ transition causes a strongly negative degree of polarization and confirms that the transition moment of the triplet–singlet phosphorescence in quinazoline, as in unsubstituted aromatic molecules, is perpendicular to the plane of the molecule.[28]

c. *Infrared Spectra*

The infrared spectra of several quinazolines in the region 1500–1700 cm^{-1} (double-bond region) were examined. Three main sets of bands between 1478–1517 cm^{-1}, 1566–1581 cm^{-1}, and 1612–1628 cm^{-1} were found and designated 'Quinazoline I, II, and III,' respectively. By comparison with 6-acetyl-2,4-dimethylquinazoline these bands were shown to be generally as intense as the carbonyl band. The possibility that 'Quinazoline I' was attributed to the benzene ring and 'Quinazoline II and III' to the pyrimidine ring, which has two C=N groups, was suggested. It was, however, considered better to associate these three bands with the conjugated quinazoline ring system as a whole without making assignments.[29]

This work was confirmed in a detailed examination of the spectra of methyl-, chloro-, methoxy-, and nitroquinazolines, and was extended to the region 700–1300 cm^{-1}. The out-of-plane CH-bending modes and band sequences which occur in the region 700–1000 cm^{-1} were found for all the position-of-substitution types. The 'umbrellas' mode, with all the hydrogen atoms on one ring moving in phase, occurred as strong bands in characteristic positions and were easily assigned, but the remaining γ-CH modes were weak. The expected five CH-in-plane bending modes in the region 1000–1300 cm^{-1} were observed. The in-plane ring stretching modes were in the region 1300–1700 cm^{-1} and generally showed a strong band near 1625, a medium-to-strong doublet near 1580, a strong band near 1485, a weak band near 1450, a well-defined triplet centered about 1395, and a medium band near 1310 cm^{-1}. The intensity of the first band (near 1625 cm^{-1}) for substituents in positions 2, 4, 5, and 7 rose sharply with the electron-donor power of the substituent. Intensity versus electronic properties of the substituents for the other bands in this region was less clear cut.[30] In the nitro-quinazolines the intensity of the symmetric stretching mode of the nitro group (near 1350 cm^{-1}) when it was α, i.e. in position 5 or 8 ($\epsilon_A = 200 \pm 50$), was significantly lower than when it was β, i.e. in position 6 or 7 ($\epsilon_A = 450 \pm 70$). Also in the methoxyquinazolines the band assigned to ν-OMe was within the region 1024–1048 cm^{-1} when the group was in a β position, i.e. position 6 or 7, but when it was in the α-position, i.e. 5 and 8, the band apparently moved to 1100 cm^{-1}.[31] The spectrum of quinazoline was correlated with the spectra of several diaza- and triazanaphthalenes.[32] The infrared spectra of quinazolines with tautomeric groups, e.g. oxo (Ch. IV, Sects. 1.B., 2.C.a., and 3.B.a.) and thio (Ch. VI, Sect. 2.D.) are described in the relevant chapters.

d. *Proton Magnetic Resonance Spectra*

The proton magnetic resonance spectrum of quinazoline at 60 Mc/sec was first measured in 1965, and partial assignments of the signals were made.[33] Later that year the assignment of all the protons in quinazoline was made at 100 Mc/sec,[34] and is shown (together with the computed spectrum) in Fig. 1. Gawer and Dailey also measured the spectrum of quinazoline and concluded that the chemical shifts appeared to be an unreliable measure of the π-electron densities, particularly in the positions adjacent to the nitrogen atoms.[18]

A detailed study of the spectra of quinazoline and its mono-substituted chloro, hydroxy, methoxy, methyl, and nitro derivatives, with these substituents in positions 5, 6, 7, and 8, was made by Katritzky and collaborators at 40, 60, and 100 mc/sec.[35] They made assignments for all the protons, but disagreed with earlier workers[34] by concluding that the 4-proton was the most deshielded atom and was at lowest

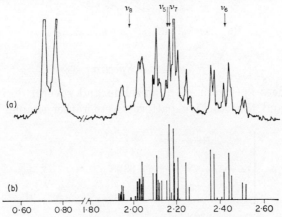

Fig. 1.   (a) Experimental and (b) Calculated P.m.r. Spectrum of Quinazoline in Carbon Tetrachloride at 100 mc/sec. (By courtesy of Drs. Heffernan and Black.)

field. This was because they found that substituents in the benzene ring caused greater changes in the chemical shift of the downfield signal than of the neighbouring signal at higher field. Substituents would be expected to affect the chemical shift of the 4-proton more than the 2-proton. Also the chemical shifts of $H_{(4)}$ and $H_{(2)}$ in 2-chloro- and 4-chloroquinazo-line, respectively, were only compatible by assigning $H_{(4)}$ to the lower field signal. Conclusive evidence that these assignments were correct was obtained by examination of the spectrum of 4-deuteroquinazoline which showed that the downfield signal was absent.[13] The signals for the 2- and 4-protons converged as the dielectric constant of the medium decreased and in cyclohexane they were virtually superimposed.[13]

In general it was found that the electron-donating hydroxy, methoxy, and methyl groups in the benzene ring caused greater upfield shifts of the protons in quinazoline than in benzene, whereas the electron-withdrawing nitro group caused less of a downfield shift. The spectra of the monosubstituted quinazolines mentioned above were computed from the measured chemical shifts. The computed chemical shifts for the spectrum of quinazoline in dry dimethyl sulphoxide are shown in **6**, and the coupling constants are $J_{2,4} \simeq 0$, $J_{5,6} = 8.40$, $J_{5,7} = 2.02$, $J_{5,8} = 0.21$, $J_{6,7} = 6.89$, $J_{6,8} = 1.63$, and $J_{7,8} = 8.62$ c/sec.[35] The spectrum of quinazoline in deuterium oxide is shown in Fig. 5.

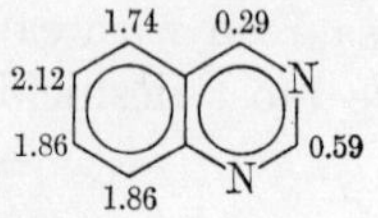

(**6**) Chemical shifts are in p.p.m. on τ scale.

e. *Mass Spectra*

The mass spectrum of quinazoline and several derivatives was measured and the cracking patterns were rather simple. Quinazoline

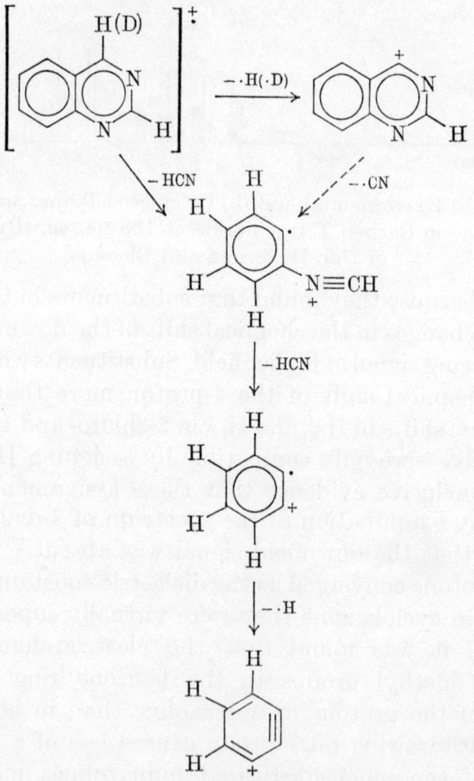

SCHEME 1

breaks down in two ways. Its molecular ion eliminates two molecules of hydrogen cyanide, stepwise, to form the benzyne radical ion which loses a hydrogen radical to give the benzyne cation. Concurrently with this, the quinazoline molecular ion loses a hydrogen radical from $C_{(4)}$, followed apparently by a cyanide radical, and then breaks down as above (Scheme 1). The mass spectrum of 4-deuteroquinazoline is consistent with this scheme. Substituted quinazolines in general break down in a similar manner.[36]

C. Covalent Hydration

a. *Covalent Hydration in Quinazoline*

The cation of quinazoline differs from the cations of the naphthyridines,[37] cinnoline,[21] phthalazine,[22] and quinoxaline[38] because it undergoes reversible water addition across the 3,4-double bond.[22,39] This water addition is described as 'covalent hydration.'[40] The anomaly in quinazoline was discovered by Albert, Brown, and Wood[41] who found that quinazoline was a stronger base (tenfold) than 4-methylquinazoline (Table II.3.). This was unusual because a methyl group was normally base strengthening. The ultraviolet spectra of the neutral species and cations of quinazoline and 4-methylquinazoline showed that it was the cation of quinazoline that was anomalous. The spectra of the neutral species of quinazoline in water and in hexane are closely similar (Sect. 2.B.a.), but the spectrum of the cation in water is displaced to shorter wavelengths (45 mμ) than that of the neutral species (Fig. 2). On the

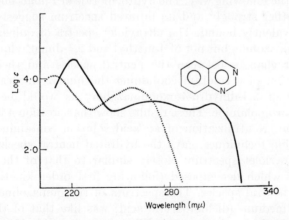

FIG. 2.   Ultraviolet Spectra of Quinazoline (——— pH 7) and its Cation (·········· pH 1).

2*

other hand, the spectrum of the 4-methylquinazoline cation in water is very similar to that of the neutral species, except for the small bathochromic shift of the long wavelength band,[22] and is typical of heterocyclic molecules that do not react with water (Fig. 3).[21]

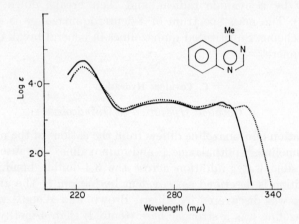

FIG. 3. Ultraviolet Spectra of 4-Methylquinazoline (———— pH 7) and its Cation (·········· pH 0).

The large change in the absorption spectrum of quinazoline on protonation suggested that the chromophore was altered, and the structure **7** was postulated for the cation.[21,42,43] This structure was deduced in the following way. The hydrochloride of **7** holds one molecule of water rather strongly and its infrared spectrum suggests that the water is covalently bound. The ultraviolet spectra of quinazoline and 2-methylquinazoline, but not of 4-methyl and 2,4-dimethylquinazoline, show major changes between the neutral species and their cations. Mild oxidation of a solution containing the quinazoline cation gives high yields of 3,4-dihydro-4-oxoquinazoline, as would be expected from an α-carbinolamine. These results show that position 4 is involved in hydration. Neutralization of an acid solution containing **7**, using rapid reaction techniques, gave the hydrated neutral species **8** which had an ultraviolet spectrum closely similar to that of the hydrated cation, but which decomposed (following first order kinetics) to the anhydrous neutral species. The spectrum of the quinazoline cation in anhydrous medium (dichloroacetic acid) was like that of the neutral species, i.e. no hypsochromy as in dilute aqueous acid. Also, when the acid concentration of a solution of quinazoline in water was increased,

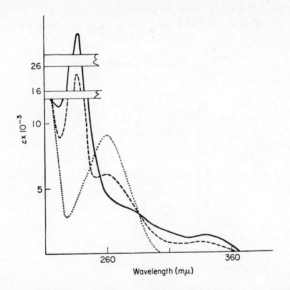

i.e. the activity of water was decreased, the spectrum altered until it
was quite similar to the one in anhydrous dichloroacetic acid (Fig. 4).[22]

The ring–chain tautomer **9** was excluded, because unlike *o*-amino-
benzaldehyde, a solution of the quinazoline cation did not react with

Fig. 4. Effect of Acidity on the Ultraviolet Spectrum of Quinazoline (———— H_0 −4.3, ------ H_0 −3.5, and ·········· H_0 0) in
Sulphuric Acid–Water Mixtures.

p-nitrophenylhydrazine.[15] Also the ultraviolet spectrum of the unstable
hydrated neutral species **8** in water was similar to that of the pseudo
base, 3,4-dihydro-4-hydroxy-3-methylquinazoline (**10**), in water. The

pseudo base **10**, which was derived from its salt **11**, had similar spectra
in water and in an anhydrous solvent (cyclohexane), and had no
carbonyl absorption in the infrared spectrum (solid and solution); thus
excluding ring–chain tautomerism in **10**, and hence in **8**. The similarity
of the spectra of **10** and **8** is paralleled by **11** and **7**, and proves the
postulated structure **7** for the quinazoline cation in dilute aqueous
acid.[39]

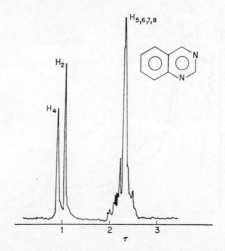

(10)   (11)

The structure **7** for the hydrated quinazoline cation gained further
support from the proton magnetic resonance spectra. The anhydrous
neutral species of quinazoline in deuterium oxide had two signals at
$\tau \simeq 1$ (Fig. 5). The downfield signal was due to the 4-proton and the

$H_{5,6,7,8}$

H_2

H_4

1   2   3
τ

Fig. 5.   Proton Magnetic Resonance Spectrum of Quinazoline in
D$_2$O.

other to the 2-proton (Sect. 2.B.d.). In the spectrum of the cation, the
downfield proton moved upfield to $\tau = 3.58$, the region where the
benzylic protons absorb (Fig. 6).[33] Ring–chain tautomerism was

excluded because an aldehydic proton (as in *o*-aminobenzaldehyde) which absorbs at $\tau \simeq 0$ was absent in this spectrum. This signal at $\tau = 3.58$ was absent in the spectrum of the 4-deuteroquinazoline cation, and is in agreement with structure **7**.

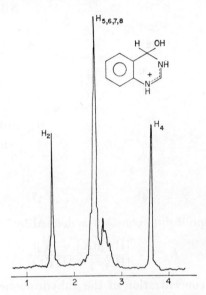

FIG. 6.   Proton Magnetic Resonance Spectrum of the Quinazoline
Cation in N DCl in D_2O.

The ionization constant of quinazoline measured by the usual potentiometric and spectrophotometric methods was shown to be a complicated value. The pK_a value of 3.51 is an equilibrium value, denoted by $pK_a^{eq.}$, and involves the equilibria in (Eq. 4) where K_1 is the ratio of hydrated to anhydrous neutral species, and K_2 the ratio of hydrated to anhydrous cation, both at equilibrium. $K_a^{anhyd.}$ and $K_a^{hyd.}$ are the ionization constants for the anhydrous and hydrated species, respectively. In quinazoline the equilibria K_1 and K_2 lie largely in favour of **12** and **7**, respectively. As is the case of the unstable hydrated neutral species (**8**), when the anhydrous neutral species (**12**) is acidified, the anhydrous cation (**13**) is formed. This readily hydrates, following first order kinetics, to establish the equilibrium K_2. The rates, i.e. $K_{obs.}$ for the establishment of the equilibria K_1 and K_2 have been sorted out into rates of hydration and rates of dehydration for other heterocyclic molecules that undergo covalent hydration.[44] Measurement of these rates for quinazoline and its derivatives would be of value.

Anomalous pK_a values are characteristic of molecules that show this behaviour because they are equilibrium values.[44]

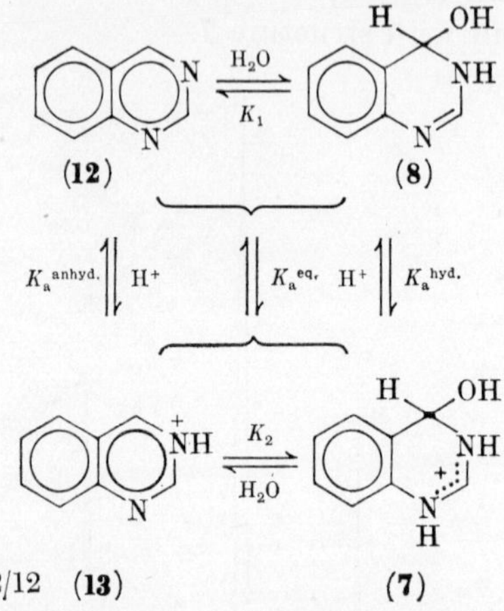

$$(4)$$

The overall equilibrium constant is defined by

$$K_a^{eq.} = \frac{[H^+]([X] + [Y])}{[HX^+] + [HY^+]}. \tag{5}$$

Where [X] is the concentration of the anhydrous neutral species, [Y] the concentration of the hydrated neutral species, and [HX$^+$], and [HY$^+$] the concentrations of the anhydrous and hydrated cations, respectively.

$$K_1 = [Y]^{eq.}/[X]^{eq.}$$

and

$$K_2 = [HY^+]^{eq.}/[HX^+]^{eq.},$$

also

$$K_a^{anhyd.} = \frac{[H^+][X]}{[HX^+]} \tag{6}$$

and

$$K_a^{hyd.} = \frac{[H^+][Y]}{[HY^+]} \tag{7}$$

By making the relevant substitutions

$$K_1 = \frac{K_a^{hyd.}(K_a^{anhyd.} - K_a^{eq.})}{K_a^{anhyd.}(K_a^{eq.} - K_a^{hyd.})} \tag{8}$$

and

$$K_2 = \frac{K_a^{anhyd.} - K_a^{eq.}}{K_a^{eq.} - K_a^{hyd.}} \tag{9}$$

It must be noted that the ratios K_1 and K_2 are independent of pH. The value of $K_a^{hyd.}$ for quinazoline was measured by adjusting the pH of an acid solution containing the hydrated cation (with the use of a stopped-flow rapid reaction apparatus[44]) to several alkaline pH values and observing the optical densities at zero time. The $pK_a^{hyd.}$ was thus found to be 7.77.[22] The $K_{obs.}$ for the rate of change of optical density is acid-base catalyzed. A typical plot is shown in Fig. 7, and is character-

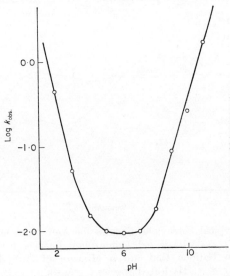

Fig. 7.   pH–Rate Profile of 2-Aminoquinazoline.

istic of heterocyclic molecules that show this phenomenon.[44] For obtaining $K_a^{anhyd.}$, the measurements had to be performed at low pH values where the rates were too fast for the apparatus mentioned above. However, by using a modified rapid reaction apparatus in conjunction with a cathode ray oscilloscope and a Polaroid camera, the optical densities at zero time of a neutral solution of quinazoline which was rapidly adjusted to various acid pH values were obtained. From these measurements[45] the $pK_a^{anhyd.}$ was 1.95. The three pK_a values obtained are so far apart from each other that equations (8) and (9) can be simplified to equations (9a) and (9b), respectively, and give the values $K_1 = 0.55 \times 10^{-4}$, and $K_2 = 35$ for quinazoline at 20°.[15,45] These equations were also used for obtaining K_1 and K_2 for many substituted quinazolines (Table II.3.).

$$K_1 = \frac{K_a^{hyd.}}{K_a^{eq.}} \tag{9a}$$

$$pK_a^{eq.} = pK_a^{anhyd.} + \log(1 + K_2) \tag{9b}$$

The ratios K_1 and K_2 require a knowledge of the $pK_a^{anhyd.}$, $pK_a^{eq.}$, and $pK_a^{hyd.}$ values. These ratios can be obtained accurately only when the differences between the pK_a values are larger than the experimental error (usually less than ± 0.05 pH units). The typical ultraviolet spectra of a hydrated cation, an anhydrous cation, and a mixture of hydrated and anhydrous cations are shown in Fig. 8.

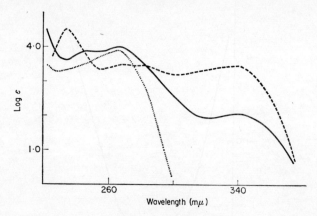

Fig. 8.   Typical Ultraviolet Spectra for Anhydrous Quinazoline Cations (- - - - - -), Hydrated Quinazoline Cations (·············), and Quinazoline Cations that are a Mixture of Anhydrous and Hydrated Species (————).

Measurement of the extinction coefficient of the long wavelength absorption band of a quinazoline cation which contains a mixture of hydrated and anhydrous species affords a second method for obtaining K_2. This method is satisfactory for ratios between 0.1 and 0.9.[11,23]

The ratio K_2 for quinazoline was measured at several temperatures and was found to increase with decrease of temperature, viz. at 4.3, 12.1, 20.0, and 29.5° the values of K_2 were 75, 48, 35, and 30, respectively. The activation energy for the uncatalyzed addition of a molecule of water on the anhydrous quinazoline cation was 9.3 kcal/mole, and the activation energy for the uncatalyzed removal of a molecule of water from the hydrated quinazoline cation was 15.3 kcal/mole.[45a] The activation energy for the former process has to be smaller than for the latter process otherwise hydration cannot take place.

Theoretical treatment showed that the 3,4-double bond is the most polarized double bond in the quinazoline molecule (Sect. 2.A.), and is in agreement with the foregoing. The bond behaves very much like an isolated double bond. Although electron deficiency is necessary in a molecule which adds water reversibly, the new resonance set up in the hydrated molecule stabilizes it. In the hydrated quinazoline cation it is of the amidinium type **7**. That this resonance is necessary is demonstrated by the findings that the cation of 4-nitroisoquinoline (**14**) is anhydrous.[46] In **14** the nitro group has comparable electron-withdrawing properties to the $N_{(1)}$ in quinazoline,[15] but if a hydrated cation is formed, amidinium resonance stabilization is not possible.[46] The reader is referred to recent reviews for further details on the qualitative[40] and quantitative[44] aspects of covalent hydration.

(**14**)

The proton in the anhydrous quinazoline cation (**13**) was placed on $N_{(3)}$ because it was known that isoquinoline (pK_a 5.42) was a stronger base than quinoline (pK_a 4.90).[47] This difference in pK_a values is not very large and it is possible that a small proportion of $N_{(1)}$-protonated species is present in the quinazoline cation. Both the $N_{(1)}$- and $N_{(3)}$-protonated quinazolines form the same hydrated cation **7**. The monocation can be further protonated to give a dication (pK_a −5.5) which has an ultraviolet spectrum similar to that of the anhydrous monocation.[22]

b. Effect of Substituents in the Pyrimidine Ring on Covalent Hydration

(i) Effect of substituents in position 4. The 4-position of quinazoline is the position which is involved in the nucleophilic attack by water molecules or hydroxyl ions in the reversible water addition (Sect. 2.C.a.). A substituent in this position should therefore have a marked effect on covalent hydration. A 4-methyl group decreases hydration in the quinazoline cation considerably,[22] and the ratio K_2 for the 4-methylquinazoline cation is ~0.1[45] as compared with 35 for quinazoline (Table II.3; and Sect. 2.C.a.). The methyl group can do this by virtue of its electronic (+I) effect or by a steric effect. It was shown that this was mainly due to the steric effect because 4-cyano- and 4-chloroquinazoline cations (in which the groups have strong −I effects) were predominantly anhydrous.[22] This was further confirmed by the cations of 4,5-dimethyl- (**15**, R = H) and 2,4,5-trimethyl-quinazoline (**15**, R = Me) which were predominantly hydrated. In these examples the electronic effect of the 4-methyl group was barely

R = H or Me

(**15**)

altered but the steric effect was decreased by a second steric effect (intramolecular overcrowding) due to the 5-methyl group. A steric effect of the latter type was also observed in which the amount of hydrated species in the cation increased in the order 4-methyl- < 4-ethyl- < 4-isopropylquinazoline (Table II.3.), because of interaction with the hydrogen atom in position 5.[11]

(ii) **Effect of substituents in position 2.** Electron-withdrawing substituents in the 2-position of quinazoline decrease the amount of hydration in the cation. The ratio K_2 for example, is in the order 2-methyl > 2-chloromethyl > 2-dichloromethyl. This has been explained by the effect that the substituent has on the polarity of the 3,4-double bond. An electron-withdrawing group ($-$I), e.g. in **16**, would decrease hydration by opposing the polarization —C$\overset{\frown}{=}$N—, whereas an electron-releasing substituent ($+$I), e.g. in **17** would enhance hydration. Mesomeric effects ($+$M) would tend to stabilize resonance structures such as **18** which decrease the amount of hydration.[48] 2-Cyano- and 2-carbamoylquinazoline ($-$I, $-$M) form anhydrous cations[49] which suggests that the inductive effect ($-$I) has the strongest influence. Covalent hydration of 2-substituted quinazoline cations depends on

(**16**)   (**17**)

(**18**)

the overall electronic effects and is summarized in table II.2. It is generally agreed[40,44] that the first step in the reversible water addition is a nucleophilic attack by H_2O or OH^- on position 4, but the above results show that the addition (and retention) of a proton on $N_{(3)}$ (or $N_{(1)}$) makes a significant contribution to the result.[48]

TABLE II.2. Electronic Effects and Hydration in 2-Substituted Quinazoline Cations.[48]

% Hydration	+I (with weak +M)	+M (with weak −I)	−I
∼ 90–100	—Me —Et —i-Pr −t-Bu[a] —CH$_2$Cl	—	—
∼ 5–50	—	—NH$_2$ —NHMe —NMe$_2$ —OMe —SMe	—
∼ 0	—	—	—Cl[b] —CHCl$_2$ —CF$_3$[c] —CN[c,d] —CONH$_2$[c,d]

[a] This group has only a +I effect.
[b] This group also has a weak +M effect.
[c] This group also has a −M effect.
[d] Ref. 49.

c. Effect of Substituents in the Benzene Ring on Covalent Hydration

Substituents in the benzene ring appear to modify the electronic property of the benzene ring as a whole and do not generally relay their electronic effects to the 3,4-double bond as in the 2-substituted quinazolines. In the cations, electron-releasing substituents decrease hydration relative to the quinazoline cation. Electron-releasing substituents in positions 5, 6, and 8 have closely similar effects on water addition across the 3,4-double bond. Substituents in position 7 have stronger effects on covalent hydration in the cations probably because they are *para* to $C_{(4)}$. Thus 7-methyl-, 7-methoxy-, and 7-hydroxyquinazoline cations are

TABLE II.3. Ionization and Covalent Hydration of Quinazolines in Water at 20°.

Quinazoline	^{a}p$K_a$$^{anhyd.}$	^{b,c}p$K_a$$^{eq.}$	^{c}p$K_a$$^{hyd.}$	$^cK_1 \times 10^4$	$^aK_2$
Unsubstituted	1.95	3.51	7.77	0.55^e	35
2-Methyl-	3.00	4.52	8.31	1.6	32
2-Ethyl-	2.95	4.51^d	8.41	1.3	36
2-Isopropyl-	—	4.29^d	8.41	0.76	—
2-t-Butyl-	—	4.17^d	8.38	0.62	—
4-Methyl-	2.80	2.84	—	—	0.1
4-Ethyl-	2.82	3.06^d	—	—	0.7
4-Isopropyl-	2.81	3.07^d	—	—	0.8
5-Methyl-	2.31	3.63	7.89	0.52	20
6-Methyl-	2.16	3.41	—	—	17
7-Methyl-	2.54	3.17	7.88	0.14	3.3
8-Methyl-	2.15	3.20	7.85	0.20	10
5-Methoxy-	2.37	3.41	7.71	0.45	10
6-Methoxy-	2.12	2.85	8.05	0.05	4.4
7-Methoxy-	2.86	2.89	7.35	0.02	~0.1
8-Methoxy-	1.93	3.51	7.82	0.48	37
5-Chloro-	—	3.75	6.95	6.3	—
6-Chloro-	—	3.55	7.15	2.5	—
7-Chloro-	—	3.29	7.00	1.95	—
8-Chloro-	—	3.30	6.55	5.6	—
5-Fluoro-^{c}	—	3.85	6.90	8.9	—
6-Fluoro-^{c}	—	3.42	7.23	1.5	—
7-Fluoro-^{c}	—	3.10	7.11	1.0	—
5-Trifluoromethyl-^{c}	—	3.20	6.90	2.0	—
6-Trifluoromethyl-^{c}	—	3.96	6.75	15	—
7-Trifluoromethyl-^{c}	—	3.90	6.85	11	—
8-Trifluoromethyl-^{c}	—	2.38	6.00	2.4	—
5-Nitro-	—	3.75	6.43^e	21^e	—
6-Nitro-	—	4.18	7.02^e	16^e	—
7-Nitro-	—	4.05	6.15^e	80^e	—
8-Nitro-	—	4.00	6.00^e	100^e	—

^{a} Ref. 45. ^{b} Ref. 23. ^{c} Ref. 50. ^{d} Ref. 11. ^{e} Ref. 15.

less hydrated than any of their 5-, 6-, or 8-isomers. The effect of the 7-methoxy group is almost as large as that of a 4-methyl group, and resonance stabilization such as in **19** is probably the cause of this large decrease in covalent hydration.[23] In the neutral species the effect of substituents is roughly in the order: OMe > Me ⩾ H > Cl > CF$_3$ > NO$_2$ of increasing covalent hydration.[50] The pK_a values and hydration ratios for several quinazolines are given in table II.3. It must be noted that K_1 and K_2 in table II.3 are obtained from ionization measurements

TABLE II.4.   Ionization Constants of Substituted
Quinazolines in Water at 20°.

Quinazoline	$pK_a^{anhyd.}$	References
2-Amino-	4.86^a	48
	4.83	48
4-Amino-	5.85	21
5-Amino-	3.57^a	21
6-Amino-	3.29^a	21
7-Amino-	4.60^a	21
8-Amino	2.81^a	21
2-Amino-4-methyl-	5.36	48
6,7-Benzo-	5.2	21
2-Carbamoyl-	0.53	49
2-Chloro-	-1.6	23
6,8-Dichloro-	3.06^a	23
2-Chloromethyl-	1.81^a	48
2-Chloro-4-methyl-	-0.75	48
2-Cyano-	-2.56	49
2-Dichloromethyl-	-0.87	48
2-Dichloromethyl-4-methyl-	0.11	48
2-Dimethylamino-	5.26^a	48
	5.24	48
2-Dimethylamino-4-methyl-	6.13	48
7-Ethylthio-	3.11^a	50
5-Hydroxy-	3.64^a	23
	7.39^b	23
6-Hydroxy-	3.12^a	23
	8.19^b	23
7-Hydroxy-	3.22^a	23
	7.37^b	23
8-Hydroxy-	8.41^a	23
	8.65^b	23
2-Methoxy-	1.60^a	48
4-Methoxy-	3.13	23
2-Methoxy-4-methyl-	2.32	48
2,4-Dimethyl-	3.60^a	22
4,5-Dimethyl-	4.16^a	11
2,4,5-Trimethyl-	4.75^a	11
4-Methyl-2-methylamino-	5.48	48
4-Methyl-2-methylthio-	1.85	48
4-Methyl-2-t-butyl-	3.87	48
4-Methyl-2-trifluoromethyl-	-1.75	48
2-Methylamino-	5.02^a	48
2-Methylthio-	1.60^a	72
2-Trifluoromethyl-	-2.23	48

^{a} These are $pK_a^{eq.}$ values.
^{b} pK_a values for the acidic group.

(19)

(10)

so that in addition to the above mentioned electronic effects, steric effects due to substituents in position 5 (and perhaps position 8) may be significant. Ionization constants of quinazolines that are not included in table II.3 are in table II.4.

D. Polarography

The polarographic behaviour of quinazoline displayed special features not shown by quinoxaline and phthalazine, but which were consistent with the equilibria (Eq. 4). The pH dependence of the limiting current of a neutral and alkaline solution had the height of a normal two-electron wave. Between pH 6 and pH 1.5 the wave split into two and the height of the two waves diminished considerably. In stronger acid the height of the waves increased again and at $H_0 \sim -2.5$ the height was the same as in the alkaline solution. This is in agreement with the presence of anhydrous species in neutral solution and in strong acid, which are capable of polarographic reduction, and hydrated species at intermediate pH values ($pK_a^{eq.}$ 3.51) which are not reduced. The polarographic changes at the intermediate pH values are time dependent and are a measure of the rate at which the system arrives at the equilibria described in equation (4).[51] The reduction probably follows the reaction (10) in alkaline solution. 3-Methylquinazolinium iodide and 6-aminoquinazoline, but not 4-chloro-, 4-methoxy-, 3,4-dihydro-4-thio-, 4-methylthio-, 4-amino-, 4-methyl-, and 2,4-dimethyl-quinazoline, show similar behaviour.[52]

From the polarographic reduction in acid and in alkaline solution a compound $(C_8H_7N_2)_2$ was isolated, and was shown to be di-3,4-dihydro-quinazolin-4-yl (**20**) on the evidence of the similarity of its ultraviolet spectrum and cathodic wave potential with those of 3,4-dihydro-quinazoline. On oxidation with ferricyanide it gave 85% yield of

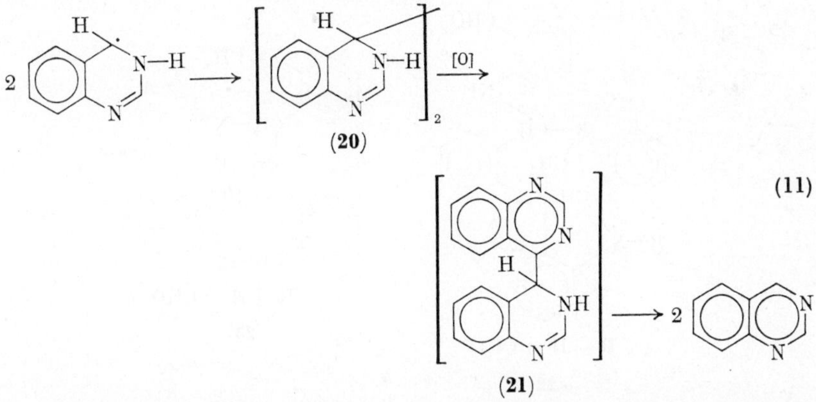

(20)

(11)

(21)

quinazoline.[52] This reaction probably involves the oxidation of half the molecule to 4-(3',4'-dihydroquinazolin-4'-yl)quinazoline (21) which then undergoes the reversal of an addition reaction of quinazoline to quinazoline (Reaction 11).

Polarographic reduction of 4-chloroquinazoline yields quinazoline in almost quantitative yield.[52]

3. Chemical Reactivity of Quinazoline

A. Hydrolysis, Oxidation, and Reduction

Quinazoline is stable in cold dilute acid and alkaline solutions, but it is destroyed when these solutions are boiled. o-Aminobenzaldehyde, ammonia, and formic acid are formed when quinazoline is boiled with hydrochloric acid.[2] In a recent detailed investigation, quinazoline was boiled in dilute acid at pH 2.5. Among other products, the anhydro tetramer of o-aminobenzaldehyde and its monoformyl derivative were isolated in 6 and 10% yields, respectively. These were assigned the structures 22 (R = H) and 22 (R = CHO),[53] and the earlier structures by Seidel and Dick,[54] 23 (R = H) and 23 (R = CHO) were shown to be incorrect. The structure 22 is related to Tröger's base (Ch. VIII, Sect. 7.).

Oxidation of quinazoline, in dilute aqueous acid, with two equivalents of hydrogen peroxide at room temperature gave a high yield of 3,4-dihydro-4-oxoquinazoline. The predominant species in this solution was the hydrated cation 7, which being an α-carbinolamine, was smoothly oxidized to the respective oxo compound[22] (Sect. 2.C.a.). Peracetic acid oxidizes quinazoline to 3,4-dihydro-4-oxoquinazoline

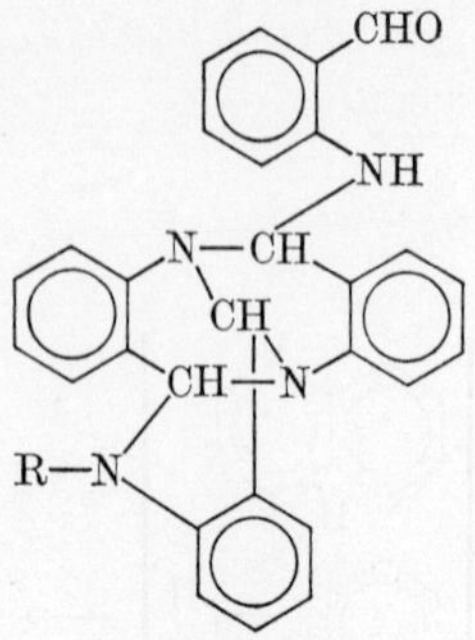

R = H or CHO

(22)

R = H or CHO

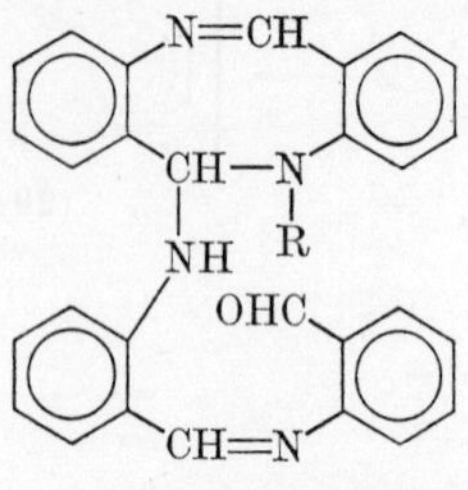

(23)

and not to the N-oxide (Reaction 12).[55] Here also, the oxidation appears to proceed via the hydrated cation **7** because trace quantities of water would form the readily oxidizable cation **7** (Ch. III, Sect. 2.B.b.). In alkaline medium, where the anhydrous neutral species of quinazoline were predominant, oxidation with potassium permanganate furnished a high yield of 4,5-dicarboxypyrimidine (**24**), although a small quantity of 3,4-dihydro-4-oxoquinazoline was also formed (Reaction 12).[56]

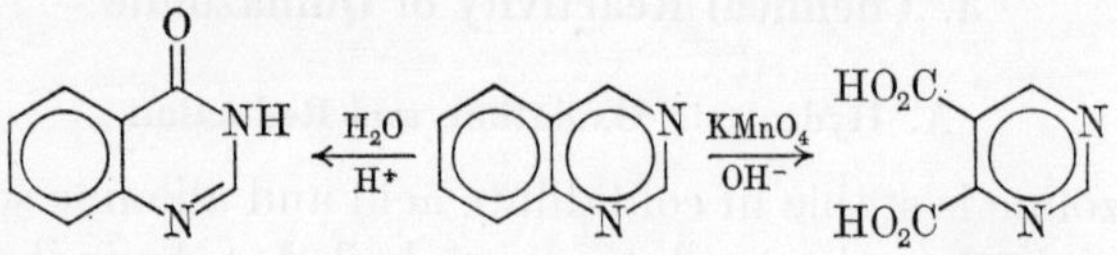

$$\begin{array}{ccc} & \xleftarrow{\;H_2O\;}{\;H^+\;} & \xrightarrow{\;KMnO_4\;}{\;OH^-\;} \end{array} \qquad (12)$$

(24)

Catalytic hydrogenation of quinazoline stopped after the absorption of one molecule of hydrogen and gave 3,4-dihydroquinazoline.[57] Reduction with sodium amalgam gave 1,2,3,4-tetrahydroquinazoline.[2] Lithium aluminium hydride and sodium borohydride gave 3,4-dihydro- and 1,2,3,4-tetrahydroquinazoline (Ch. VIII, Sects. 4.D and 5.C.b.).[58]

B. Electrophilic and Nucleophilic Substitution, and Alkylation

Nitration is the only known electrophilic substitution reaction of quinazoline. Theoretical considerations show that the expected order of reactivity is at positions $8 > 6 > 5 > 7 \gg 4 > 2$.[59] Nitration with fuming nitric acid in concentrated sulphuric acid gave a 56% yield of 6-nitroquinazoline,[8,60] and no other isomers were reported in this reaction. It was considered that the nitration proceeded via the hydrated cation **7**,[61] however we now know that in concentrated sulphuric acid the anhydrous dication is the predominating species (Sect. 2.C.a.).

The two known nucleophilic substitution reactions of quinazoline, namely with sodamide and hydrazine, presumably proceed via the intermediate addition products, and give 4-amino- and 4-hydrazino-quinazoline.[9]

Alkylation of quinazoline takes place on $N_{(3)}$. 3-Methyl-,[56,62,63] 3-ethyl-,[62] 3-allyl-[63–65] and 3-benzylquinazolinium[66] salts readily take up a molecule of alcohol to form the corresponding 4-alkoxy-3-alkyl-3,4-dihydroquinazolinium salts (**25**). These salts yield the pseudo bases, 3-alkyl-3,4-dihydro-4-hydroxyquinazolines (**26**) on treatment with strong alkali (Reaction 13).[39,56,63,64,67] 3,4-Dihydro-4-hydroxy-3-methylquinazoline did not exhibit ring–chain tautomerism[39] (Sect. 2.C.a.), and its structure was deduced by oxidation to the known 3,4-dihydro-3-methyl-4-oxoquinazoline.[67] 3-Allyl- and 3-methyl- 3,4-dihydro-4-hydroxyquinazolines react with nitromethane to form 3-allyl- and 3-methyl- 3,4-dihydro-4-nitromethylquinazolines.[64] Alkylation on $N_{(3)}$ does not necessarily mean that $N_{(3)}$ is the more basic centre because the steric requirements for alkylation are larger than for protonation.

(13)

C. Addition Reactions

Quinazoline is very reactive towards anionoid reagents which attack position 4. Sodium bisulphite,[9,22] hydrogen cyanide,[9,68] aceto-phenone,[69] acetone, 2-butanone, and cyclohexanone[70] add across the 3,4-double bond of quinazoline. Methyl,[9,22] ethyl, isopropyl,[11,71] benzyl,[71] *t*-butyl,[11] and phenyl[9] magnesium halides, and phenyl lithium[9] also add across the 3,4-double bond to give the corresponding 4-substituted 3,4-dihydroquinazolines (Scheme 2).

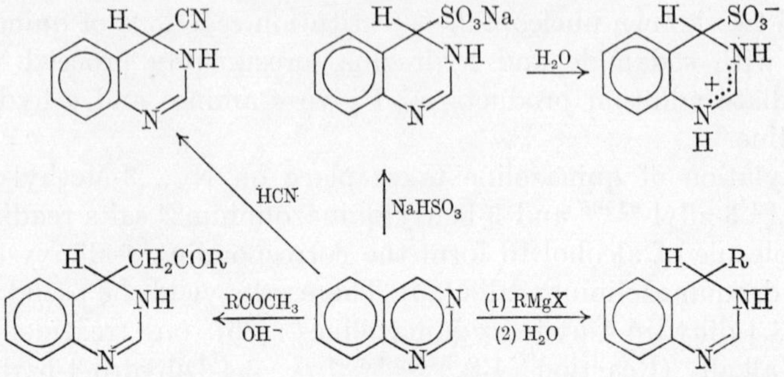

SCHEME 2

In aqueous sodium cyanide, quinazoline forms a product which on mild oxidation yields 4,4′-biquinazolinyl (**27**, R = H). The structure of this compound was deduced from its nuclear magnetic resonance spectrum. It gave a dihydrated cation **28** (R = H) which was readily oxidized to 3,4-dihydro-4-oxoquinazoline (Reaction 14). 2-Methyl-, but not 4-methylquinazoline also gave a biquinazolinyl. A benzoin type of reaction was postulated because sodium hydroxide solution with the same pH as the cyanide solution did not bring about this reaction.[33]

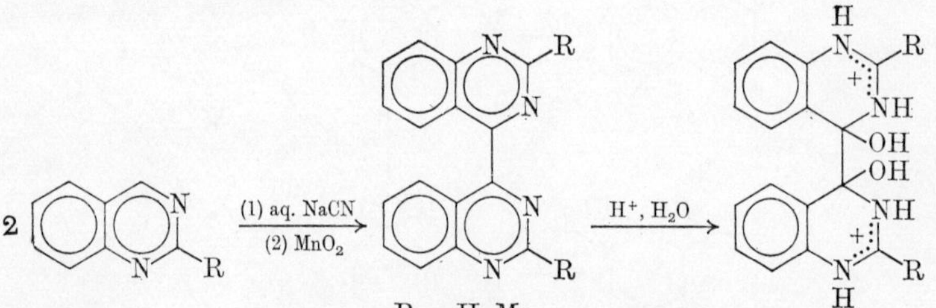

$$(14)$$

4. References

1. Bischler and Lang, *Ber. Deut. Chem. Ges.*, **28**, 279 (1895).
2. Gabriel, *Ber. Deut. Chem. Ges.*, **36**, 800 (1903).
3. Riedel, *Ger. Pat.*, 174, 941 (1905); *Chem. Zentr.*, **II**, 1372 (1906).
4. Adachi, *J. Pharm. Soc. Japan*, **75**, 1423 (1955).
5. Bogert and McColm, *J. Am. Chem. Soc.*, **49**, 2650 (1927).
6. Sidhu, Thyagarajan, and Rao, *Indian J. Chem.*, **1**, 346 (1963).
7. Dewar, *J. Chem. Soc.*, **1944**, 619.

8. Elderfield, Williamson, Gensler, and Kremer, *J. Org. Chem.*, **12**, 405 (1947).
9. Higashino, *J. Pharm. Soc. Japan*, **80**, 245 (1960).
10. Armarego, *J. Appl. Chem.*, **11**, 70 (1961).
11. Armarego and Smith, *J. Chem. Soc.*, **1965**, 5360.
12. Albert, *The Acridines*, Edward Arnold, London, 1966, p. 12.
13. Armarego and Batterham, *J. Chem. Soc.* (C), **1966**, 750.
14. Albert and Catterall, unpublished results (1966).
15. Armarego, *J. Chem. Soc.*, **1962**, 4094.
16. Tanabe and Kamiya, *Ann. Rept. Fac. Pharm.*, *Kanazawa Univ.*, **6**, 12 (1956), *Chem. Abstr.*, **51**, 2455 (1957).
17. Longuet-Higgins and Coulson, *J. Chem. Soc.*, **1949**, 971.
18. Gawer and Dailey, *J. Chem. Phys.*, **42**, 2658 (1965).
19. Brown, personal communication, Monash University, Melbourne, Australia (1966).
20. Nakajima and Pullman, *J. Chim. Phys.*, **55**, 793 (1958).
21. Osborn, Schofield, and Short, *J. Chem. Soc.*, **1956**, 4191.
22. Albert, Armarego, and Spinner, *J. Chem. Soc.*, **1961**, 2689.
23. Armarego, *J. Chem. Soc.*, **1962**, 561.
24. Müller and Dörr, *Z. Elektrochem.*, **63**, 1150 (1959).
25. Vanderhaeghe and Claesen, *Bull. Soc. Chim. Belges*, **66**, 276 (1957).
26. Mason, *J. Chem. Soc.*, **1962**, 493; Mason, in *Physical Methods in Heterocyclic Chemistry* (Ed. Katritzky), Academic Press, 1963, Vol. 2, p. 24.
27. Favini and Simonetta, *Gazzetta*, **90**, 369 (1960).
28. Dörr, Gropper, and Mika, *Ber. Bunsen. Phys. Chem.*, **67**, 202 (1963); *Chem. Abstr.*, **58**, 13310 (1963).
29. Culbertson, Decius, and Christensen, *J. Am. Chem. Soc.*, **74**, 4834 (1952).
30. Armarego, Katritzky, and Ridgewell, *Spectrochim. Acta*, **20**, 593 (1964).
31. Katritzky and Ridgewell, *Spectrochim. Acta*, **20**, 589 (1964).
32. Armarego, Barlin, and Spinner, *Spectrochim. Acta*, **22**, 117 (1966).
33. Armarego and Willette, *J. Chem. Soc.*, **1965**, 1258.
34. Black and Heffernan, *Australian J. Chem.*, **18**, 707 (1965).
35. Katritzky, Reavill, and Swinbourne, *J. Chem. Soc.* (B), **1966**, 351.
36. Batterham, Triffit, and Wunderlich, unpublished results (1966).
37. Albert, *J. Chem. Soc.*, **1960**, 1790.
38. Armarego, *J. Chem. Soc.*, **1963**, 4304.
39. Albert, Armarego, and Spinner, *J. Chem. Soc.*, **1961**, 5267.
40. Albert and Armarego, *Advan. Heterocyclic Chem.*, **4**, 1 (1965).
41. Albert, Brown, and Wood, *J. Chem. Soc.*, **1954**, 3832.
42. Albert, *Chem. Soc. (London) Spec. Publ.* (3) 138 (1955).
43. Albert, *Heterocyclic Chemistry*, Athlone Press, London, 1959, p. 121.
44. Perrin, *Advan. Heterocyclic Chem.*, **4**, 43 (1955).
45. Bunting and Perrin, *J. Chem. Soc.* (B), **1966**, 436.
45a. Bunting and Perrin, unpublished results (1966).
46. Albert and Armarego, *J. Chem. Soc.*, **1963**, 4237.
47. Perrin, *Dissociation Constants of Organic Bases in Aqueous Solution*, London, Butterworths, 1965.
48. Armarego and Smith, *J. Chem. Soc.* (C), **1966**, 234.
49. Biffin, personal communication (1966).
50. Armarego and Smith, unpublished results (1966).

51. Lund, *Nature*, **204**, 1087 (1964).
52. Lund, *Acta Chem. Scand.*, **18**, 1984 (1964).
53. Albert and Yamamoto, *J. Chem. Soc.* (B), **1966**, 956.
54. Seidel and Dick, *Ber. Deut Chem. Ges.*, **60**, 2018 (1927).
55. Landquist, *J. Chem. Soc.*, **1956**, 1885.
56. Gabriel and Colman, *Ber. Deut. Chem. Ges.*, **37**, 3643 (1904).
57. Bogert and Marr, *J. Am. Chem. Soc.*, **57**, 729 (1935).
58. Smith, Briggs, Kent, Albright, and Walsh, *J. Heterocyclic Chem.*, **2**, 157 (1965).
59. Dewar and Maitlis, *J. Chem. Soc.*, **1957**, 2521.
60. Schofield and Swain, *Nature*, **161**, 690 (1948); *J. Chem. Soc.*, **1949**, 1367.
61. Schofield, *J. Soc. Chem. Ind.* (*London*), **1957**, 1068; Ridd, in *Physical Methods in Heterocyclic Chemistry* (Ed. Katritzky), Academic Press, 1963, Vol. 1, p. 128.
62. Gabriel and Colman, *Ger. Pat.*, 101, 401 (1904); *Chem. Zentr.*, **II**, 182 (1905).
63. Schöpf and Oechler, *Ann. Chem.*, **523**, 1 (1936).
64. Reynolds and Robinson, *J. Chem. Soc.*, **1936**, 196.
65. Hanford, Liang, and Adams, *J. Am. Chem. Soc.*, **56**, 2780 (1934).
66. Armarego, unpublished results (1966).
67. Fry, Kendall, and Morgan, *J. Chem. Soc.*, **1960**, 5062.
68. Teshigawara, Hayashi, and Tono, *Japan Pat.*, 8,133 (1963); *Chem. Abstr.*, **59**, 11527 (1963).
69. Hayashi and Higashino, *Chem. Pharm. Bull.* (*Japan*), **12**, 1111 (1964).
70. Hayashi and Higashino, *Chem. Pharm. Bull.* (*Japan*), **13**, 291 (1965).
71. Higashino, *Chem. Pharm. Bull.* (*Japan*), **10**, 1043 (1962).
72. Albert and Barlin, *J. Chem. Soc.*, **1962**, 3129.

CHAPTER III

C-Alkyl- and C-Arylquinazolines

This chapter is concerned with derivatives which have alkyl, aryl, and heterocyclic groups attached directly to the quinazoline nucleus. Alkyl, aryl, and heterocyclic substituents which have functional groups, e.g. halogen, cyano, are also included, but quinazolines that have, in addition to these, other functional groups directly attached to the quinazoline system are found in subsequent chapters.

1. Methods of Preparation

A. Bischler's Synthesis

This synthesis was first described by Bischler[1] in 1891 who prepared 2-methylquinazoline by heating o-acetamidobenzaldehyde (1, R = H, R^1 = Me) with alcoholic ammonia in a sealed tube at 100°. By using the N-acyl derivatives of o-aminobenzophenone and alcoholic ammonia at 170°, several 4-phenylquinazolines were later prepared.[2] The method has been widely used for obtaining 2-, 4-, and 2,4-substituted quinazolines (Reaction 1) where the substituents could be branched alkyl groups, e.g. isopropyl[2,3,4] or t-butyl,[5] or unsaturated, e.g. styryl.[3]

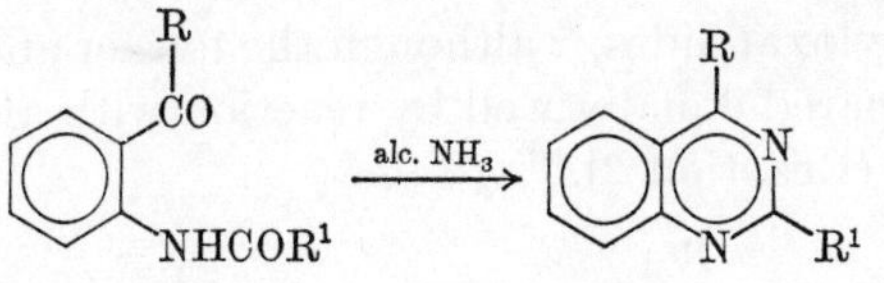

(1)

(1)

The reaction is of general applicability,[6] gives high yields, and has been used to prepare alkylquinazolines with a methoxy group in the benzene ring[7] and with a carboxyphenyl group in position 2.[8] Because

quinazoline can be prepared in high yield from *o*-formamidobenzalde-
hyde and alcoholic ammonia[9] (Ch. II, Sect. 1.), it should be possible to
prepare quinazolines with alkyl or aryl groups in positions 5, 6, 7, or 8 in
this way. The synthesis has proved satisfactory also for 4,5-dimethyl-
quinazolines[10] (**2**, R = H or Me) in which there is steric interaction
between the *peri* methyl groups.

(2)

Various conditions of temperature and time such as 1 hour at
$105°$[11] and 16 hours at $150°$[12] have been used, but high temperatures
and prolonged heating may not always be necessary. Although these
do not usually cause a drop in yield, they may be too drastic if there is a
sensitive substituent on R or R^1 in **1**. A study of the conditions for this
ring closure using saturated ethanolic ammonia has revealed that at
$20°$, when in **1**, R = H and R^1 = CF_3, $CHCl_2$, or CH_2Cl; or R = Me
and R^1 = CF_3 or $CHCl_2$, the reaction is complete in 12 hours. When
R = Me and R^1 = H it requires 18 hours, and when R = Me and
R^1 = Me or CMe_3, 4 to 5 days are necessary for completion. Acyl
substituents with electron-withdrawing groups therefore increase the
ease of ring closure.

In an endeavour to avoid the use of high pressures and sealed
tubes, Schofield, Swain and Theobald[13] carried out the ring closure by
bubbling ammonia gas through a fused mixture of *o*-formamidoaceto-
phenone and ammonium acetate at $155–160°$. 4-Methylquinazoline was
thus prepared in good yield. For 4-phenylquinazoline[14] the yield was
only 20%. This synthesis has been extended to the preparation of
4,4′-dimethyl- and 4,4′-diphenyl-2,2′-biquinazolinyl from the corresponding *o,o*-diacyloxanilides,[15] although the former and 2,2′-biquinazo-
linyl can be prepared equally well by reaction with alcoholic ammonia
in a sealed tube (Reaction 2).[16]

(2)

R = H, Me or Ph

A reaction which may proceed by a route similar to the above is the formation of 4-phenylquinazoline, in almost quantitative yield, by heating *o*-aminobenzophenone with formamide and formic acid at 150°. When formic acid is omitted the reaction requires longer periods at 210°, and when *o*-amidobenzophenones are used no significant products can be isolated.[17] Another reaction which makes use of alcoholic ammonia in a sealed tube is the preparation of 6-methyl- and 6,8-dimethyl- 2,4-diphenylquinazolines[18,19] as shown in reaction (3).

$$\text{(3)}$$

The hydroxy dihydroquinazoline was obtained from *p*-toluidine or *as-m*-xylidine and benzyl chloride in the presence of anhydrous zinc chloride (Ch. VIII, Sect. 4.F.); the action of ammonia must involve breakdown of the dihydroquinazoline with loss of one molecule of toluidine or xylidine followed by the usual ring closure.

B. Oxidation of 3,4-Dihydroquinazolines

The oxidation of 2-alkyl-[20,21,22,23] and 2-aryl-[23]3,4-dihydro-quinazolines takes place readily and smoothly with potassium ferri-cyanide in alkaline medium. The 2-aryl substituent may be *p*-methoxy-phenyl, *o*-nitrophenyl, or *α*- or *β*-naphthyl.[23] The same reagent is capable of oxidizing 4-substituted 3,4-dihydroquinazolines where the substituent is Ph,[14,24] PhCOCH$_2$,[25] PhCH$_2$,[24] Me,[26,27] Et, or isoPr[10,26]

$$\text{(4)}$$

(Reaction 4). The yields are usually above 50%. Other oxidizing agents have not been used and attempts to oxidize **3** (R = *t*-Bu) with alkaline potassium ferricyanide yielded quinazoline with loss of the *t*-butyl group. The oxidation is generally carried out in dilute aqueous alkali hydroxide or carbonate solution using a little more than two molecular equivalents of potassium ferricyanide. A mixture of water and benzene has occasionally been used as solvent in order to minimize the attack, by alkali, of the starting material or product.[10,24]

C. Decarboxylation of Acids

Acids with the carboxyl groups on $C_{(2)}$ or $C_{(4)}$ are readily obtained (Ch. X, Sects. 2.A. and 2.B.) and can be decarboxylated in good yields by boiling in dilute aqueous acid solutions, or better by heating at their melting points (Reaction 5). 2-Methyl-, 2-ethyl-, and 2-phenyl-6-methylquinazolines,[28] 2-methyl- and 2-phenylquinazoline[8] were prepared from the corresponding 4-carboxylic acids. 4-Methyl-[8] and 4-phenylquinazoline,[2] were similarly obtained from the corresponding 2-carboxylic acids. 4-Methylquinazoline was also obtained by boiling a

$$-CO_2 \qquad\qquad (5)$$

20% aqueous hydrochloric acid solution of 2-carbamoyl-4-methylquinazoline.[12] For the decarboxylation of acids with a carboxyl group on an alkyl side chain see section 1.H.

D. From N'-Toluene-p-sulphonylhydrazino Derivatives

The action of dilute alkali on alkyl 4-N'-toluene-p-sulphonylhydrazinoquinazolines or their hydrochlorides, as in the preparation of other quinazolines (Ch. V, Sect. E.b.(v)), gives yields of over 60% of 5-, 6-, 7-, and 8-methylquinazoline (Eq. 6).[29] This method was used successfully to prepare 4-phenylquinazoline from 4-phenyl-2-N'-toluene-p-sulphonylhydrazinoquinazoline. The method proceeds equally well with derivatives containing a trifluoro group in place of a methyl group.[30] For a possible mechanism of this reaction see Chapter II, Section 1.

$$\qquad (6)$$

E. From Imidoyl Chlorides and Nitriles

N-Phenyl alkyl(or aryl)imidoyl chlorides, with at least one unsubstituted *ortho* position in the phenyl group, react with aliphatic or aromatic nitriles in the presence of anhydrous aluminium chloride[31] to give C-alkyl or C-aryl substituted quinazolines (Reaction 7). The reaction is described as being similar to an Houben-Hoesch synthesis.

$$(7)$$

It can be carried out by complexing the imidoyl chloride with the Lewis acid and reacting it with the nitrile, complexing the nitrile with the Lewis acid and then adding the imidoyl chloride, or by mixing the three reagents together. The reaction can also be performed in one step, e.g. by mixing benzanilide in excess of benzonitrile with thionyl chloride and aluminium chloride, which gives an 86% yield of 2,4-diphenylquinazoline. Anhydrous zinc chloride or titanium tetrachloride can be used in place of aluminium chloride, and the reaction temperatures vary from 90 to 160°. The solvent may be the nitrile itself, whereby excess of it can be used, tetrachloroethane, o-dichlorobenzene, or nitrobenzene, depending on the temperatures required. R and R^1 in **4** can be similar or different, alkyl or aryl, di- or trichloromethyl, and the benzene ring of the quinazoline may also be substituted. The yields are generally well over 50%, and the imidate esters, e.g. $PhNH=C(OEt)Ph$, can be used instead of the imidoyl chlorides. N-β-Naphthylbenzimidoyl chloride and benzonitrile furnish 5,6-benzo-2,4-diphenylquinazoline in 88% yield.[31,32]

F. From Aryl Diazonium Salts and Nitriles

Aryl diazonium borofluorides, with at least one *ortho* position unsubstituted, react with two molecules of a nitrile at 20 to 50° to give 40–80% yields of quinazolines in which the 2- and 4-substituents are similar (Reaction 8).

$$(8)$$

Diazonium salts other than the borofluorides can be used and their stabilities are in the order $BiCl_5^{2-}$ > $SnCl_6^{2-}$ = $HgBr_3^-$ = BF_4^- > $ZnCl_6^{2-}$ > $FeCl_4^-$. Hence the reaction temperatures with the bismuthates, hexachlorostannates, and tetrachloroferrates are 80–90°, 70° and

3+Q.

45°, respectively, but the yields are similar when the different salts of the same aryl diazonium cation are used. 6-Methyl-, 5,7-dimethyl-, and 6-chloro- 2,4-diphenylquinazolines and 2,4-dibenzyl-5,8-dimethyl-quinazoline, among others, have been similarly synthesized.[31,33] The method is not particularly satisfactory when methylnitrile is used, because further condensation of the 4-methyl group with some of the N-arylacetonitrilium salt formed in the reaction (Eq. 9) may take place with the formation of the anil (5) from which the acetonyl derivative (6) could be obtained by alkaline hydrolysis.

$$\tag{9}$$

(5)   (6)

G. From 4-Chloro- or 4-Cyanoquinazoline and Grignard Reagents

The reaction of 4-chloroquinazoline and Grignard reagents has been described[24] but it is not a satisfactory one. Isopropyl magnesium bromide gives a 38% yield of 4-isopropylquinazoline together with a high molecular weight substance which is not 4,4'-biquinazolinyl as claimed.[16] Phenyl magnesium bromide yields the high molecular weight substance and uncrystallizable materials, and benzyl magnesium chloride afforded a 30% yield of 4-benzylquinazoline together with resinous products. A much cleaner reaction is that of a Grignard

$$+ \; RMgBr \longrightarrow \quad + \; MgBrCN \tag{10}$$

reagent and 4-cyanoquinazoline (Eq. 10), in which the 4-substituted quinazolines are isolated with loss of the cyano group. Thus 4-methyl-, 4-ethyl-, 4-isopropyl-, 4-phenyl-, and 4-benzylquinazoline were

$$
\underset{\text{CN}}{\overset{\text{CH}\underset{\text{CH}_3}{\overset{\text{CH}_3}{\big<}}}{\bigg|}} + \text{PhMgBr} \longrightarrow \underset{\text{COPh}}{\overset{\text{CH}_3-\text{CH}-\text{CH}_3}{\bigg|}} \tag{11}
$$

obtained in 87, 80, 74, 45, and 42% yields, respectively. Although there is no evidence of attack of the Grignard reagent on the cyano group on $C_{(4)}$, 2-cyano-4-isopropylquinazoline reacts with phenyl magnesium bromide to give an 80% yield of 2-benzoyl-4-isopropylquinazoline (Reaction 11).[34] This is attributed to the greater ease with which the cyano group is substituted when in position 4. The condensation of 2,4-dichloroquinazoline with aryl magnesium halide is described in a patent.[35]

H. From Chloro- or Cyanoquinazolines and Substances with an Active Methylene Group

4-Chloroquinazoline reacts with compounds with an active methylene group in the presence of sodium ethoxide[36,37] or in the presence of sodamide[38,39] in an anhydrous solvent (Eq. 12). The yields of 4-substituted alkylquinazolines thus obtained are usually under 50%

$$
\underset{(7)}{\overset{\text{Cl}}{\bigg|}} + \underset{R^1}{\overset{}{\big\backslash}}\text{CH}\underset{R^2}{\overset{R}{\big/}} \xrightarrow{\text{NaOEt}} \underset{(8)}{\overset{\overset{R^1 \quad R^2}{\big\backslash \text{CR} /}}{\bigg|}} \tag{12}
$$

but the synthesis does lead to products which are otherwise difficultly accessible. The active methylene compounds used were $PhCH_2CN$, $CH_2(CO_2Et)_2$, $CH_2(CN)CO_2Et$, $PhCH(CN)CO_2Et$, $EtCH(CO_2Et)_2$,[36,38] $PhCH(CN)(CH_2)_nNR_2$,[39] $CH_2(CN)CO_2CH_2Ph$,[40] and $CH_3COCH_2 \cdot CO_2Ph$.[40] However, when one of the groups in 7 is an acetyl group as in ethyl acetoacetate[36] or benzyl acetoacetate,[40] the acetyl group is lost in the reaction and the products are 8 ($R = R^1 = H$, $R^2 = CO_2Et$) or 8 ($R = R^1$, $R^2 = CO_2CH_2Ph$). The mechanism proposed by Elderfield and Serlin[36] is shown in reaction (13). It is probably correct because a simple retro acetoacetic ester synthesis of **9** would involve OH⁻ ions

(13)

which cannot be present in the anhydrous medium in which the reaction is carried out. Ethoxide ions can bring about this reaction but the concentration of these is very small, if at all present, in the medium. Aqueous alkaline hydrolysis of 4-(α,α-diethoxycarbonyl)methyl- (**8**, R = H, R^1 = R^2 = CO_2Et) and 4-(α,α-diethoxycarbonyl)propylquinazoline (**8**, R = Et, R^1 = R^2 = CO_2Et) followed by decarboxylation gives 4-methyl- and 4-propylquinazoline in 71 and 63% yields.[36] Hydrolysis of the former with sodium ethoxide, on the other hand, gives an 82% yield of 4-ethoxycarbonylmethylquinazoline (**8**, R = R^1 = H, R^2 = CO_2Et). However, this is not always the case, because 4-(α-cyano-α-ethoxycarbonyl)methylquinazoline resists hydrolysis, due, probably, to the formation of a stable alkali salt.[40] Acid hydrolysis, on the other hand, invariably caused fission of a carbon–carbon bond with the formation of 3,4-dihydro-4-oxoquinazoline.[36] Substitution of the chlorine atom in the 2-position of quinazoline by nucleophiles in a manner similar to the above has also been achieved. 2-Chloroquinazoline reacted with benzyl cyanide or ethyl cyanoacetate in the presence of sodamide to give 2-α-cyanobenzylquinazoline and 2-(α-cyano-α-ethoxycarbonyl)methylquinazoline, respectively.[38]

Similar to the synthesis described above is the reaction of the more versatile 4-cyanoquinazoline with ethyl acetoacetate, ethyl cyanoacetate, and diethyl malonate in the presence of sodamide in benzene, which affords the respective 4-quinazolinyl compounds related to **8**. The reaction with nitromethane can be carried out in aqueous potassium carbonate, and gives 4-nitromethylquinazoline in 20% yield.[41] The reactions of 4-cyanoquinazoline have been extended by Higashino to the condensations in 50% aqueous sodium hydroxide solutions,[42] and were carried out at room temperature. Acetone and acetophenone gave the required 4-acetonyl- and 4-benzoylmethylquinazoline in 66 and 50% yields, respectively. Ethyl methyl ketone and isopropyl methyl ketone gave two products resulting from the condensation at each of the active methylene groups of the ketone (Eqs. 14 and 15). Because the products

$$\text{(quinazoline-CN)} + CH_3COCH_2CH_3 \xrightarrow{OH^-}$$

$$\underset{\textbf{(10)}}{\text{quinazoline-}CH_2COCH_2CH_3} + \underset{\textbf{(11)}}{\text{quinazoline-}CH_3-CH-COCH_3} \qquad (14)$$

$$\text{(quinazoline-CN)} + CH_3COCH\overset{CH_3}{\underset{CH_3}{\diagup}} \xrightarrow{OH^-} \qquad (15)$$

$$\underset{\textbf{(12)}}{\text{quinazoline-}CH_2COCH\overset{CH_3}{\underset{CH_3}{\diagup}}} + \underset{\textbf{(13)}}{\text{quinazoline-}CH_3-\overset{CH_3}{\underset{}{C}}-COCH_3}$$

11 and **13** are unstable in the presence of alkali, loss of the acetyl group occurs and 4-ethyl- and 4-isopropylquinazoline are formed, respectively. Condensation of 4-cyanoquinazoline with diethyl ketone and propiophenone (ethyl phenyl ketone) gave the intermediate, 4-1'-propionylethyl- and 4-1'-benzoylethylquinazoline, respectively, which decomposed in the alkaline medium of the reaction to the same 4-ethylquinazoline; the alkaline solution from the latter reaction furnished benzoic acid on acidification. Hydrolysis of 4-acetonyl-, 4-benzoylmethyl-, 4-butan-2'-onyl-(**10**), and 4-(3'-methylbutan-2'-onyl)quinazoline (**12**) with 30% aqueous sodium hydroxide gave 4-methylquinazoline in each case.[42] A similar condensation with cyclopentanone gave a very good yield of 4-cyclopentan-2'-onylquinazoline, but cyclohexanone gave a 44% yield of 4-5'-carboxypentylquinazoline (Eq. 16) without isolation of the intermediate 4-cyclohexan-2'-onylquinazoline (**14**). Hydrolysis of the quinazolinylpentanone with hot alkali gave 4-4'-carboxybutylquinazoline.[42] 4-Chloroquinazoline

$$\text{CN} \quad \text{O} \qquad \qquad \text{O} \qquad \qquad CH_2(CH_2)_4CO_2H$$

(14)

(16)

under similar aqueous alkaline conditions hydrolyzes to 3,4-dihydro-4-oxoquinazoline, and 4-cyanoquinazoline behaves in a similar way only when the ketone is omitted from the reaction medium.

I. Reidel's Synthesis

This synthesis, the reductive cyclization of bisformamido derivatives of o-nitrobenzaldehydes (15), is used successfully for the synthesis of quinazoline (Ch. II, Sect. 1.) and several derivatives (Reaction 17).[29]

$$\text{H} \quad \text{HNCOR}^1$$
$$R \quad \text{NHCOR}^1 \quad \longrightarrow \quad R$$
$$\text{NO}_2$$

(15)

(17)

The reaction is limited by the availability of the respective o-nitrobenzaldehydes. The preparation of o-nitrobenzaldehydes from o-nitrobenzene diazonium salts and formaldehyde oxime[43] has widened the scope of this synthesis. The preparation of 7-methyl- and 2-methylquinazoline, among several other quinazolines, by this method, is described.[44] The reducing agent is zinc and acetic acid or hydrochloric acid. Reduction of o-nitrobenzaldehydes in the presence of formamide containing Raney nickel also gives quinazolines.[44] The reaction can be adopted only for the preparation of alkylquinazolines which lack a substituent on $C_{(4)}$ because o-nitroacetophenones do not condense with aliphatic amides to yield bisamido derivatives as do the aldehydes. When R^1 is a phenyl group in 15, cyclization to 2-phenylquinazoline does not take place.

J. Miscellaneous

The following methods are not likely to be of general use for the preparation of alkyl- and arylquinazolines but deserve mention. 2-Chloro-4-2'-pyridylquinazoline is reduced with 5% Pd/C to give a poor yield of 4-2'-pyridylquinazoline.[15] Normally catalytic reduction of 2- and 4-chloroquinazoline is difficult to stop at the quinazoline stage and tends to give 3,4-dihydro derivatives. Thus 2-chloro-4-phenylquinazoline gives 3,4-dihydro-4-phenylquinazoline (Ch. V, Sect. 1.E.b.(iv)).[14] Reduction of 2-phenyl-4-trichloromethylquinazoline and 4-phenyl-2-trichloromethylquinazoline with zinc and hydrochloric acid gives the corresponding methylphenylquinazolines.[31] Alkyl- and arylquinazoline N-oxides are reduced smoothly to the corresponding quinazolines with phosphorus trichloride or Raney nickel and hydrogen[6,45] (Ch. IX, Sects. 1. and 2.C.). When 2-methyl- or 2-phenyl-5,6,7,8-tetrahydroquinazolines are heated with 10% Pd/C at about 285°, dehydrogenation takes place with evolution of hydrogen.[46] 2-Phenylquinazoline was isolated in 80% yield, and although the theoretical volume of hydrogen was evolved from the 2-methyl derivative, no satisfactory yield of 2-methylquinazoline was obtained. The same reactions can be carried out with 5% Pd/C in boiling decalin but the yields are inferior (Reaction 18).[47] The formation of 4,4'-biquinazolinyls[16] from quinazolines which are unsubstituted in position 4 is described in chapter II, section 3.C.

$$\text{(18)}$$

2. Properties

A. Physical Properties

The alkylquinazolines are low-melting solids or liquids, and a substituent with a branched chain lowers the melting point. They can be distilled at atmospheric pressure with little decomposition and sublime readily in a vacuum. Aryl substituents raise the melting point and this depends largely on whether or not the aryl group is further substituted. The solubilities of these compounds in water are much larger than those of the corresponding naphthalene analogues, as would be predicted from the presence of the ring nitrogen atoms whose non-bonded pair of electrons are available for solvation with water molecules. Thus 2- and 4-methylquinazoline are soluble in water to more than 30%. The lower members of the alkyl series are sometimes hygroscopic. So great is the affinity that 8-methylquinazoline has for water, for example, that unless a dry-box sampling technique is used for microanalysis, good figures cannot be obtained for the anhydrous material.[29] 2,4-Dimethylquinazoline is a liquid which is converted to a solid with two molecules of water per molecule of substance on standing in air,[48] but is dehydrated under vacuum. Solid alkylquinazolines can be crystallized from light petroleum or benzene. The arylquinazolines are less soluble in water and can be crystallized also from alcohols.

When kept for long periods at room temperature in the dark, 2- and 4-methylquinazoline show an intense band in the infrared spectrum at ~ 1700 cm^{-1} which is not present in the purified material. The remainder of the spectrum is barely altered. This band could be removed only by passage of a benzene solution of these quinazolines through a column of alumina and magnesium oxide prior to distillation.[49] Alkyl- and arylquinazolines form well-defined and stable picrates (see Tables III.1, 2, 3, and 5) from which the quinazolines can be regenerated by passage through an alumina column in a suitable solvent, e.g. benzene or by shaking with aqueous alkali—preferably lithium hydroxide which forms a more water-soluble picrate. They can be readily extracted into, and recovered from, chloroform.

The quinazolines dissolve in aqueous hydrochloric acid. Those that lack a substituent on $C_{(4)}$ are likely to exist in aqueous acid solution as the hydrates, which have covalently bound water. They have the structure 16 which is stabilized by an amidinium resonance.[40] Hence their

(16)

salts, prepared in aqueous solution, are likely to possess the elements of one molecule of water. Because of this resonance the pK_a values are larger, i.e. stronger bases than would be expected from the normal base-strengthening effect of the substituents on the $pK_a{}^{anhyd.}$ of quinazoline. Covalent hydration in these quinazolines is discussed in chapter II together with the ultraviolet,[10,27,29,40] infrared,[50,51] and nuclear magnetic resonance[16] spectra. The ultraviolet spectra of the neutral species show the typical three-band spectrum of the parent quinazoline.

B. Chemical Properties

a. The Heightened Reactivity of 2- and 4-Methyl Groups

Methyl groups on $C_{(2)}$ and $C_{(4)}$ of quinazoline behave in a manner similar to methyl groups that are placed α or γ to the nitrogen heteroatoms in pyridine and quinoline.[52] They react like 'active methylene' groups. Bogert and Nabenhauer[12] were the first to test the reactivity of methyl groups by condensing 2-methyl-, 4-methyl-, 2,4-dimethyl-, and 4-methyl-2-phenyl- quinazolines with phthalic anhydride. They fused the mixture for a few hours and obtained insoluble products (Reaction 19). Addition of anhydrous zinc chloride did not appear to improve the

(19)

(17)

reaction. The nature of the products made purification difficult but the analyses clearly indicated that condensation had taken place and that only one phthalic anhydride molecule per molecule of quinazoline was involved in each case. These products did not have good melting points and only some of the analyses were satisfactory. They attempted to compare the relative reactivity of the 2- and 4-methyl groups by carrying out the reaction under strictly similar conditions, but were unable to make a comparison. The phthalone (17) was insoluble in dilute caustic alkali whereas the phthalone from 4-methylquinazoline dissolved in dilute alkali to give a brown-coloured solution from which it could be precipitated by addition of acid. Because the phthalone obtained from 2,4-dimethylquinazoline was difficultly soluble in dilute alkali, the authors concluded[12] that it was the 4-methyl-2-phthalone and that the 2-methyl group was more reactive than the 4-methyl group.

2-Methylquinazoline condenses with many aldehydes[53] viz: benzaldehyde, *p*-methoxybenzaldehyde, terephthalaldehyde, furfural, thiophene-2-aldehyde, pyridine-3-aldehyde, and 6-methylpyridine-2-aldehyde, to give the ethylenic compounds 18. The reaction (20) is carried out in boiling methanol containing potassium methoxide but the yields are only between 4 and 12%. With chloral, in pyridine, the reaction stops at the intermediate hydrate stage[54] giving a 99% yield of 2-(3′,3′,3′-trichloro-2′-hydroxy)propylquinazoline (19) which has to be treated with potassium hydroxide to furnish 2-2′-carboxyethenyl-quinazoline (20). Studies of the relative reactivity of 2- and 4-methyl groups towards aldehydes have not been made, but Adachi[37] prepared 4-*p*-nitrostyrylquinazoline (21) in about 10% yield in ethanol (Reaction

3*

$$(20)$$

$$(18)$$

$$(19)$$

$$(20)$$

21). When the ethanolic solution was not allowed to boil, the intermediate 4-(2'-hydroxy-2'-p-nitrophenyl)ethylquinazoline (**22**) was isolated
and was in turn dehydrated to **21** by boiling in ethanol for 1 hour. A
comparison of these results with the previous condensations of 2-methyl-
quinazoline suggests that the 4-methyl group is more reactive towards

$$(21)$$ $$(21)$$

$$(22)$$

aldehydes than the 2-methyl group. Supporting evidence is shown in
the Mannich reactions described below. Other workers, however, have
found that the condensation of 4-methylquinazoline with benzaldehyde
was difficult[55] and gave tars. 2,4-Dimethylquinazoline failed to react
with p-dimethylaminobenzaldehyde and other aromatic aldehydes,
even in the presence of condensing agents, e.g. anhydrous zinc chloride.[56] A similar condensation was later carried out successfully by
heating a mixture of 4-methylquinazoline with p-dimethylamino-

benzaldehyde in the presence of anhydrous zinc chloride,[57] but the resulting styryl compound was isolated in 12% yield only.

The relative reactivity of methyl groups on $C_{(2)}$ and $C_{(4)}$ in quinazolines was clearly demonstrated by Siegle and Christensen[55] who carried out Mannich reactions (Eq. 22). Whereas 4-methyl- and 2,4-dimethylquinazoline gave the required products (23) with dimethylamine, and morpholine in 20–40% yields, 2-methylquinazoline failed to react, or gave a tar, under the various conditions used. The reactivity of the 4-methyl group, however, is lower than that in an acetyl group because 7-acetyl-2,4-dimethylquinazoline gave 2,4-dimethyl-7-3'-dimethyl aminopropionylquinazoline (24) under similar conditions.

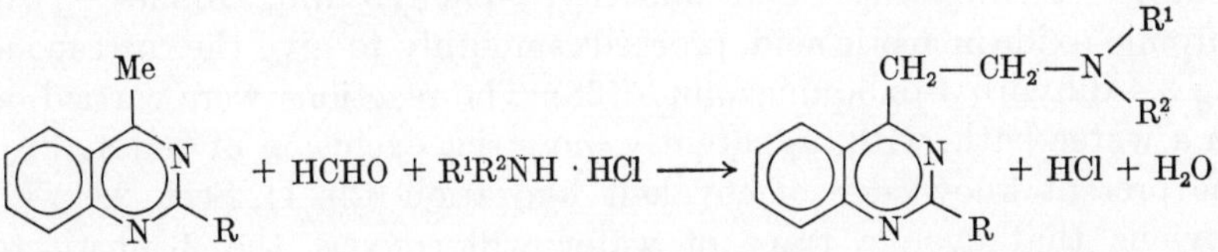

$$ \text{(Eq. 22)} $$

(23)

(22)

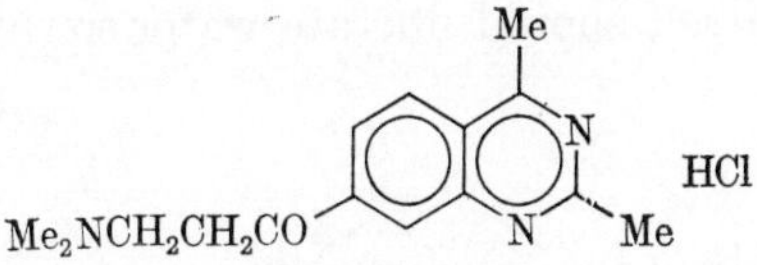

(24)

4-Methyl-2-phenylquinazoline, in nitrobenzene, condenses with N-phenyl benzimidoyl chloride in the presence of anhydrous aluminium chloride[31] to give a 93% yield of 2-phenyl-4-2'-phenyliminophenethyl-

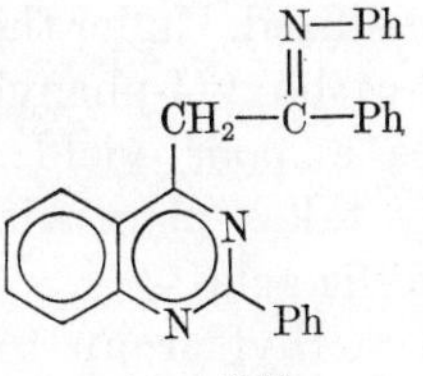

(25) 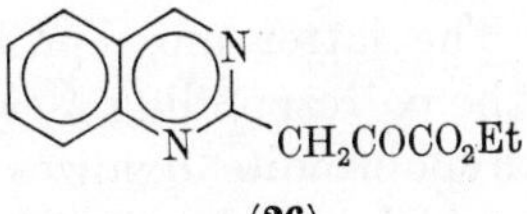   (26)

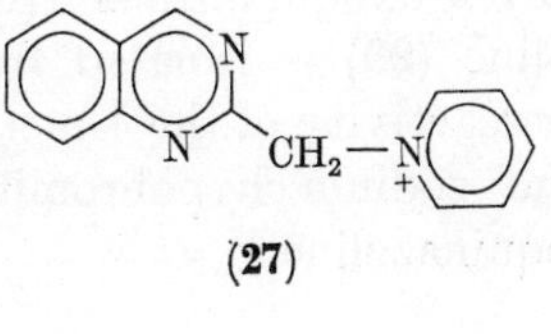

(27)

quinazoline (25). 2-Methylquinazoline, in acetic acid, reacts with diethyl oxalate[58] to give 2-ethoxalylmethylquinazoline (26) which is a useful intermediate. 2-Methylquinazoline also reacts with pyridine containing iodine to give the pyridinium salt (27) which can be isolated as the perchlorate in 78% yield.[59] The iodine in this reaction may be responsible for partial oxidation of the methyl group. For the reactivity of substituted alkyl groups see section 2.B.e.

b. *Oxidation and Reduction*

The oxidation of 2-methyl-, 2-ethyl-, 2-propyl-, 2-isopropyl-, 2-benzyl-,[4] 2,6-dimethyl- and 6-methyl-2-phenyl- quinazolines,[28] with chromic oxide in acetic acid, proceeds smoothly to give the corresponding 3,4-dihydro-4-oxoquinazolines (28). The reactions were carried out on a water bath, with, apparently, no strict exclusion of water. From the present knowledge of covalent hydration (Ch. II, Sect. 2.C.) it is obvious that even a trace of water will convert the 2-substituted quinazolines to the hydrated cations. The reaction is therefore the oxidation of α-carbinolamines and should take place readily (Reaction 23). The oxidation itself should liberate water so that very little water

(23)

is necessary to carry the oxidation to completion. When a substituent is present on $C_{(4)}$ then the hydrated cation is not readily formed and the more sensitive substituent, therefore, is oxidized. Under these conditions 2-methyl-4-phenylquinazoline gives 2-carboxy-4-phenylquinazoline,[2] and 4-methyl-2-phenylquinazoline gives a poor yield of 2-phenylquinazoline.[3] The latter most probably takes place via the decarboxylation of the corresponding 4-carboxylic acid.

Sodium hypobromite oxidizes a 4-methyl group to a tribromomethyl group which can then be hydrolyzed to give bromoform and the corresponding 3,4-dihydro-4-oxoquinazoline (Reaction 24). 2-Methyl-4-tribromomethylquinazoline (29) is isolated from this reaction[55] and demonstrates the higher reactivity of the 4-methyl group. 7-Acetyl-2,4-dimethylquinazoline and sodium hypobromite gives 7-carboxy-3,4-dihydro-2-methyl-4-oxoquinazoline.[55]

(24)

(29)

(30)

Catalytic reduction of alkyl quinazolines lacking in a substituent on $C_{(4)}$ proceeds rapidly and then almost stops after the absorption of one molecule of hydrogen. In neutral medium 2-methylquinazoline is reduced, in the presence of 5% Pd/C, to give a 60% yield of 3,4-dihydro-2-methylquinazoline.[60] Reduction stops at the dihydro stage apparently due to the poisoning of the catalyst by the reduced base. Under the same conditions reduction of 4-alkylquinazolines also takes place, but at a considerably slower rate and furnishes only the 3,4-dihydro derivatives[10] (for further details see Ch. VIII, Sect. 4.D.).

Reduction of 2,4-dimethyl-[48] and 2-methyl-4-phenylquinazoline[2] with sodium and amyl alcohol gives the corresponding 1,2,3,4-tetrahydroquinazolines. A substituent in a side chain is reduced in the normal fashion, for example 24 is reduced to 7-(3'-dimethylamino-1'-hydroxy)propyl-2,4-dimethylquinazoline (30) with Adams' platinum as catalyst.[11]

c. *Electrophilic Substitution*

Very little work has been done on the electrophilic substitution of alkyl- and arylquinazolines. Attempted Friedel Crafts reactions with 2-methyl- and 2,4-dimethylquinazoline failed,[11] and nitration of 2,6-dimethylquinazoline gives 3,4-dihydro-2-methyl-6-nitro-4-oxoquinazoline.[61] When smaller quantities of nitric acid are used in the nitration, a mixture of the starting material and the oxoquinazoline is obtained. Moreover, nitration of 3,4-dihydro-2-methyl-4-oxoquinazoline yields the same mononitro compound, and it appears that elimination of the methyl group precedes nitration. This reaction also reflects the higher reactivity of the 4-methyl group.

d. *Alkylation*

Bogert and Clark[56] were unable to alkylate 2,4-dimethyl-, 4-methyl-2-styryl-, and 4-methyl-2-phenylquinazoline with methyl iodide, ethyl iodide, or dimethyl sulphate under a variety of conditions. They found that either the reaction does not take place or extensive decomposition occurs. 4-Methylquinazoline and methyl iodide at room temperature, on the other hand, give the methiodide in good yield.[62] The structure of the very deliquescent quaternary salt was shown to be 1,4-dimethylquinazolinium iodide. Although it could not be purified, it gave the same cyanine dye, 1-methyl-4-(1′-methylbenzothiazolidin-2′-ylidenemethyl)quinazolinium toluene-*p*-sulphonate (**31**), when condensed with 3-methyl-2-methylthiobenzothiazolinium toluene-*p*-sulphonate (Eq. 25) as did 1-methyl-4-methylthioquinazolinium iodide (**32**) when condensed with 2-methylbenzothiazole methiodide (**33**).

$$p\text{-}CH_3C_6H_4SO_3^- \qquad (25)$$

(**31**)

(**32**)   (**33**)

1-Methyl-4-methylthioquinazolinium iodide was prepared unambiguously from 1,4-dihydro-1-methyl-4-thioquinazoline and methyl iodide.[62] 1-Methyl- and 1-ethyl-4-methylquinazolinium toluene-*p*-sulphonate are prepared from 4-methylquinazoline by heating with methyl and ethyl toluene-*p*-sulphonic esters respectively.[62] Because alkylation of 2,4-disubstituted quinazolines is not satisfactory,[56] 1,2-dimethyl-4-phenylquinazolinium iodide (**34**), is obtained by a Grignard reaction between 1,4-dihydro-1,2-dimethyl-4-oxoquinazoline and phenyl magnesium bromide followed by boiling with hydriodic

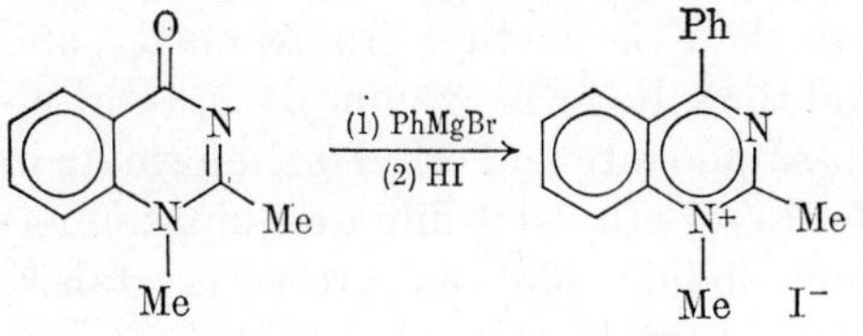

(26)

(34)

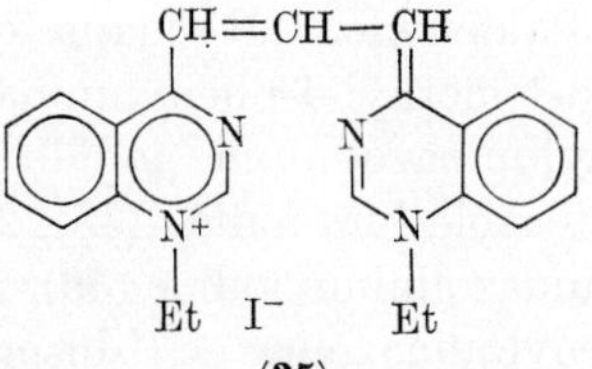

(35)

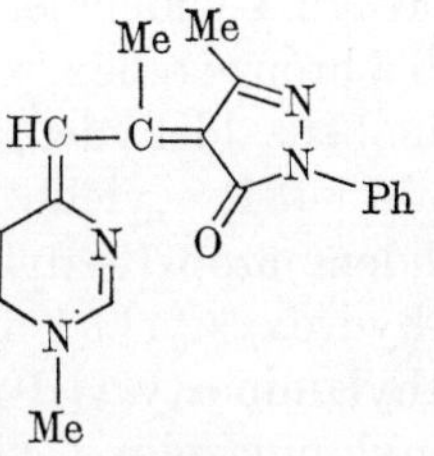

(36)

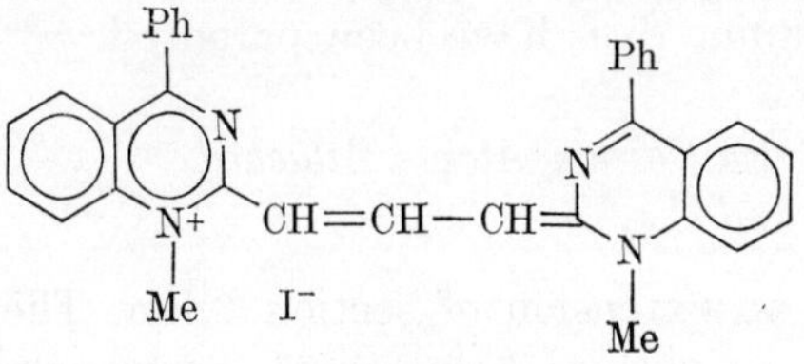

(37)

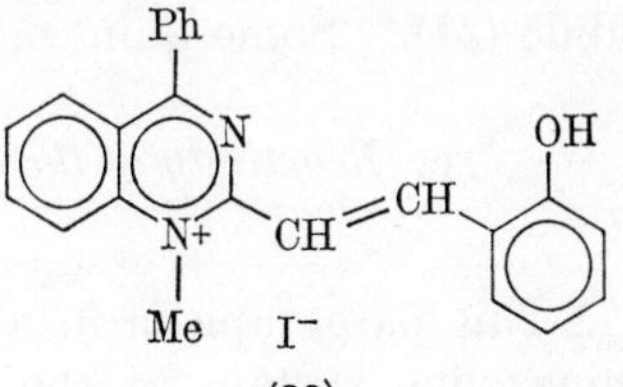

(38)

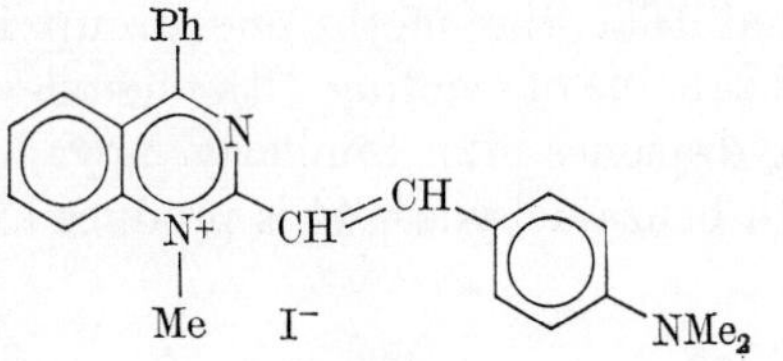

(39)

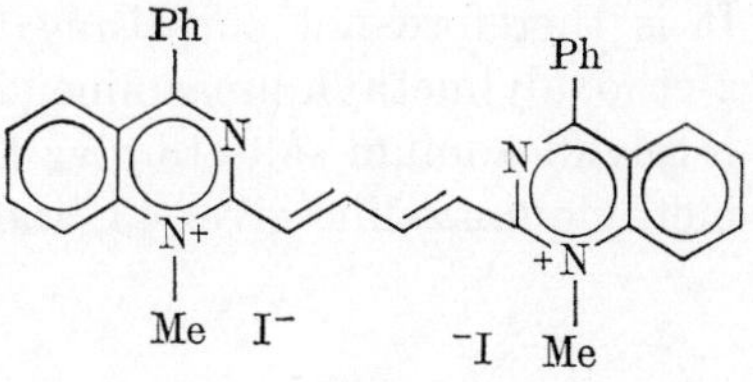

(40)

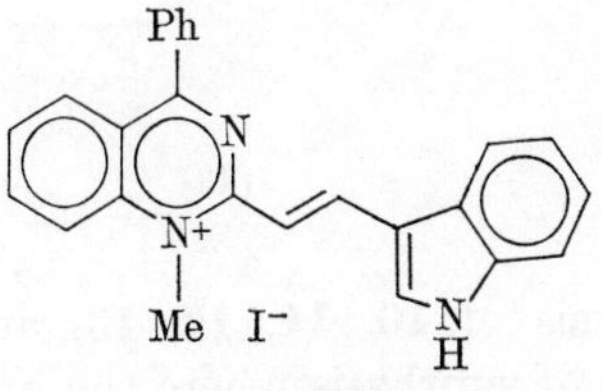

(41)

acid (Reaction 26).[63] The methyl groups on $C_{(2)}$ and $C_{(4)}$ in these quaternary salts are more reactive than the methyl groups on $C_{(2)}$ and $C_{(4)}$ in the parent quinazolines, and the salts form cyanine dyes. 1-Ethyl-4-methylquinazolinium toluene-p-sulphonate and ethyl orthoformate in boiling pyridine gives 1-ethyl-4-(3'-(1-ethyl-1,4-dihydroquinazolin-4-ylidene)prop-1'-enyl)quinazolinium iodide (35) as green crystals.[62] 1,4-Dimethylquinazolinium toluene-p-sulphonate, 3-methyl-1-phenyl-pyrazol-5-one, ethyl orthoacetate, and triethylamine in boiling ethanol formed 1,4-dihydro-1-methyl-4-(β-methyl-β-(3-methyl-5-oxo-1-phenyl-pyrazolin-4-ylidene)ethylidene)quinazoline (36) as dark brown crystals with a bronze reflex.[62] Ethyl orthoformate, salicylaldehyde, p-dimethyl-aminobenzaldehyde, glyoxal, and indol-3-aldehyde, and the quaternary iodide (34) yield 2-(3'-(1,2-dihydro-1-methyl-4-phenylquinazolin-2-ylidene)prop-1'-enyl)-1-methyl-4-phenylquinazolinium iodide (37), 2-o-hydroxystyryl-1-methyl-4-phenylquinazolinium iodide (38), 2-p-di-methylaminostyryl-1-methyl-4-phenylquinazolinium iodide (39), 2-(δ-4' phenylquinazolin-2'-yl)butadienyl-4-phenylquinazoline 1,1'-bismethio-dide (40), and 2-β-indol-3'-ylethenyl-1-methyl-4-phenylquinazolinium iodide (41).[63] Some quinazoline cyanine dyes have been patented.[64,65]

e. *Reactivity of the Substituted Carbon Atoms Attached to $C_{(2)}$ and $C_{(4)}$*

This paragraph is in a sense an extension of section 2.B.a. The quinazoline system in the alkyl derivatives behaves as a strongly electron-withdrawing group akin to a cyano or ethoxycarbonyl group. It is therefore not surprising to find that the methylene group in 2-ethoxalylmethylquinazoline (26) is capable of reacting with phenyl- or p-tolyldiazonium salts to give the hydrazones (42). Similarly 2-cyano-methylquinazoline gives 43, and with benzaldehydes, 44 is produced.[58]

C—COCO$_2$Et
‖
NNHR
(42)

C—CN
‖
NNHR
(43)

C—CN
‖
CHR
(44)

The alkaline hydrolysis of 10, 11, 12, 13, and 14 involves a retro acetoacetic ester type of synthesis where the quinazoline nucleus takes the place of an ethoxycarbonyl group. A trihalomethyl group on $C_{(2)}$ and $C_{(4)}$ is readily eliminated as haloform with alkali, e.g. reaction (24).

When 2-phenyl-4-trichloromethylquinazoline is heated with alkali, chloroform is liberated, and the 3,4-dihydro-4-oxo-2-phenylquinazoline (45) is formed (Reaction 27).[31] The quinazoline moiety here behaves like the aldehyde group in chloral.

$$(27)$$

The cleavage of a carbon–carbon bond as above takes place readily when the methyl group is loaded with strongly electron-attracting substituents, e.g. CO_2Et or CN. In these examples, e.g. 4-(α,α-diethoxycarbonyl)methylquinazoline (46), however, alkali can hydrolyse the ester group and stabilizes the compounds by formation of an anion. Acid hydrolysis, by contrast, degrades the molecule, to give 3,4-dihydro-4-oxoquinazoline (48) (Sect. 1.H.). Thus when 47 (R = H, $R^1 = R^2 = CO_2Et$), (R = Et, $R^1 = R^2 = CO_2Et$), (R = Ph, $R^1 = R^2 = CO_2Et$), (R = H, $R^1 = CN$, $R^2 = CO_2Et$), and (R = H, $R^1 = Ph$, $R^2 = CN$) are boiled with 3 N hydrochloric acid, 3,4-dihydro-4-oxoquinazoline (48) is formed in good yields (Reaction 28).[36] In some

$$(28)$$

cases 10 minutes is sufficient for complete hydrolysis, but longer periods are required when a cyano group is present. With a halogen substituent on $C_{(2)}$, for example 2-chloro-4-(α-cyano-α-ethoxycarbonyl)-methylquinazoline, acid hydrolysis requires longer periods of heating and the product is benzoylene urea. The most labile compound appears to be 4-(α,α-diethoxycarbonyl)propylquinazoline (47, R = Et, $R^1 = R^2 = CO_2Et$) whose picrate decomposes to the 3,4-dihydro-4-oxo-quinazoline picrate on standing in alcoholic solution. The acid hydrolysis may involve the hydrated intermediate cation 49 (R = H) as in 16 because it was shown that the larger the substituent on $C_{(4)}$ the greater was the tendency to form a hydrated cation when compared with 4-methylquinazoline[10] (Ch. II, Sect. 2.C.b.(i)). Further evidence for this mechanism, is derived from the hydrolysis of **47** (R = Et, R^1 = R^2 = CO_2Et) in ethanolic hydrochloric acid solution which results in a 56% yield of 4-ethoxyquinazoline (Reaction 29).[36] Similarly, acid hydrolysis of **47** (R = Ph, R^1 = CN, R^2 = $(CH_2)_nNR_2{}^3$) gives **48** (Reaction 28).[39]

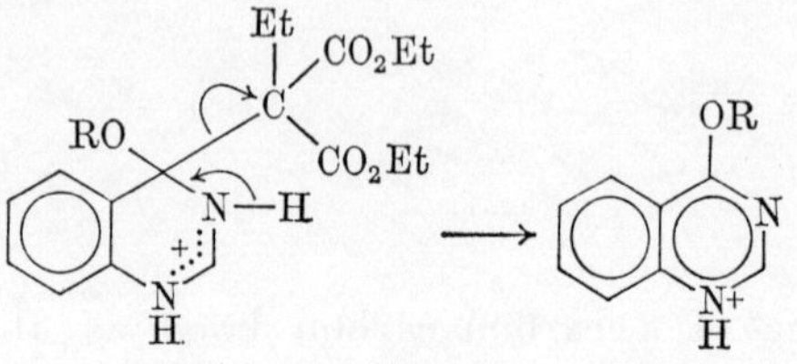

(29)

(49) R = H or Et

3. Tables

TABLE III.1. 2-Alkyl- and Aryl- (including Heteroaryl-) quinazolines.

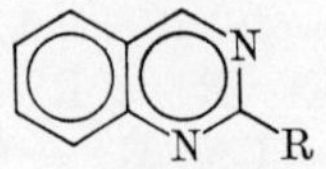

Quinazoline	M.p. (°c)	References
2-Benzyl-	59–60°, 350–355°/atm; picrate 230–232°	4, 38
2-2′-Carboxyethenyl-	250° (dec.)	54
2-2′-Carboxyethyl-	205°	54
2-o-Carboxyphenyl-	208–209°	68
2-p-Chlorobenzyl-	picrate 208–209°	23
2-(α-Cyano-α-p-dimethylamino-phenylimino)methyl-	232–233°	58
2-(α-Cyano-α-ethoxycarbonyl)-methyl-	127–129°	38
2-α-Cyano-p-methoxystyryl-	173–174°	58
2-(α-Cyano-α-p-tolylhydrazono)-methyl-	233°	58
2-Cyanomethyl-	100–103°	58
2-α-Cyanostyryl-	198–199°	58
2-Dichloromethyl-	132°	5
2-(α-Ethoxalyl-α-phenyl-hydrazono)methyl-	134–136°	58
2-(α-Ethoxalyl-α-p-tolylhydrazono)methyl-	165°	58
2-Ethoxalylmethyl-	160–161°	58

(Table continued)

TABLE III.1 (*continued*)

Quinazoline	M.p. (°c)	References
2-Ethyl-	77°/0.9 mm, 247–249°/722 mm	4, 5
2-β-2′-Furylethenyl-	119°	53
2-(Indan-1′,3′-dion-2′-yl)-	—	12
2-Isopropyl-	95°/0.5 mm, 235–255°/722 mm	4, 5
2-*p*-Methoxyphenyl-	95–96°; picrate 161–162°	23
2-*p*-Methoxystyryl-	145°	53
2-Methyl-	41–42°, 255°/atm,	
	253–255°/720 mm;	1, 4, 22, 23,
	picrate 92°, 97–98°	44
2-(β-6′-Methyl-2′-pyridylethenyl)-	131°	53
2-Monochloromethyl-	93°	5
2-1′-Naphthyl-	127–128°; picrate 149–150°	23
2-*o*-Nitrophenyl-	108–109°; picrate 114–115°	23
2-Phenyl-	101°, 103–104°; picrate	4, 8, 23, 46,
	162–163°	47
2-Propyl-	257–259°/722 mm	4
2-β-3′-Pyridylethenyl-	129°	53
2-*N*′-Pyridyl-	perchlorate 143–144°	59
2-Quinazolin-2′-yl-	285–286°	16
2-β-Quinazolin-2′-ylethenyl-	293°	53
2-Styryl-	129°	53
2-*t*-Butyl-	74°/0.3 mm	5
2-β-2′-Thienylethenyl-	132°	53
2-(3′,3′,3′-Trichloro-2′-hydroxy)-propyl-	172°	54
2-Trifluoromethyl-	63°, 72°/0.2 mm	5

TABLE III.2.   4-Alkyl- and Aryl- (including Heteroaryl-) quinazolines.

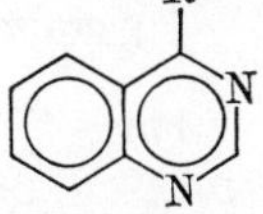

Quinazoline	M.p. (°c)	References
4-Acetonyl-	121–122°	42
4-Benzoyl-	160–161°	25, 42
4-Benzyl-	picrate 154°	42
4-(α-Benzyloxycarbonyl-α-cyano)-methyl-	150–151°	40

(*Table continued*)

TABLE III.2 *(continued)*

Quinazoline	M.p. (°c)	References
4-Benzyloxycarbonylmethyl-	139–140°	40
4-Butan-2'-onyl-	111–112°	42
4-(1'-Carbamoyl-1'-methyl)ethyl-	192° (dec.)	34
4-4'-Carboxybutyl-	136°	42
4-5'-Carboxypentyl-	100–101°	42
4-1'-Cyanobenzyl-	112°	38
4-(1'-Cyano-4'-diethylamino-2'-phenyl)butyl-	182–185°/0.005 mm	39
4-(1'-Cyano-3'-diethylamino-1'-phenyl)propyl-	195–198°/0.025 mm	39
4-(1'-Cyano-4'-dimethylamino-1'-phenyl)butyl-	182–186°/0.005 mm	39
4-(1'-Cyano-3'-dimethylamino-1'-phenyl)propyl-	183–186°/0.015 mm	39
4-(α-Cyano-α-ethoxycarbonyl)-benzyl-	96–102°; picrate 209.5–210° (dec.)	36
4-(α-Cyano-α-ethoxycarbonyl)-methyl-	172–173°	36, 38, 41
4-(1'-Cyano-3'-morpholino-1'-phenyl)propyl-	202–205°/0.015 mm	39
4-(1'-Cyano-3'-piperidino-1'-phenyl)propyl-	200–202°/0.025 mm	39
4-Cyclopentan-2'-onyl-	154–155°	42
4-α,α-Diethoxycarbonylbenzyl-	102–103°	36
4-α,α-Diethoxycarbonylmethyl-	85.5–86.5°	36, 38
4-α,α-Diethoxycarbonylpropyl	63.5–65°	36
4-2'-Dimethylaminoethyl-	HCl 133–134.4°	55
4-p-Dimethylaminostyryl-	138°	57
4-Ethoxycarbonylmethyl-	108–109°	36, 38, 41
4-Ethyl-	15–16°, 94–96°/0.6–0.7 mm; picrate 170–171°	10, 24, 42
4-(2'-Hydroxy-2'-p-nitrophenyl)ethyl-	173°	37
4-(Indan-1',3'-dion-2'-yl)-	—	12
4-Isopropyl-	96°/0.7 mm; picrate 170–171°	10, 24
4-Methyl-	36–37°, 78°/0.15 mm, 130–132°/17 mm, 260°/atm; picrate 183–185°	8, 12, 13, 36, 37
4-(4'-Methylbutan-2'-onyl)-	111–112°	42
4-2'-Morpholinoethyl-	HCl 156.2–158.2°	55
4-1'-Nitroethyl-	142°	41
4-Nitromethyl-	225–228° (dec.)	41

(Table continued)

TABLE III.2 (*continued*)

Quinazoline	M.P. (°c)	References
4-*p*-Nitrostyryl-	245°	37
4-Phenyl-	99–100°; picrate 178°	2, 14, 17, 24
4-Propyl-	87°/0.2 mm; picrate 166–166.5°	36
4-2′-Pyridyl-	89–90°	15
4-Quinazolin-4′-yl	246–247°	16

TABLE III.3.   2,4-Disubstituted Alkyl- and Arylquinazolines.

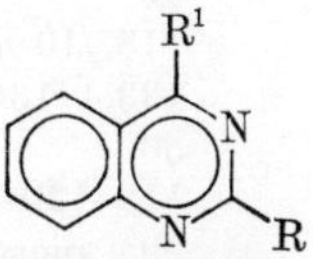

Quinazoline	M.p. (°c)	References
4-*p*-Acetamidophenyl-2-methyl-	202–203°	6
2-*N*′-Aminoamidino-4-isopropyl-	156° (dec.)	34
2-Benzyl-4-methyl-	76°	3
2-*N*′-Butylaminoamidino-4-isopropyl-	picrate 197°	34
2-*o*-Carboxyphenyl-4-methyl-	185–186°	8
4-*o*-Chlorophenyl-2-dichloromethyl-	134°	31
4-*o*-Chlorophenyl-2-phenyl-	163°	31
4-*o*-Chlorophenyl-2-trichloromethyl-	133°	31
2-Dichloromethyl-4-methyl-	141°	5
2-Dichloromethyl-4-phenyl-	129°	31
4-2′-Dimethylaminoethyl-2-methyl-	HCl 131.8–141.8°	55
4-Diphenylmethyl-2-phenyl-	132°	31
2-Ethyl-4-methyl-	259–260°/atm; picrate > 100° (dec.)	3
2-Ethyl-4-phenyl-	83°; picrate > 150° (dec.)	2
4-Ethyl-2-phenyl-	45°	31
2,4-Dimethyl-	$2H_2O$ 72°, 249°/713 mm; picrate 170° (dec.)	6, 12, 48
4-Methyl-2-isopropyl-	268–269°/760 mm	3
2-Methyl-4-(2′-methylquinazolin-4′-yl)-	219–220°	16
4-Methyl-2-(4′-methylquinazolin-2′-yl)-	249–250°, 245–246°	15, 16
4-Methyl-2-4′-(4-methylquinazolin-2-yl)butyl-	116–117°	13

(*Table continued*)

TABLE III.3 (*continued*)

Quinazoline	M.p. (°c)	References
4-Methyl-2-8′-(4-methylquinazolin-2-yl)octyl-	101–102°	13
2-Methyl-4-2′-morpholinoethyl-	HCl 151.6–152.6°	55
2-Methyl-4-*p*-nitrophenyl-	170°	6
2-Methyl-4-phenyl-	90°, 47–48°, 198–200°/23 mm; picrate 170°; chloroplatinate 100–110°	6, 2, 31
4-Methyl-2-phenyl-	90°	3, 12, 32
4-Methyl-2-propyl-	269–270°/atm	3
4-Methyl-2-styryl-	96°	3
4-Methyl-2-*t*-butyl-	118°/10 mm	5
2-Methyl-4-tribromomethyl-	133.4–135.4°	55
4-Methyl-2-trifluoromethyl-	50°	5
2,4-Diphenyl-	119–120°; picrate 192°	2, 31, 32, 33
4-Phenyl-2-isopropyl-	99°; picrate 140° (dec.)	2
2-Phenyl-4-(2′-phenylimino)-phenethyl-	214–215°	31
4-Phenyl-2-(4′-phenylquinazolin-2′-yl)-	295–296°	15
4-Phenyl-2-propyl-	99–100°; picrate 150°	2
2-Phenyl-4-trichloromethyl-	129°	31
4-Phenyl-2-trichloromethyl-	109°	31
2,4-bisTrichloromethyl-	133°	31

TABLE III.4.   Alkylquinazolines Substituted in the Benzene Ring.

Quinazoline	M.p. (°c)	References
6,7-Benzo-[a]	163–165°	66, 67
5-Methyl-	58–59°	29
6-Methyl-	62–63°	29
7-Methyl-	65–66°, 150–151°	29, 44
8-Methyl-	47–48°	29
5-Trifluoromethyl-	64°/0.5 mm	30
6-Trifluoromethyl-	75°	30
7-Trifluoromethyl-	52°	30
8-Trifluoromethyl-	130°	30

[a] This is not an alkylquinazoline.

TABLE III.5.   Alkyl- and Arylquinazolines Substituted in Both Rings.

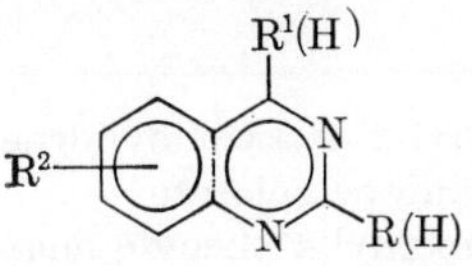

$R^1(H)$

R^2

$R(H)$

Quinazoline	M.p. (°c)	References
4-Acetonyl-2,5,8-trimethyl-	135°; picrate 205°	31
6,7-Benzo-4-(α,α-diethoxycarbonyl)- methyl-	172–175°	66
6,7-Benzo-4-methoxycarbonylmethyl-	207–209°	66
6,7-Benzo-4-methyl-	163–165°	66, 67
5,6-Benzo-2,4-diphenyl-	153°	31
7,8-Benzo-2,4-diphenyl-	160°	31
2,4-Dibenzyl-5,8-dimethyl-	98–99°	31, 33
6-Chloro-2-4′-(6-chloro-4-methyl- quinazolin-2-yl)butyl-4-methyl-	166–167°	13
6-Chloro-2-8′-(6-chloro-4-methyl- quinazolin-2-yl)octyl-4-methyl-	147–148°	13
6-Cyano-2-4′-(6-cyano-4-methyl- quinazolin-2-yl)butyl-4-methyl-	238–239°	13
6-Cyano-2-8′-(6-cyano-4-methyl- quinazolin-2-yl)octyl-4-methyl-	197–198°	13
7-(3′-Dimethylamino-1′-hydroxy)- propyl-2,4-dimethyl-	78–80°	11
2-Dimethylaminomethyl-6,7- dimethyl-4-phenyl-	109–110°; HCl 198–199°	45
2-Ethyl-6-methyl-	38°, 265–266°/730 mm	28
2,6-Dimethyl-	79°, 255°/726 mm; picrate 145°	28
4,5-Dimethyl-	88°	10
2,4,5-Trimethyl-	83°	10
2,4,5,8-Tetramethyl-	oil; picrate 207–208° (dec.)	31
4-Methyl-2-4′-(4-methyl-6-nitro- quinazolin-2-yl)butyl-6-nitro-	219–220°	13
6-Methyl-2-phenyl-	133°, > 360°/760 mm	28
6-Methyl-2,4-diphenyl-	117°	31
5,7-Dimethyl-2,4-diphenyl-	154–155°	31
5,6-(or 6,7)-Dimethyl-2,4-diphenyl-	173–174°	31

TABLE III.6.   Miscellaneous Alkyl- and Arylquinazolines (including
Quinazolinium Salts).

Compound	M.p. (°c)	References
4-(1'-*m*-Chlorophenyl-4'-methyl-2'-tetrazolinylidene-methyl)-1-ethylquinazolinium perchlorate	183°	65
2-*p*-Dimethylaminostyryl-1-methyl-4-phenylquinazo-linium iodide	202° (dec.)	63
1-Ethyl-4-(3'-ethylbenzothiazolin-2'-ylidenemethyl)-quinazolinium iodide	295°	62
1-Ethyl-4-(3'-ethylbenzoxazolin-2'-ylidenemethyl)-quinazolinium iodide	285°	62
1-Ethyl-4-(3'-(1-ethyl-1,4-dihydroquinazolin-4-ylidene)-prop-1'-enyl)quinazolinium iodide	286°	62
1-Ethyl-4-(3'-ethylnaphtho(1,2-d)oxoazolin-2'-ylidene)methylquinazolinium iodide	265°	62
1-Ethyl-4-(1'-ethylquinazolin-4'-ylidenemethyl)-quinazolinium iodide	258°	62
1-Ethyl-4-(1'-ethyl-4'-quinolylidenemethyl)-quinazolinium iodide	278°	62
1-Ethyl-4-(3'-methylnaphtho(2,1-d)thiazolin-2'-ylidenemethyl)quinazolinium iodide	> 300°	62
1,4-Dihydro-1-methyl-4[β-methyl-β-(3-methyl-5-oxo-1-phenylpyrazolin-4-ylidene)ethylidene]-quinazoline	224° (dec.)	62
2-(3'-(1,2-Dihydro-1-methyl-4-phenylquinazolin-2-ylidene)prop-1'-enyl)-1-methyl-4-phenyl-quinazolinium iodide	270°	63
2-*o*-Hydroxystyryl-1-methyl-4-phenylquinazolinium iodide	182° (dec.)	63
2-β-3-Indolylethenyl-1-methyl-4-phenyl-quinazolinium iodide	252° (dec.)	63
1-Methyl-4-(3'-methylbenzoxazolin-2'-ylidene-methyl)quinazolinium iodide	285°	62
1-Methyl-4-(1'-methylbenzoselenazolin-2'-ylidene-methyl)quinazolinium bromide	> 300°	62
1-Methyl-4-(1'-methylbenzothiazolidin-2'-ylidene-methyl)quinazolinium toluene-*p*-sulphonate	306.5–308°	62
1-Methyl-4-((1,4,4-trimethyl-3-methylthio)2'-pyrazolenine-5'-ylidenemethyl)quinazolinium perchlorate	210°	64
1-Methyl-4-(3'-methylnaphtho(1,2-d)oxazolin-2'-ylidenemethyl)quinazolinium iodide	258°	62
1-Methyl-4-(3'-methylnaphtho(2,1-d)thiazolin-2'-ylidenemethyl)quinazolinium iodide	> 300°	62

(*Table continued*)

TABLE III.6 (continued)

Compound	M.p. (°c)	References
1-Methyl-4-(1'-methyl-2'-quinolylidenemethyl)-quinazolinium iodide	262°	62
1,2-Dimethyl-4-phenylquinazolinium iodide	208° (dec.)	63
1,4-Dimethylquinazolinium iodide	101–108°	62
4-Phenyl-2-δ-4'-phenylquinazolin-2'-ylbutadienyl-quinazoline 1,1'-bismethiodide	250° (dec).	63

4. References

1. Bischler, *Ber. Deut. Chem. Ges.*, **24**, 506 (1891).
2. Bischler and Barad, *Ber. Deut. Chem. Ges.*, **25**, 3080 (1892).
3. Bischler and Howell, *Ber. Deut. Chem. Ges.*, **26**, 1384 (1893).
4. Bischler and Lang, *Ber. Deut. Chem. Ges.*, **28**, 279 (1895).
5. Armarego and Smith, *J. Chem. Soc.* (C), **1966**, 234.
6. Kövendi and Kircz, *Chem. Ber.*, **98**, 1049 (1965).
7. Albert and Hampton, *J. Chem. Soc.*, **1954**, 505.
8. Bogert and Nabenhauer, *J. Am. Chem. Soc.*, **46**, 1702 (1924).
9. Armarego, *J. Chem. Soc.*, **1962**, 4094.
10. Armarego and Smith, *J. Chem. Soc.*, **1965**, 5360.
11. Christensen, Graham, and Griffith, *J. Am. Chem. Soc.*, **67**, 2001 (1945).
12. Bogert and Nabenhauer, *J. Am. Chem. Soc.*, **46**, 1932 (1924).
13. Schofield, Swain, and Theobald, *J. Chem. Soc.*, **1952**, 1924.
14. Schofield, *J. Chem. Soc.*, **1952**, 1927.
15. Schofield, *J. Chem. Soc.*, **1954**, 4034.
16. Armarego and Willette, *J. Chem. Soc.*, **1965**, 1258.
17. Palazzo, *Boll. Sedute Accad. Gioenia Sci. Nat. Catania*, **71**, (227) 75 (1959); *Chem. Abstr.*, **55**, 12412 (1961).
18. Dziewónski and Sternbach, *Bull. Intern. Acad. Polonaise, Classe Sci. Math. Nat.*, **1953A**, 327; *Chem. Abstr.*, **30**, 2971 (1936).
19. Dziewónski and Sternbach, *Bull. Intern. Acad. Polonaise, Classe Sci. Math. Nat.*, **1953A**, 333; *Chem. Abstr.*, **30**, 2971 (1936).
20. Gabriel and Colman, *Ber. Deut. Chem. Ges.*, **37**, 3643 (1904).
21. Gabriel, *Ber. Deut. Chem. Ges.*, **36**, 800 (1903).
22. Ried and Stahlhofen, *Chem. Ber.*, **87**, 1814 (1954).
23. Muñoz, Lora-Tamayo, and Madroñero, *Chem. Ber.*, **94**, 208 (1961); *Anales Real Soc. Españ. Fis. Quim.*, **57**, 277 (1961); *Chem. Abstr.*, **56**, 7273 (1962).
24. Higashino, *Chem. Pharm. Bull. (Japan)*, **10**, 1043 (1962).
25. Hayashi and Higashino, *Chem. Pharm. Bull. (Japan)*, **12**, 1111 (1964).
26. Higashino, *J. Pharm. Soc. Japan*, **80**, 245 (1960).
27. Albert, Armarego, and Spinner, *J. Chem. Soc.*, **1961**, 5267.
28. Bischler and Muntendam, *Ber. Deut. Chem. Ges.*, **28**, 723 (1895).
29. Armarego, *J. Chem. Soc.*, **1962**, 561.
30. Armarego and Smith, unpublished work (1966).

31. Meerwein, Laasch, Mersch, and Nentwig; *Chem. Ber.*, **89**, 224 (1956).
32. Meerwein, *Ger. Pat.*, 1,074,047 (1960); *Chem. Abstr.*, **55**, 21152 (1961).
33. Meerwein, *Ger. Pat.*, 1,109,180 (1953); *Chem. Abstr.*, **56**, 8726 (1962).
34. Hayashi and Higashino, *Chem. Pharm. Bull. (Japan)*, **12**, 43 (1964).
35. Hentrich, Hardtmann, and Knoche, *U.S. Pat.*, 1,780,879 (1931); *Chem. Abstr.*, **25**, 216 (1931).
36. Elderfield and Serlin, *J. Org. Chem.*, **16**, 1669 (1951).
37. Adachi, *J. Pharm. Soc. Japan*, **77**, 514 (1957).
38. Mizuno, Adachi, and Ikeda, *Pharm. Bull. (Japan)*, **2**, 225 (1954).
39. Castle and Onda, *J. Pharm. Sci.*, **51**, 1110 (1962).
40. Albert, Armarego, and Spinner, *J. Chem. Soc.*, **1961**, 2689.
41. Higashino, *Chem. Pharm. Bull. (Japan)*, **10**, 1052 (1962).
42. Higashino, *Chem. Pharm. Bull. (Japan)*, **10**, 1048 (1962).
43. Beech, *J. Chem. Soc.*, **1954**, 1297.
44. Sidhu, Thyagarajan, and Rao, *Indian J. Chem.*, **1**, 346 (1963).
45. Sternbach, Kaiser, and Reeder, *J. Am. Chem. Soc.*, **82**, 475 (1960).
46. Baumgarten, Greger, and Villars, *J. Am. Chem. Soc.*, **80**, 6609 (1958).
47. Burnett, Jr. and Ainsworth, *J. Org. Chem.*, **23**, 1382 (1958).
48. Bischler and Burkart, *Ber. Deut. Chem. Ges.*, **26**, 1349 (1893).
49. Armarego and Katritzky, unpublished work (1963).
50. Culbertson, Decius, and Christensen, *J. Am. Chem. Soc.*, **74**, 4834 (1952).
51. Armarego, Katritzky, and Ridgewell, *Spectrochim. Acta.*, **20**, 593 (1964).
52. Albert, *Heterocyclic Chemistry*, Athlone Press, 1959, p. 97.
53. Ried and Hinsching, *Ann. Chem.*, **600**, 47 (1956).
54. Ried and Keller, *Chem. Ber.*, **89**, 2578 (1956).
55. Siegle and Christensen, *J. Am. Chem. Soc.*, **73**, 5777 (1951).
56. Bogert and Clark, *J. Am. Chem. Soc.*, **46**, 1294 (1924).
57. Bahner, Wilson, West, Browder, Goan, Cook, Fain, Franklin, and Myers, *J. Org. Chem.*, **22**, 683 (1957).
58. Borsche and Doeller, *Ber. Deut. Chem. Ges.*, **76**, 1176 (1943).
59. Ried and Bender, *Chem. Ber.*, **89**, 1893 (1956).
60. Armarego, *J. Chem. Soc.*, **1961**, 2697.
61. Tomisek and Christensen, *J. Am. Chem. Soc.*, **70**, 2423 (1948).
62. Fry, Kendall, and Morgan, *J. Chem. Soc.*, **1960**, 5062.
63. Hamer, Heilbron, Reade, and Walls, *J. Chem. Soc.*, **1932**, 251.
64. Kendall and Duffin, *Brit. Pat.*, 730,489 (1955); *Chem. Abstr.*, **49**, 15580 (1955).
65. Waddington, Duffin, and Kendall, *Brit. Pat.*, 785,334 (1957); *Chem. Abstr.*, **52**, 6030 (1958).
66. Osborn, Schofield, and Short, *J. Chem. Soc.*, **1956**, 4191.
67. Etienne and Legrand, *Compt. Rend.*, **229**, 220 (1949).
68. Gabriel, *Ber. Deut. Chem. Ges.*, **45**, 713 (1912).

CHAPTER IV

Oxoquinazolines and 5-, 6-, 7-, and 8-Hydroxyquinazolines

The hydroxyquinazolines described and discussed in this chapter have the oxygen atoms attached to $C_{(2)}$, $C_{(4)}$, to both $C_{(2)}$ and $C_{(4)}$, and to the carbon atoms of the benzene ring. The nomenclature used throughout is the one adopted by 'The Chemical Society,' London.[1] 2-Hydroxy-, 4-hydroxy-, and 2,4-dihydroxyquinazoline will be named 1,2- or 2,3-dihydro-2-oxo-, 1,4- or 3,4-dihydro-4-oxo-, and 1,2,3,4-tetrahydro-2,4-dioxoquinazoline. These are not reduced quinazolines but the names given usually refer to the parent quinazoline from which they are theoretically (and sometimes practically) derived. The name 'oxo' suggests that they exist as cyclic amides rather than hydroxy compounds. Indeed the amide forms are, in all cases, the predominant tautomers (Sects. 1.B., 2.C.a., and 3.B.a.). When one nitrogen atom in these compounds bears a substituent, then the name given is the only correct one. This chapter does not include the detailed chemistry of oxoquinazolines that have in addition to the oxo group, alkoxy, amino, thio, carboxy, and N-hydroxy substituents directly attached to the ring system, nor reduced derivatives. These will be found in the respective chapters dealing with alkoxy (Ch. V), amino (Ch. VII), thio (Ch. VI), carboxy (Ch. X), N-hydroxy (Ch. IX), and reduced (Ch. VIII) quinazolines. For clarity, occasional mention of these compounds, however, is made here. Quinazolines with a hydroxyl group in the benzene ring are true hydroxyquinazolines and are named as such.

1. 2-Oxoquinazolines

A. Preparation

Few 1,2-dihydro-2-oxoquinazolines are known and the most useful synthesis involves the fusion of o-acylanilines with urea. This

69

method was first used in 1895[2] when *o*-aminobenzaldehyde (**1**, R = H) was fused with four times its weight of urea at 150–155° for 10 minutes (Eq. 1). The reaction was later extended to the phenyl derivative by

$$ (1) $$

fusion of *o*-aminobenzophenone with half its weight of urea at 195° for 20 minutes.[3] This reaction was carried out on a 50 g scale[4] but vigorous stirring was necessary because of considerable frothing due to the liberation of ammonia and water. Similarly, 4-*p*-tolyl-,[5] 6-methyl-4-phenyl-,[6] 4-2′,4′-xylyl-,[7] 4-2′-pyridyl-[8] and 8-methoxy-[9]1,2-dihydro-2-oxoquinazolines were prepared. The reaction usually takes place above 150° whereby it becomes vigorous and exothermic, and then the melt solidifies as the oxoquinazoline is formed. The reaction time varies from 10 minutes to 1 hour and the yields are high. Urea is always used in excess and the quinazolines are readily separated from by-products by virtue of the much lower solubilities of the oxoquinazolines in water.

Under similar conditions *o*-aminoacetophenone yields a charred mass.[10] 1,2-Dihydro-4-methyl-2-oxoquinazoline is obtained by condensing *o*-aminoacetophenone with ethyl chloroformate followed by cyclization of the resulting *o*-ethoxycarbonylaminoacetophenone with ethanolic ammonia as in the typical Bischler synthesis (Reaction 2) (see Ch. III, Sect. 1.A.). The oxoquinazoline is thus obtained in 75%

$$ (2) $$

yield and the method should be capable of wide usage.[10] Hydrolysis of the silver salt of the cyclic imino sulphone (**3**), obtainable by oxidation of the thiazine (**2**), with hydrochloric acid gives 1,2-dihydro-2-oxoquinazoline (Reaction 3).[2] The intermediate urea (**4**) formed prior to cyclization suggests that reaction in (2) may also proceed via the *o*-ureido compound.

Hydrolysis of 2-alkoxy- and 2-halogenoquinazolines gives the corresponding 2-oxoquinazoline (see Ch. V, Sects. 1.E.b.(ii) and 2.E.b.(i)). Thus acid hydrolysis of 2-chloro-4(α-cyano-α-ethoxycar-

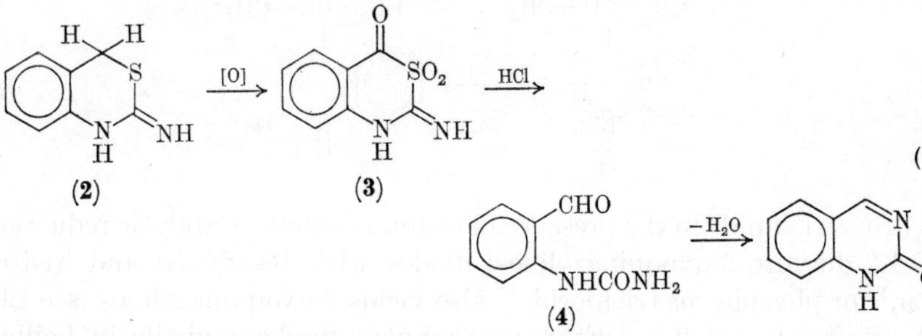

(3)

(3)

(4)

bonyl)methylquinazoline[11] and of 2-methoxyquinazoline[12] yields the corresponding 1,2-dihydro-2-oxoquinazoline.

Decarboxylation of 4-carboxy-1,2-dihydro-2-oxoquinazoline by boiling water for 6 hours gives a 95% yield of 1,2-dihydro-2-oxoquinazoline[13] (Reaction 4). The method could be profitably used for preparing

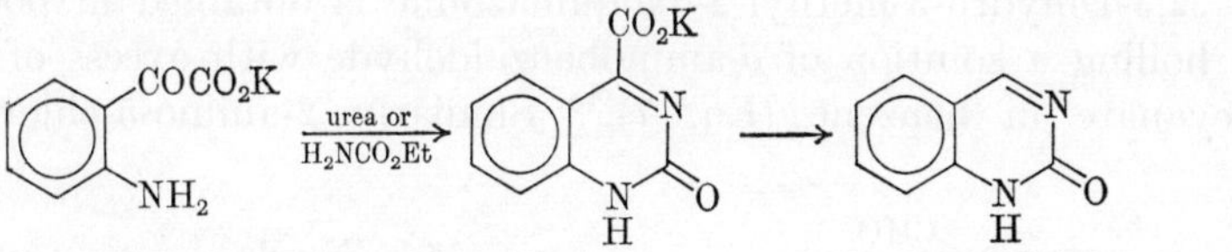

(4)

benzene-substituted 2-oxoquinazolines because a large number of isatins are known and from these the alkali salts of the isatinic acids are readily obtained (see Ch. X, Sect. 2.B.).

The N-oxides are another source of 1,2-dihydro-2-oxoquinazolines. 4-Alkoxyquinazoline-1-oxides react with toluene-p-sulphonyl chloride in the presence of sodium carbonate to give the respective 4-alkoxy-1,2-dihydro-2-oxoquinazolines (Reaction 5).[14,15] With acetic anhydride,

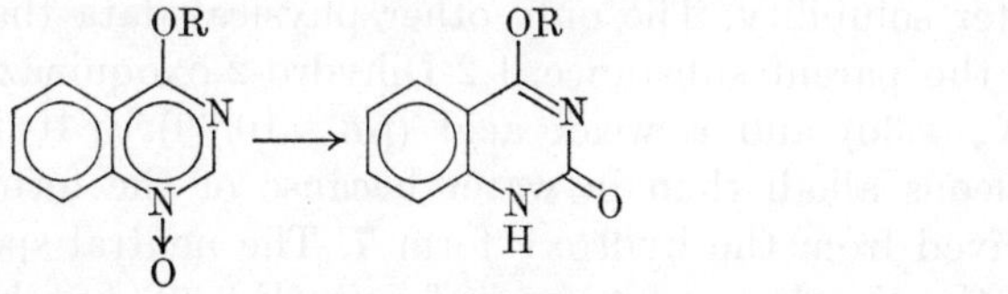

(5)

the 2-acetoxyquinazoline is formed and it hydrolyzes to the 2-oxoquinazoline.[15] 4-Isopropylquinazoline-1-oxide is known to undergo this reaction by treatment with 15% sodium hydroxide at 100° (but not at room temperature) and yields 1,2-dihydro-4-isopropyl-2-oxoquinazoline (Reaction 6).[16] This rearrangement has also been effected with sulphur dioxide in methanol (a reagent which normally deoxygenates N-oxides), or sodium hydrogen sulphite solution, and even with

$$\text{(6)}$$

hydrogen cyanide in the presence of sodium cyanide. Catalytic reduction of 1,2-dihydro-2-oxoquinazoline-1-oxides with Raney Ni and hydrogen,[14] or phosphorus trichloride[17] also yields 2-oxoquinazolines (see Ch. IX, Sects. 1 and 2.). o-Ethoxycarbonylaminophenylnitrile in boiling ethanol containing sodium ethoxide gave a 92% yield of 4-ethoxy-1,2-dihydro-2-oxoquinazoline after 16 hours.[18] 5,6-Benzo-1,2-dihydro-4-methyl-2-oxoquinazoline was prepared in 66% yield by refluxing 5,6-benzo-2-guanidino-4-methylquinazoline with 6 N hydrochloric acid for 18 hours.[19]

2,3-Dihydro-3-methyl-2-oxoquinazoline is obtained in poor yield by boiling a solution of o-aminobenzaldehyde with excess of methyl isocyanate in benzene (Eq. 7).[20] Similarly 2-amino-5-chlorobenzo-

$$\text{(7)}$$

phenone and methyl isocyanate yield 6-chloro-2,3-dihydro-3-methyl-2-oxo-4-phenylquinazoline.[20a]

B. Properties

1,2-Dihydro-2-oxoquinazolines are high-melting solids with low water solubility. The only other physical data that are available are for the parent substance. 1,2-Dihydro-2-oxoquinazoline is a weak base (pK_a 1.30) and a weak acid (pK_a 10.69).[21] It is more soluble in aqueous alkali than in water because of the formation of the anion derived from the hydroxy form 7. The neutral species are capable of existing in three tautomeric forms (Eq. 8), but because the infrared spectrum in chloroform[22] shows strong bands at 1680 and 1608 cm^{-1}, a weak band at 3313 cm^{-1}, and a strong band at 3194 cm^{-1}, it evidently exists largely in the forms 6 and 8 in this solvent. The infrared spectrum of a nujol mull shows these bands also.[23] The proportion of 8 must be less than 6 because it has an o-quinonoid structure in the benzene ring which would be less stable than 6 where there is a fully aromatic benzene ring. Tautomeric ratios in water cannot be calculated because

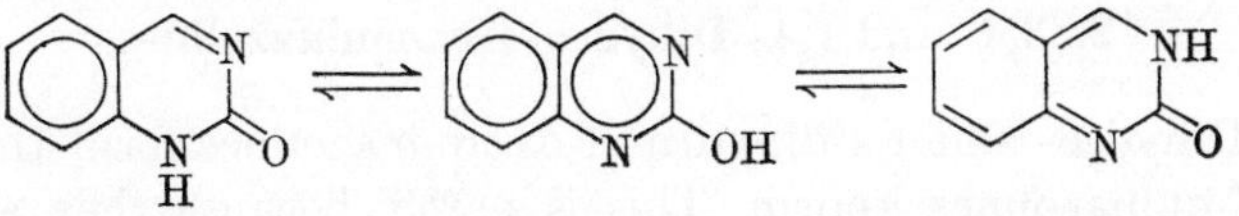

$$(8)$$

(6)   (7)   (8)

although the ionization and ultraviolet spectral data are available for 1,2-dihydro-2-oxoquinazoline[20,24] and 2,3-dihydro-3-methyl-2-oxo-quinazoline,[20] 1,2-dihydro-1-methyl-2-oxoquinazoline (the model for tautomer 6) has not yet been synthesized.[20]

There is evidence that the neutral species of 1,2-dihydro-2-oxo-quinazoline in aqueous solution has water bound in a covalent manner to the extent of 25%.[25] By analogy with 1,2-dihydro-2-oxopteridine, which is largely in the covalent hydrate form,[25] the hydrated form of 1,2-dihydro-2-oxoquinazoline almost certainly has this molecule of water bound across the 3,4-double bond.

The two known chemical reactions of 1,2-dihydro-2-oxoquinazo-lines are the methylation of the parent substance with methyl iodide in methanol at 100° which yields 1,2-dihydro-3-methyl-2-oxoquinazo-linium iodide (9),[20] and the benzoylation of 1,2-dihydro-6-methyl-2-oxo-4-phenylquinazoline which gives 1-benzoyl-1,2-dihydro-6-methyl-2-oxo-4-phenylquinazoline.[6]

6-Chloro-2,3-dihydro-3-methyl-2-oxo-4-phenylquinazoline adds the elements of water and methanol across the 1,4-positions to yield 4-hydroxy- and 4-methoxy- 6-chloro-1,2,3,4-tetrahydro-3-methyl-2-oxo-4-phenylquinazolines respectively. The pK for the equilibrium (9a ⇌ 9b, R = H) is 1.7 ± 0.1 (compare Ch. VI, Sect. 1.B.). Sodium boro-hydride, in dimethyl formamide, reduces 9a to 6-chloro-1,2,3,4-tetrahydro-3-methyl-2-oxo-4-phenylquinazoline.[20a]

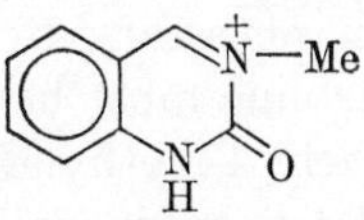

(9)

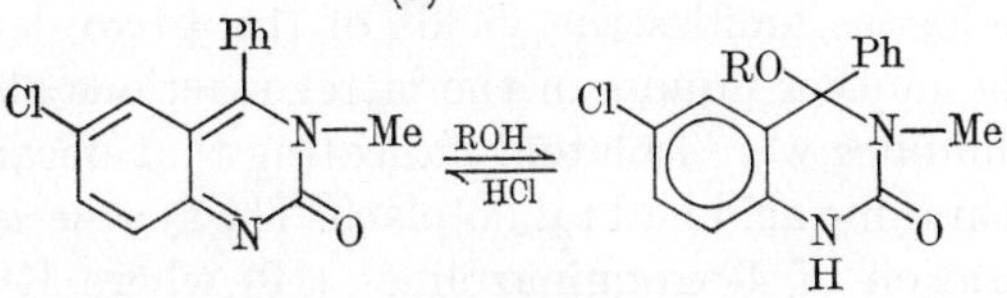

(9a)   (9b)

R = H or Me

2. 3,4- and 1,4- Dihydro-4-oxoquinazolines

3,4-Dihydro- and 1,4-dihydro- 4-oxoquinazolines form the largest group of quinazolines known. This is partly because they are easily prepared and partly because the 4-oxoquinazoline moiety is found in several quinazoline alkaloids and also in a number of derivatives which possess biological activities of various types (see Ch. XI).

A. Preparation of 3,4-Dihydro-4-oxoquinazolines

a. *Niementowski's Synthesis*

In 1895 Niementowski prepared 3,4-dihydro-4-oxoquinazoline by fusing anthranilic acid with formamide (Reaction 9).[26] He realized

$$R\overset{CO_2H}{\underset{NH_2}{\bigodot\!\!-\!\!\bigodot}} \xrightarrow{R^1CONH_2} R\overset{O}{\underset{N}{\bigodot\!\!-\!\!\bigodot}}\overset{NH}{\underset{R^1}{}} \qquad (9)$$

$$(10)$$

the potentialities of this reaction and studied the condensation of anthranilic acid with acetamide, propionamide, and isobutyramide. The reaction with formamide required 3 hours at 120–130° and the yield was high, but with the homologous amides higher temperatures and longer heating periods were necessary. Thus with propionamide heating for 6 hours at 140–160° gave only a moderate yield of 2-ethyl-3,4-dihydro-4-oxoquinazoline. From the mother liquors of the reaction with isobutyramide, which required long heating at 150 to 200°, o-isobutyr-amidobenzoic acid was isolated. The condensation was so slow that only a small amount of 3,4-dihydro-2-isopropyl-4-oxoquinazoline was formed and the nitrogen atom necessary to convert the o-isobutyr-amidobenzoic acid to the quinazoline must have been lost, presumably in the form of ammonia. Similarly 4-methylanthranilic acid gave good yields of 3,4-dihydro-7-methyl-4-oxoquinazoline with formamide, but with the homologous amides the yields of the 4-oxo derivatives were poor. From the mother liquors of the latter reactions also, the corresponding m-toluidines were isolated, indicating that decarboxylation of the methylanthranilic acid had taken place. The synthesis is best suited for the preparation of 4-oxoquinazolines (10) where $R^1 = H$, i.e. by the fusion of substituted anthranilic acids with formamide. The condensation of anthranilic acid with formamide at 125–130° for 4 hours can be carried out on a 0.5 kilogram scale to give an 86% yield of 3,4-dihydro-4-oxoquinazoline.[27] The reaction proceeds equally well when the anthranilic acid is substituted in the benzene ring with halogen,[28-37] alkyl,[26,31,36-43] aryl,[31] alkyl and halogen,[43] alkoxy,[31,44-47] halogen and alkoxy,[43] mononitro,[33,35,36,48-54] dinitro,[33] alkoxy and nitro,[55,57] carboxy,[31] phenyl,[31] benzo (i.e. from o-aminonaphthoic acids),[37,53,56] and trifluoromethyl[57,58] groups.

Although formation of 4-oxoquinazolines from anthranilic acid and homologues of formamide, e.g. acetamide, leads to poor yields and extensive decarboxylation of the amino acid, the use of thioamides offers considerable advantages. The formation of 3,4-dihydro-4-oxo-2-phenylquinazoline[59] from anthranilic acid and thiobenzamide at 175–180° was reported as early as 1903. This reaction is also said to take place at 135–160°. After 2 hours, evolution of H_2S is complete and the oxoquinazoline is obtained in 50% yield.[60] More recently Sen and Gupta[61] found that whereas the yields of oxoquinazoline from anthranilic acid and acetamide were 35–40%, thioacetamide (one molar excess) at 135–140° for 2 hours, or 150–160° for 30 minutes, raised the yields to 75–98% (Eq. 10). The reaction was equally successful

$$+ H_2S + H_2O \qquad (10)$$

with mono- or dihalogen substituted anthranilic acids. By replacing thioacetamide by 2-thioformamidofuran, the derivatives 11 (R^1 = 2-furyl) can be prepared.[62]

Fusion of N-substituted formamides with anthranilic acid yields 3-substituted 3,4-dihydro-4-oxoquinazolines but the yields are not always good (for possible reason see below). By heating 4-nitro-anthranilic acid with N-methylformamide a 60% yield of 3,4-dihydro-3-methyl-7-nitro-4-oxoquinazoline is obtained.[33] When phosphoryl chloride is added to this mixture, the yield of oxoquinazoline is raised to 82%. 3-Nitro- and 3-nitro-5-chloro- anthranilic acids and N-methyl-formamide give a negligible yield of the oxoquinazoline, but addition of phosphoryl chloride raises the yield to $\sim 60\%$. With 3,5-dinitro-anthranilic acid, however, the yields in both cases are negligible.[33] The method has been extended to the fusion of anthranilic acid with N,N-diethyl-N'-formylethylenediamine which gives an 82% yield of 3-2'-diethylaminoethyl-3,4-dihydro-4-oxoquinazoline (12, $R = NEt_2$).

4+q.

Similarly 6-chloro-3-2'-diethylaminoethyl-3,4-dihydro-4-oxoquinazoline
(**13**) is prepared in 85% yield, but 3-(4'-diethylamino-1'-methyl)butyl-
3,4-dihydro-4-oxoquinazoline (**14**) is obtained in 31% yield only after
heating at 140–155° for 8 hours.[63] Also, by heating the anthranilic acids
with N-formyl-2-chloroethylamine at 150° for 3 hours 3-2'-chloroethyl-
3,4-dihydro-4-oxoquinazoline (**12**, R = Cl) and its 7-chloro and
6-methyl derivatives are obtained.[64] The condensations are usually
carried out in the absence of a solvent, but a solvent, e.g. methyl
cellosolve, has occasionally been used.[36] When formanilide is heated
with an equimolecular quantity of anthranilic acid, 3,4-dihydro-4-
oxo-3-phenylquinazoline (**15**) is obtained.[65-67] The yield is low (40%)

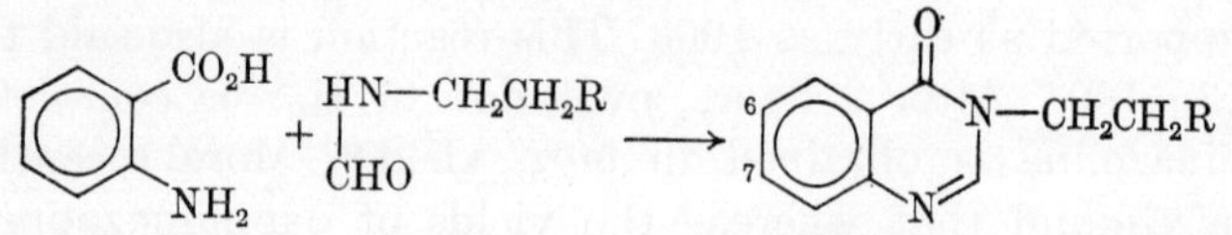

(**12**)

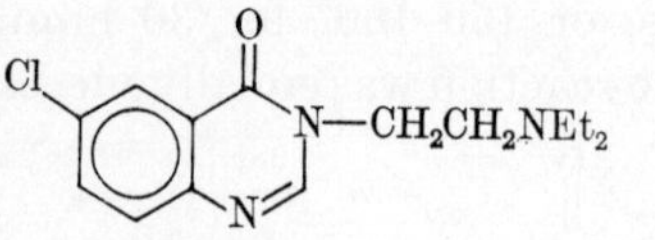

(**13**) 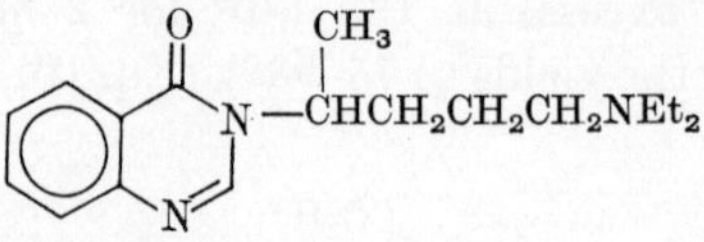   (**14**)

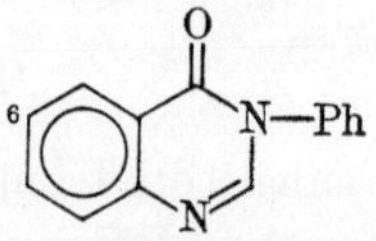

(**15**)

because the anthranilate salt of **15** is formed, thus consuming half
of the reactant. When 2 moles of amino acid per mole of formanilide
are used the yield is raised to 75%.[67] 6-Chloro-3,4-dihydro-4-oxo-3-
phenylquinazoline[68,69] and 6-bromo-3-P-bromophenyl-3,4-dihydro-4-
oxoquinazoline are prepared in a similar manner, and the yields are
improved by application of a vacuum to the reaction mixture.[69]

The mechanism of the Niementowski synthesis was first suggested by Bogert and Gotthelf.[70] It involves the stages depicted in
reaction (11). The acylation of the anthranilic acid by the amide
liberates ammonia. The latter forms the ammonium salt of the
o-amidobenzoic acid, and this salt is dehydrated, by the high temperature of the reaction, to the corresponding amide. Finally the amide
cyclizes with loss of another molecule of water to the 4-oxoquinazoline.

Meyer and Wagner[67] investigated the reaction in more detail and confirmed that no doubtful assumptions were made in any of the steps in the postulated mechanism. In step 1 the reaction proceeds better with

$$(11)$$

formamide than acetamide (or homologous amides) because it is a better acylating agent than acetamide. If this step is slow, then extensive thermal decarboxylation takes place resulting in a poor yield of oxoquinazoline,[26,44] and the mother liquors of the reaction contain the anilide without the carboxyl group. In order to avoid decarboxylation, esters of the anthranilic acid can be used, provided that higher temperatures and longer heating are used.[67] This use of esters offers no advantage because, although acylation occurs, the alkoxycarbonyl group is converted to an amide only very slowly. Methyl anthranilate in methanol, for example, when treated with excess of concentrated ammonium hydroxide at 100° in a sealed vessel, showed no evidence of forming benzamide. If a strong electron-attracting substituent, e.g. NO_2, is in the benzene ring, however, formation of the amide may proceed more rapidly. The yields of oxoquinazolines prepared from methyl esters are very poor as is understandable because the high temperature and slow reaction cause loss of ammonia from the reaction medium and give a poor yield of the amide. Step 3 and step 4 have a precedent in the action of heat on ammonium o-acetamidobenzoate which gives 3,4-dihydro-2-methyl-4-oxoquinazoline.[71,72] Step 4 can be accomplished by the action of heat, dilute alkali, or ammonia and is a good method for preparing oxoquinazolines (Sect. 2.A.b.).

This clear picture of the mechanism suggests the experimental methods which can give the best yields of the oxoquinazolines. The fusion is best carried out at 120–130° in an open vessel (to remove liberated water) until a solid mass is formed. At this stage which requires 1–2 hours, steps 1 and 2 are almost complete. The mixture is then heated at a higher temperature, e.g. 170–180° for a further 1–2 hours in order to complete steps 3 and 4. The best molar ratio of anthranilic acid and amide was the subject of an investigation.[67] Although it was found that 3,4-dihydro-4-oxo-3-phenylquinazoline formed salts, e.g. formates, benzoates, phenylacetates, salicylates, and anthranilates which lowered the yield in this example, generally, 3,4-dihydro-4-oxoquinazolines did not form salts under the normal conditions and when they were formed they readily hydrolyzed even on recrystallization. The optimum ratio is 4 moles of amide to one mole of anthranilic acid. When the reaction in its original form fails or gives poor yields it can be modified in order to give maximum yields of product. Thus if the anthranilic acid gives low yields, its ammonium salt is used in its place.[50] Methyl anthranilate and formamide heated at 175° for 4 hours, give a 35% yield of 3,4-dihydro-4-oxoquinazoline, but if ammonium acetate is added to the fusion mixture the yield is raised to 71%.[73] Also fusion of the anthranilamides with formamide[31] can be used, and several other modifications described under separate headings are found in this section (see below). Failure of this synthesis to take place may be due to the great ease with which thermal decarboxylation occurs, for example 6-ethylanthranilic acid decarboxylates at its melting point, 97–99°; or to some intramolecular interaction with the carboxyl group as in 6-acetylanthranilic acid.[57]

b. Cyclization of o-Amidobenzamides

When ammonium o-formamidobenzoate is heated to 220° over an open flame, water is evolved and 3,4-dihydro-4-oxoquinazoline is formed.[71] Similarly ammonium 2-acetamido-4-nitrobenzoate gives 3,4-dihydro-2-methyl-7-nitro-4-oxoquinazoline (Reaction 12).[74] The

$$\text{(12)}$$

cyclization must involve the prior formation of the amide as in step 3 of the Niementowski reaction (Reaction 11). Ethyl 2-acetamido-5-nitro-benzoate and alcoholic ammonia, heated in a sealed tube at 170°, yield 3,4-dihydro-2-methyl-6-nitro-4-oxoquinazoline.[75] If alcoholic methylamine is used instead of ammonia, the 3-methyl derivative is formed. 3,4-Dihydro-2-methyl-4-oxoquinazoline,[76] 3,4-dihydro-2-methyl-8-nitro-4-oxoquinazoline and its 3-methyl derivative,[77,78] 3,4-dihydro-4-oxo-2-phenylquinazoline and its 3-methyl derivative[77] can be prepared from the ethyl esters of the respective anthranilic acids with alcoholic ammonia or methylamine (Reaction 13). These also would involve initial formation of the amide before ring closure because on heating o-acetamidobenzmethylamide, 3,4-dihydro-2,3-dimethyl-4-oxoquinazoline is formed.[76] Heating o-amidobenzamides above their melting points until elimination of water is complete gives the respective 3,4-dihydro-4-oxoquinazolines, or their 3-methyl derivatives if one of the two hydrogen atoms of the amide nitrogen is substituted (Eq. 14).[79-84] This thermal

$$R \underset{NHCOR^1}{\overset{CO_2Et}{\bigcirc}} \xrightarrow{\text{alc. } R^2NH_2} R \underset{NHCOR^1}{\overset{O}{\overset{\|}{\bigcirc}} NHR^2} \longrightarrow R \underset{N}{\overset{O}{\bigcirc}} \underset{R^1}{\overset{N-R^2}{\bigcirc}} \quad (13)$$

$$\underset{NHCOR}{\overset{O}{\overset{\|}{\bigcirc}} NHR^1} \xrightarrow{\text{heat}} \underset{N}{\overset{O}{\bigcirc}} \underset{R}{\overset{R^1}{\bigcirc}} \quad (14)$$

(16)

cyclization is also possible with o-benzamidobenz-β-naphthylamide (16, R = phenyl, R^1 = β-naphthyl), o-benzamidobenz-m-tolylamide (16, R = Ph, R^1 = m-tolyl), and o-benzamidobenzanilide (16, R = R^1 = Ph).[85] Although o-propionamidobenzanilide (16, R = Et, R^1 = Ph) and o-butyramidobenzanilide (16, R = Pr, R^1 = Ph) give 44 and 53% yields, respectively, of the oxoquinazoline after 30 minutes at 240–250°, o-2′-methylbenzamido-(16, R = o-tolyl), o-4′-methylbenzamido-(16, R = p-tolyl), o-4′-chlorobenzamido-(16, R = p-chlorophenyl), o-4′-nitrobenzamido-(16, R = p-nitrophenyl), and o-nicotinamido- (16, R = 3-nicotinyl) benzanilides give useful yields (16–58%) only after addition of a few milligrams of anhydrous zinc chloride.[86] The cyclization can also be carried out in the presence of sodium benzenesulphonate[87] and the application of a vacuum during the heating facilitates the reaction.[88] The yields in the cyclization are generally reasonable and it is advisable to use an oil bath rather than a naked flame so as to minimize charring. The resulting oxoquinazolines are normally stable at high temperature.[71,89] 4-Oxoquinazolines can sometimes be formed in one step by heating the o-aminobenzamide with the appropriate acid, e.g. formic acid[44,72] or phenylacetic acid.[90]

o-Formamidobenzamide can be cyclized to 3,4-dihydro-4-oxo-quinazoline by boiling water, boiling ethanol, or by boiling in dilute potassium hydroxide, all of which are considerably milder than the above conditions.[80] This affords a more satisfactory means of bringing about the cyclization but appears to be more effective for 4-oxoquinazo-lines which are unsubstituted in position 3. By heating the amides in aqueous alkali, or sometimes in ethanol containing a few drops of aqueous sodium hydroxide solution for a short while, many substituted 4-oxoquinazolines can be prepared.[31,37,57,76,91-94] Boiling with 1.3 N sodium hydroxide for 15 minutes[95] or allowing to stand for 1 day in 2.5 N sodium hydroxide[96] has been used for effecting the cyclization, but still milder conditions such as 10 minutes at 50° in dilute alkali can be used when a sensitive side chain, for example in o-α-bromo-butyramidobenzamide, is present in the amide.[97] N-Phenyl-3-acetamido-phthalimide undergoes ring opening in alkaline solution followed by cyclization to 5-carboxy-3,4-dihydro-2-methyl-4-oxo-3-phenylquinazo-line.[98] The ring closure of 16 can also be brought about in acidic media,[99] e.g. in thionyl chloride. By heating o-formamidobenzanilide (16, R = H, R¹ = Ph) with acetic anhydride, 3,4-dihydro-4-oxo-3-phenylquinazoline is formed without exchange of the formyl group.[100] o-Benzamidobenzanilide (16, R = R¹ = Ph) cannot be cyclized with acetic anhydride but boiling benzoyl chloride furnishes 3,4-dihydro-4-oxo-2,3-diphenylquinazoline as does boiling o-aminobenzanilide with the same reagent.[100] In this connection it is important to note that nitration of o-acetamidobenzamide with fuming nitric acid yields 3,4-dihydro-2-methyl-6-nitro-4-oxoquinazoline.[78] When 5-bromoanthranilic acid is heated with formic acid and ammonium carbonate at 210–220°, 6-bromo-3,4-dihydro-4-oxoquinazoline is formed.[101]

c. *From o-Aminobenzonitriles*

o-Aminobenzonitriles and acid anhydrides at temperatures above 200° for 6–10 hours give poor yields of 3,4-dihydro-4-oxoquinazolines with substituents in position 2 depending on the anhydride used, and with substituents in the benzene ring depending on the nitrile used.[102,103]

3,4-Dihydro-2,6,8-trimethyl-4-oxoquinazoline can be prepared by heating 2-acetamido-3,5-dimethylbenzonitrile with 2.5 N sodium hydroxide.[104] Excellent yields, on the other hand, can be obtained by heating o-amidobenzonitriles with alkaline hydrogen peroxide at

35–$40°.$[38,102,103,105,106] This reaction (15) must involve the formation of the intermediate amide (17), as in the usual preparation of amides from

$$(15)$$

$$(17)$$

nitriles by alkaline hydrogen peroxide.[107] The cyclization of the intermediate 17, also in alkali, follows as described in section 2.A.b. From a study of a number of similar types of reactions the last synthesis emerges as the best of all because the yields are very high and there are few side reactions.[101] This method, however, is best suited for the preparation of oxoquinazolines which lack a substituent in position 3.

d. From Anthranilic Acid Derivatives and Nitriles

Heating a mixture of anthranilic acid and acetonitrile in a sealed tube gives a low yield of 3,4-dihydro-2-methyl-4-oxoquinazoline.[70,108] Bogert and Gotthelf[70] argued that the water formed in the reaction was the cause of the poor yield. They repeated the preparation, heated the mixture in the presence of acetic anhydride, and succeeded in increasing the yield of this oxoquinazoline to 45%. Gotthelf studied this reaction in great detail and found that addition of anhydride could almost double the yields although the yields were still below 50%.[109] When the corresponding acid replaced the anhydride, little reaction occurred and anilides, amides, and decarboxylation products resulted. The use of nitriles with their corresponding anhydrides or with anhydrides derived from other acids showed that the anhydride, not the nitrile, determined the nature of the oxoquinazoline formed, at least when the lower numbers of the aliphatic series were used. Thus when anthranilic acid, propionitrile, and acetic anhydride were heated in a sealed tube at 140–150° for 3 hours, 180–190° for 5 hours, followed by 6 hours at 200–205°, only 3,4-dihydro-2-methyl-4-oxoquinazoline was formed. On the other hand, when anthranilic acid, isocapronitrile and isobutyric anhydride were heated, a mixture of 3,4-dihydro-2-isopropyl- and 3,4-dihydro-2-isoamyl- 4-oxoquinazolines was obtained. The postulated reaction scheme is shown in (16). When the acid is used in these reactions instead of the anhydride, the nitrile usually determines which oxoquinazoline is formed, particularly with the higher acids. Actually the

$$(16)$$

outcome depends on the ease with which the acid forms an anhydride, and so acylates the anthranilic acid.[109] 2-Benzyl- and 2-p-chlorobenzyl-3,4-dihydro-4-oxoquinazolines[110] can be prepared by this method. The synthesis offers no great advantages because long periods of heating are necessary and the yields are usually only between 10 and 40%.

o-Aminobenzamide hydrochloride reacts with methyl, propyl, or phenyl nitriles in a sealed tube at 200° for 2 hours to give the respective 2-methyl-, 2-propyl-, or 2-phenyl- 3,4-dihydro-4-oxoquinazolines in 19, 22, and 18% yields, respectively (Eq. 17).[111] The yield of 3,4-dihydro-2-methyl-4-oxoquinazoline formed when o-aminobenzamide, instead of its hydrochloride, was used was less than 6% and the authors therefore postulated that the imidoyl chloride might be the reactive intermediate. o-Aminobenzamide hydrochloride, heated with acetic anhydride, butyric acid, or benzoic acid gave slightly better yields than the preceding reactions.[111] Hardman and Partridge[112] found that by heating the benzenesulphonate salt of ethyl anthranilate with ethyl cyanoacetate at 140°, the sulphonate salt of 2-ethoxycarbonylmethyl-3,4-dihydro-4-oxoquinazoline (18) together with 3,4-dihydro-2-(2',4'-dihydroxy-3'-quinolinyl)-4-oxoquinazoline (19) were formed in 19 and 31% yields, respectively (Eq. 18). When the reaction temperature was raised to 210° the products were 19 and the benzenesulphonate salt of 3,4-dihydro-2-methyl-4-oxoquinazoline. The latter was also obtained by boiling 18 in acetic acid.

The condensation of phenylnitrile with 4-nitroanthranilic acid in alcoholic sodium ethoxide containing 1% of ammonia is reported to yield 3,4-dihydro-7-nitro-4-oxo-2-phenylquinazoline.[54] Methyl anthranilate, powdered sodium, and methylnitrile in benzene react exothermically to give 68% yield of dianthranilide and a poor yield of 2-o-aminobenzoylmethyl-3,4-dihydro-4-oxoquinazoline.[113] Similarly, by using phenylnitrile in place of methylnitrile, dianthranilide and 3,4-dihydro-4-oxo-2-phenylquinazoline are formed in 49 and 45% yields, respectively.[113,114]

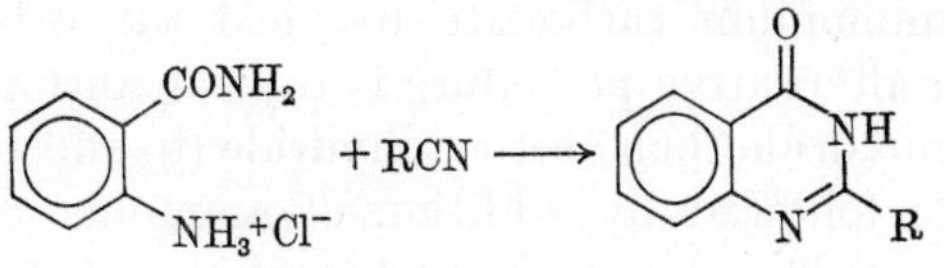

(17)

R = Me, Pr, or Ph

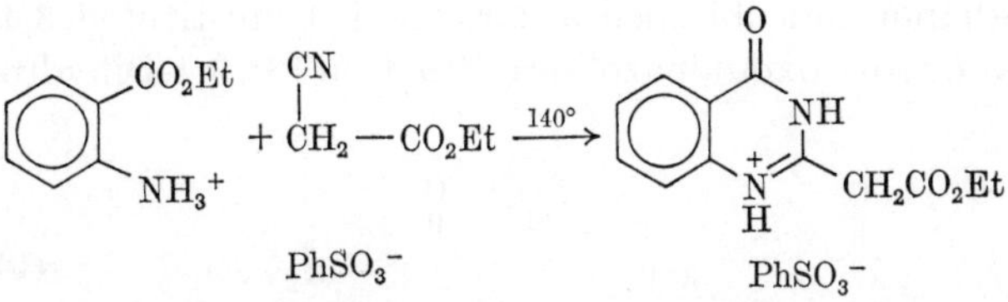

(18)

(18)

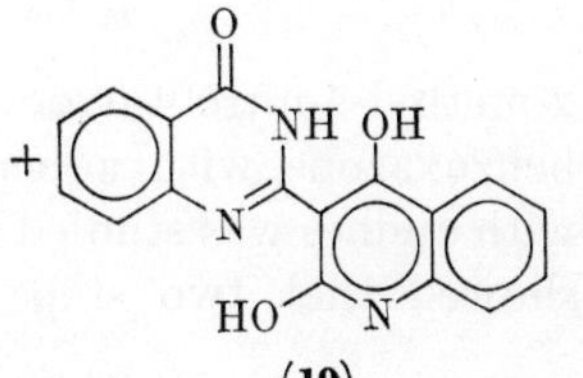

(19)

e. From 3,1,4-Benzoxazones (Acylanthranils) and Amines

3,1,4-Benzoxazones (20) are commonly called acylanthranils. In the quinazoline literature the latter name is still currently used even though it is very misleading. The name anthranil is also used for benzoxazoles (21) because both classes of compounds are derived from anthranilic acid. The *Chemical Abstracts* treats the acylanthranils discussed in this section as 3,1,4-benzoxazones (Ring Index No. 947)[115] and this nomenclature will be used in this monograph.

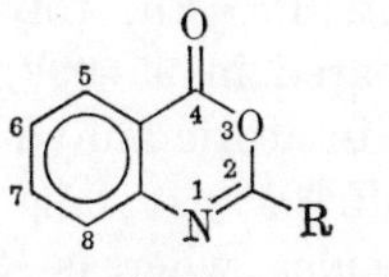

(20) 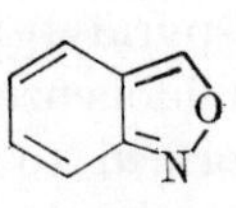   (21)

3,1,4-Benzoxazones react with amines to give 3,4-dihydro-4-oxoquinazolines. In the simplest form of this reaction anthranilic acid was heated with an acid anhydride in the presence of ammonium carbonate.[101] The anhydride acylated the anthranilic acid, the resulting o-amidobenzoic acid was dehydrated to a 3,1,4-benzoxazone which

4*

reacted with ammonium carbonate to yield the 3,4-dihydro-4-oxo-quinazoline. An alternative procedure is to heat anthranilic acid with say propionic anhydride then acetic anhydride (to effect the cyclization to **20**, R = Et) followed by addition of ammonia to give 2-ethyl-3,4-dihydro-4-oxoquinazoline.[12] Bogert and Seil[116] reacted primary aliphatic amines and anilines, with 2-methyl-5-nitro-3,1,4-benzoxazone in boiling dilute ethanol and obtained a variety of 3-substituted 3,4-dihydro-2-methyl-5-nitro-4-oxoquinazolines (Reaction 19). 3,4-Dihydro-

$$
\begin{array}{ccc}
\text{NO}_2 \;\; \text{O} & \xrightarrow{\text{RNH}_2} & \text{NO}_2 \;\; \text{O} \\
& &
\end{array}
\qquad (19)
$$

2-methyl-5-nitro-4-oxoquinazoline is obtained simply by shaking the benzoxazone with aqueous ammonia. The reaction of benzoxazones with amines was studied in some detail by Zentmyer and Wagner[86] who showed that two steps are involved (Reaction 20). The first step

$$
\xrightarrow[\text{step 1}]{\text{R}^1\text{NH}_2} \qquad \xrightarrow{\text{step 2}} \qquad (20)
$$

necessitates opening of the oxazone ring because water hydrolyzes benzoxazones to *o*-amidobenzoic acids. The ease of ring opening is dependent on the substituent in position 2 and is in the order H > Me > Et ≫ Ph. 3,1,4-Benzoxazone (**20**, R = H) is so unstable that it hydrolyzes to the benzoic acid even on standing in a stoppered flask for 24 hours[86] and has to be used as soon as it is prepared. Incidentally benzoxazones (**20**, R = H, Me, Et, Pr, Ph, tolyl, *p*-chlorophenyl, nitrophenyl, or 3′-pyridyl) are prepared in 95–99% yields by boiling the respective *o*-amidobenzoic acids in acetic anhydride while allowing the acetic acid formed to distil off.[86,117] It fails with isovaleroyl-, caproyl-, and laurylanthranilic acids, whereas 3,5-dinitrobenzoyl-anthranilic acid undergoes transacylation prior to cyclization to form 2-methyl-3,1,4-benzoxazone.[86] Step 2 is in itself a general method for preparing 3,4-dihydro-4-oxoquinazolines and is promoted either by heat or by dilute base (Sect. 2.A.b.). The reaction (20) explains all the results obtained from the reaction of 3,1,4-benzoxazones with amines. The first step is subject to the nucleophilic nature of the amine used and, depending on R and R^1, the steric nature of the reactants. Thus when R and R^1 are small groups and R^1NH_2 a strong nucleophile the reaction proceeds to completion giving the oxoquinazoline. When R and R^1 are large and R^1NH_2 is a weak nucleophile, more severe conditions are necessary, and the product is the intermediate o-amidobenzamide. This is a very useful synthesis because even if it stops at the o-amidobenzamide stage more severe conditions can be applied to effect the second step. Moreover the steric conditions must be really large to obstruct the reaction completely. The reaction of amines having a primary amino group directly attached to a tertiary carbon atom, for example 2-amino-2-methyl-1,3-propanediol and 2-methyl-3,1,4-benzoxazone,[118] and the reaction of amines with 2-o-substituted phenyl-3,1,4-benzoxazones[86] fail entirely.

The nature of the substituent in the benzene ring of the benzoxazone has some effect on the ease of ring opening of the heterocyclic ring in step 1 and on the ease of ring closure in step 2. Thus, although 2-methyl-5-nitro-3,1,4-benzoxazone yields the respective oxoquinazoline[116] on shaking with ammonia, 6-chloro-2-methyl-3,1,4-benzoxazone gives 2-acetamido-5-chlorobenzamide under the same conditions.[119]

3,4-Dihydro-4-oxoquinazolines have been prepared from 3,1,4-benzoxazone and ammonia,[86] p-acetamidoaniline,[120] and 2-aminobenzthiazoles,[121] and the conditions varied from boiling in ethanol for a short period to boiling for 4 hours in benzene. 3,4-Dihydro-2-methyl-4-oxoquinazolines have also been prepared from 2-methyl-3,1,4-benzoxazone and ammonia,[49,86,116,122–126] aliphatic amines[12,49,50,122,123,126–129] (conditions varying from boiling in ethanol for an hour to heating in a suitable solvent at 200° for a few hours), and aromatic amines.[99,117,120,129–133] In the last case the conditions varied from heating at 100° for 10 minutes[127] to fusion above 150° for 5 minutes then boiling the product with potassium hydroxide solution.[117] Similarly, other 2-alkyl- or 2-aralkyl- 3-aryl-3,4-dihydro-4-oxoquinazolines can be prepared,[86,96,123,128,134,135] and addition of excess copper powder to the fused mixture has been used to promote the reaction.[136] Heterocyclic amines, e.g. aminopyridines, and 2-methyl-3,1,4-benzoxazone give good yields of oxoquinazolines when heated with a naked flame.[137]

The conditions for preparing 2-aryl-3,4-dihydro-4-oxoquinazolines are more drastic. 2-Phenyl-3,1,4-benzoxazone requires heating with ammonia in ethanol at 240–250° for 0.75 hours for conversion to 3,4-dihydro-4-oxo-2-phenylquinazoline.[138] 7-Nitro-2-phenyl-3,1,4-benzoxazone and aromatic amines ranging from aniline to naphthylamine, yield the respective o-amidobenzamides which have to be heated at 250° or at their melting points to give the required 3-aryl-3,4-dihydro-7-nitro-4-oxo-2-phenylquinazolines.[139] In some examples the addition of anhydrous zinc chloride to the melt assists the reaction.[86] The yields in the preparation of oxoquinazolines from 3,1,4-benzoxazones decrease as the severity of the conditions are increased in order to effect reaction. Nevertheless the yields are rarely below 40% and more usually about 70–80%.

3,1,4-Benzoxazones react with dibasic amines to give mono- or dioxoquinazolines depending on the ratios of reactants used (Eq. 21).

$$\text{(structures)} + H_2N\!-\!\langle\ \rangle\!-\!NH_2 \longrightarrow \text{(structures)} -NH_2 + H_2O$$

(21)

Both products can be obtained with p-phenylenediamine[117] and hydrazine.[132] 2-Alkyl-3,1,4-benzoxazones also give oxoquinazolines with substituted sulphanilamides which are weak bases. The reagents are heated to 120–140° for 1 hour, then at 160–170° for 4–7 hours to give over 60% yields of 3,4-dihydro-4-oxo-3-4'-sulphamoylphenyl-quinazolines substituted on the sulphonamide nitrogen atom.[140,141] 3,1,4-Benzoxazones also react with aminoacetonitriles and ethyl aminoacetate (glycine ethyl ester) to yield the respective 3-cyano-methyl- and 3-ethoxycarbonylmethyl- 3,4-dihydro-4-oxoquinazolines, but glycine is said to fail to react.[49] More recently, however, Baker and coworkers have shown that 2-methyl-3,1,4-benzoxazone reacts with glycine in diethyl carbitol at 180–190°, as evidenced by the dissolution of the glycine, to give a 60% yield of 3-carboxymethyl-3,4-dihydro-2-methyl-4-oxoquinazoline.[142] Anet and Somasekhara[143] found that Bogert and Beal's[144] 3-benzyl-3,4-dihydro-2-methyl-4-oxoquinazoline, obtained from 2-methyl-3,1,4-benzoxazone and benzylamine, was an equimolecular complex of the oxoquinazoline and o-acetamido-benzoylbenzylamine. Anschütz, Schmidt, and Greiffenberg,[145,146] showed that the product obtained by Kowalski and Niementowski[147] from the reaction of anthranilic acid and acetic anhydride was 3-o-carboxyphenyl-3,4-dihydro-4-oxoquinazoline because they prepared the same compound from 2-methyl-3,1,4-benzoxazone and anthranilic acid.

f. From Isatoic Anhydrides

Isatoic anhydrides readily react with an equimolecular quantity of amines to form o-aminobenzamides,[148] and these in turn can be converted to 3-substituted 3,4-dihydro-4-oxoquinazolines by refluxing with formic acid for 3 hours[149] or ethyl orthoformate[64,150] for 1.5 to 6 hours without isolating the intermediate amides (Reaction 22). The first stage of the reaction can be followed by the evolution of carbon dioxide. When using formic acid, boiling for 1.5 hours gives the o-formamidobenzamides which can be cyclized to the oxoquinazolines by further boiling with acetic anhydride containing a trace of phosphoric acid.[151,152] 3-Methyl-, ethyl-, propyl-, isopropyl-, allyl-, butyl- and isobutyl- 3,4-dihydro-4-oxoquinazolines can be prepared in this manner.[151,152]

$$(22)$$

The reaction was unsuccessful with ethyl orthoacetate. It was suggested that the reactive intermediate might be the amidine which can be formed from the reaction of ethyl orthoformate and the amine.[153] The synthesis in one step is unsatisfactory when isatoic anhydride and cyclohexylamine in ethyl orthoformate are used. For steric reasons the product formed is o-ethoxymethyleneamino-N-cyclohexylbenzamide (22) and it requires further boiling with acetic anhydride containing a catalytic amount of 85% phosphoric acid to give a 38% yield of 3-cyclohexyl-3,4-dihydro-4-oxoquinazoline.[118]

Isatoic anhydride reacts with equivalent quantities of N,N'-diphenyl-, N,N'-di-m-tolyl-, or N,N'-di-p-tolylformamidine at

120–130° to give 3-pheny 1-,3-*m*-tolyl-, or 3-*p*-tolyl- 3,4-dihydro-4-
oxoquinazolines in 80 to 90% yields with liberation of an equivalent
quantity of the respective aromatic amine and carbon dioxide (Eq. 23).

(23)

With N,N'-phenylacetamidine, however, the yield of 3,4-dihydro-2-
methyl-4-oxo-3-phenylquinazoline is 39%, and no aromatic amine is
liberated. This infers that the reaction may proceed as in (23) but that
the free aniline liberated reacts with isatoic anhydride (perhaps more
rapidly than the acetamidine) to form anthranilanilide, thus consuming
the anhydride.[67] Anthranilanilide is known not to give an oxoquinazoline when heated with N,N'-diphenylacetamidine even at 190°, but
N,N'-*p*-bromophenyl- and N,N'-diphenylformamidine at 130–160° give
a 75% yield of 3-*p*-bromophenyl- and 3-phenyl- 3,4-dihydro-4-oxo-
quinazolines.[150] Consumption of anhydride by the liberated amine is
demonstrated by the reaction of isatoic anhydride with half an
equivalent of N,N'-diphenylformamidine, whereby the theoretical
amount of carbon dioxide is liberated and 3,4-dihydro-4-oxo-3-phenyl-
quinazoline (73% yield based on formamidine) and anthranilanilide
(53% based on isatoic anhydride) are formed.[67] It is possible that the
methyl group in the acetamidine sterically hinders the attack on isatoic
anhydride.

g. *From Anthranilic Acids or Esters and Imidoyl*
Chlorides

Mumm and Hesse[154] recorded the first synthesis of 3,4-dihydro-4-
oxo-2,3-diphenylquinazoline in 1910 from sodium anthranilate and
N-phenyl benzimidoyl chloride in dilute alcohol, but the yield was low.
Levy and Stephen[155] studied the reaction in detail and explained that
the poor yield previously obtained was due to extensive hydrolysis of
the imidoyl chloride. They found that the reaction progressed better in
acetone and that the synthesis of the oxoquinazoline followed two
pathways (Reaction 24). When equimolar quantities of ammonium
anthranilate and *N*-phenyl benzimidoyl chloride were reacted in

acetone at 20° a 35% yield of the oxoquinazoline (23) was obtained. The low yield was explained by route 2. Ammonium anthranilate hydrolyzes to a large extent in acetone (hydrolysis being appreciable even at 0°) and leads to the formation of 2-phenyl-3,1,4-benzoxazone (24) which reacts with aniline to give o-benzamidobenzanilide (25) which slowly cyclizes to 23. (The reactants were shown previously to give 2-phenyl-3,1,4-benzoxazone when pyridine was used as solvent.) By adding solid ammonium anthranilate to the dry acetone solution of benzimidoyl chloride, the dissociation is minimized and a 70% yield of 23 is obtained. Methyl anthranilate can be used in place of the acid but in this case attack takes place on the amino group with the liberation of HCl. In order to obtain high yields (80–90%) of the oxoquinazoline two moles of anthranilate must be used, the second mole removes the HCl from the reaction. 2,3-Diphenyl-, 2-phenyl-3-m-tolyl-, 3-o-methoxyphenyl-2-phenyl-, 3-p-methoxyphenyl-2-phenyl-, 3-2′-naphthyl-2-phenyl-, 3-2′,4′-xylyl-2-phenyl-, 2-p-chlorophenyl-3-phenyl-, and 2-1′-naphthyl-3-phenyl- 3,4-dihydro-4-oxoquinazolines were prepared in this manner.[155] A variant of this method makes use of sodium o-nitrobenzoate and benzimidoyl chloride which give the intermediate N-acyl-N-aryl-o-nitrobenzamide (26). After reduction of this with dithionite and rapid ring closure with ammonia, the oxoquinazoline can be obtained in yields higher than 70% (Reaction 25).[155]

Anthranilic acid, its potassium or ammonium salt, or its methyl

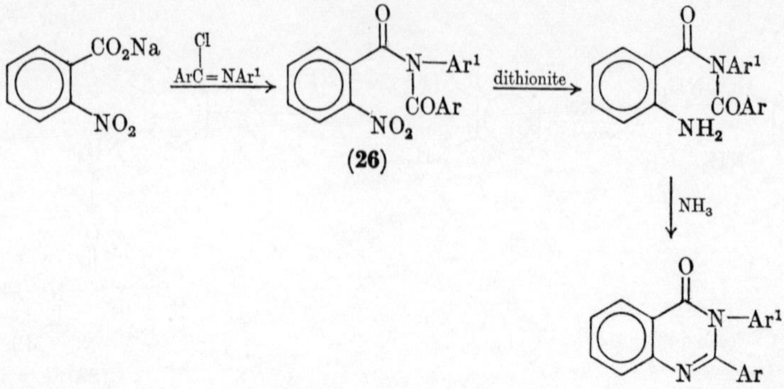

(26)

(25)

ester, react with ψ-saccharin chloride to give the 3-o-carboxyanilino-4,5-benzo-1,2-thiazole 1,1-dioxide derivative (26a), which with 0.25 N sodium hydroxide, gives 3,4-dihydro-4-oxo-2-o-sulphamoylphenylquinazoline (27), but with acetic anhydride 7-oxobenzo(d)quinazo(3,2-b)-thiazole 5,5-dioxide (28) is obtained (Reaction 26).[156] Imidoyl

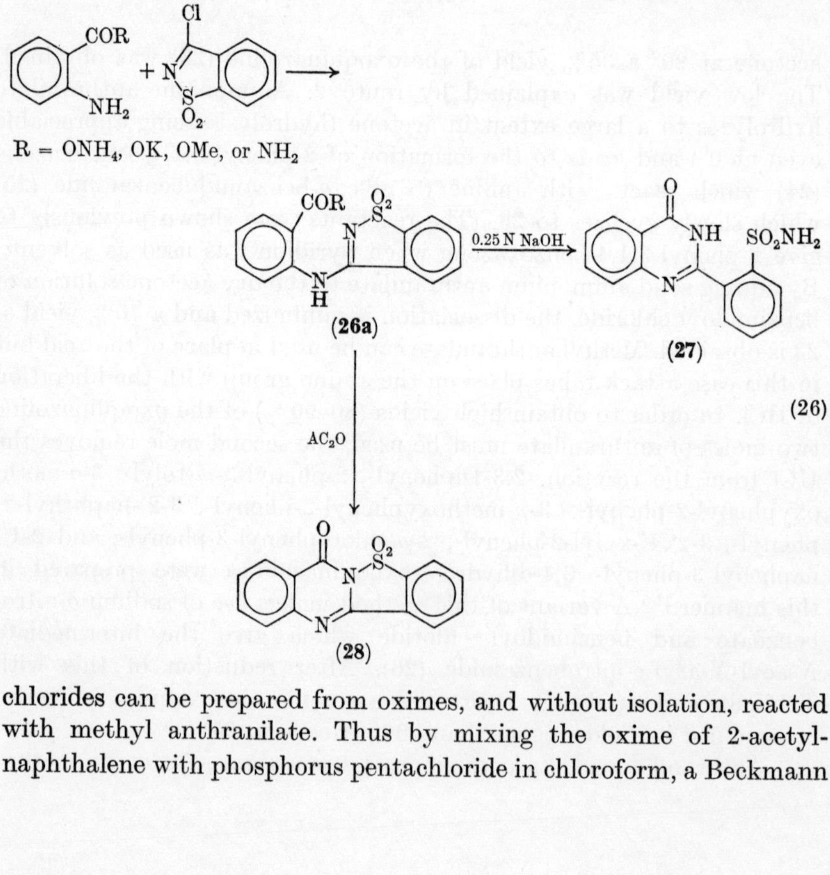

R = ONH$_4$, OK, OMe, or NH$_2$

(26a)

(27)

(26)

(28)

chlorides can be prepared from oximes, and without isolation, reacted with methyl anthranilate. Thus by mixing the oxime of 2-acetyl-naphthalene with phosphorus pentachloride in chloroform, a Beckmann rearrangement occurs with the formation of N-2′-naphthyl methyl-imidoyl chloride (29) after storing at 20°. If this cooled solution is then treated with methyl anthranilate at 20°, a 71% yield of 3,4-dihydro-2-methyl-3-2′-naphthyl-4-oxoquinazoline is obtained (Reaction 27).

(29)   (27)

Similarly 2,3-diphenyl- and 2-methyl-3-p-tolyl- 3,4-dihydro-4-oxoquina-zolines were prepared in 80 and 69% yields respectively.[157] A reaction which these authors think shows much promise is that of N-toluene-p-sulphonyl benzimidoyl chloride[158] with methyl anthranilate to give N-toluene-p-sulphonyl-$N′$-o-methoxycarbonylphenyl phenylformamid-ine (30). With aqueous ammonia it gives a 92% yield of 3,4-dihydro-4-oxo-2-phenylquinazoline (Reaction 28).[95]

(30)   (28)

h. *From Anthranilic Acids or Esters and Imidates*

Imidates react with anthranilic acid or its methyl ester in much the same way as the imidoyl chlorides. Anthranilic esters and ethyl benzimidate in boiling ethanol[159] or on fusion at 210–220° give a 30–40% yield of 3,4-dihydro-4-oxo-2-phenylquinazoline. 2-2′-Furyl-3,4-dihydro-4-oxoquinazoline,[62,160] and its 7-chloro[161] derivative are prepared in 74 and 83% yields, respectively from the imidate and the acid by fusion. Fusion is not always necessary because the condensation of 3-amino-2-naphthoic acid with a variety of imidates,[162] and anthranilic acid with mono- and diimidates[163] give satisfactory yields

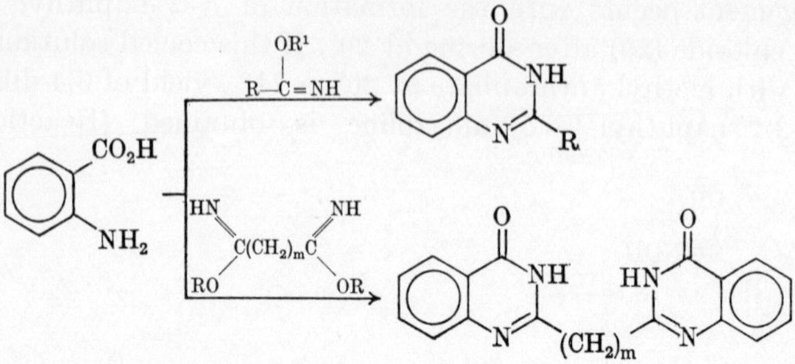

(29)

of mono- and dioxoquinazolines in boiling ethanol (Reaction 29). When the imidate of cyanogen is used then 2-(2′-amino-4′-hydroxy-3′-quinolinyl)-3,4-dihydro-4-oxoquinazoline (31) and not the biquinazo-

(31)

linyl is formed, indicating that one of the imino groups reacted in the usual manner with the carboxyl group of anthranilic acid and the other reacted with the amino group.[163] The yields in these condensations depend on the stability of the imidates and the ability to liberate the free bases from their hydrochlorides. This can be done in one operation by adding sodium alkoxide at low temperature to the solution.[164,165] o-Aminobenzamide also reacts with imidates to give oxoquinazolines.[166]

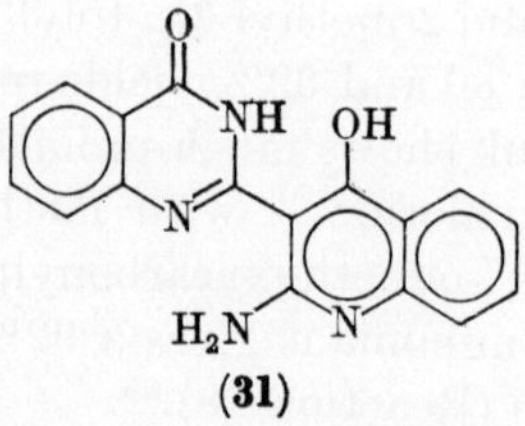

N,N'-Diphenyl-, di-m-tolyl-, and di-p-tolylformamidine, and N,N'-diphenylacetamidine react with methyl anthranilate at 200–230° to give 89, 81, 86 and 49% yields of 3-phenyl-, 3-m-tolyl-, 3-p-tolyl- and 3-phenyl-2-methyl- 3,4-dihydro-4-oxoquinazolines, respectively (Reaction 30). With anthranilic acid the reactions have to be carried out at lower temperatures (130–150°) to minimize decarboxylation and the yields are poorer (30–40%).[67] The mechanism suggested[67] (Reaction 30) is supported by the findings that O-ethyl-N-arylimidates of hydrocyanic acid react with methyl anthranilate to give good yields of 3-aryl-3,4-dihydro-4-oxoquinazolines (Reaction 31).[167] Several 4-oxoquinazolines are prepared in 40–80% yields from this reaction by heating equivalent amounts of methyl anthranilate, an arylamine, and ethyl ortho-

$$
\begin{array}{c}
\text{ArN} \\
\overset{\diagdown}{\underset{\diagup}{C}}-R \\
\text{ArHN}
\end{array}
\qquad
\begin{array}{c}
\text{CO}_2\text{Me} \\
\overset{\diagdown}{C}=\text{NAr} \\
\text{NH}\overset{|}{}R
\end{array}
\longrightarrow
\begin{array}{c}
\text{O} \\
\parallel \\
\text{N--Ar} \\
\text{N}\quad R
\end{array}
\qquad (30)
$$

$$
\begin{array}{c}
\text{EtO} \\
\overset{\diagdown}{\underset{\diagup}{C}}-H \\
\text{ArN}
\end{array}
\longrightarrow
\begin{array}{c}
\text{O} \\
\parallel \\
\text{N--Ar} \\
\text{N}
\end{array}
\qquad (31)
$$

formate in boiling decalin for 9 hours.[167] The arylimidates (ArN = CHOEt) formed from the amine and ethyl orthoformate are presumably the reactive intermediates.

i. *Grimmel, Guenther, and Morgan's Synthesis*

The largest number of 4-oxoquinazolines have been prepared by this synthesis. It was discovered by Grimmel, Guenther, and Morgan[168] in 1946 and was used for the preparation of 2,3-disubstituted 3,4-dihydro-4-oxoquinazolines. The reason for its wide applicability followed from the discovery of the hypnotic activity of 2-alkyl-3-aryl-3,4-dihydro-4-oxoquinazolines by the Indian workers, Gujral, Saxena, and Tiwari (Ch. XI, Sect. 2.).[169] When 3 moles of o-amidobenzoic acids are heated with 3 moles of an amine together with one mole of phosphorus trichloride in toluene for 2 hours, 2,3-disubstituted 3,4-dihydro-4-oxoquinazolines are formed in high yields (Eq. 32). The yields are not

$$
3\;
\begin{array}{c}
\text{CO}_2\text{H} \\
 \\
\text{NHCOR}
\end{array}
+ 3\,\text{R}^1\text{NH}_2 + \text{PCl}_3 \longrightarrow
\qquad (32)
$$

$$
3\;
\begin{array}{c}
\text{O} \\
\parallel \\
\text{N}\diagdown \text{R}^1 \\
\text{N}\quad R
\end{array}
+ \text{H}_3\text{PO}_4 + 3\,\text{HCl} + 3\,\text{H}_2\text{O}
$$

increased by using more than one mole of phosphorus trichloride, and phosphoryl chloride can be used in its place. The reaction proceeds via the phosphazo compounds (formed from the phosphorus halide and the amine) because equivalent quantities of phenylphosphazoanilide and o-acetamidobenzoic acid also give an 82% yield of 3,4-dihydro-2-methyl-4-oxo-3-phenylquinazoline.[168,170] In its original form this synthesis has been used to prepare a large number of 2,3-disubstituted oxoquinazolines.[131,171-188] In one instance 2-methyl-3,1,4-benzoxazone was used instead of o-acetamidobenzoic acid.[189] In addition to aromatic amines, aliphatic amines (with long and short chains),[128] N-methyl-pyrrolidin-3-ylmethylamine,[149] and β-3,4-dimethoxyphenylethyl-amine[190] have been used successfully. The reaction is said to have failed with α-naphthylamine, 2-amino-6-ethoxybenzothiazole, allylamine, and 2-aminopyridine,[168] but successful condensations with allyl-amine[190] and 2-aminopyridine,[191] using the normal conditions, have been reported. In most cases the acyl groups in the o-amidobenzoic acids were formyl, acetyl or propionyl, and 5-methyl-2-furoylamido-benzoic acid also condensed satisfactorily.[192,193] Toluene was most commonly used as solvent, but xylene,[182] pyridine,[128] nitrobenzene[194] and also phenol[195] have been used. The last named solvent has been found successful when the bases were weak, for example with sulphanil-amide. The usual time for reaction is 2 hours but times up to 6 hours have been used.[196] Other condensing agents are phosphoryl chlor-ide,[133,197,198] benzenesulphonyl chloride in pyridine,[128,199] dicyclo-hexylcarbodiimide in tetrahydrofuran at 20°,[128,199] phosphoric acid in the absence of a solvent at 185–195° (but using only 10 grams of phosphoric acid for 0.05 mole of o-amidobenzoic acid),[200] and poly-phosphoric acid at 140–160° then at 180–200°,[201] in addition to phosphorus trichloride. 3,4-Dihydro-2-methyl-4-oxo-3-o-tolylquinazo-line-2-^{14}C was prepared from anthranilic acid and acetyl chloride-1-^{14}C followed by condensation with o-toluidine and phosphorus trichloride as above.[202]

j. Sen and Ray's Synthesis

During the investigations of the structure of the alkaloid vasicine (see Ch. XI, Sect. 1.B.) De and Ray found that boiling a solution of normal or isobutyrylanilides with urethane and phosphorus pentoxide in xylene gave 2-propyl- and 2-isopropyl- 3,4-dihydro-4-oxoquinazo-lines.[203] They named this method of preparation after Sen and Ray who first mentioned its feasibility in 1926.[204] Phosphoric acid has also been used without advantage over phosphorus pentoxide, but no reaction occurred in the absence of a condensing agent.[205] A detailed study showed that aniline, N-acetylurethane and phosphorus pentoxide gave an amidine while m-toluidine gave carbamides, but acetanilide reacted with urethane to give 3,4-dihydro-2-methyl-4-oxoquinazoline.[206] Acetyl-,[206] phenylacetyl-,[207] and benzoylanilide[206] and urethane give 2-methyl-, 2-benzyl-, and 2-phenyl- 3,4-dihydro-4-oxoquinazolines. Toluidides, anisidides, anethidides, and xylidides also give the respective 4-oxoquinazolines by this reaction (Reaction 33).[206,207] The yields are usually higher when the weight of phosphorus pentoxide is 3 to 4 times that of the anilide and the weight of urethane about equal to that of the anilide. Efficient stirring is evidently necessary for obtaining high

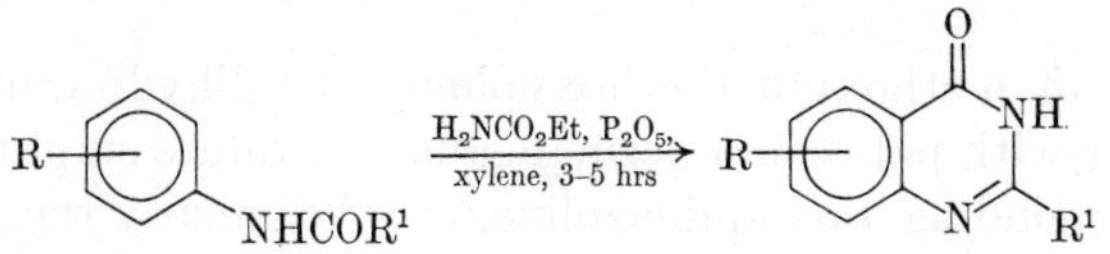

(33)

(R = Me, OMe, OEt; R^1 = Me, Et, Pr, iso-Pr, $PhCH_2$, Ph)

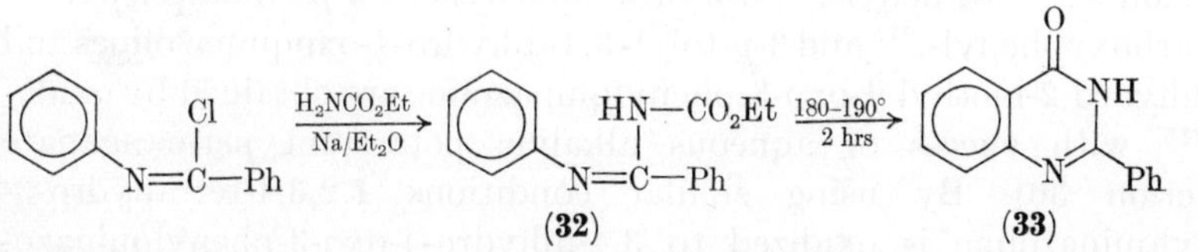

(34)

yields. A similar type of reaction is that of N-phenyl benzimidoyl chloride and the sodium derivative of urethane to give the intermediate N-ethoxycarbonyl-N'-phenyl phenylformamidine (**32**) which cyclizes to the oxoquinazoline (Reaction 34).[208] Similarly N-phenyl α- and β-naphthimidoyl chlorides give 7,8- and 6,7-benzo-3,4-dihydro-4-oxo-2-phenylquinazoline. Whereas 3,4-dihydro-4-oxo-2-phenylquinazoline (**33**) cannot be acetylated easily, the synthesis (34) using N-acetylurethane produces the N-acyl derivative of **32** which cyclizes satisfactorily to 3-acetyl-3,4-dihydro-4-oxo-2-phenylquinazoline.[208]

N-Ethoxymethyleneurethane (**34**), prepared from urethane and ethyl orthoformate, condenses with β-naphthylamine to form N-ethoxycarbonyl-N'-β-naphthylformamidine (**35**) which cyclizes to 5,6-benzo-3,4-dihydro-4-oxoquinazoline in boiling diphenyl ether (Reaction 35).[209] Although a 98% yield is obtained in this case, only a 10% yield of 3,4-dihydro-4-oxoquinazoline is formed when aniline is used.

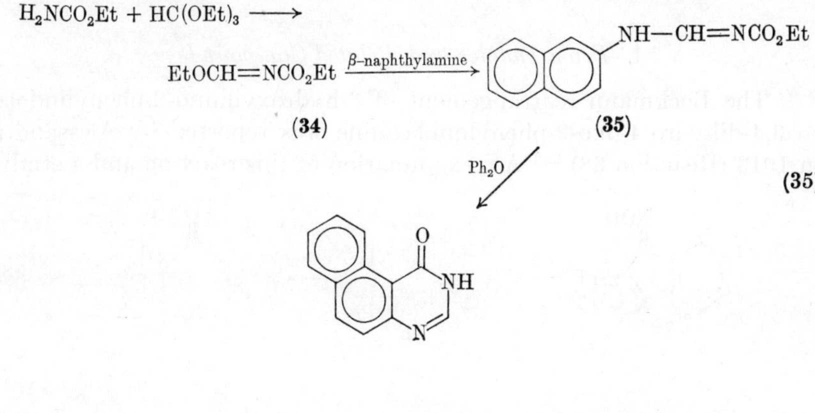

$H_2NCO_2Et + HC(OEt)_3 \longrightarrow$

(35)

k. *Oxidation of Reduced Quinazolines*

The oxidation of quinazolines without a substituent on $C_{(4)}$ with chromic oxide[210–212] in acetic acid is described in chapter III, section 2.B.b.

Oxidation of 6-ethoxy-3-4′-ethoxyphenyl-3,4-dihydroquinazoline, in air at 150° or with potassium permanganate in dilute sulphuric acid, gives the corresponding 4-oxoquinazoline.[213,214] Similarly the methoxy derivative gives 3,4-dihydro-6-methoxy-3-4′-methoxyphenyl-4-oxo-quinazoline.[214] 3-Phenyl-,[215] 3-*p*-bromophenyl-,[216] 3-*p*-chlorophenyl-[217] 3-*p*-carboxyphenyl-,[218] and 3-*p*-tolyl- 3,4-dihydro-4-oxoquinazolines and 3,4-dihydro-2-methyl-4-oxo-3-phenylquinazoline are obtained by oxidation[215] with excess of aqueous alkaline potassium permanganate (Reaction 36). By using similar conditions 1,2,3,4-tetrahydro-3-phenylquinazoline is oxidized to 3,4-dihydro-4-oxo-3-phenylquinazoline.[218] The oxidation is also successfully carried out with potassium permanganate in acetone.[66,219] This reagent oxidizes several 2- and 3-substituted 1,2,3,4-tetrahydro-4-oxoquinazolines to 3,4-dihydro-4-oxoquinazolines in high yields[220,221] (Reaction 37), and chromium trioxide can be used to oxidize 3-methyl- and 3-vinyl-1,2-dihydroquinazolinium salts to 3-methyl- and 3-vinyl- 3,4-dihydro-4-oxoquinazolines[222] (see Ch. VIII, Sect. 6.).

(36)

(37)

l. *From Indoles and Related Compounds*

The Beckmann rearrangement of 3-hydroxyimino-2-phenylindole to 3,4-dihydro-4-oxo-2-phenylquinazoline was reported by Alessandri in 1913 (Reaction 38).[223] A reexamination of this reaction and a study

(38)

of the rearrangement of 2-methyl-, 2-t-butyl-, 5-methyl-2-t-butyl-, 5,7-dimethyl-2-t-butyl-, and 5-methyl-2-phenyl- 3-hydroxyiminoindoles showed that the yields of oxoquinazolines were poor but the other products isolated consisted of intermediates in the synthesis of oxoquinazolines. Thus o-acetamidobenzonitrile, o-t-valeramidobenzamide, 2-t-valeramido-5-methylbenzamide, 2-t-valeramido-3,5-dimethylphenylnitrile, and 2-benzamido-5-methylphenylnitrile were obtained respectively, when the above were treated with phosphorus pentachloride in cold chloroform. In boiling chloroform, on the other hand, all gave the phenylnitriles. When polyphosphoric acid was used instead of phosphorus pentachloride, the nitriles, o-amidobenzoic acids and 2-substituted 3,1,4-benzoxazones were formed.[224] All the intermediates can be converted to oxoquinazolines as described earlier (Sects. 2.A.a, b, c, and e). 2-Phenylindole in 3% alcoholic ammonia gives, after standing at 20° for 9 months, 3,4-dihydro-4-oxo-2-phenylquinazoline (Reaction 39).[225] Sunlight is required for this reaction which is similar to the

(39)

formation of 3,4-dihydro-4-oxo-2,6-diphenylpyrimidine from 2,5-diphenylpyrrole. The latter reaction proceeds via oxidation of the 2,3-double bond of the pyrrole (elemental oxygen is necessary) and ring opening, followed by cyclization with ammonia (Reaction 40).[226] Isatin and ammonia yields isammic acid (36) which can be oxidized with alkaline hydrogen peroxide to 2-o-aminophenyl-3,4-dihydro-4-oxoquinazoline (Reaction 41).[227] By some unknown mechanism, 3-oxo-2-phenylindole-1-oxide reacts with tetracyanoethylene in boiling xylene to give 3,4-dihydro-4-oxo-2-phenylquinazoline. This reaction cannot be brought about by heating the indole-1-oxide with potassium cyanide.[228] 1-Benzylindazole rearranges with oxidation, in boiling xylene containing sodamide, to give a 20–30% yield of 3,4-dihydro-4-oxo-2-phenylquinazoline together with o-benzylaminobenzamide and benzonitrile, but 1-benzoylindazole does not react in this way.[229] 2-o-(o-Aminobenzamido)phenylbenzimidazole cyclizes, by heating at 330° or by boiling in toluene containing phosphoryl chloride to 3-o-benzimidazol-2′-ylphenyl-3,4-dihydro-2-methyl-4-oxoquinazoline (37).[230]

$$\text{Ph}-\underset{\overset{|}{\text{H}}}{\text{N}}-\text{Ph} \xrightarrow{[O]} \underset{\underset{\overset{|}{\text{H}}}{\text{N}}}{\overset{\text{CO}_2\text{H}}{\underset{\text{COPh}}{|}}} \xrightarrow{\text{NH}_3} \underset{\text{Ph}\quad\text{N}\quad\text{Ph}}{\overset{O}{\parallel}} \quad (40)$$

$$\underset{\overset{|}{\text{H}}}{\overset{O}{\parallel}}O \xrightarrow{\text{NH}_3} \underset{\text{N}\quad\text{O}\quad\text{CO}_2\text{H}\quad\text{NH}_2}{\overset{\text{OH}}{\underset{|}{-\text{N}-\text{C}}}} \xrightarrow[\text{OH}^-]{\text{H}_2\text{O}_2} \underset{\text{N}}{\overset{O}{\parallel}}\text{NH NH}_2 \quad (41)$$

(36)

(41)

$$(37)$$

m. *Miscellaneous*

Fusion of *o*-benzamidobenzoic acid with urea at 140–150° gives 3,4-dihydro-4-oxo-2-phenylquinazoline in 60% yield.[231] *o*-Acetamidobenzoic acid also gives 3,4-dihydro-2-methyl-4-oxo-3-*o*-tolylquinazoline by fusion with *N,N′*-di-*o*-tolylurea or thiourea or *N*-*o*-tolylurethane.[232] This oxoquinazoline can also be obtained by heating *o*-acetamidobenzoic acid with *o*-tolyl isothiocyanate at 180° for 5 hours. Similarly 3-allyl-, 3-isobutyl-, 3-3′,4′-dimethoxyphenethyl-, and 3-(4′-bromo-2′-methyl)phenyl- 3,4-dihydro-4-oxoquinazolines are prepared (Reaction 41a).[232] 2-Acetamido-4-chloro-5-sulphamoylbenzoic acid condenses

$$\underset{\text{NHAc}}{\overset{\text{CO}_2\text{H}}{\bigcirc}} \xrightarrow{\text{RNCS}} \underset{\text{N}\qquad\text{Me}}{\overset{O}{\overset{\parallel}{\bigcirc}}\text{N}-\text{R}} \quad (41\text{a})$$

with urethane at 180–190° to give 7-chloro-3,4-dihydro-2-methyl-4-oxo-6-sulphamoylquinazoline.[233] When an aqueous solution of 2-amino-4-hydroxyquinoline in alkaline N potassium permanganate is kept for

4 days, 3,4-dihydro-4-oxoquinazoline is formed.[234] Two molecules of methyl anthranilate react with one molecule of ethyl orthoformate in decalin to give 3,4-dihydro-2-o-methoxycarbonylphenyl-4-oxoquinazoline.[167] o-Aminobenzamide and dihydropyran in concentrated hydrochloric acid at 100° for 1 hour give 3,4-dihydro-2-4'-hydroxybutyl-4-oxoquinazoline in 20% yield.[235] Although o-propionamidobenzophenone reacts with hydrazoic acid and rearranges to give, finally, 2-ethyl-3,4-dihydro-4-oxo-3-phenylquinazoline (Reaction 42), o-acetamidobenzophenone gives o-acetamidobenzanilide, and o-butyrylamido- and o-benzylamidobenzophenone give the corresponding acyl derivatives of o-phenylenediamine (38).[236]

(42)

(38) R = Pr or Ph

Fusion of amides of malonic acid with anthranilic acid failed to give oxoquinazolines.[237] The hydrolysis of chloro- and alkoxyquinazolines (Ch. V, Sects. 1.E.b.(ii) and 2.E.b.(i)), reduction of oxoquinazoline-N-oxides (Ch. IX, Sect. 2.C.), and decarboxylation of oxoquinazoline carboxylic acids (Ch. X, Sect. 2.) to oxoquinazolines are described elsewhere. Desulphurization of oxothioquinazolines and conversion of thioquinazolines to oxoquinazolines are treated in chapter VI, section 4.

B. Preparation of 1,4-Dihydro-4-oxoquinazolines

The substances described in this section are known for certain to be 1,4-dihydro-4-oxoquinazolines because the 1-substituent so fixes this structure that it cannot tautomerize to the 3,4-dihydro isomer. These substances can be synthesized by methods detailed in section A as long as the intermediate has a substituent which will occupy $N_{(1)}$ in the oxoquinazoline. Weddige,[76] who in 1887 was aware of the tautomerism in 4-oxoquinazolines, synthesized 1,4-dihydro-1,2-dimethyl-4-oxoquinazoline (39) by heating o-N-acetyl-N-methylaminobenzamide at its melting point (Eq. 43). Knape later obtained 1,4-dihydro-1-methyl-4-oxoquinazoline by heating o-N-formyl-N-methylaminobenz-amide at 150–160° for long periods,[80] and o-methylaminobenzamide and formamide heated at 130° for 18 hours gave the same product.[238] Formamide has also been used to convert N-p-chlorophenyl- and N-benzyl-5-chloroanthranilic acid to 1-p-chlorophenyl- and 1-benzyl-6-chloro-1,4-dihydro-4-oxoquinazolines.[239] Starting from 1-substituted isatoic anhydrides and ammonia, N-substituted aminobenzamides can be prepared, and these give high yields of 1-substituted 1,4-dihydro-2-methyl-4-oxoquinazolines on boiling with acetic anhydride (Reaction 44)[122] or 2-unsubstituted derivatives with boiling formic acid or ethyl orthoformate.[239] o-N-Formyl-N-methylaminobenzonitrile cyclizes to

$$\text{(43)}$$

$$\text{(39)}$$

$$\text{(44)}$$

1,4-dihydro-1-methyl-4-oxoquinazoline by boiling in 2 N hydrochloric acid or N sodium hydroxide solution.[240] When N-methylanthranilic acid is acylated with α-hydroxyacetyl chloride or α-hydroxypropionyl chloride and the acyl derivative heated in dimethylformamide, 1,3-disubstituted benzo-4,1-oxazepines are formed. When these are kept in aqueous ammonia for one week good yields of 2-hydroxymethyl- and 2-1'-hydroxyethyl- 1,4-dihydro-1-methyl-4-oxoquinazolines are obtained. If the starting material is replaced by anthranilic acid, then the corresponding 3,4-dihydro-4-oxoquinazolines are formed.[241]

In a synthesis of anthranilamides, salicylamide is condensed with N-phenyl benzimidoyl chloride in the presence of sodium alkoxide to give o-(N-pheny benzimidoyloxy)benzamide which on boiling in diphenyl ether for 2, 12, or 24 hours undergoes a Chapman rearrangement and gives a 10% yield of 1,4-dihydro-4-oxo-1,2-diphenylquinazoline (**42**). The yield of oxoquinazoline is greatly improved when methyl salicylate is the starting material. Methyl o-(N-phenyl benzimidoyloxy) benzoate (**40**, R $=$ H) rearranges to N-(o-methoxycarbonylphenyl)-N-phenylbenzamide (**41**, R $=$ H) at 270–275° during 10 minutes. This is hydrolyzed to the acid and converted to the amide, via the acid chloride, which on heating at 300° for a few minutes gives a good yield of 1,4-dihydro-4-oxo-1,2-diphenylquinazoline (**42**, R $=$ H). Derivatives of **42** with R $=$ OMe, F, and Cl are prepared in this way in 44, 69, and 53% yields, respectively (Reaction 45).[242] Oxidation of 3-amino-1,2-

diphenylindole gave an intermediate, which on heating with acid or with alkali, formed what was presumed to be **42** (R $=$ H).[243] This was

shown to be correct.[242] 3-N-(o-Chlorocarbonylphenyl)methylcarbamoyl-
1,4-dihydro-1,2-dimethyl-4-oxoquinoline and ammonia give 1,4-di-
hydro-2-(1',4'-dihydro-1',2'-dimethyl-4'-oxo-2'-quinolyl)-1-methyl-4-
oxoquinazoline.[244] 1,4-Dihydro-1,2-dimethyl-4-oxoquinazoline is readily formed by the aerial oxidation of 1,4-dihydro-1,2-dimethylquinazo-
line[245] (see Ch. VIII, Sect. 6.).

C. Properties of 4-Oxoquinazolines

a. *Physical Properties*

4-Oxoquinazolines are easily crystallizable solids, and stable to
mild acid and alkaline treatment. They can be sublimed and the parent
substance can be distilled.[71] They form salts with organic acids that
are stable in air, but hydrolyze readily in solution[67] as is expected from
their weak basic properties. 2-Nitroindan-1,3-dione forms highly insoluble salts with 3,4-dihydro-4-oxoquinazoline and its 7-chloro derivative which are useful for isolation purposes.[246] Salts with inorganic
acids have also been prepared (see Tables IV, 2, 3, and 6). Tautomerism of dihydro-4-oxoquinazoline was recognised by Weddige[76] in
1887. As in dihydro-2-oxoquinazoline, dihydro-4-oxoquinazoline can also
exist in three tautomeric forms (Eq. 46). The presence of 4-hydroxy-

$$\text{(43)} \qquad \text{(44)} \qquad \text{(45)} \tag{46}$$

quinazoline in the tautomeric mixture is shown by its ready solubility
in aqueous alkali at pH 12.0 to give the anion whose ultraviolet
spectrum is similar to that of the neutral species of 4-methoxyquinazo-
line.[20] The 4-oxoquinazolines are insoluble in alkali when a substituent
is present on $N_{(1)}$ or $N_{(3)}$. The presence of the oxo form is demonstrated by
the strong carbonyl band at 1681 cm^{-1} (in chloroform), 1663 cm^{-1} (in
potassium bromide disc)[22] or 1704 cm^{-1} (Nujol mull),[23] and the N—H
stretching bands at 3402 cm^{-1} (inflexion), 3397 cm^{-1} (in chloroform
solution), or at 3365 cm^{-1} (weak), 3205 cm^{-1} (strong, in a potassium
bromide disc).[22] Methyl groups in positions 2 and 3 have about the same
effect in causing the carbonyl frequency to be lowered by 20 to 30
cm^{-1}; methyl groups in the 1- and 2-position cause a lowering in
frequency by 67 cm^{-1}. This large change is attributed to the presence

of the α,β-double bond which is conjugated with the carbonyl group in the latter compounds.[23] An intense carbonyl band is also present in 3,4-dihydro-6-methyl-4-oxoquinazoline[39] and 2-benzyl-3,4-dihydro-4-oxoquinazoline,[247] and presumably it is present in all 4-oxoquinazolines.

Hearn, Morton, and Simpson[248] measured the ultraviolet spectra, apparently in 95% ethanol, of 4-oxoquinazoline, 3,4-dihydro-3-methyl-4-oxoquinazoline, 1,4-dihydro-1-methyl-4-oxoquinazoline and 4-meth-

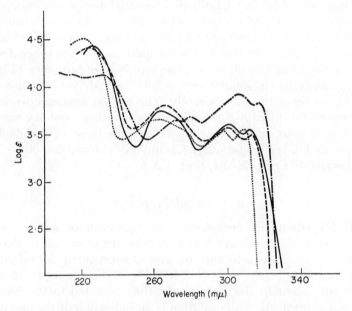

Fig. 1.   Ultraviolet spectra,——— 4-Oxoquinazoline,————3,4-Dihydro-3-methyl-4-oxoquinazoline,   —·—·—   1,4-Dihydro-1-methyl-4-oxoquinazoline, ·········· 4-Methoxyquinazoline, all in pH 7 Aqueous Buffer (plotted from refs. 20 and 403, and from spectral charts kindly supplied by the authors).

oxyquinazoline. From a careful examination of the curves they concluded that the curve for 4-oxoquinazoline could be accounted for by a mixture of tautomers **43**, **44**, and **45** in the ratio, 7 $\pm$ 0.25: 2 $\pm$ 0.25: 1 $\pm$ 0.5 respectively, but noted that their argument may be weakened by second order effects of the methyl groups on the extinction coefficients on which their estimations depended. The ultraviolet spectra of these compounds measured in aqueous buffers at pH values such as to ensure that they are all neutral species are given in Fig. 1. Ultraviolet spectroscopic data showed that also in 3,4-dihydro-6-nitro-4-oxoquinazoline the mobile hydrogen atom resides mainly on $N_{(3)}$.[248] Grammaticakis[99] measured the ultraviolet spectra of several 3-substituted 3,4-dihydro-2-methyl-4-oxoquinazolines and found them to be very similar to that of 3,4-dihydro-2-methyl-4-oxoquinazoline but different from those of the o-amidobenzamides from which they were derived. Dihydro-4-oxoquinazoline has a basic pK_a value of 2.12 and an acidic pK_a value of 9.81.[21] From a knowledge of the pK_a values of 1,4-dihydro-1-methyl-4-oxoquinazoline (3.19) and 3,4-dihydro-3-methyl-4-oxoquinazoline (2.18) the tautomeric ratio of tautomer **43** to tautomer **45** was shown to be 9:1.[20] This is in close agreement with the previous ratio of 7:1 calculated from spectra data,[22,248] but does not appear to take the concentration of the tautomer **44** into account. The percentage of tautomer **44** in the mixture, however, is small ($\sim 20 \pm 2.5\%$ see above) and does not affect the order of the ratio severely. The nuclear magnetic resonance spectrum of 1,4-dihydro-1-methyl-4-oxoquinazoline, and its cracking pattern in a mass spectrometer together with those of 2-benzyl-3,4-dihydro- and 2-benzyl-1-methyl-1,4-dihydro- 4-oxoquinazolines have been described[247] (see Ch. XI, Sect. 1.A.).

b. *Chemical Properties*

(i) **Alkylation and acylation.** 4-Oxoquinazolines which are not substituted on $N_{(1)}$ or $N_{(3)}$ react with alkyl halides in alcohol, or alcoholic alkaline or alkoxide solutions to give 3-substituted 3,4-dihydro-4-oxoquinazolines.[12,79,80,103,109,130,206,207,223,249] The quantity of alkali used is equivalent to the amount of halide liberated in the reaction, hence the neutral pH of the solution is an indication of the end of the reaction. The alkylation is effected either by refluxing the solution or by heating in a sealed tube up to 120°. Dimethyl sulphate in alkaline solution also leads to alkylation on $N_{(3)}$.[123,250] Large groups in the 2-position, e.g. phenyl, do not appear to alter the course of the reaction.[223] Although a low yield of 3,4-dihydro-3-methyl-4-oxoquinazoline together with 20% of 4-methoxyquinazoline was recorded from methylation with diazomethane,[251] recently it was shown that in ethereal solution this reagent gave a 68% yield of the 3-methyl derivative, and that the yield was raised to 91% when a methanolic solution was used.[252] 3,4-Dihydro-3-methyl-8-nitro-4-oxoquinazoline was prepared by alkylation with diazomethane.[33] Methylation of 2-methyl- and 2-ethyl- 3,4-dihydro-5-nitro-4-oxoquinazolines with methyl iodide in alcoholic alkaline solution gave the corresponding 3-methyl derivatives, but with ethyl iodide the products were 2-methyl- and

2-ethyl- 4-ethoxy-5-nitroquinazolines. The latter ether rearranged to the $N_{(3)}$ derivative on boiling with ethanol. 3,4-Dihydro-2-methyl-7-nitro-4-oxoquinazoline similarly gave only the O-ethyl- and O-amyl ethers with ethyl and amyl iodides, respectively, but these ethers showed no inclination to rearrange to the $N_{(3)}$ derivatives.[123] The alkylation on $N_{(3)}$, which takes place in the majority of cases, is not an indication that there is a preponderance of the tautomer **43** in the mixture because alkylation reactions are slow relative to tautomeric changes and are seriously affected by steric interference. Thus even if the tautomer **45** predominates in the mixture, alkylation would occur on **43** or **44** because of the smaller steric effects on $N_{(3)}$ or the oxygen atom, and thus upset the equilibrium until alkylation is complete. The reason why alkylation on oxygen occurs occasionally is not yet clear. Although there is no record of alkylation on $N_{(1)}$ in dihydro-4-oxoquinazolines, in none of the reactions previously studied has a deliberate effort been made to look for the 1-substituted isomer, for example by paper chromatography.

Further alkylation of 3-substituted 3,4-dihydro-4-oxoquinazolines takes place on $N_{(1)}$,[130,253,254] and of 1-substituted 1,4-dihydro-4-oxoquinazoline on $N_{(3)}$[243,255] to give in each case the quaternary salt. When 1,3-dialkyl-4-oxoquinazolinium salts are heated at 250–300° for 0.25 hours, the alkyl group on $N_{(1)}$ is lost as alkyl iodide irrespective of whether it is a methyl or ethyl group and whether there is a methyl or ethyl group on $N_{(3)}$ (Eq. 47). The quaternary salts (**46**) are unstable to

$$(47)$$

(**46**) R = R¹ = Me; R = Me, R¹ = Et;
or R = Et, R¹ = Me

cold aqueous alkali and decompose to give the o-alkylaminobenzalkylamides.[255]

When long chains containing large groups are to be introduced on $N_{(3)}$ in 3,4-dihydro-4-oxoquinazolines, the corresponding halide is reacted with the sodium salt of 3,4-dihydro-4-oxoquinazoline. The latter is prepared by heating the oxoquinazoline in a methanolic solution containing an equivalent amount of sodium methoxide. The solution can be used as such or evaporated to dryness, the salt dissolved in a suitable solvent, e.g. methyl cellosolve, tetrahydrofuran, or diethyl carbitol depending on the temperature required for reaction, and heated with the halide. A large number of 3-substituted derivatives with complex side chains have been prepared in this way (Reaction 48).[31,36,37,43,46,57,143,256-263] The yields in these condensations

(48)

(47)

are usually high. The sodium salt of 4-oxoquinazoline is believed to have the structure **47**.[251,264] The sodium salt of 3,4-dihydro-2-methyl-4-oxoquinazoline and phenacyl bromide failed to give the desired product but the lithium salt gave satisfactory results.[265] It is the most reactive halogen that reacts when the alkyl halide contains two halogen atoms, thus 1-bromo-5-chloropentan-2-one yields 3-(5'-chloro-2'-oxo)pentyl-3,4-dihydro-4-oxoquinazoline.[266] Propargyl bromide condenses with 3,4-dihydro-4-oxoquinazoline to give 3,4-dihydro-4-oxo-3-propargyl-quinazoline.[267,268] With acrylonitrile, cyanoethylation occurs and the product is 3-2'-cyanoethyl-3,4-dihydro-4-oxoquinazoline.[269] Several 3,4-dihydro-3-2'-hydroxyethyl-4-oxoquinazolines are obtained from 3,4-dihydro-4-oxoquinazoline and the respective ethylene oxide in the presence of pyridine.[269a] Xanthydrol condenses with 3,4-dihydro-4-oxoquinazoline[270] and its 2-methyl[271] derivative in acetic acid solution at room temperature to give, apparently, the 3-xanthydryl derivatives.

Acetylation of 3,4-dihydro-4-oxoquinazoline with acetic anhydride in dry benzene gives the 3-acetyl derivative (**48**) as a hygroscopic substance. It takes up one molecule of water from the atmosphere which cannot be removed by heating at 100° in a vacuum.[51] The sodium salt of 4-oxoquinazoline, on the other hand, reacts with acetyl chloride in dry dioxan to give 4-acetoxyquinazoline (**49**). The acetoxy compound

(48)   (49)

readily hydrolyzes with water to give equimolar quantities of 3,4-dihydro-4-oxoquinazoline and acetic acid. A good yield of the former and not 3-ethyl-3,4-dihydro-4-oxoquinazoline is obtained when the acetoxyquinazoline is reduced with lithium aluminum hydride.[272] With toluene-p-sulphonyl chloride and 4-oxoquinazoline, 3,4-dihydro-4-oxo-3-toluene-p-sulphonylquinazoline is obtained as shown by its hydrolysis to N-o-aminobenzoyl toluene-p-sulphonamide.[273]

(ii) **The heightened reactivity of the 2-methyl group.** The 2-methyl group in 3,4-dihydro-2-methyl-4-oxoquinazoline is more reactive than the methyl group in 2-methylquinazoline (Ch. III, Sect. 2.B.a.) as is shown by the ease with which it condenses with aldehydes and the high yields of products formed. 3,4-Dihydro-2-methyl-4-oxoquinazoline reacts with benzaldehyde, piperonal, o-nitro- and p-nitrobenzaldehyde, and propriophenone by heating at 150–180° for 1–2 hours, or until spattering ceases (due to loss of water) to give the respective 2-styryl derivatives. Methyl, ethyl, phenyl, p-methoxyphenyl, and α- or β-naphthyl groups on $N_{(3)}$ do not interfere with the reaction (Eq. 49).[144]

$$\text{(49)}$$

Many similar condensations are carried out in the absence of a solvent[129,134,250,274,275] but the reaction proceeds equally well in acetic anhydride,[276] and in ethanol containing piperidine.[122] In order to compare the reactivity of a 2-methyl group with a 3-methyl group, it was shown that, whereas 3,4-dihydro-2-methyl-4-oxoquinazoline reacted with benzaldehyde at its boiling point in 10 minutes to give 3,4-dihydro-4-oxo-2-styrylquinazoline, 3,4-dihydro-3-methyl-4-oxoquinazoline did not react after 8 hours at 180°.[277] 1,4-Dihydro-1,2-dimethyl-4-oxoquinazoline and p-N-β-chloroethyl-N-methylaminobenzaldehyde at 145–150° for 20 minutes gives 2-p-N-β-chloroethyl-N-methylaminostyryl-1,4-dihydro-1-methyl-4-oxoquinazoline.[278] Heilbron and collaborators[122] showed that although, 1,4-dihydro-1,2-dimethyl-4-oxoquinazoline, its 6- and its 7-methoxy derivatives, and 3,4-dihydro-2,3-dimethyl-4-oxoquinazoline and its 7-methoxy derivative condensed with benzaldehyde in ethanolic sodium ethoxide, 3,4-dihydro-2,3-dimethyl-6-methoxyquinazoline failed to react under a variety of conditions, even when anhydrous zinc chloride was added to the melt. They also found that the 2-methyl group in the 1,4-dihydro-2-methyl-4-oxoquinazolines was more reactive than in the 3,4-dihydro-2-methyl-4-oxoquinazolines.

5+Q.

Reduction of these styryl compounds with 3% sodium amalgam in ethanol yields the corresponding ethyl derivatives.[134] Quaternary salts of 2-methyl-4-oxoquinazolines condense more readily with aldehydes than the above examples[279] as was observed in the quaternary salts of 2-alkylquinazolines (Ch. III, Sect. 2.B.d.). The styryl compounds **50** have been isolated in two forms, apparently *cis* and *trans*.[280]

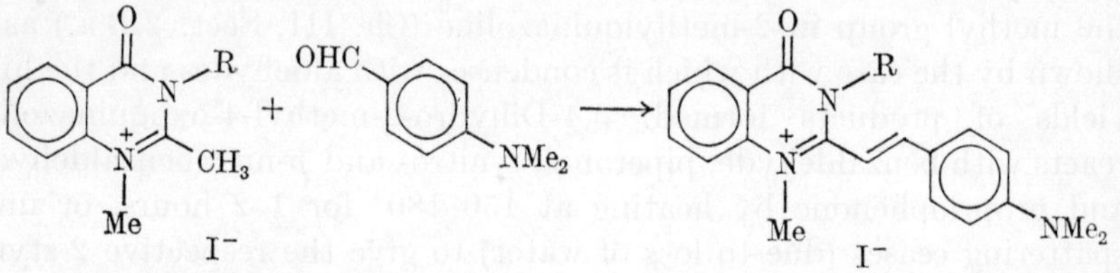

R = H, Me, or Et

(50)

3,4-Dihydro-2-methyl-4-oxoquinazolines condense with phthalic anhydride at the fusion point of the mixture to give the respective phthalones, e.g. **51**. The structure of **51** is assigned on the evidence that phthalone gives a red disodium salt (**52**), can be reduced with zinc and boiling sodium hydroxide to the hydrindone (**53**), hydrolyzes to the oxoquinazoline and phthalic acid with concentrated hydrochloric acid, and condenses with aniline in the presence of anhydrous zinc chloride to give 3,4-dihydro-2-(1'-oxo-3'-phenylimino-2'-indanyl)-4-oxoquinazoline (**54**). Anhydrous zinc chloride is necessary to bring about the

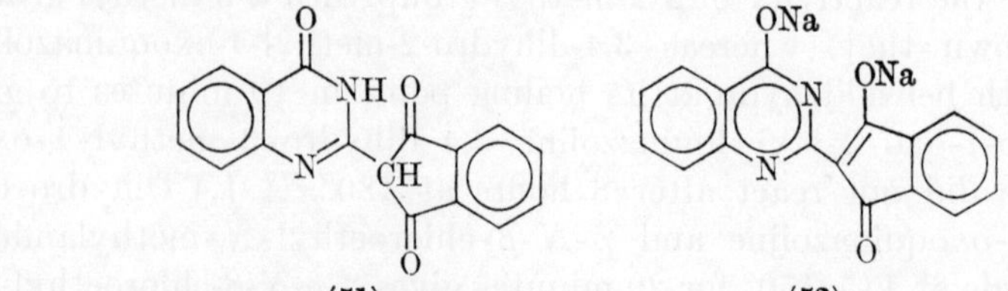

(51)   (52)

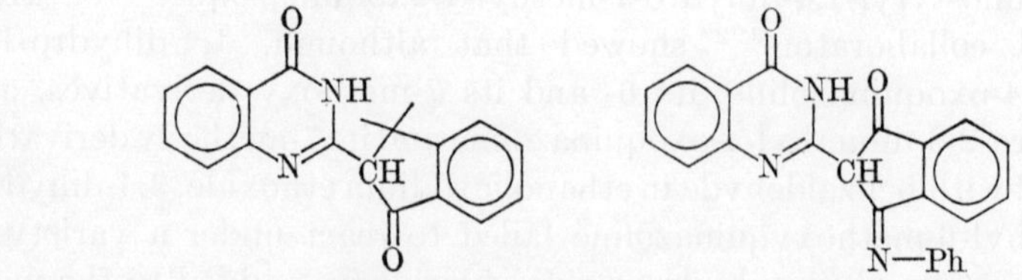

(53)   (54)

condensation of 3,4-dihydro-2-methyl-4-oxoquinazoline with phthalimide at 200°.[281] 3,4-Dihydro-2-methyl-4-oxoquinazoline condenses with chloral to give 2-(3',3',3'-trichloro-2'-hydroxy)propyl-3,4-dihydro-4-oxoquinazoline[276,282] (55), which on boiling with acetic anhydride containing one drop of sulphuric acid gives 2-3',3',3'-trichloropropenyl-3,4-dihydro-4-oxoquinazoline.[282] Alkaline treatment of compound 55 gives 2-carboxyethenyl-3,4-dihydro-4-oxoquinazoline.[282] Although 3,4-dihydro-2-methyl-4-oxoquinazoline was reported to fail to react with diethyl oxalate in alcoholic sodium ethoxide,[144] the 2,3-dimethyl derivative yielded 2-ethoxalylmethyl-3,4-dihydro-3-methyl-4-oxoquinazoline (56) which readily condensed with o-phenylenediamines to give 3,4-dihydro-2-(3',4'-dihydro-3'-oxoquinoxalin-2'-yl)methyl-3-methyl-4-oxoquinazolines (57).[283] Acetylation of 1,4-dihydro-2-methyl-4-oxo-1-phenylquinazoline leads to 2-acetonylidene-1,2,3,4-tetrahydro-4-oxo-1-phenylquinazoline (58) whose structure is shown by infrared and nuclear magnetic resonance spectroscopy to contain the 'chelated' proton.[242]

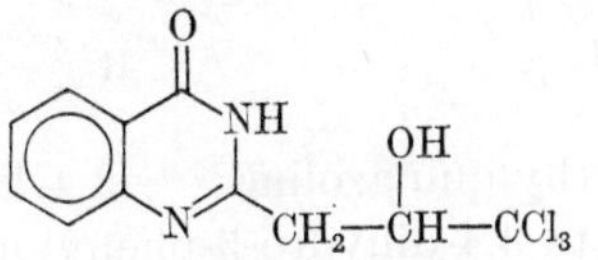

(55)

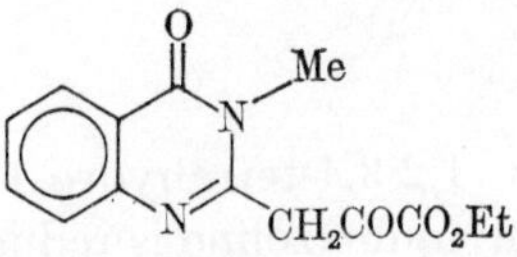

(56)

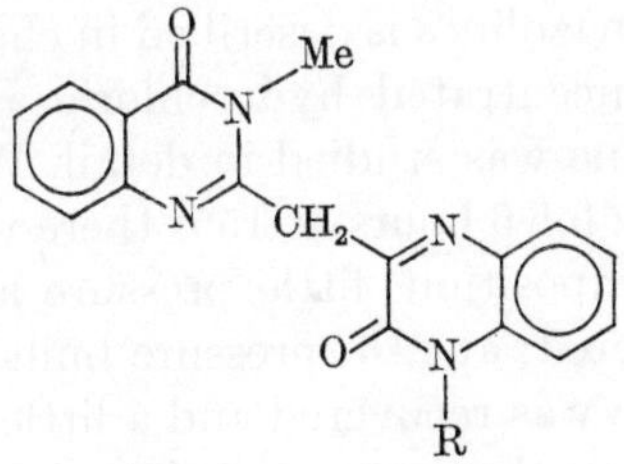

(57) R = Me, Ph

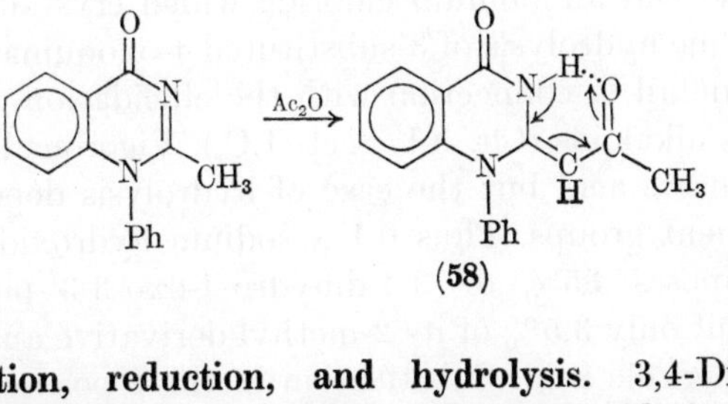

(58)

(iii) **Oxidation, reduction, and hydrolysis.** 3,4-Dihydro-4-oxoquinazoline is oxidized very slowly by chromic oxide in acetic acid at 100° to 1,2,3,4-tetrahydro-2,4-dioxoquinazoline.[284] With chromic acid it forms a stable chromate salt, but is slowly oxidized to 2,4-dioxo-quinazoline (2% yield) by heating with acidified potassium permanganate at 55° for 1 hour.[285] 3,4-Dihydro-2-methyl-4-oxoquinazoline is oxidized to 2-formyl-3,4-dihydro-4-oxoquinazoline with selenium dioxide.[286] Oxidation of 3,4-dihydro-2-methyl-4-oxo-3-o-tolylquinazoline with hydrogen peroxide in acetic acid at 60–70° for 7 hours gives a 32% yield of N-o-tolyl 2-nitrobenzamide[287] (see Ch. IX, Sect. 1.).

Reduction of 3,4-dihydro-3-methyl-4-oxoquinazoline with a limited amount of lithium aluminium hydride in benzene gives 1,2,3,4-tetra-hydro-3-methyl-4-oxoquinazoline, but with excess of reagent in tetrahydrofuran 1,2,3,4-tetrahydro-3-methylquinazoline is formed (Reaction 50).[288,289] Similarly, reduction of 1,4-dihydro-1-methyl-4-oxoquinazo-

(50)

line gives 1,2,3,4-tetrahydro-1-methylquinazoline.[289] 3,4-Dihydro-4-oxo-3-phenylquinazoline is reduced to 3,4-dihydro-3-phenylquinazoline with tin and hydrochloric acid.[65] The reduction of nitro groups in the benzene ring of oxoquinazolines is described in chapter VII, section 3.A.

The action of concentrated hydrochloric acid on 3,4-dihydro-2-methyl-4-oxoquinazoline was studied in detail. When the mixture was heated in a sealed tube for 6 hours at 155° there was no change; at 190° there was slight decomposition, little pressure and much of the oxoquinazoline was recovered; at 216° pressure built up in the tube, about 60% of oxoquinazoline was recovered and a little aniline hydrochloride was formed; and at 250° there was complete decomposition to aniline, carbon dioxide and ammonium chloride which crystallized out in the tube.[130] Alkaline hydrolysis of 3-substituted 4-oxoquinazolines was also examined in detail in connection with the elucidation of the structure of Hydrangea alkaloids (Ch. XI, Sect. 1.C.). Vigorous hydrolysis leads to o-aminobenzoic acid but the ease of hydrolysis depends largely on the 2-substituent groups. Thus 0.1 N sodium hydroxide at 100° for 3 hours decomposes 35% of 3,4-dihydro-4-oxo-3-3'-piperidinopropyl-quinazoline but only 3.5% of its 2-methyl derivative and yields in each case o-aminobenzoic acid. Substitution in the 2-position stabilizes the oxoquinazoline to alkaline cleavage and 2,3-disubstituted derivatives are about ten times more stable than the 3-substituted compounds.[290]

6- and 7-Nitro-3,4-dihydro-3-methyl-4-oxoquinazoline are hydrolyzed to 5-, and 4-nitroanthranilic acids respectively by boiling with 2 N hydrochloric acid for 30 minutes. 6- and 7-Nitro-1,4-dihydro-1-methyl-4-oxoquinazoline are degraded by 2 N sodium hydroxide in the cold to 5- and 4-nitro-2-methylaminobenzamides respectively, whereas boiling of the solution for 10–40 minutes hydrolyzes them to the corresponding benzoic acids with liberation of ammonia.[52]

(iv) **Electrophilic substitution.** Nitration of 3,4-dihydro-4-oxoquinazoline with fuming nitric acid and sulphuric acid gives the 6-nitro derivative.[35,130] The highest yield (85%) is obtained by keeping the nitration temperature below 95°.[52] In 1890 Dehoff[78] nitrated the 2-methyl and 2,3-dimethyl derivatives and the mono nitration products were later shown to be 2-methyl-6-nitro-[75] and 2,3-dimethyl-6-nitro-[132] 3,4-dihydro-4-oxoquinazoline. 3-Ethyl- and 3-ethyl-2-methyl- 3,4-dihydro-4-oxoquinazolines also give the 6-nitro derivatives (**59**) but nitration of 3,4-dihydro-2-methyl-4-oxo-3-phenylquinazoline gives a dinitro derivative. This was not 3,4-dihydro-2-methyl-6-nitro-3-p-nitrophenyl-4-oxoquinazoline because the latter was obtained by nitration of 3,4-dihydro-2-methyl-3-p-nitrophenyl-4-oxoquinazoline.[130] The authors believe that it was the o-nitrophenyl derivative, however if steric effects are considered and the phenyl group imagined as having a deactivating group, then the most probable product would be 3,4-dihydro-2-methyl-6-nitro-3-m-nitrophenyl-4-oxoquinazoline.　3,4-Dihydro-2-methyl-4-oxo-3-p-tolylquinazoline also gives a dinitro derivative.[130] 3,4-Dihydro-4-oxo-2-styrylquinazoline gives the 6-nitro derivative and a dinitro compound, which is the 6-nitro-2-p-nitrostyryl derivative.[144] Nitration of 2,4-dimethyl- and 3,4-dihydro-2-methyl-4-oxo- quinazolines give the same 3,4-dihydro-2-methyl-6-nitro-4-oxoquinazoline.　1,4-Dihydro-1-methyl-6-nitro-4-oxoquinazoline can be obtained by direct nitration of 1,4-dihydro-1-methyl-4-oxoquinazoline.[254]

3,4-Dihydro-4-oxoquinazoline has been sulphonated with fuming sulphuric acid but the sulphonic acid gave, with bromine, a monobromo compound of unknown structure.[130] Chlorosulphonation of 3,4-dihydro-4-oxoquinazoline and its 2-methyl and 7-chloro derivatives gave the corresponding 6-chlorosulphonyl derivatives (**60**) which were easily converted to their sulphonamides.[291,292] The sulphonamide from the last named compound was identical with 7-chloro-3,4-dihydro-4-oxo-6-sulphamoylquinazoline obtained from the respective anthranilic acid.[233] Mercuric oxide is used as a catalyst in the sulphonation of 7-chloro-3,4-dihydro-4-oxoquinazoline with oleum which gives the

$$O_2N \underset{(59)}{\overset{O}{\bigotimes}} \underset{R}{\overset{R^1}{N}} \qquad ClO_2S \underset{(60)}{\overset{O}{\bigotimes}} \underset{R^1}{\overset{NH}{N}} \qquad Cl \underset{(61)}{\overset{O}{\bigotimes}} \overset{NH}{N}$$

6-sulphonic acid.[291] Sulphonation of 3,4-dihydro-2-(1',3'-dioxoindan-2'-yl)-6-nitro-4-oxoquinazoline gives apparently the 6-sulphonic acid with loss of the nitro group because hydrolysis of the product yields 3,4-dihydro-2-methyl-4-oxo-6-sulphoquinazoline. Bromination of this compound gave a pentabromooxoquinazoline of unknown structure.[281]

Bromination of 3,4-dihydro-4-oxoquinazoline with bromine in acetic acid is reported to have failed but the sulphonic acids readily give mono- and polybromooxoquinazolines with elimination of the sulphonic acid group.[130,281] 2-Styryloxoquinazolines undergo substitution rather than addition reactions with bromine.[144] Chlorination of 3,4-dihydro-4-oxoquinazoline in acetic acid containing ferric chloride at 97–100° gave a 50% yield of 6-chloro-3,4-dihydro-4-oxoquinazoline (61) together with small amounts of the 8-chloro and the 6,8-dichloro derivatives. Further chlorination of 61 was unsuccessful.[28]

(v) **Substitution reactions involving ring opening.** In an attempt to prepare 4-butylaminoquinazoline from 3,4-dihydro-4-oxoquinazoline and butylamine at 140°, Leonard and Curtin[251] obtained 3-butyl-3,4-dihydro-4-oxoquinazoline together with a small amount of o-amino-benzbutylamide. 3-Diethylaminopropylamine similarly gave 3-3'-diethylaminopropyl-3,4-dihydro-4-oxoquinazoline and they proposed the mechanism in reaction (51). The mechanism was later shown to be correct because reaction with moist morpholine or piperidine gave the benzamide derivative (62, R = morpholyl or piperidyl); and with dry piperidine, the dipiperidino compound (64) was obtained.[293] A detailed investigation of this reaction revealed that the ease of displacement of R in compound 63 is H > Ph > $NH_2 \approx$ Bu, a series in which each group can replace the preceding one (or two)—(the bases are aniline, hydrazine and butylamine). Aniline and hydrazine but not butylamine react with 3,4-dihydro-2-methyl-4-oxoquinazoline to give the respective 3-phenyl- and 3-amino- 3,4-dihydro-2-methyl-4-oxoquinazolines.[238] The reaction of compound 63 (R = Ph) with hydrazine gives compound 63 (R = NH_2)[68] and not the hydrazone as previously stated.[69] Reaction of 3,4-dihydro-3(6-methyl-3-methylmercapto-1,2,4-triazin-5-yl)-4-oxoquinazoline with aniline or p-toluidine in ethanol gives 3-phenyl- or 3-p-tolyl-3,4-dihydro-4-oxoquinazoline, respectively.[294]

$$(51)$$

(62)   (63)

(64)

(vi) Reaction with Grignard reagents. In 1948 Sen and Sidhu[295] reported that the reaction of phenyl, propyl, and butyl magnesium halides with 3,4-dihydro-2-methyl-4-oxo-3-phenylquinazoline was normal and that the respective alcohols (65) were formed. Koelsch observed that benzyl magnesium bromide did not give the required material with 3,4-dihydro-4-oxo-3-phenylquinazoline and showed that the product was o-N-dibenzylmethylaminobenzanilide (66) and postulated the reaction (52).[296] Sen and Upadhyaya found that 2-methyl-3-1′-naphthyl- and 3-butyl-2-methyl- 3,4-dihydro-4-oxoquinazoline reacted in the normal way with propyl, phenyl, and p-tolyl magnesium

(65) R = Ph, Pr, or Bu   (52)

(66)   (67)

halides, and the hydroxy compounds formed gave the corresponding acetyl derivatives.[174] Kacker and Zaheer reexamined this work but were unable to obtain the normal products,[297] and Mustafa and coworkers reported that 3,4-dihydro-4-oxo-2,3-diphenylquinazoline and phenyl magnesium bromide gave 2,2,4-triphenyl-3,1,4(H)-benzoxazine (**67**, R = Ph).[298] Kacker and Zaheer further reported that the reactions of 3-substituted 3,4-dihydro-4-oxoquinazolines with phenyl magnesium bromide do not follow the normal course.[173] The 3-phenyl derivative gave *o*-*N*-diphenylmethylaminobenzanilide (cf. **66**), and the 2-methyl-3-phenyl derivative did not react (the normal product previously obtained[174,295] was in fact the hydrochloride of the starting material). 2-Ethyl-3-phenyl- and 3-phenyl-2-propyl- oxoquinazolines gave aniline and the benzoxazines (**67**, R = Et) and (**67**, R = Pr). 2-Ethyl-3-*p*-tolyl- and 2-propyl-3-*p*-tolyloxoquinazolines gave *p*-toluidine and the same benzoxazines (**67**, R = Et) and (**67**, R = Pr) as obtained with the 3-phenyl derivatives.[299]

1,4-Dihydro-1,2-dimethyl-4-oxoquinazoline reacted with phenyl magnesium bromide in the normal way because, when the product was heated with hydriodic acid, 1,2-dimethyl-4-phenylquinazolinium iodide was formed[300] (Ch. III, Sect. 2.B.d.).

(vii) **Mannich reactions.** 3,4-Dihydro-2-methyl-4-oxoquinazoline (**68**), paraformaldehyde, and ammonium chloride in liquid paraffin react exothermically when heated at 180° and give 3-aminomethyl-3,4-dihydro-4-oxoquinazoline (**69**).[301] This product is identical with that

obtained by acid hydrolysis of the condensation product of the same oxoquinazoline (**68**) with *N*-hydroxymethylbenzamide.[302,303] Dimethylamine, diethylamine and piperidine hydrochlorides also react with formaldehyde and **68** at 180–190° to give the *N*,*N*-dimethyl and *N*,*N*-diethyl derivatives of **69**, and the 3-piperidinomethyl derivative.[301] The last two compounds are different from the alternative structures:

2-2′-diethylaminoethyl- and 2-2′-piperidinoethyl- 3,4-dihydro-4-oxo-quinazolines prepared unambiguously.[91] Also 3,4-dihydro-4-oxoquin-azoline gives similar products[301] but its 2,3-dimethyl derivative fails to condense.[303] By contrast 3,4-dihydro-2-methyl-4-oxoquinazoline, for-maldehyde and sulphanilamide heated at 160–170° for 15 minutes apparently give 3,4-dihydro-4-oxo-2-sulphanilamidoethylquinazoline because 3,4-dihydro-4-oxoquinazoline does not react under similar conditions.[304] Several 2- and 2,3-substituted 3,4-dihydro-8-hydroxy-4-oxoquinazolines undergo this reaction in the benzene ring to give the 7-aminomethyl derivatives (70). This, however, is possibly a Lederer–Manasse reaction. Piperazine condenses with two molecules of oxoquinazoline to form 71.[305]

(70)

(71)

(viii) **Miscellaneous.** The conversion of oxoquinazolines to thio-quinazolines (Ch. VI, Sect. 2.A.) and to 4-chloroquinazolines (Ch. V, Sect. 1.B.) is described elsewhere. Nitro groups in the benzene ring are reduced in the usual manner to amino groups (Ch. VII, Sect. 3.A.). Groups on a side chain or aryl substituent react in the usual way without being affected by the oxoquinazoline ring. Thus the chlorine atom in 2-(2′-chloro-5′-nitro)phenyl-3,4-dihydro-6-nitro-4-oxoquinazo-line can be replaced by an amino group,[106] the amino group in 3-p-aminophenyl-3,4-dihydro-4-oxoquinazoline is readily acylated,[120] and a carboxyl group in a 3-phenyl substituent can be esterified[144] or decarboxylated[147] in the usual way. Catalytic reduction of 3-allyl-3,4-dihydro-4-oxoquinazoline furnishes 3,4-dihydro-4-oxo-3-propylquinazo-line. If, however, the substituent is close enough to the oxoquinazoline ring, then ring-closure reactions may take place. 3,4-Dihydro-2-4′-hydroxybutyl-4-oxoqinazoline could be brominated with hydrobromic acid and cyclized to 2,3-tetramethylene-4-oxoquinazoline (72).[235]

5*

2-o-Aminophenyl-3,4-dihydro-4-oxoquinazoline and acetic anhydride
gives 6-methylquinazo(4,3-b)quinazol-8-one (73),[306] and with formaldehyde it gives 5,6-dihydroquinazo(4,3-b)quinazol-8-one (74).[307]

(72)   (73)   (74)

3. 2,4-Dioxoquinazolines

Although benzoylene urea is the common name for 2,4-dioxo-
quinazoline, it will be referred to as 1,2,3,4-tetrahydro-2,4-dioxo-
quinazoline throughout the present work.

A. Preparation of 1,2,3,4,-Tetrahydro-2,4-dioxoquinazolines

a. *From Anthranilic Acid (or Derivatives) and Cyano
Compounds*

The first quinazoline, 2-cyano-3,4-dihydro-4-oxoquinazoline, was
synthesized by Griess[308] in 1869. It was prepared by the action of cyanogen on an ethanolic solution of anthranilic acid. When the ethanolic
solution was stored for a few days it gave the 2-ethoxy derivative (75).
He did not know the structure of 75 at that time, but on boiling with
hydrochloric acid it gave the base $C_8H_6N_2O_2$ (76) (later shown to be
1,2,3,4-tetrahydro-2,4-dioxoquinazoline) and by heating with alcoholic
ammonia at 100° for 1 day it gave the base $C_8H_7N_3O$ (77) (later shown
to be 2-amino-3,4-dihydro-4-oxoquinazoline). He did not know the
structure of this base also, but wrote that it was related to anthranilic
acid as creatinine (78) was to sarcosine (79). He therefore recognized
the cyclic guanidine nature of this compound. With barium hydroxide
the base gave the dioxo compound (76). In 1872 he prepared the same
dioxo compound (76) by fusing anthranilic acid with urea[309] and he also
showed that it can be obtained directly from the reaction of anthranilic
acid with cyanogen in water.[310] Griess recognized the bicyclic nature of
the intermediate in his reaction which he formulated as 80, and gave
the formula 81 to the product he obtained from the reaction in alcohol.[310]
The sequence of reactions is shown in scheme 1.

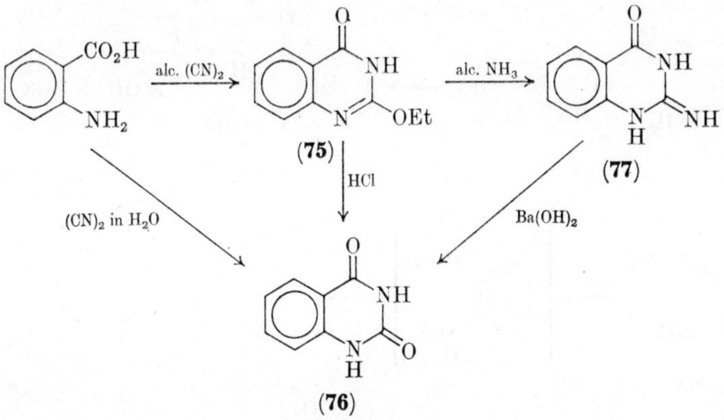

(75)

(76)

(77)

SCHEME 1

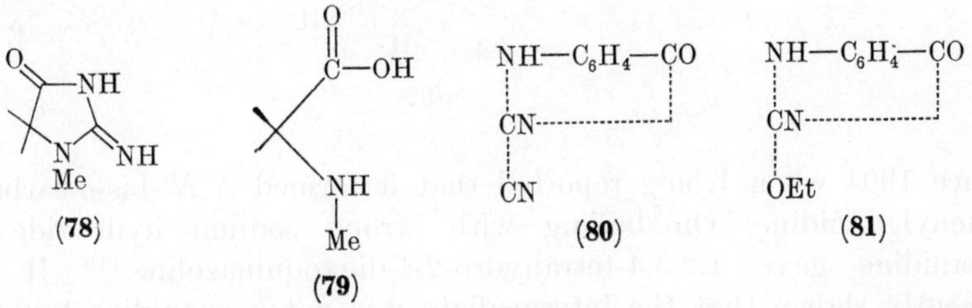

(78)

(79)

(80)

(81)

The formula **81** was adjusted to that of **75** by Finger and Günzler who synthesized the compound by reacting methyl or ethyl anthranilate with ethyl cyanimidocarbonate (Eq. 53).[311] By heating ethyl anthranilate with methyl cyanimidocarbonate in the presence of copper at 80° the corresponding 2-methoxy compound was prepared,[312] and at high temperatures in the presence of cuprous chloride 1,2,3,4-tetrahydro-2,4-dioxoquinazoline was formed.[313] The intermediate ethyl o-cyanamino-benzoate can be methylated and the product cyclized to give 1,2,3,4-tetrahydro-3-methyl-2,4-dioxoquinazoline.[314]

Cyanogen bromide reacts with sodium anthranilate to give the unstable intermediate o-cyanaminobenzoic acid which cyclizes to the imino isatoic anhydride (**82**). The structure of this imino compound is consistent with its infrared and ultraviolet spectra and it behaves very much like isatoic anhydride. Mild treatment with methanol, ethanol, isopropanol or butanol yields the methyl, ethyl, isopropyl, or butyl esters of o-ureidobenzoic acid respectively. With alkali or 20% hydrochloric acid it rearranges to 1,2,3,4-tetrahydro-2,4-dioxoquinazoline.[315] The reaction of anthranilic acid and cyanogen bromide has been known

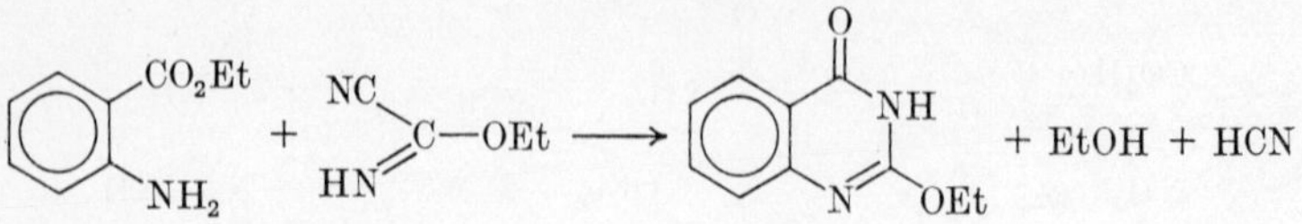

$$+ \text{ EtOH } + \text{ HCN} \qquad (53)$$

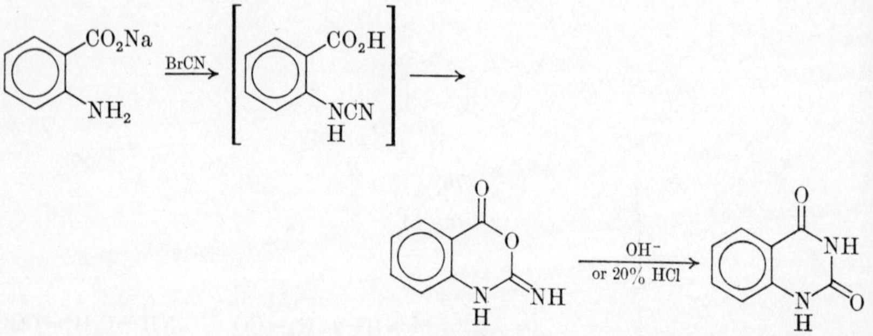

(82)

since 1904 when König reported that it formed N,N'-bis-o-carboxy-phenylguanidine. On boiling with strong sodium hydroxide the guanidine gave 1,2,3,4-tetrahydro-2,4-dioxoquinazoline.[110] It was recently shown that the intermediate was not a guanidine but N-o-ureidobenzoylanthranilic acid because it could be prepared by reaction of the imino compound (82) and anthranilic acid. Although alkaline treatment of this intermediate did give 1,2,3,4-tetrahydro-2,4-dioxo-quinazoline as reported by König, refluxing for 10 hours in dry pyridine yields 3-o-carboxyphenyl-1,2,3,4-tetrahydro-2,4-dioxoquinazoline.[316] The imino compound 82 is a very useful intermediate for the prepara-tion of $N_{(3)}$-substituted derivatives of 1,2,3,4-tetrahydro-2,4-dioxo-quinazoline. With methyl-, ethyl-, and benzylamine, and aniline in ethanol or dioxan it gives the respective o-ureidobenzamides which can be cyclized in high yields to the dioxoquinazolines by boiling with 5% potassium hydroxide (Reaction 54). Secondary amines also give the

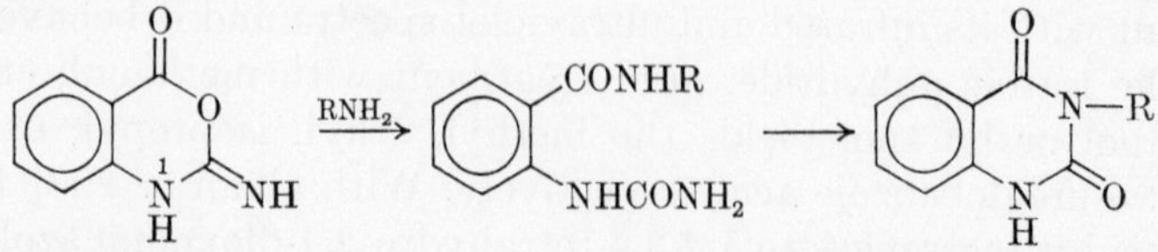

$$(54)$$

(82)

amides but these cannot be cyclized.[317] N-Benzyl-, N-carbamoyl-
methyl-, and N-methylanthranilic acid react with cyanogen bromide
to give the $N_{(1)}$ derivatives of **82** which rearrange easily to 1-benzyl-,
1-carbamoylmethyl-, and 1-methyl-1,2,3,4-tetrahydro-2,4-dioxoquin-
azoline in good yields.[318] 6,7-Benzo-, 8-carboxy-, 6,8-dibromo-, 6,8-
dichloro-, and 7-trifluoromethyl- 1,2,3,4-tetrahydro-2,4-dioxoquinazo-
lines can be obtained from their respective anthranilic acids by reaction
with cyanogen bromide followed by treatment with 1.7 N sodium
hydroxide at 80°.[319]

b. From Anthranilic Acid (or Derivatives) and Ureas

The fusion of anthranilic acid with urea to give 1,2,3,4-tetrahydro-
2,4-dioxoquinazoline was first described by Griess[309] (Sect. 3.A.a.), and
has been used to prepare the 6-[39] and 7-methyl,[72] 7-t-butyl,[320] and
6-bromo,[321] 7- and 8-nitro,[322] and 6,8-dibromo,[323] dichloro,[323,324,325]
and diiodo[323] derivatives of 1,2,3,4-tetrahydro-2,4-dioxoquinazoline
(Reaction 55). The reaction failed with 5-nitroanthranilic acid.[48] The

$$ R \text{—} \underset{NH_2}{\overset{CO_2H}{\bigcirc}} \xrightarrow{\text{urea}} R \text{—} \bigcirc \overset{O}{\underset{H}{\overset{\|}{N}}} NH \\ O \qquad (55) $$

yields are not always good. The reaction of 3,5-dihalogenoanthranilic
acids and urea was studied in detail. When the molar ratio of acid to
urea was 1:3.3 the yields of dioxoquinazoline for the chloro, bromo, and
iodo compounds were 67, 45, and 23%, and the product was accompanied
by the respective 3,5-dihalogenoanthranilamides which were isolated
in 11, 40, and 69% yields.[323] The parent compound has also been
prepared from o-nitrobenzoyl chloride and urea followed by reduction
and cyclization of the o-aminobenzoylurea by heating at 200° or boiling
with acid.[326] Condensations have been successfully carried out by
fusion with substituted ureas. Thus anthranilic acid can be fused with
N-phenyl-, N-p-tolyl-, N-m-bromophenyl-, and N-benzoylurea to give
3-phenyl-,[327,328] 3-p-tolyl-, 3-m-bromophenyl-,[327] and 3-benzoyl-1,2,3,4-
tetrahydro-2,4-dioxoquinazoline.[231] N-Methyl-,[329,330] N-benzyl-, N-
phenyl-, and N-2,4,6-trinitrophenylanthranilic acid and urea give
respectively 1-methyl-, 1-benzyl-, 1-phenyl-, and 1-2′,4′,6′-trinitro-
phenyl-[331] 1,2,3,4-tetrahydro-2,4-dioxoquinazolines, respectively. Anthranilic esters[332] and amides[324,333–335] have been used successfully in

this reaction. Fusion of o-methylaminobenzamide with urea at 200–210° for 30 minutes gave mainly 1,2,3,4-tetrahydro-1-methyl-2,4-dioxoquinazoline, but careful work-up of the mother liquors during the purification gave some 1,2,3,4-tetrahydro-3-methyl-2,4-dioxoquinazoline.[255] 1,2,3,4-Tetrahydro-1,3-dimethyl-2,4-dioxoquinazoline can be prepared from equimolar quantities of o-methylaminobenzmethylamide and urea by heating at 180°.[255] 1,2,3,4-Tetrahydro-2,4-dioxoquinazoline has also been obtained from isatoic anhydride and urea but the reaction is not a general one[153] (see following section). 1,2,3,4-Tetrahydro-7-nitro-2,4-dioxoquinazoline is the only recorded example where a dioxoquinazoline is formed from an anthranilic acid and urea by boiling in water.[336]

c. Cyclization of o-Ureidobenzoic Acids and Derivatives

o-Ureidobenzoic acids are readily prepared from the corresponding anthranilic acid and potassium cyanate. The ureido acids are then easily cyclized to the respective 1,2,3,4-tetrahydro-2,4-dioxoquinazolines by heating with acid[337] or alkali.[338,339] Anthranilic esters[336,340] and amides[336,341] as well as acids[342] undergo this reaction (56). 6-

$$R^1 = OH, OMe, OEt, NH_2 \qquad (56)$$

and 7-Chloro-, 6-bromo-,[321,343] 7-methyl-,[336] 8-methyl-,[342] 5-, 6-, 7-, and 8-methoxy-, 6,7-dimethoxy-,[336] 6- and 7-hydroxy-,[344] 5-[322] and 7-nitro-,[336] and 5-carboxy-[345,346] 1,2,3,4-tetrahydro-2,4-dioxoquinazolines have been prepared in a similar manner. o-Methylamino- and o-ethylaminobenzoic acid give 1-methyl-[330] and 1-ethyl-1,2,3,4-tetrahydro-2,4-dioxoquinazoline[347] in an analogous fashion. The 1-phenyl derivative can be prepared directly by heating ethyl o-anilinobenzoate and sodium cyanate in trifluoroacetic acid.[347a] 5-Nitroanthranilic acid fails to react with potassium cyanate (this also failed with urea, Sect. 3.A.b.) but nitration of methyl o-ureidobenzoate gave a dinitro derivative which on treatment with ammonia formed 1,2,3,4-tetrahydro-6-nitro-2,4-dioxoquinazoline[48] (see Sect. 3.B.b.). o-Ureidobenzonitriles also give dioxoquinazolines with alkali or acid.[336,348] Phenyl and p-tolyl isocyanates react with anthranilic acid and o-methylaminobenzoic acid to give 3-phenyl-,[349,350] and 3-p-tolyl-1,2,3,4-tetrahydro-2,4-dioxo-quinazoline, and 3-phenyl- and 3-p-tolyl-1,2,3,4-tetrahydro-1-methyl-2,4-dioxoquinazoline.[351] Methyl anthranilate also reacts with propyl, butyl, cyclohexyl, phenyl, p-tolyl, and α-naphthyl isocyanates to give the substituted o-ureidobenzoic esters which cyclize to the respective 3-substituted 1,2,3,4-tetrahydro-2,4-dioxoquinazolines in 70–90% yields with 1:1 ethanolic hydrochloric acid; lower yields are obtained when sulphuric acid is used as cyclizing agent.[352] N,N'-di-o-ethoxycarbonyl-phenylurea, prepared from ethyl anthranilate and phosgene, cyclizes to 3-o-carboxyphenyl-1,2,3,4-tetrahydro-2,4-dioxoquinazoline after boiling in ethanolic alkali for 0.5 hours.[353] N,N'-Diphenylcarbodiimide reacts with anthranilic acid in benzene to give 1,2,3,4-tetrahydro-2,4-dioxo-3-phenylquinazoline and aniline, presumably via the intermediate N-o-phenylcarbamoylphenyl-N'-phenylurea.[354] Methanolic ammonia at room temperature converts N-o-methoxycarbonylphenyl-N'-p-chlorosulphonylphenylurea to 1,2,3,4-tetrahydro-2,4-dioxo-3-p-sulpha-moylphenylquinazoline in 4 hours.[355]

o-N'-Phenylureidobenzoic acid cyclizes to 1,2-dihydro-2-phenyl-imino-3,1,4-benzoxazone (the phenylimino derivative of **82**) with polyphosphoric acid at 80–100°, but at 150° this rearranges to 1,2,3,4-tetrahydro-2,4-dioxo-3-phenylquinazoline.[355a]

Attempts have been made to prepare dioxoquinazolines from isatoic anhydride and amines but the yields and products vary depending on the substituents in the benzene ring and on the amine used (Reaction 57). 5,7-Dibromoisatoic anhydride and aniline give a mixture

consisting mostly of 2-amino-3,5-dibromobenzanilide and a trace of 6,8-dibromo-1,2,3,4-tetrahydro-2,4-dioxoquinazoline. The yield of the latter is increased to 17.5 and 36.1% when 0.1 and 0.35 moles of water, respectively, are added to the mixture. No dioxoquinazoline is formed when 0.07 moles of acetic acid is added to the mixture.[356] 5,7-Dichloro-, dibromo-, and diiodoisatoic anhydride and ethylamine give 6,8-dichloro-, dibromo-, and diiodo-3-ethyl-1,2,3,4-tetrahydro-2,4-dioxoquinazoline in 71, 86, and 87% yields, respectively.[323] A detailed study of the reactions of methyl-, ethyl-, propyl-, isopropyl-, butyl-, t-butyl-, cyclohexyl-, and benzylamine with isatoic anhydride (83) indicated that in all cases fission at both (a) and (b) occurs, and that in all these cases the yields of 84 or 85 reach an optimum at a molar ratio 83 to amine of about 4 to 8. The yields of 84 are higher in aqueous solution than in alcoholic solution. The reaction with s-butylamine, on the other hand, favours 85. When the o-ureidobenzoic acids (84) are heated with 10% sulphuric acid until clear, then cooled, the 3-methyl-, ethyl-, propyl-, isopropyl-, butyl-, cyclohexyl-, and benzyl-1,2,3,4-tetrahydro-2,4-dioxoquinazoline are formed in 61, 73, 82, 41, 87, 48, and 70% yields, respectively.[357]

d. From o-Ethoxycarbonylaminobenzoic Esters or Amides

When o-ethoxycarbonylaminobenzamide and its 4-methyl derivative are heated above their melting points, they lose water and form 1,2,3,4-tetrahydro-2,4-dioxoquinazoline[334] and its 7-methyl derivative.[358] The reaction can also be carried out by heating the o-ethoxycarbonylaminobenzoic esters with the required amine (Reaction 58),[126,359] or in two steps from o-aminobenzamides.[360] o-Ethoxy-

carbonylaminobenzamides cyclize to dioxoquinazolines in very good yield with alcoholic potassium hydroxide.[360] Although cyclization of N-t-butyl-N'-o-carboxyphenylurea to the corresponding dioxoquinazoline has been reported to form 1,2,3,4-tetrahydro-2,4-dioxoquinazoline with loss of the t-butyl group,[357] the preparation of 1,2,3,4-tetrahydro-2,4-dioxo-3-t-butylquinazoline from o-ethoxycarbonylaminobenz-t-butylamide is accomplished with difficulty.[360]

e. From Phthalic Acid Derivatives

The use of derivatives of phthalic acid for the preparation of dioxoquinazolines necessitates rearrangements of the Hofmann, Curtius, or Lossen type. The first is exemplified by the formation of 1,2,3,4-tetrahydro-2,4-dioxoquinazoline, its 3-methyl and 3-ethyl derivatives, by reaction of alkali hypobromite with phthalamide[361,362] or phthalimide,[361] N-methyl- and N-ethylphthalimide (Reaction 59).[362] o-Cyanobenzamide and sodium hypochlorite react similarly.[363] The second rearrangement is shown by phthaloyldiazide which gives 1,2,3,4-tetrahydro-2,4-dioxoquinazoline with ammonia, and 1,2,3,4-tetrahydro-2,4-dioxo-3-phenylquinazoline with aniline followed by concentrated hydrochloric acid.[364] A Lossen rearrangement occurs when N-methanesulphonyloxyphthalimide (86) is treated with primary amines (Reaction 60). The reaction is carried out at 50° for a short time after

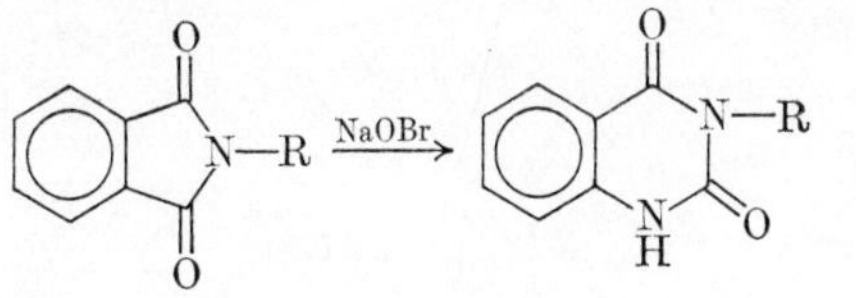

$$\text{R = Me or Et}$$

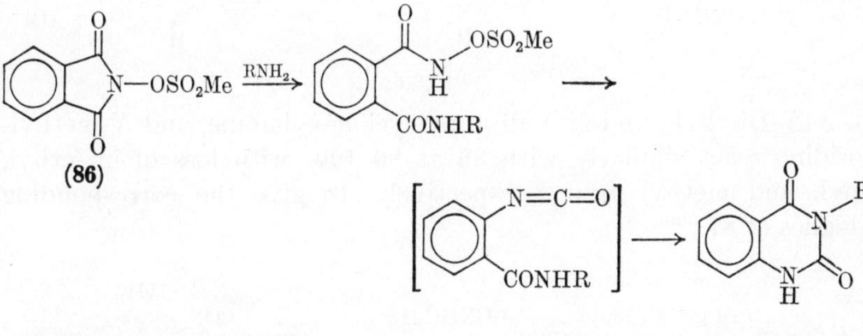

(59)

(60)

the initial exothermic reaction. The bases that have been used are methylamine, ethanolamine, glycine, α-picolinic hydrazide, benzenesulphonylhydrazine, hydrazine, and hydroxylamine, and the yields are usually high.[365,366] This reaction has the peculiarity of taking place also with tertiary amines. Hence N,N-dimethylcyclohexylamine reacts with compound 86 at 150° with the formation of the zwitterion 87 and the liberation of a methyl group. The infrared spectrum of compound 87 has no band for the N=C=O group but has one carbonyl stretching frequency at 1765 cm^{-1}. Its constitution was derived from the reactions in scheme 2 and has been synthesized according to the route in reaction

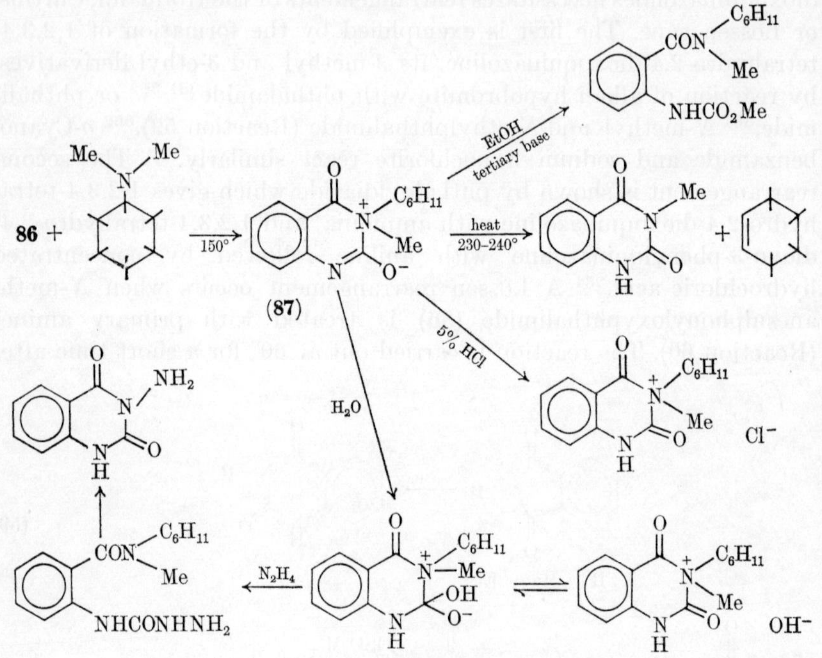

SCHEME 2

(61). N,N-Diethyl-, and N,N-dipropylcyclohexylamine, and N-methyl-piperidine react similarly with **86** at 90–100° with loss of an ethyl, propyl, and methyl group, respectively, to give the corresponding analogues of **87**.[366]

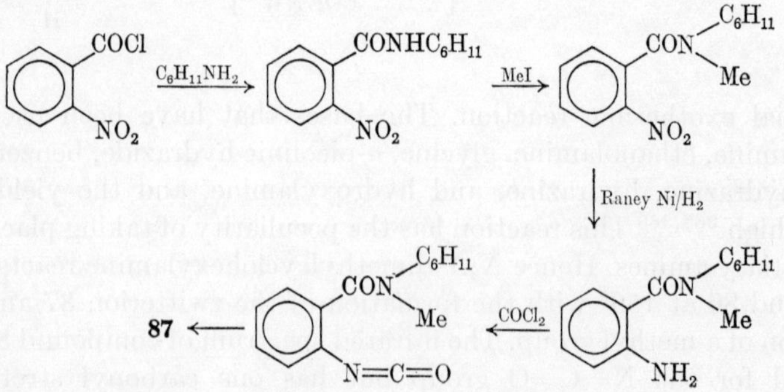

(61)

f. From Isatins

α-Isatinoxime rearranges to 1,2,3,4-tetrahydro-2,4-dioxoquinazoline on heating with dilute sodium hydroxide.[367] β-Imino derivatives of isatin, on the other hand, require oxidation with hydrogen peroxide in alkaline solution in order to form the dioxoquinazoline. Thus β-imino- and N-phenyl-, N-p-tolyl-, N-p-aminophenyl-, N-p-methoxyphenyl-, and N-1-naphthyl-β-iminoisatin and hydrogen peroxide give the respective 3-substituted 1,2,3,4-tetrahydro-2,4-dioxoquinazolines in 47 to 92% yields.[368] The reaction assumably goes through the imino isatoic anhydride derivative (Reaction 62). The product obtained by Dorsch[369] by the action of ammonia on the chromic oxide oxidation product of 5,7-dichloroisatin was shown to be 6,8-dichloro-1,2,3,4-tetrahydro-2,4-dioxoquinazoline.[324] When isatin is heated with alcoholic ammonia at 100° for 20 hours it forms three products, and alkaline treatment of the compound melting at 270° gives 1,2,3,4-tetrahydro-2,4-dioxoquinazoline.[370] The latter is also obtained from the oxidation of isammic acid (36) (see Sect. 2.A.l.) with potassium permanganate or nitric acid.[371] N-Phenyl-N-3-oxo-2-indolylhydroxylamine (88) reacts with thionyl chloride to form the N-chloro compound which rearranges to 2-chloro-3,4-dihydro-4-oxo-3-phenylquinazoline and finally hydrolyzes to 1,2,3,4-tetrahydro-2,4-dioxo-3-phenylquinazoline (Reaction 63).[372]

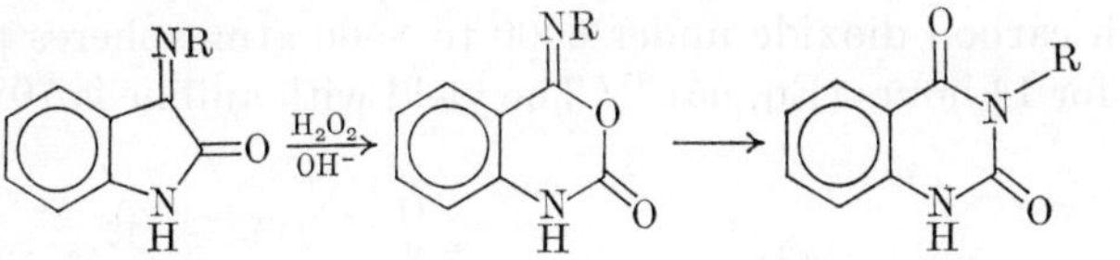

(62)

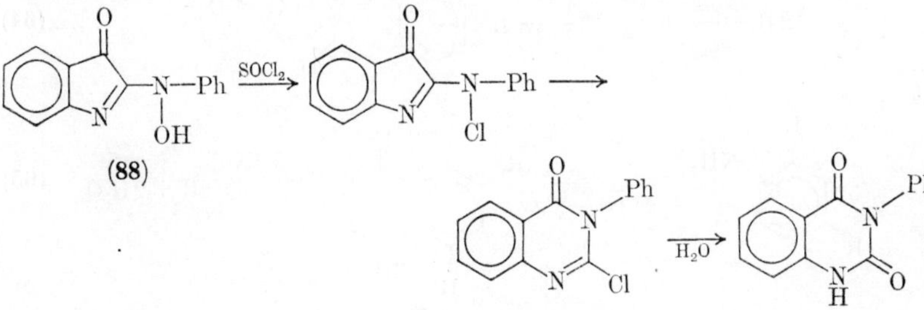

(88)

(63)

g. From Anilines and Related Compounds

When a mixture of an aryl isocyanate (or its dimer), anhydrous aluminium chloride, and sodium chloride are heated above 135°,

3-aryl-2,4-dioxoquinazolines are formed in moderate yields.[373] Since
the isocyanate (in a sense) dimerizes to the oxoquinazoline, the substituent in the aryl groups will be present in both the benzene ring of the
quinazoline and the 3-phenyl substituent (Eq. 64). 3-Phenyl-,[373,374]
6-methyl-3-*p*-tolyl-, 7-methyl-3-*m*-tolyl-, 8-methyl-3-*o*-tolyl-, 6-chloro-
3-*p*-chlorophenyl-, 7-chloro-3-*m*-chlorophenyl-, 8-chloro-3-*o*-chloro-
phenyl-, 6,8-dimethyl-3-2',4'-xylyl-, and 5,8-dichloro-3-2',5'-dichloro-
phenyl-[373] 1,2,3,4-tetrahydro-2,4-dioxoquinazolines are prepared from
the corresponding aryl isocyanates in 23–51% yields. 4-Diphenyl
isocyanate yields 5-phenylanthranilic acid by this treatment, presumably via the dioxoquinazoline.[373] The reaction proceeds equally
well in high-boiling inert solvents such as 1,2-dichloro- or 1,2,4-trichloro-
benzene.[375] A variant of this method makes use of N,N-diarylureas and
potassium carbonate under about 50 atmospheres of carbon dioxide
pressure, at temperatures above 200°. The yields are rather low.
Dioxoquinazolines with different substituents in the benzene ring and
the 3-aryl group can be prepared if a substituted aniline is heated with
potassium anthranilate at 220–230° under carbon dioxide pressure in
the absence of potassium carbonate. The reaction can also be carried
out with the acetyl derivative of the amine, e.g. α-acetamidonaphthalene
gives a poor yield of 7,8-benzo-1,2,3,4-tetrahydro-3-1'-naphthyl-2,4-
dioxoquinazoline.[376] A further variation on this reaction is the formation of 3-aryl-1,2,3,4-tetrahydro-2,4-dioxoquinazolines by heating
anilines with carbon dioxide under 6000 to 8500 atmospheres pressure
and at 200° for 14 hours (Eq. 65).[377] The yield with aniline is 70% when

$$2\,R\!-\!\!\bigcirc\!\!-\!\!NCO \xrightarrow[\text{NaCl}]{\text{AlCl}_3} R\!-\!\!\bigcirc\!\!-\!\!\text{(dioxoquinazoline)}\!-\!\bigcirc\!\!-\!\!R \qquad (64)$$

$$2\;\bigcirc\!\!\begin{smallmatrix}R^1\\ NH_2\end{smallmatrix} + 2\,CO_2 \longrightarrow R\!-\!\text{(dioxoquinazoline)}\!-\!\bigcirc\!\!-\!\!R + 2\,H_2O \qquad (65)$$

the temperature is 200°, but at 150° and 3300 atmospheres the yield
drops to less than 1%. Alkali or acid catalysts can be used but the latter
give more by-products. The reaction fails with amino-, chloro-, and
nitroanilines, and α- and β-naphthylamines,[378] but is satisfactory with

toluidines, xylidines, anisidines, and anilines with long aliphatic chains substituted in the benzene ring.[377]

Azobenzenes can be converted to 3-aryl-1,2,3,4-tetrahydro-2,4-dioxoquinazolines by heating at 230° with carbon monoxide at 100–200 atmospheres pressure in the presence of cobalt carbonyl (Reaction 66).

Oxygen has to be excluded from the reaction because it decomposes the catalyst. The reaction can be carried out in the presence of inert solvents such as benzene, toluene, or xylene. Other catalysts, e.g. iron carbonyl, nickel carbonyl, and cobalt-containing salts, can be used but are inferior to cobalt carbonyl. Several by-products are formed and the major ones are the respective 2-arylindazolones (91), and diarylureas. These are suspected as intermediates because they are converted in high yield to the respective dioxoquinazolines under similar conditions. The yields vary from 17 to 65%. The reaction can be carried out with symmetrical as well as unsymmetrical azobenzenes.[379]

When R is 4-methyl, chloro, dimethylamino, or methoxy and R¹ is H in 89, then the substituents are found in the 6-position in the benzene ring of 90, and no mixed quinazolines are formed. The reaction with azonaphthalenes yields only traces of dinaphthylureas, and when R or R¹ in 89 are nitro or cyano the reactions fail.[379]

h. *Miscellaneous*

1,2,3,4-Tetrahydro-2,4-dioxo-1-phenylquinazoline can be prepared in 80% yield by heating ethyl N-phenylanthranilate with urethane at 180–200° for 2 hours then at 200–220° for a further hour.[380] A variant on this theme is the formation of 1,2,3,4-tetrahydro-2,4-dioxoquinazoline from isatoic anhydride and urethane.[142]

The oxidation of 1,2,3,4-tetrahydro-2-oxoquinazolines with potassium permanganate[381,382,383] or chromic oxide[384] gives 1,2,3,4-tetrahydro-2,4-dioxoquinazolines (Ch. VIII, Sect. 6.). When 4-nitroanthranilic acid and cyanoguanidine are heated in hydrochloric acid,

1,2,3,4-tetrahydro-7-nitro-2,4-dioxoquinazoline is formed.[385] 7-Chloro-
5-phenyl-3,1,4-benzoxadiazepin-2(1*H*)-one (92) rearranges to 6-chloro-
1,2,3,4-tetrahydro-2,4-dioxo-3-phenylquinazoline on heating. The latter
is identical with the product obtained from 5-chloroanthranilic acid
and phenyl isocyanate. A Beckmann rearrangement is postulated for
this thermal reaction (67).[386] 2-(*N*-Chloroacetyl-*N*-methyl)amino-*N*-
methylbenzamide and the benzanilide (93) lose the —CH$_2$Cl group on
boiling in pyridine for 1 and 2.5 hours respectively, to give 3-methyl-
and 3-phenyl-1,2,3,4-tetrahydro-1-methyl-2,4-dioxoquinazoline in 50
and 56% yields respectively (Reaction 68).[387] Hydrolysis of 12*H*-benz-

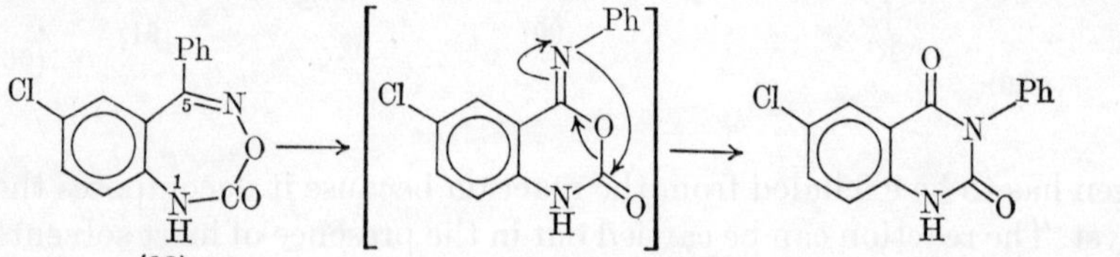

(67)

(92)

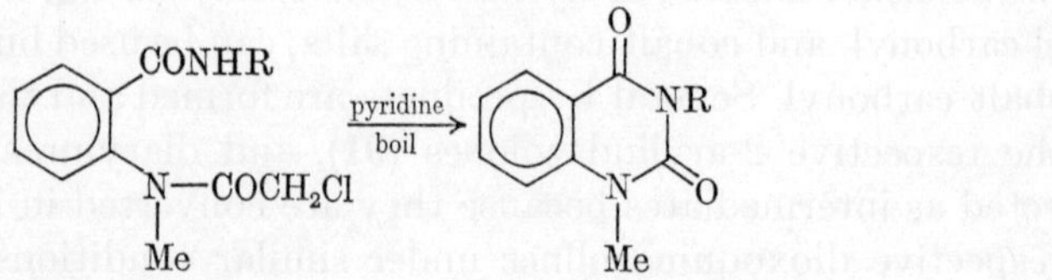

(68)

(93) R = Me or Ph

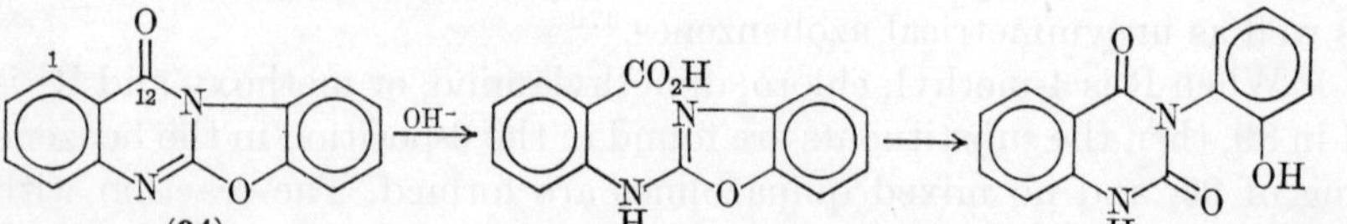

(94)

(69)

oxazolo(2,3-b)quinazolin-12-one (94) with dilute alkali afforded 1,2,3,4-
tetrahydro-3-*o*-hydroxyphenyl-2,4-dioxoquinazoline via the intermediate *N*-2-benzoxazolylanthranilic acid which can also be isolated
(Reaction 69).[388] For the formation of dioxoquinazolines from chloro-,
alkoxy- (Ch. V, Sects. 1.E.b.(ii) and 2.E.b.(i)), thio- (Ch. VI, Sects. 3
and 4.), amino- (Ch. VII, Sects. 1.E.a. and 3.A.), and *N*-hydroxy-
quinazolines (Ch. IX, Sect. 4.) see the references cited.

B. Properties of 1,2,3,4-Tetrahydro-2,4-dioxoquinazolines

a. *Physical Properties*

1,2,3,4-Tetrahydro-2,4-dioxoquinazolines are high-melting solids
(see Tables IV.41–47) with a poor solubility in water. They form

insoluble salts, and the 6,8-dichloro and dibromo derivatives form insoluble salts with sodium, potassium, lithium, lead and caesium ions.[321] Although the dichloro compound had been suggested as reagent for sodium ions[324] careful study showed that it cannot be recommended because precipitation is incomplete, the reagent hydrolyzes readily, and cannot detect sodium ions in the presence of potassium ions.[389] 1,2,3,4-Tetrahydro-2,4-dioxoquinazoline and its 1,3-dimethyl derivative form soluble complexes with phenol derivatives in aqueous solution at 30°. The stability of the complexes is in the order: hydroquinone > resorcinol > catechol > phenol.[390] In non-aqueous media, e.g. carbon tetrachloride, the 1,3-dimethyl derivative forms well-defined insoluble complexes. The ratio of 1,2,3,4-tetrahydro-1,3-dimethyl-2,4-dioxoquinazoline to phenol in the complexes obtained with catechol, resorcinol, and hydroquinone are 2 : 5, 1 : 4, and 1 : 1 respectively.[391] Nitro derivatives have been suggested as indicators because of their resemblance to p-nitrophenol.[339] They give colour reactions with reducing sugars,[392] Lewisite, and ethyl dichloroarsine.[393]

   1,2,3,4-Tetrahydro-2,4-dioxoquinazoline is capable of existing in six possible tautomeric structures. Two pK_a values 9.78 and 2.5 have been measured for it, and are apparently for the loss of each of the protons in the heterocyclic ring.[21] The 1-methyl and 3-methyl derivatives have pK_a values of 9.85 and 10.6 respectively.[394] The infrared spectra show two very intense bands in the frequency regions 1720–1780 cm^{-1} and 1655–1712 cm^{-1} in the solid state[23,380] and in dioxan solution,[395] and are consistent with the structure 95 which is probably the

(95)

predominating tautomer. The former frequency is attributed to the carbonyl in position 4 because of its proximity to the benzene ring, and the latter to the carbonyl in position 2.[23] Other 1-, 3-, and 1,3-substituted dioxoquinazolines that have been examined also showed two strong bands in the frequency regions cited above.[357,380] The ultraviolet spectra of several 1-, 3-, and 1,3-substituted dioxoquinazolines have been measured and they are quite similar to the parent compound in showing two peaks, one at ~ 220 mμ and the second at ~ 320 mμ.[380,396] A detailed study of the tautomerism of 1,2,3,4-tetrahydro-2,4-dioxoquinazoline has not yet been made. The mass spectrum of 1,2,3,4-tetrahydro-1-methyl-2,4-dioxoquinazoline has been measured.[247]

b. Chemical Properties

1,2,3,4-Tetrahydro-2,4-dioxoquinazolines are stable to mild acid and alkaline treatment, but boiling with 10% sodium hydroxide causes extensive hydrolysis. The time of heating depends on the substituents and varies from 2 to 6 hours.[373,375,376,379] The hydrolysis leads to the respective anthranilic acids. Indeed this is considered as a good method for preparing anthranilic acids which are otherwise difficult to obtain (Reaction 70),[373,375] particularly when the starting material for the preparation of the dioxoquinazoline is an aniline (Sect. 3.A.g.).

$$ R \text{—} \underset{H}{\overset{O}{\underset{N}{\bigcirc}}} N \text{—} \bigcirc R^1 \quad \xrightarrow[\text{2-6 hrs reflux}]{\text{10\% NaOH}} \quad R \text{—} \bigcirc \overset{CO_2H}{\underset{NH_2}{}} \quad + \quad \underset{R^1}{\overset{NH_2}{\bigcirc}} \qquad (70) $$

Alkylation of 1,2,3,4-tetrahydro-2,4-dioxoquinazoline has been the subject of study for many years because Abt in 1889 reported that methylation with methyl iodide in a sealed tube at 100–120° gave 1,2,3,4-tetrahydro-1-methyl-2,4-dioxoquinazoline[334] and recorded a melting point of 147°. He synthesized this product from o-metnylaminobenzamide and urea. Mayeda in 1916 prepared the 1-methyl derivative from o-methylaminobenzoic acid and potassium cyanate but his melting point was 265°.[330] He stated that the properties of his compound were, however, very similar to those reported by Abt. Bogert and Scatchard in 1919 repeated the methylation and found that the 1,3-dimethyl derivative melting at 167–168° was formed together with the 3-methyl derivative which had a melting point of 237–238°.[48] These melting points agree reasonably well with very recent work (1963)[255] and it is clear that either Abt was wrong in recording his melting points or his synthesis was incomplete.[346] The 3-ethyl derivative is formed with ethyl iodide and this can be further alkylated with dimethyl sulphate to the 3-ethyl-1-methyl derivative.[347] Excess of ethyl iodide in the presence of alkali,[12] dimethyl sulphate,[345] or diazomethane[397] forms the respective 1,3-dialkyldioxoquinazoline. Although the 1,3-dimethyl and 1,3-diethyl derivatives are formed with excess of alkylating agent, propyl iodide with sodium propoxide gives a monopropyl derivative which resists further alkylation by propyl iodide.[12] Caprolactim O-methyl ether methylates 1,2,3,4-tetrahydro-2,4-dioxoquinazoline to the 1,3-dimethyl derivative (63% yield).[398] Dimethyl sulphate reacts with 5-carboxy-1,2,3,4-tetrahydro-2,4-dioxoquinazoline to form a trimethyl derivative which was assigned the structure 2,4-dimethoxy-5-methoxycarbonylquinazoline (m.p. 144°).[345] This was later corrected to 1,2,3,4-tetrahydro-5-methoxy-carbonyl-1,3-dimethyl-2,4-dioxoquinazoline on the evidence that it was stable to dilute acid whereas 2,4-dimethoxy-5-methoxycarbonyl-quinazoline (m.p. 134.5–135.5), prepared (unequivocally) from 2,4-dichloro-5-chlorocarbonylquinazoline and sodium methoxide, was readily hydrolyzed by dilute hydrochloric acid to 1,2,3,4-tetrahydro-5-methoxycarbonyl-2,4-dioxoquinazoline.[399] The 1,3-dimethyl derivative of the latter (m.p. 142–143°, see above), prepared from the dioxo acid and diazomethane, was hydrolyzed to the acid and converted to the acid chloride. Treatment of this with diazomethane and hydrobromic acid resulted in the loss of one N-methyl group. The monomethyl compound (96) was oxidized to the carboxylic acid which was decarboxy-lated to 97 (Reaction 71). The melting point of this monomethyl dioxo-

(71)

(97) m.p. 198–199°

quinazoline did not correspond with either the 1- or the 3-methyl derivative (see above). The authors postulate that the difference may be stereochemical which is rather difficult to accept.[400] Perhaps dimorphism would be a better explanation or the product may be a mixture of the 1- and 3-methyl derivatives.

Nitration of 1,2,3,4-tetrahydro-2,4-dioxoquinazoline gave a mono- and a dinitro derivative. The former was presumed to be the 6-nitro derivative but it could not be prepared from 5-nitroanthranilic acid and urea or potassium cyanate. However, methyl o-ureidobenzoate could be nitrated to a dinitro derivative which was shown to be methyl 5-nitro-2-N'-nitroureidobenzoate (98) because it hydrolyzed to the known 5-nitroanthranilic acid (Reaction 72) (Sects. 3.A.b. and 3.A.c.).

$$ (72) $$

$$ (98) $$

The dinitro compound (98) then cyclized to 1,2,3,4-tetrahydro-6-nitro-2,4-dioxoquinazoline which was identical with the product from direct mononitration.[48] The dinitro compound was later shown to be the 6,8-derivative by reduction to the diamino compound followed by tetraazotization and reaction with cuprous bromide to give 6,8-di-bromo-1,2,3,4-tetrahydro-2,4-dioxoquinazoline of known structure.[321] Supporting evidence came from the nitration of either the 6-nitro[48] or the 8-nitro[322] derivatives which gave the same product as in the direct dinitration of 1,2,3,4-tetrahydro-2,4-dioxoquinazoline. Nitration of 1,2,3,4-tetrahydro-7-methyl-2,4-dioxoquinazoline gave high yields of mono and dinitro compounds, presumably the 6- and 6,8-dinitro derivatives.[358]

Sulphuryl chloride in glacial acetic acid for 14 hours failed to chlorinate 1,2,3,4-tetrahydro-2,4-dioxoquinazoline.[324] Sodium hypochlorite gives the 1- or 3-, or 1,3-chloro derivatives.[345] 1,3-Dichloro-1,2,3,4-tetrahydro-2,4-dioxoquinazolines are claimed to be useful bleaching agents.[401] Phosphorus pentachloride converts oxo- to chloro-quinazolines (Ch. V, Sects 1.A., 1.B., and 1.C.), and benzoyl chloride in pyridine gives the 1,3-dibenzoyl derivatives.[231] For the reaction of hydrazine with dioxoquinazolines see chapter VII, section 2.A.c. Zinc-dust distillation of 1,2,3,4-tetrahydro-7-methyl-2,4-dioxoquinazoline yields 2-amino-4-methylbenzonitrile.[72] 1,2,3,4-Tetrahydro-2,4-di-oxoquinazoline undergoes a coupling reaction with diazonaphthionic acid to form a red-coloured dye.[402]

4. Quinazolines with Hydroxy Groups in the Benzene Ring

A. Preparation

The literature of quinazolines substituted with hydroxy groups in the benzene ring is small. 7-,[403] and 8-Hydroxy-,[404] 8-hydroxy-4-methyl-, and 8-hydroxy-4-propylquinazoline[405] are prepared by demethylating the corresponding methyl ethers with anhydrous aluminium chloride. After the initial exothermic reaction on mixing, the complex is heated at 125–135° for 3 to 4 hours. The hydroxyquinazo-line is then isolated by extraction with chloroform after the pH is adjusted to such a value as to ensure the maximum amount of neutral species in the aqueous medium. The yields vary from 40 to 65% and this large difference could be due to incomplete extraction, particularly in the examples where the acidic and basic pK_a values are close to each other. Demethylation can also be effected with hydrobromic acid (density 1.5) as for the preparation of 2,4-dimethyl- and 4-methyl-2-phenyl-8-hydroxyquinazoline,[8] and several 3,4-dihydro-8-hydroxy-4-oxoquinazolines.[129]

The Riedel synthesis (Ch. II, Sect. 1. and Ch. III, Sect. 1.I.) has been successfully used to prepare 5-,[403] 6-,[404] and 8-hydroxyquinazoline, and 6,8-dimethyl-5-hydroxyquinazoline[406] from 2-hydroxy-6-nitro-, 3-hydroxy-6-nitro-, 3-hydroxy-2-nitro-, and 3,5-dimethyl-2-hydroxy-6-nitrobenzylidenebisformamide respectively. The Bischler synthesis as modified by Schofield, Swain, and Theobald (Ch. III, Sect. 1.A.) was adopted for the preparation of 8-hydroxy-4,5,7-trimethyl-2-o-nitro-phenylquinazoline from 3-hydroxy-4,5-dimethyl-2-o-nitrobenzamido-acetophenone.[407] A synthesis which is specific for the preparation of 6,8-dimethyl-5-hydroxyquinazolines (100) involves the condensation of 2,4-dimethyl-6-formyl (or acetyl)-2-acetoxycyclohexadienone (99) with formamidine, acetamidine, or phenylformamidine (Reaction 73). The reaction takes place in ethanol on standing for 12 hours at room temperature or boiling for 30–45 minutes. The yields of 6,8-dimethyl-, 2,6,8-trimethyl-, 2,4,6,8-tetramethyl-, and 6,8-dimethyl-2-phenyl- 5-hydroxyquinazolines are 70, 86, 86, and 63%.[406] The authors[406] say that a 1,4-addition takes place without describing a mechanism. A probable mechanism would be the formation of the azomethene (101) followed

by the addition of the imino group across the 'enone' to give **102** which
would lose the elements of acetic acid as shown by the arrows (Reaction
74). 7-Allyl-8-hydroxyquinazoline is prepared by a Claisen rearrangement of 8-allyloxyquinazoline.[405]

(73)

(**99**)   (**100**)

R = H or Me, R¹ = H, Me, or Ph

(74)

(**101**)   (**102**)

   3,4-Dihydro-7-hydroxy-2-methyl-4-oxoquinazoline is prepared
from the corresponding 7-amino compound by diazotization and boiling
with water,[408] and 3,4-dihydro-5,7-dihydroxy-4-oxo-2-phenylquinazo-
line is claimed to have been prepared from diethyl 2,4,6-trihydroxy-
isophthalic acid and phenylformamidine.[409]

B. Properties

   The hydroxyquinazolines are crystalline solids which have the
characteristic properties of phenols. 5-, 6-, and 7-Hydroxyquinazolines
are generally high melting whereas the 8-hydroxy derivatives melt some
80–90° lower (see Table IV.39.). This is probably due to intra-, rather
than intermolecular hydrogen bonding of the 8-OH with $N_{(1)}$ which
would tend to weaken the crystal lattice forces. 8-Hydroxyquinazolines
have been the subject of considerable study because they are nitrogen
analogues of oxine (8-hydroxyquinoline). They form 1:1 and 2:1
complexes with Cu^{2+}, Ni^{2+}, Zn^{2+}, Fe^{2+}, UO_2^{2+}, and Mg^{2+}.[405,410,411] In
the stability constant measurements of 8-hydroxyquinazoline,[405,410]
its 4-methyl-,[405] 2,4-dimethyl-, 4-methyl-2-phenyl-[410] derivatives and
oxine, it is found that, irrespective of the nature of the ligand, the
stability of the metal complex follows the order $Mg^{2+} < Zn^{2+} <$
$Ni^{2+} < UO_2^{2+} < Cu^{2+}$.[410] 8-Hydroxy-4-methyl-2-phenylquinazoline

shows no evidence of complex formation with magnesium,[410] and because of poor solubility, the stability constants of 7-allyl- and 4-propyl- 8-hydroxyquinazolines cannot be measured.[405] 2(2(4,5-Dimethylimidazol-2-yl)-azophenyl)-8-hydroxy-4,5,7-trimethylquinazoline (103) has been developed for the spectrophotometric determination of Li at 530 mμ. This reagent in dimethylformamide reacts selectively with Li and the sensitivity is 0.1γ of Li in 5.75 cm^3 of solution. Fifty-fold amounts of Ca, Sr, and Mg, 100-fold amounts of Na, Ba, Al and Fe, and 200-fold amounts of Rb and Cs do not interfere with the estimation.[412] The partition coefficients between oleyl alcohol and water for several 8-hydroxyquinazolines have been measured in connection with their bactericidal activity.[405,413]

The hydroxyquinazolines are amphoteric, and unlike the 2- and 4-oxoquinazolines the acidic and basic pK_a values lie closer to each other[21,403] indicating that contributions from quinonoid structures such as 104 are small. The presence of hydroxyl bands and the lack of carbonyl bands is shown in the infrared spectra and intramolecular hydrogen bonding occurs in the 8-hydroxy compound 105.[22,414] The tautomeric ratio of NH to OH forms in 8-hydroxyquinazoline is 1.4 $\times$ 10^{-4}.[414] The effect of the hydroxyl group in the benzene ring on the covalent hydration of the cation of quinazoline, and the ultraviolet spectra of hydroxyquinazolines are discussed in chapter II, section 2.C.c. The ionization constants are in Table II.4 (Ch. II, Sect. 2.C.c.). The anions of 5-, 6-, 7-, and 8-hydroxyquinazoline are anhydrous in aqueous solutions and only the 5- and 7-isomers, which are the stronger acids (pK_a 7.39 and 7.37), can be written in three resonating structures, e.g. 106, 107, and 108. Of the weaker acids, i.e. 6- (pK_a 8.19) and 8- (8.65) hydroxyquinazolines, the latter is the weaker and this is attributed to the greater difficulty in removing the proton from the hydrogen bonded structure 105.[403] By using the spectrophotometric method developed for the determination of pK_a values that lie close to each other, the values for 8-hydroxy and 2,4-dimethyl-8-hydroxy-quinazolines have been determined.[415]

The hydroxy groups in the benzene ring can be acetylated in the usual way.[408] Methylation of 8-hydroxyquinazoline occurs on N$_{(3)}$, but reaction with allyl bromide in alcoholic alkali produces 8-allyloxy-quinazoline.[405] Attempts to correlate the position of protonation with results from methylation experiments[416] can be dangerous for reasons described earlier (see Sect. 2.C.b.(i) and Ch. II, Sect. 3.B.). The Mannich reactions with 8-hydroxyquinazolines[305] are given in section 2.C.b(vii). The reactions of a group on any substituent which does not interfere

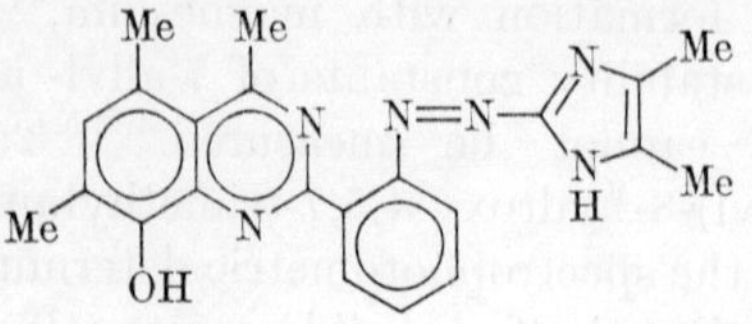

(103)

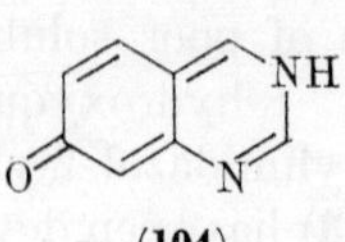

(104)

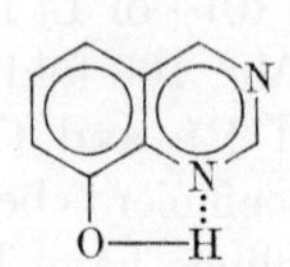

(105)

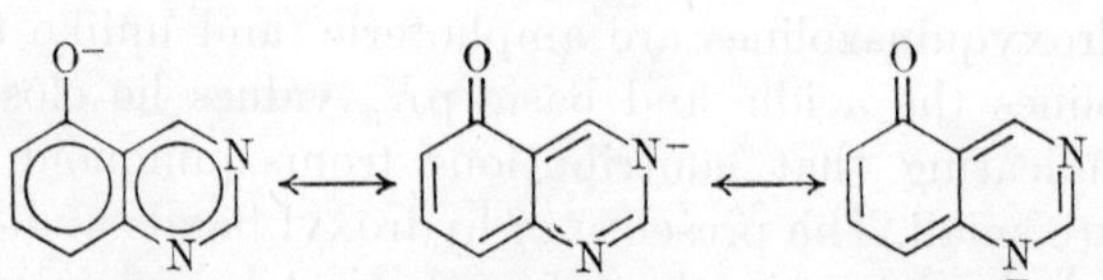

(106)   (107)   (108)

with the quinazoline nucleus are normal. Thus the nitro group in 8-hydroxy-4,5,7-trimethyl-2-o-nitrophenylquinazoline can be reduced with sodium dithionite to an amino group which can be diazotized, and this in turn can be coupled with phenols, deaminated, or hydrolyzed to the respective hydroxy compound.[407]

5. Tables

TABLE IV.1.   1,2-Dihydro-2-oxoquinazolines.

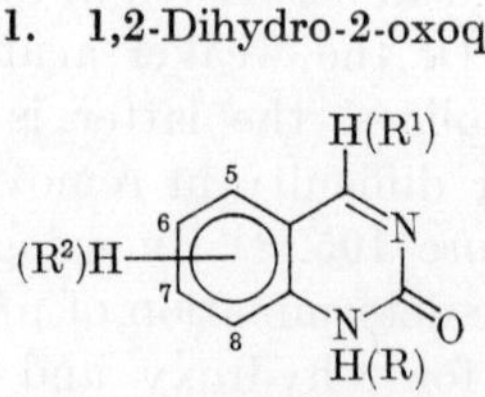

1,2-Dihydro-2-oxoquinazoline	M.p. (°c)	References
Unsubstituted	282–284°; HCl > 300° 3-methiodide[a] 238–239.5°	2, 3, 12, 13, 20
5,6-Benzo-4-methyl-	292–294°	19
1-Benzoyl-6-methyl-4-phenyl-	121–122°	6
6-Chloro-4-phenyl-[b]	310–312°	386

(*Table continued*)

TABLE IV.1 *continued*

1,2-Dihydro-2-oxoquinazoline	M.P. (°c)	References
4-(1′-Cyano-1′-ethoxycarbonyl)- methyl-	290–291°	11
4-Ethoxy-	218–221°, 225–240° (dec.)	14, 18
4-Isopropyl-	231–232°	16
4-Methoxy-	233°, 210–225° (dec.)	14, 18
8-Methoxy-	205°	9
4-Methyl-	230°	10
6-Methyl-4-phenyl-	283.5°	6
4-Phenyl-	250–251°	3, 4
4-2′-Pyridyl-	278–280°	8
4-p-Tolyl-	286°; aurichloride 251–252° (dec.)	5
4-2′,4′-Xylyl-	260–261°; H_2SO_4 261° (dec.); picrate 214°	7

[a] 2,3-Dihydro-3-methyl-2-oxoquinazoline has m.p. 204–208°.[20]

[b] 6-Chloro-2,3-dihydro-3-methyl-2-oxo-4-phenylquinazoline has m.p. 307–309°; HCl 267–269° (dec.).[20a]

TABLE IV.2.   1,4-Dihydro-4-oxoquinazolines.

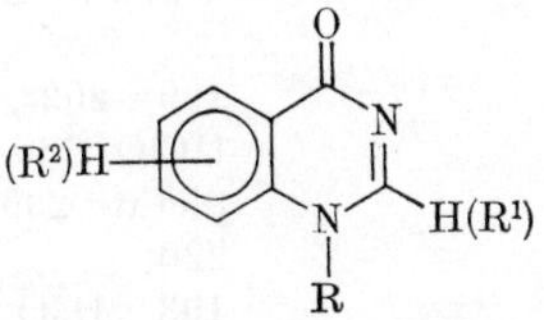

1,4-Dihydro-4-oxoquinazoline	M.p. (°c)	References
1-Benzyl-	203–205°	239
2-Benzyl-1-2′-dimethylaminoethyl	149°	427
2-Benzyl-1-2′-morpholinoethyl-	153°	427
6-Chloro-1-p-chlorophenyl-	156–159°	239
2-p-Chlorophenyl-1-2′-dimethylamino- ethyl-	130°	427
2-p-Chlorophenyl-1-3′-dimethylamino- propyl-	150°	427
1-p-Chlorophenyl-2-phenyl-	243–245°	242
2-(1′,4′-Dihydro-1′,2′-dimethyl-4′- oxo-3′-quinolinyl)-1-methyl-	260°	244

(*Table continued*)

TABLE IV.2 (continued)

1,4-Dihydro-4-oxoquinazoline	M.p. (°c)	References
1-2'-Diethylaminoethyl-2-phenyl-	124°	427
1-3',4'-Dimethoxyphenyl-	225.5–228°	239
1-2'-Dimethylaminoethyl-2-phenyl-	85°	427
1-2'-Dimethylaminoethyl-2-2'-pyridyl-	117°	427
1-2'-Dimethylaminoethyl-2-3'-pyridyl-	107°	427
1-2'-Dimethylaminoethyl-2-4'-pyridyl-	oxalate 140°	427
1-3'-Dimethylaminopropyl-2-phenyl-	oxalate 199°	427
2-p-Dimethylaminostyryl-7-methoxy-1-methyl-	266°	122
2-p-Dimethylaminostyryl-1-methyl-	274°	122
1-p-Fluorophenyl-2-phenyl-	289–290°	242
2-1'-Hydroxyethyl-1-methyl-	155–157°	241
2-Hydroxymethyl-1-methyl-	178–180°	241
7-Methoxy-1-methyl-2-3',4'-methylenedioxystyryl-	280°	122
1-p-Methoxyphenyl-2-phenyl-	241–243°	242
2-p-Methoxystyryl-1-methyl-	156°; H$_2$O 94°	122
1-Methyl-	123–124°, 136–137°, 141–142°;	80, 238, 254
	H$_2$O 65–66°;	254
	HCl 245–246°;	238
	picrate 249–250° (dec.)	238, 240, 254
1,2-Dimethyl-	199°, 203°, 205–206°;	76, 122, 245
	HClO$_4$ 260–261°;	245
	picrate 236–237°	245
1,2-Dimethyl-6-methoxy-	220°	122
1,2-Dimethyl-7-methoxy-	193°; H$_2$O 135°	122
1-Methyl-2-3',4'-methylenedioxystyryl-	264°	122
1-Methyl-6-nitro-	270–272°	254
1-Methyl-2-styryl-	245°, 261–262°	122, 245
1,2-Diphenyl-	273–275°, 280–281°; 3-methiodide 260–263°	242, 243

TABLE IV.3.   2-Alkyl-3,4-dihydro-4-oxoquinazolines.

3,4-Dihydro-4-oxoquinazoline	M.p. (°c)	References
2-Acetoxymethyl-	196–197°	475
2-o-Aminobenzyl-	> 250°; acetyl deriv. 258°	96
2-Anilinomethyl-	222–224°	475
2-Benzyl-	253–254°, 256°, 242°, 252–253°,	90, 95, 110
	177°, 247°	165, 211,
		207
2-4′-Bromobutyl-	HBr 289–290° (dec.)	235
2-2′-Bromoethyl-	114°	64
2-1′-Bromopropyl-	218° (dec.)	97
2-4′-Carboxybutyl-	203°	163
2-2′-Carboxyethenyl-	258°, 262–263°	276, 282
2-2′-Carboxyethyl-	225° (dec.)	163
2-5′-Carboxypentyl-	197°	163
2-3′-Carboxypropyl-	270° (dec.)	163
2-4′-Chlorobenzyl-	246° (dec.); benzoyl deriv. 210°	110
2-p-N-2′-Chloroethyl-N- methylaminostyryl-	1-methiodide 220° (dec.)	278
2-Chloromethyl-	247–248°	475
2-4′-Cyanobutyl-	166°	163
2-2′-Cyanoethyl-	342° (dec.)	163
2-Cyanomethyl-	235° (dec.)	163
2-5′-Cyanopentyl-	140°	163
2-3′-Cyanopropyl-	173°	163
2-Dichloromethyl-	210°	433
2-2′-Diethylaminoethyl-	122°	91
	2 HCl 290°; picrate 198°	61
2-Diethylaminomethyl-	85°	91
2-3′-(1,2-Dihydro-1-methyl- 2-quinolinylidene)prop-2′- enyl-	methiodide 172°	439
2-3′-(1,2,3,4-Tetrahydro-1- methyl-4-oxoquinazolin-2- ylidene)prop-2′-enyl-	methiodide 240°	439
2-4′-(3,4-Dihydro-4-oxo- quinazolin-2-yl)butyl-	345° (dec.)	163

(*Table continued*)

6+Q.

TABLE IV.3 *(continued)*

3,4-Dihydro-4-oxoquinazoline	M.p. (°c)	References
2-2'-(3,4-Dihydro-4-oxo-quinazolin-2-yl)ethyl-	>310°	110
2-6'-(3,4-Dihydro-4-oxo-quinazolin-2-yl)hexyl-	310° (dec.)	163
2-8'-(3,4-Dihydro-4-oxo-quinazolin-2-yl)octyl-	260°	163
2-5'-(3,4-Dihydro-4-oxo-quinazolin-2-yl)pentyl-	300° (dec.)	163
2-3'-(3,4-Dihydro-4-oxo-quinazolin-2-yl)propyl-	320° (dec.)	163
2-3',4'-Dimethoxyphenethyl-	209–210°	134
2-3',4'-Dimethoxystyryl-	268–269°	134
2-2'-Dimethylaminoethyl-	122°; 2 HCl 283°; picrate 202°	61, 91
2-4'-*p*-Dimethylamino-phenylbutadienyl-	1-methosulphate 231–232°	279
2-*p*-Dimethylaminostyryl-	300–302°; picrate 214–215°; 1-methiodide 214° and 255–256° (dec.) (two forms)	275, 279, 280
2-Ethoxycarbonylmethyl-	163–164°; phenylsulphonate 205–206° (dec.)	112
2-Ethyl-	225°, 234°; picrate 193–194°	12, 26, 86, 102, 109, 206
2-Fluoromethyl-	210–211°	480
2-2'-Furylethenyl-	206–208°, 267°; picrate 224–226°	275, 276, 301
2,4'-Hydroxybutyl-	178°	235
2-1'-Hydroxyethyl-	190–191°	241
2-Hydroxymethyl-	>214° (dec.), 236–237°	241, 475
2-(1'-Hydroxy-2'-nitro)ethyl-	216–218°	286
2-*o*-Hydroxystyryl-	283°, 307° (dec.)	276, 277
2-(2'-Indan-1',3'-dionyl)-	318°	281
2-(2'-Indan-1'-onyl)-	~328°	281
2-Isobutyl-	194–195°; H₂SO₄ 228–229°; HNO₃ 171–173° (dec.); oxalate 204–205°; picrate 192°	102, 109
2-Isopentyl-	184°; picrate 164–165°	109
2-Isopropyl-	224°, 233°; H₂SO₄ 219–220°; picrate 208.5–209.5°, 213–214°	26,102,109, 276
2-Methoxycarbonylmethyl-	184–185°; tosylate 221–223° (dec.)	112
2-*p*-Methoxyphenethyl-	213–214°	250
2-*p*-Methoxystyryl-	284–285°, 278°	250, 276

(Table continued)

TABLE IV.3 (continued)

3,4-Dihydro-4-oxoquinazoline	M.p. (°c)	References
2-Methyl-	234–236°, 240–241°; tosylate 276–277°; picrate 207.5–208.5°; 1-methiodide 223.7°	61, 76, 102, 109, 112, 124, 131, 280, 475
2-3′,4′-Methylenedioxyphenethyl-	239–240°	250
2-3′,4′-Methylenedioxystyryl-	305°, 316–317°	144, 250
2-o-Methylphenacyl-	166–167°	114
2-2′-Morpholinoethyl-	2 HCl 346° (dec.); picrate 204°	61
2-Morpholinomethyl-	187–188°; picrate 247–248°	475
2-o-Nitrobenzyl-	254–255° (dec.)	96
2-Nitromethyl-	200–202° (dec.)	164
2-o-Nitrostyryl-	300°, 288°	144, 276
2-p-Nitrostyryl-	350°, 310°	144, 276
2-(3′-Oxo-2′-indolinylidene)-methyl-	~ 349°	281
2-Phenacyl-	260–262°, 255–263° (dec.)	165, 469
2-Phenethyl-	209.5–210.5°	134
2-Phenoxymethyl-	209°	95
2-3′-Phenoxypropyl-	181°	88
2-4′-Phenylbutadienyl-	257–258°; 1-methiodide 232.5° (dec.)	144, 253
2-(1′-Phenylhydrazono-3′-oxo-2′-indanyl)-	225°	281
2-(3′-Phenylimino-2′-indan-1′-onyl)-	284–285°	281
2-1′-Phenylpropyl-	225°	131
2-2′-Piperidinoethyl-	148°; 2 HCl 325°; picrate 205°	61, 91, 301
2-Piperidinomethyl-	170°; picrate 225–226°	91, 475
2-Propyl-	200–201°; H_2SO_4 227–228°; HNO_3 159–160° (dec.); oxalate 193–194°; picrate 184.5–185°	86, 97, 102, 109, 111, 203, 211
2-Styryl-	248°, 252–253°; HCl 310° (dec.)	95, 144, 220, 276, 277
2-Sulphanilamidomethyl-	230–240°	304
2-t-Butyl-	187°	224
2-o-Tolyloxymethyl-	185°	95
2-m-Tolyloxymethyl-	233°	95
2-Trichloromethyl-	206–207°	78
2-(3′,3′,3′-Trichloro-2′-hydroxy)propyl-	197–198°	275
2-(3′,3′,3′-Trichloroprop-1′-enyl)-	212°	282

TABLE IV.4.   2-Aryl-(and Heteroaryl-)3,4-dihydro-4-oxoquinazolines.

3,4-Dihydro-4-oxoquinazoline	M.p. (°c)	References
2-o-Acetamidophenyl-	278° (dec.)	479
2-m-Acetoacetamidophenyl-	202–205°	93
2-(5′-Amino-4′-cyano-1′-pyrazolyl)-	> 300°	476
2-(5′-Amino-4′-ethoxycarbonyl-1′-pyrazolyl)-	> 300°	476
2-o-Aminophenyl-	225–227°, 236–237°; HCl 278–280°; picrate 256°; acetyl deriv. 277°, 274–275° (dec.)	92, 93, 227
2-m-Aminophenyl-	251°	93
2-p-Aminophenyl-	277–279°, > 300°	93, 187
2-o-Benzoylacetamidophenyl-	240–241°	93
2-m-Benzoylacetamidophenyl-	275–277°	93
2-p-Benzoylacetamidophenyl-	> 300°	93
2-p-Bromophenyl-	313–315°	199
2-p-Chlorophenyl-	306°	86
2-2′,4′-Diethoxyphenyl-	174°	220
2-(2′,4′-Dihydroxy-3′-quinolinyl)-	353–355°	112
2-2′,4′-Dimethoxyphenyl-	207°	220
2-3′,4′-Dimethoxyphenyl-	247°	95, 220
2-(3′,5′-Dimethyl-1′-pyrazolyl)-	165–167°	476
2-(3′-Ethoxy-4′-methoxy)phenyl-	239°	220
2-(4′-Ethoxycarbonyl-5′-methyl-1′-pyrazolyl)-	160–162°	476
2-2′-Furyl-	220°	160
2-m-2′-Furoylacetamidophenyl-	261–263°	93
2-(3′-Hydroxy-2′-naphthyl)-	—	82
2-m-(p-Methoxybenzoyl)-acetamidophenyl-	245°	93
2-o-Methoxyphenyl-	208°	220
2-p-Methoxyphenyl-	247°	95, 220
2-3′,4′-Methylenedioxyphenyl-	279°	220
2-o-Nitrophenyl-	226–227°, 232°, 237°	92, 93, 220, 300
2-m-Nitrophenyl-	> 300°, 354° (dec.)	93, 220
2-p-Nitrophenyl-	351–352°, > 360°, 365° (dec.)	86, 93, 106, 220

(*Table continued*)

TABLE IV.4 (*continued*)

3,4-Dihydro-4-oxoquinazoline	M.p. (°c)	References
2-Phenyl-	235°, 238°; picrate 197–197.5°	59, 60, 79, 95, 113, 117, 138, 211, 212, 165
2-3'-Pyridyl-	275.5–276.5°	86, 165
2-o-Sulphamoylphenyl-	283°	156
2-m-Thenoylacetamidophenyl-	257–259°	93
2-o-Tolyl-	236°	95
2-m-Tolyl-	212°	95
2-p-Tolyl-	235°, 241–242°	86, 95, 220
2-3',4',5'-Trimethoxyphenyl-	255°	95

TABLE IV.5.   3,4-Dihydro-4-oxoquinazolines with Alkoxy, Aryloxy, or Chloro Substituents in Position 2.

3,4-Dihydro-4-oxoquinazoline	M.p. (°c)	References
2-Butoxy-	135–137°	138
2-Chloro-	218–220°, 212°	432, 453, 463
2-Ethoxy-	173°, 176°, 179°	138, 308, 310, 311, 312, 313, 453
2-Methoxy-	214–218°, 231–232° (dec.), 218°	138, 312, 453
2-2'-Methoxyethoxy-	117.5–118.5°	441
2-Propoxy-	149–150°	138
2-Phenoxy-	272°	453

TABLE IV.6.   3-Alkyl- (other than Oxygen-containing Alkyl)
3,4-dihydro-4-oxoquinazolines.

3,4-Dihydro-4-oxoquinazoline	M.p. (°c)	References
3-Allyl-	64–65°, 67°, 66–68°, 156–157°/4 mm; HCl 200–202° (dec.); picrate 157–158°	36, 89, 97, 118, 222, 249
3-2'-Aminoethyl-	2 HCl 260° (dec.)	118
3-o-Aminobenzyl-	178°; acetyl deriv. 258°	96
3-Aminomethyl-	2 HCl 242–244°; picrate 200–202° (dec.)	302
3-3'-Aminopropyl-	2 HCl 250–252° (dec.)	118
3-3'-Anilinopropyl-	2 HCl 203–205° (dec.)	118
3-Benzyl-	117–118°, 120°; HCl 230°; 1-methiodide 188°	100, 118, 130, 172, 253
3-2'-Bromoallyl-	65–67°	118
3-6'-Bromohexyl-	HCl 188–190° (dec.)	118
3-Butyl-	72–73°	12, 152, 249, 251
3-2'-Butylaminoethyl-	2 HCl·H₂O 100–130° (dec.)	118
3-2'-Chlorobutyl-	HCl 204–206°	269a
3-2'-Chloroethyl-	98–100°, 120°, 125°; picrate 160°	64, 118, 449
3-2'-Chlorophenethyl-	HCl 198–200°	269a
3-2'-Chloropropyl-	48–50°; HCl 192–196°	269a
3-Cyclohexyl-	115–115.5°; 2 HCl 236°	36, 118, 128
3-2'-Cyclohexylaminoethyl-	2 HCl 242–244° (dec.)	118
3-6'-Cyclohexylamino-hexyl-	2 HCl 211–213° (dec.)	118
3-3'-Cyclohexylamino-propyl-	2 HCl 238–240° (dec.)	118
3-3'-Diamylaminopropyl-	210–215°/1 mm	262
3-2'-Dibutylaminoethyl-	194–195°/1 mm; 2'-N-methiodide 160° (dec.)	262
3-3'-Dibutylaminopropyl-	205–210°/1 mm	262
3-2'-Diethylaminoethyl-	153–156°/0.17 mm, 184–185°/3 mm; HCl 182–183°; 2 HCl 210–213° (dec.); picrate 160°; 2'-N-methiodide 152–154° (dec.)	63, 262, 449
3-4'-Diethylaminopentyl-	158–160°/0.1 mm; dipicrate 169–170°	63

(Table continued)

TABLE IV.6 *(continued)*

3,4-Dihydro-4-oxoquinazoline	M.p. (°c)	References
3-3′-Diethylaminopropyl-	196–199°/3.5 mm; dipicrate 160–161°; 3′-*N*-ethiodide 111–112°; 3′-*N*-methiodide 133–135°; 3′-*N*-*p*-nitrobenzyl bromide 205–206°	262
3-2′-Diisobutylamino- ethyl-	192–194°/1 mm; 2′-*N*-methiodide 154–155°	262
3-2′-Dimethylamino- ethyl-	174–176°/2 mm; 2′-*N*-allyl bromide 225–227°; 2′-*N*-benzyl bromide 148–149°; 2′-*N*-ethiodide 228–229° (dec.); 2′-*N*-methiodide 270° (dec.); 2′-*N*-*p*-nitrobenzyl bromide 227–229° (dec.); 2′-*N*-phenethyl bromide 202–203°; 2′-*N*-propyl iodide 178–180°	262
3-3′-(2,6-Dimethyl- piperidino)propyl-	2 HCl·H₂O 216.5–218°	259
3-2′-Dipropylaminoethyl-	176–178°/1 mm; 2′-*N*-benzyl bromide 148–150°; 2′-*N*-methiodide 170–172°; 2′-*N*-*p*-nitrobenzyl bromide 204–205° (dec.)	262
3-Ethyl-	99–100°, 104–105°; 182°/15 mm; 1-ethiodide 181°; 1-methiodide 258° (dec.)	36, 130, 152, 249, 253
3-2′-Ethylaminoethyl-	2 HCl·H₂O 220–221° (dec.)	118
3-(1′-Ethylpyrrolidin- 3′-yl)methyl-	2 HCl 133–135° (dec.)	149
3-2′-Iodoethyl-	124–125°	118
3-3′-Iodopropyl-	120–122°	118
3-Isobutyl-	62–63°; HCl 228–229°	152, 249
3-Isopropyl-	92–93°; HCl 202–203°	249
3-Methyl-	106–107°; H₂O 71–72°; picrate 208–210°, 215–216°; 1-ethiodide 230° (dec.); 1-methiodide 274°, 275–277°	80, 130, 152, 222, 252, 253, 254, 280, 302, 303
3-(3′-Methyl-1′-iso- quinolinyl)methyl-	182°	261
3-(1′-Methylpyrrolidin- 3′-yl)methyl-	2 HCl 218–220° (dec.)	149

(Table continued)

TABLE IV.6 (*continued*)

3,4-Dihydro-4-oxoquinazoline	M.p. (°c)	References
3-Phenyl-	135–136°	36
3-4'-Piperidinobutyl-	118–120°	118
3-2'-Piperidinoethyl-	180°; 2 HCl 228–230° (dec.);	
	picrate 165°	118, 449
3-Piperidinomethyl-	105°	118
3-3'-Piperidinopropyl-	2 HCl 230–232° (dec.)	118
3-2'-(2-Piperidyl)ethyl-	2 HCl 234–237° (dec.)	118
3-3'-(4-Piperidyl)propyl-	2 HCl·0.5 H$_2$O 228–231° (dec.)	118
3-Propyl-	82–83°, 95–96°, 98–99°	12, 36, 89, 152, 249
3-Prop-2'-ynyl-	116–118°	36, 267
3-3'-Pyrazolylmethyl-	187–188°	267
3-2'-(2-Pyridyl)ethyl-	2 HCl 222–223° (dec.)	118
3-Pyrrolidin-2'-ylmethyl-	HCl 196–198° (dec.)	118

TABLE IV.7. 3-Alkyl- (with Oxygen-containing Side Chain other than Acetonyl) 3,4-dihydro-4-oxoquinazolines.

3,4-Dihydro-4-oxoquinazoline	M.p. (°c)	References
3-(3'-Allylamino-2'-hydroxy)propyl-	117–120°; 2 HCl 203–207° (dec.)	118
3-(3'-Amino-2'-hydroxy)propyl-	2 HCl·0.5 H$_2$O 240–242° (dec.)	118
3-(3'-Anilino-2'-hydroxy)propyl-	152–153°	118
3-Benzamidomethyl-	180–182°	118, 302
3-Benzyloxycarbonylmethyl-	114–115°	458
3-(3'-Butylamino-2'-hydroxy)propyl-	HCl 238–240° (dec.)	118
3-2'-Carbamoylethyl-	192–193°	269
3-Carbamoylmethyl-	230°	263
3-2'-Carboxyethyl-	HCl·H$_2$O 212–214° (dec.)	118
3-Carboxymethyl-	237–239°, 260–262.5°	118, 263
3-(3'-Chloro-2'-hydroxy)propyl-	118–120°; HCl 242–244°	269a
3-(2'-Chloro-3'-methoxy)propyl-	HCl 166–169° (dec.)	118
3-Chloroacetamidomethyl-	180–182°	118

(*Table continued*)

TABLE IV.7 (continued)

3,4-Dihydro-4-oxoquinazoline	M.p. (°c)	References
3-2'-Chlorocarbonylethyl-	HCl 165–170° (dec.)	118
3-Chlorocarbonylmethyl-	HCl 232° (dec.)	258, 458
3-(3'-Cyclohexylamino-2'-hydroxy)propyl-	144–146°	118
3-(3'-Diethylamino-2'-hydroxy)propyl-	2 HCl 217–219° (dec.)	118
3-2'-(4-3',4'-Dihydro-4'-oxoquinazolin-3'-yl-2''-ethylpiperazin-1-yl)ethyl-	260°; picrate 270°	449
3-(3'-{3-[3-(3,4-Dihydro-4-oxoquinazolin-3-yl)-2-hydroxypropoxy]butoxy}-2'-hydroxy)-propyl-	oil; 2 HCl 196–198°	269a
3-(3'-{4-[3-(3,4-Dihydro-4-oxoquinazolin-3-yl)-2-hydroxypropoxy]butoxy}-2'-hydroxy)propyl-	oil; 2 HCl 186–187°	269a
3-(3'-{2-[3-(3,4-Dihydro-4-oxoquinazolin-3-yl)-2-hydroxypropoxy]ethoxy}-2'-hydroxy)propyl-	oil; 2 HCl 184–186°	269a
3-(3'-(3,4-Dihydro-4-oxoquinazolin-3-yl)-2'-hydroxy)propyl-	231–232°	118
3-3'-(1,1-Di(hydroxymethyl)ethylamino)propyl-	2 HCl 213–215° (dec.)	118
3-2',3'-Dihydroxypropyl-	230–232° (dec.)	118
3-(3'-(1,1-Dimethyl-2-hydroxyethylamino)-2'-hydroxy)propyl-	2 HCl·0.5 H₂O 228–230° (dec.)	118
3-(3'-Dodecyloxy-2'-hydroxy)propyl-	62–64°; HCl 124–126°	269a
3-2'-Epoxypropyl-	82–84°	118
3-2'-Ethoxycarbonylethyl-	HCl 177–179°	118
3-Ethoxycarbonylmethyl-	74.5–75.5°, 76–77°, 199–203°/5 mm	118, 263, 431
3-bisEthoxycarbonylmethyl-	64–67°; 2 HCl 208–209° and 143–145° (dec.) (two forms)	118
3-(3'-N-Ethyl-N-tosylamino-2'-hydroxy)propyl-	HCl 128° (dec.)	118
3-2'-N-Ethyl-N-tosylaminoethyl-	HCl 207–211° (dec.)	118
3-(3'-Ethylamino-2'-hydroxy)propyl-	2 HCl·0.5 H₂O 213–216° (dec.)	118

(Table continued)

6*

TABLE IV.7 (continued)

3,4-Dihydro-4-oxoquinazoline	M.p. (°c)	References
3-2'-Hydroxybutyl-	64–65°; HCl 208–210°	269a
3-2'-(2-Hydroxy-1,1-dimethylethyl-amino)ethyl-	2 HCl 246° (dec.)	118
3-(2'-Hydroxy-3'-β-hydroxyethyl-amino)propyl-	2 HCl 140–190° (dec.)	118
3-(2'-Hydroxy-1'-hydroxy-methyl)ethyl-	2 HCl 172–174°	118
3-(2'-Hydroxy-3'-β-hydroxypropyl-amino)propyl-	2 HCl 160–170° (dec.)	118
3-(2'-Hydroxy-3'-isopropyl-amino)propyl-	HCl 209–212° (dec.)	118
3-(2'-Hydroxy-3'-methoxy)propyl-	121–124°	118
3-(2'-Hydroxy-3'-morpholino)propyl-	106–108°	118
3-β-Hydroxyphenethyl-	166–168°; HCl 232–234°	269a
3-(2'-Hydroxy-3'-piperidino)propyl-	2 HCl 205–207° (dec.)	118
3-(5'-Hydroxy-2'-piperidyl)methyl-	120–132°; 2 HCl·H₂O 175–177° (dec.)	459
3-2'-Hydroxypropyl-	60–62°	269a
3-(5'-Hydroxy-1',4',5',6'-tetrahydro-2'-pyridyl)methyl-	172–174°; 2 HCl 213–214° (dec.); dipicrate 214° (dec.)	459
3-2'-Hydroxyethyl-	155°; picrate 180°	118, 449
3-2'-β-Hydroxyethylaminoethyl-	2 HCl 203–205° (dec.)	118
3-3'-β-Hydroxyethylaminopropyl-	2 HCl 205–207° (dec.); 2 HCl·0.5 H₂O 170–180° (dec.)	118
3-Hydroxymethyl-	186° (dec.)	438
3-3'-(1-Hydroxymethyl-1-methylethyl-amino)propyl-	2 HCl 215–217° (dec.)	118
3-2'-(1,1-bisHydroxymethylethyl-amino)ethyl-	2 HCl·0.5 H₂O 160° (dec.)	118
3-2'-Hydroxypropyl-	HCl 196–198° (dec.)	118
3-3'-Hydroxypropyl-	HCl 162–164°	118
3-2'-Morpholinoethyl-	> 280°; picrate 237°	449
3-Morpholinomethyl-	93–95°	118
3-3'-Morpholinopropyl-	2 HCl·0.5 H₂O 220–222° (dec.)	118
3-o-Nitrobenzyl-	169–170°	96
3-3'-Oxobutyl-	HCl 165–170° (dec.); phenylhydrazone 148–150°	118
3-4'-Oxopentyl-	85–87°	118

(Table continued)

TABLE IV.7 *(continued)*

3,4-Dihydro-4-oxoquinazoline	M.p. (°c)	References
3-Phenoxycarbonylmethyl-	122–124°; HCl 205–213° (dec.)	458
3-2'-N-Phenylcarbamoylethyl-	222–224°	118
3-N-Phenylcarbamoylmethyl-	243–245°	458
3-3'-Phthalimidoethyl-	207–209°	118
3-3'-Phthalimidopropyl-	152–154°	118
3-3'-(1-Tosyl-3-piperidyl)propyl-	HCl·H_2O 190–193° (dec.)	118
3-2'-Tosyloxyethyl-	160° (dec.)	118
3-3'-Tosyloxypropyl-	173–175°	118

TABLE IV.8.   3-Acetonyl-3,4-dihydro-4-oxoquinazolines.

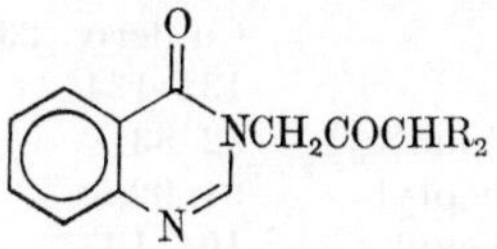

3,4-Dihydro-4-oxoquinazoline	M.p. (°c)	References
3-Acetonyl-	157–159°; HBr 230–232°; oxime 189–190°	118, 258
3-(4'-Amino-8'-bromo-5'-hydroxy-2'-oxo)octyl-	2 HBr 244–245°	464
3-(6'-Amino-5'-hydroxy-2'-oxo)hexyl-	197–198° (dec.)	459
3-(3'-Amino-2'-oxo)propyl-	198–202° (dec.)	57
3-(4'-Amino-2'-oxo-4'-(2'-tetrahydrofuryl))butyl-	2 HCl·H_2O 205–206° (dec.)	464
3-(8'-Benzamido-7'-methoxy-2',4'-dioxo)octyl-	113–116°; HCl 178–180° (dec.); Cu deriv. 218–220° (dec.)	457, 459
3-(8'-Benzamido-2',4'-dioxo)octyl-	125–127°; Cu deriv. 227–229° (dec.)	142, 431
3-(4'-Benzamido-4'-(2-furyl)-2'-oxo)butyl-	218–219°	464
3-(3'-Benzyloxycarbonyl-2'-oxo)propyl-	134–136°; Cu deriv. 214° (dec.)	458

(Table continued)

TABLE IV.8 (*continued*)

3,4-Dihydro-4-oxoquinazoline	M.p. (°c)	References
3-(3′,3′-bisBenzyloxycarbonyl-2′-oxo)propyl-	oil; Cu deriv. 210–211° (dec.)	458
3-(7′-Benzyloxycarbonylamino-2′,4′-dioxo)heptyl-	Cu deriv. 183–184°; 2,4-dinitrophenyl-hydrazone 134.5°	142, 431
3-(8′-Benzyloxycarbonylamino-2′,4′-dioxo)octyl-	Cu deriv. 184–185°; 2,4-dinitrophenyl-hydrazone 106–108°	142, 431
3-(12′-Bromo-2′-oxo)dodecyl-	90–91°; oxime 140–142°	266
3-(7′-Bromo-2′-oxo)heptyl-	136–137°; oxime 158–159°	266
3-(6′-Bromo-2′-oxo)hexyl-	156–157°	266
3-(3′-Bromo-2′-oxo)propyl-	211–213°	258
3-(5′-Chloro-2′-oxo)pentyl-	150–150.5°	266
3-(4′-Cyano-4′-hydroxy-2′-oxo)heptyl-	Cu deriv. 237° (dec.)	431
3-(3′-Diazo-2′-oxo)propyl-	132–134°	258
3-(12′-Diethylamino-2′-oxo)dodecyl-	82–83°	266
3-(7′-Diethylamino-2′-oxo)heptyl-	91–92.5°	266
3-(6′-Diethylamino-2′-oxo)hexyl-	104–105°	266
3-(5′-Diethylamino-2′-oxo)pentyl-	94–95°	266
3-(3′-Diethylamino-2′-oxo)propyl-	HCl 144–145°	253
3-(3′-(3,4-Dihydro-4-oxo-quinazolin-3-yl)-2′-oxo)propyl-	240°, 309–311° (dec.); 2 H_2SO_4 227–229°	258, 458, 258
3-(2′,4′-Dioxo-5′-phenoxy-8′-phthalimido)octyl-	Cu deriv. 140–145 °(dec.)	431, 460
3-(2′,4′-Dioxo-7′-phthalimido)heptyl-	Cu deriv. 230–233°, 232–235° (dec.)	142, 431
3-(2′,4′-Dioxo-8′-phthalimido)octyl-	Cu deriv. 235° (dec.); bisulphite 66–68°	142, 431, 457
3-2′,4′-Dioxoheptyl-	Cu deriv. 252° (dec.)	458
3-2′,4′-Dioxohexyl-	Cu deriv. 225–227° (dec.)	142, 431
3-2′,4′-Dioxopentyl-	124°, 130–130.5°; Cu deriv. 260° (dec.)	142, 431
3-(2′,4′-Dioxooct-7′-enyl)-	96–97°; Cu deriv. 241° (dec.)	431
3-(3′-Ethoxycarbonyl-2′-oxo)propyl-	123–125°	458
3-(3′,3′-bisEthoxycarbonyl-2′-oxo)propyl-	oil; Cu deriv. 224° (dec.)	458
3-(8′-Ethoxycarbonylamino-2′,4′-dioxo)octyl-	Cu deriv. 208–210° (dec.); 2,4-dinitrophenyl-hydrazone 128–129°	142, 431

(*Table continued*)

TABLE IV.8 (*continued*)

3,4-Dihydro-4-oxoquinazoline	M.p. (°c)	References
3-(4'-Ethoxycarbonylamino-4'-furyl-2'-oxo)butyl-	212–213°	464
3-(4'-Ethoxycarbonylamino-2'-oxo-5'-(2-tetrahydrofuryl))butyl-	pseudo 130–131°; normal 125–127°	464
3-(4'-(2-Furyl)-2',4'-dioxo)butyl-	129–130°	431
3-(5'-Hydroxy-2'-oxo-6'-phthalimido)hexyl-	224–225°	459
3-(5'-Methoxy-2',4'-dioxo-8'-phthalimido)octyl-	Cu deriv. 168–171° (dec.)	431
3-(3'-Methoxy-2',4'-dioxo-8'-phthalimido)octyl-	105–108°; Cu deriv. 218° (dec.)	458
3-(3'-(4-Methylpyrrolidin-2-yl)-2'-oxo)propyl-	2 HCl·0.5 H$_2$O 241° (dec.)	450
3-(6'-Methyl-2',4'-dioxohept-5'-enyl)-	Cu deriv. 229–232° (dec.)	431, 458
3-(12'-Morpholino-2'-oxo)dodecyl-	2 HCl 155–157°	266
3-(5'-Morpholino-2'-oxo)pentyl-	2 HCl 202–203°	266
3-(7'-Morpholino-2'-oxo)heptyl-	2 HCl 165–166°	266
3-(6'-Morpholino-2'-oxo)hexyl-	2 HCl·H$_2$O 166–167°	266
3-(3'-Morpholino-2'-oxo)propyl-	149–150°	258
3-(3'-(9-3,9-Oxazabicyclo-3(3,3,1)nonyl)-2'-oxo)propyl-	138–139°; 230–240°/0.7 mm	260
3-(2'-Oxo-3'-phthalimido)propyl-	254–256°	57
3-(2'-Oxo-12'-piperidino)dodecyl-	105–106°; oxime 120–121.5°	266
3-(2'-Oxo-7'-piperidino)heptyl-	2 HCl 204–205°	266
3-(2'-Oxo-6'-piperidino)hexyl-	2 HCl 191–192°	266
3-(2'-Oxo-5'-piperidino)pentyl-	2 HCl 213–214°; oxime 154–155°	266
3-(2'-Oxo-3'-piperidino)propyl-	114–115°; HCl 166–167°	258
3-(2'-Oxo-3'-(2-piperidyl))propyl-	2 HCl 228–230° (dec.)	57
3-(2'-Oxotetrahydro-3'-furoyl)methyl-	150–151°	464

TABLE IV.9.   3-Aryl-3,4-dihydro-4-oxoquinazolines.

3,4-Dihydro-4-oxoquinazoline	M.p. (°c)	References
3-o-Acetamidophenyl-	276.5–278°	307
3-p-Acetamidophenyl-	226°	120, 436
3-o-Aminophenyl-	241°, 244°	306, 445
3-p-Aminophenyl-	180°	120, 436
3-o-Benzamidophenyl-	284–285°	307
3-p-Bromophenyl-	190–191°; picrate 171–173°	150, 167, 221
3-o-Carboxyphenyl-	280–281° (dec.)	146, 437
3-p-Carboxyphenyl-	> 320° (dec.)	218
3-(2′-Chloro-4′-nitro)phenyl-	HCl 232–234°	198
3-p-Chloroacetamidophenyl-	230° (dec.)	120, 436
3-m-Chlorophenyl-	165–166°	167
3-p-Chlorophenyl-	176°, 180–181°; HCl 236° (dec.); chloroplatinate 315°	167, 172, 217
3-p-2′-Chloropropionamidophenyl-	245°	120, 436
3-o-Ethoxyphenyl-	HCl 220° (dec.)	172
3-p-Ethoxyphenyl-	154°, 158°; HCl 234° (dec.)	172, 216
3-o-Formamidophenyl-	230–231°	307
3-p-2′-(bis-2-Hydroxyethyl)-aminopropionamidophenyl-	120°	120
3-p-Hydroxyphenyl-	212°; HCl 244° (dec.)	172
3-o-Methoxyphenyl-	HCl 222° (dec.)	172
3-p-Methoxyphenyl-	170°, 194–195°	153, 167, 181, 221
3-Phenyl-	139°; HCl 222–223°; picrate 177–178°	65, 69, 100, 153, 167, 180, 218, 221, 294
3-p-2′-Piperidinopropion-amidophenyl-	202°	120, 436
3-o-Propionamidophenyl-	247–248°	307
3-o-Tolyl-	104–105°, 131°; HCl 235°	180, 194
3-m-Tolyl-	123.5–125°, 127–128°	67, 167
3-p-Tolyl-	146–147°; HCl 213–214°; chloroplatinate > 300°	67, 153, 167, 218, 294
3-2′,6′-Xylyl-	93°	194

TABLE IV.10.   3,4-Dihydro-4-oxoquinazolines with a Heterocyclic Group in Position 3.

3,4-Dihydro-4-oxoquinazoline	M.p. (°c)	References
3-(4′-*p*-Chlorophenyl-2′-thiazolyl)-	172°	121, 436
3-(4′,5′-Dimethyl-2′-thiazolyl)-	202°	121, 436
3-(4′-*p*-Methoxyphenyl-2′-thiazolyl)-	182°	121, 436
3-(6′-Methyl-3′-methylthio-1′,2′,4′-triazin-5′-yl)-	200–201°	294
3-(4′-Methyl-2′-thiazolyl)-	184°	121, 436
3-(4′-Phenyl-2′-thiazolyl)-	162°	121
3-2′-Pyridyl-	132–134°, 140°	100, 167, 118
3-2′-Quinazolinyl-	242°	468
3-4′-Quinazolinyl-	232.5°	12, 306, 445
3-Xanthenyl-	198–200°	270

TABLE IV.11.   3,4-Dihydro-4-oxoquinazoline and Derivatives with Substituents in the Benzene Ring.

3,4-Dihydro-4-oxoquinazoline	M.p. (°c)	References
Unsubstituted	209°, 215.5–216.5°; picrate 203.5–204.5°; 3-tosylate 185–188°	81, 71, 102, 273, 337
6,7-Benzo-	273–274°, 278°	37, 53, 56
6,7-Benzo-x-chloro-	329°	56
5-Bromo-	237–238°	31, 430
6-Bromo-	258°, 272–272.5°	31, 32, 101, 130
7-Bromo-	258–259°	31
5,7-Dibromo-	295–296°	37

(*Table continued*)

TABLE IV.11 (continued)

3,4-Dihydro-4-oxoquinazoline	M.p. (°c)	References
6,8-Dibromo-	279°, > 300° (dec.)	33, 103
6-Bromo-8-chloro-	336° (dec.)	32
8-Bromo-6-chloro-	341° (dec.)	32
6-Bromo-8-iodo-	329° (dec.)	32
8-Bromo-6-iodo-	316–317° (dec.)	32
5-Chloro-	210°, 211–212°	28, 31, 430
6-Chloro-	220–221.5°, 264–265°;	28, 30, 31, 32,
	picrate 199.5–200°	35, 36, 45
7-Chloro-	242–245°, 254–255.5°	28, 29, 31, 105
8-Chloro-	299–300°, 306–307° (dec.)	28, 31, 430
5,6-Dichloro-	271–272°	37
5,8-Dichloro-	297–298°	37
6,7-Dichloro-	287–288°	37
6,8-Dichloro-	> 320°, 337–338° (dec.),	28, 32, 33, 37,
	348–349°	430
6-Chloro-8-iodo-	301–302° (dec.)	32
8-Chloro-6-iodo-	309–310° (dec.)	32
5-Chloro-6-methoxy-	0.5 H$_2$O 233–235° (dec.)	43
5-Chloro-8-methoxy-	311–313° (dec.)	43, 268, 431
7-Chloro-6-methoxy-	0.5 H$_2$O 262–264°	43
5-Chloro-6-methyl-	248–249° (dec.)	43
5-Chloro-8-methyl-	276–278°	43
6-Chloro-5-methyl-	274–276°	43
6-Chloro-8-methyl-	307–308°	43
7-Chloro-6-methyl-	248–249° (dec.)	43
7-Chloro-8-methyl-	260–261° (dec.)	43
8-Chloro-6-methyl-	298–300°	43
6-Chloro-8-nitro-	245–246°	470
7-Chloro-6-sulphamoyl-	310–315°, 318°	233, 291, 292
7-Chloro-6-sulpho-	> 320°	291
5-Ethyl-	215–216°	57
5-Fluoro-	225–227°	57, 430
6-Fluoro-	252°	58
7-Fluoro-	232°	58
5-Iodo-	268–270°, 281°	32, 34, 57
6,8-Diiodo-	287° (dec.), > 320°	32, 34
5-Methoxy-	208–209°	31, 430
6-Methoxy-	242–245°, 248–249°;	
	picrate 231.5–232°	31, 44, 45
7-Methoxy-	238–240°, 269–270°	31, 45
8-Methoxy-	298°	46
6-Methoxy-7-nitro-[a]	275–277° (dec.), 270°	51, 55
6-Methoxy-7-phenylsulphonyl-[a]	301–303° (dec.)	51

(*Table continued*)

TABLE IV.11 *(continued)*

3,4-Dihydro-4-oxoquinazoline	M.p. (°c)	References
6-Methoxy-7-phenylthio-[a]	260–261°	51
5-Methyl-	210–211°, 224°	31, 42
6-Methyl-	242–245°, 255°	31, 36, 39, 40, 41, 337
7-Methyl-	239–240°	26, 31, 72
8-Methyl-	243–245°, 251°	31, 41, 337
5,6-Dimethyl-	247–248° (dec.)	37
5,7-Dimethyl-	288–291° (dec.)	37
5,8-Dimethyl-	255–256° (dec.)	37
6,7-Dimethyl-	248–249° (dec.)	37
6,8-Dimethyl-	244–245°	37
7,8-Dimethyl-	252–254°	37
5-Methylsulphonyl-	275–276°	57
5-Methylthio-	271–272°	57
5-Nitro-	218°, 255–256°	50, 53, 57
6-Nitro-	275°, 286–287°	31, 35, 48, 52, 130
7-Nitro-	263–266°, 276°	31, 33, 49, 52
8-Nitro-	250–251°	33, 51
6,8-Dinitro-	235°	33
6-Phenyl-	229–230°	31
7-Phenyl-	261–262°	31
5-Phenylthio-	250–252°	57
5-Propyl-	198–199°	57
6-Sulphamoyl-	217–220°	291
5,6-Tetramethylene-	219–220°	37
6,7-Tetramethylene-	238–239°	37
5-Trifluoromethyl-	236–237°	57, 58
6-Trifluoromethyl-	210°	58
7-Trifluoromethyl-	227°	58
8-Trifluoromethyl-	239°	58

[a] See chapter V, section 2.D.

TABLE IV.12.   3-Alkyl- (other than Oxygen-containing Alkyl) 3,4-dihydro-2-
               methyl-4-oxoquinazolines.

3,4-Dihydro-2-methyl-4-oxoquinazoline	M.p. (°c)	References
3-Allyl-	75°, 80–81°	190, 232, 264
3-Aminomethyl-	> 268–270° (dec.); picrate	
	> 240° (dec.)	301
3-Butyl-	42°, 250°/8 mm; HCl 225°	128, 170
3-Benzyl-	74°, 123°; HCl 233° (dec.)	143, 144, 168,
		172, 179
3-2′-Chlorobutyl-	HCl 204–206°	269a
3-β-Chlorophenethyl-	HCl 194–196°	269a
3-Cyclohexyl-	86°, 172–174°; HCl 252°, 270°	128, 190
3-3′-Cyclohexylaminopropyl-	oil; HCl 248–250°	197
3-2′-Diethylaminoethyl-	HCl 216°, > 210° (dec.)	197, 264
3-Diethylaminomethyl-	282–284° (dec.); picrate	
	220–225°	301
3-2′-Dimethylaminoethyl-	HCl 260–263°, > 250° (dec.)	197, 264
3-Dimethylaminomethyl-	295–296°; picrate > 250°	
	(dec.)	301
3-2′-Dimethylaminopropyl-	HCl 220° (dec.)	264
3-3′-Dimethylaminopropyl-	HCl 225°, 220° (dec.)	197, 264
3-Dodecyl-	90–92°	168, 171
3-Ethyl-	67°; chloroplatinate 329°;	
	1-ethiodide 177°;	253, 280, 281,
	1-methiodide 220°	456
3-(1′-Ethylpyrrolidin-3′-yl)-	2 HCl 247–250°	149
3-Heptyl-	75°; HCl 160°	128
3-Hexyl-	70°; HCl 169°	128
3-Imidazolin-2′-ylmethyl-	202°	264
3-Isobutyl-	75–76°; HCl 228°, 256–258°	128, 232
3-Methyl-	108–109°, 112–113°; H₂O	
	70–72°; 1-ethiodide 242°;	76, 131, 206,
	1-methiodide 246°	280, 253
3-(1′-Methyl-3′-phenyl)propyl-	203.5–204°	131
3-2′-Methylcyclohexyl-	72°; HCl 246°	128
3-3′-Methylcyclohexyl-	HCl 265°	128
3-4′-Methylcyclohexyl-	112°; HCl 266°	128
3-1′-Methylphenethyl-	213–214°, 132–134°; HCl	
	254–256°	131, 197

(*Table continued*)

TABLE IV.12 (*continued*)

3,4-Dihydro-2-methyl-4-oxoquinazoline	M.p. (°c)	References
3-(1'-Methylpyrrolidin-3'-yl)methyl-	2 HCl 232–240°; hemimucate 177–179°	149
3-(18'-Octadec-9'-enyl)-	77°; HCl 149°	128
3-Octyl-	73°; HCl 155°	128
3-Pentyl-	HCl 206°	128
3-2'-Piperidinoethyl-	150°; HCl 250°	264
3-Piperidinomethyl-	288–290° (dec.); picrate 205–210° (dec.)	301
3-3'-Piperidinopropyl-	2 HCl 226–228° (dec.)	118
3-Propyl-	82°	264
3-2'-Pyridylmethyl-	130–133°, 122°	131, 137
3-3'-Pyridylmethyl-	116°	137
3-4'-Pyridylmethyl-	127°	137

TABLE IV.13.   3-Alkyl- (with Oxygen-containing Side Chain) 3,4-dihydro-2-methyl-4-oxoquinazolines.

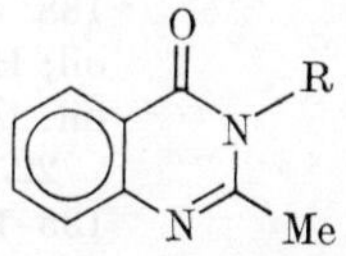

3,4-Dihydro-2-methyl-4-oxoquinazoline	M.p. (°c)	References
3-Benzamidomethyl-	184–186°	302
3-*p*-Bromophenacyl-	196–197°	265
3-2'-Carbamoylethyl-	210–211°	269
3-Carbamoylmethyl-	276–277°	263
3-Carboxymethyl-	263° (dec.)	142, 457
3-(3'-Chloro-2'-hydroxy)propyl-	112–114°	269a
3-(3'-Cyclohexylamino-2'-hydroxy)propyl-	110–112°	118
3-*N*,*N*-Diethylcarbamoylmethyl-	128–130°	474
3-2'-(3,4-Dihydro-2-methyl-4-oxoquinazolin-3-yl)ethyl-	299°	131
3-(3'-{3-[3-(3,4-Dihydro-2-methyl-4-oxoquinazolin-3-yl)-2-hydroxypropyl]butoxy}-2'-hydroxy)propyl-	oil; 2 HCl 178–180°	269a

(*Table continued*)

TABLE IV.13 (*continued*)

3,4-Dihydro-2-methyl-4-oxoquinazoline	M.p. (°c)	References
3-(3′-{2-[3-(3,4-Dihydro-2-methyl-4-oxoquinazolin-3-yl)-2-hydroxypropyl]-ethoxy}-2′-hydroxy)propyl-	2 HCl 238–240°	269a
3-2′,3′-Dihydroxypropyl-	145°	264
3-3′,4′-Dimethoxyphenethyl-	135–137°	232
3-(3′-Dodecyloxy-2′-hydroxy)propyl-	40–42°; HCl 118–120°	269a
3-2′-Epoxypropyl-	90–92°	118
3-(8′-Ethoxycarbonylamino-2′,4′-dioxo)octyl-	Cu deriv. 201–202° (dec.)	142, 431, 457
3-Ethoxycarbonylmethyl-	134–136°	263
3-p-Fluorophenacyl-	175–176°	265
3-(2′-Hydroxy-3′-piperidino)propyl-	120–122°	118
3-(1′-Hydroxy-2′,2′,2′-trichloro)ethyl-	207–208° (dec.)	131
3-2′-Hydroxybutyl-	48–50°; HCl 224–226°	269a
3-2′-Hydroxyethyl-	160°	264
3-β-Hydroxyphenethyl-	153–155°	269a
3-3′-Isopropoxypropyl-	oil; HCl 248–250°	197
3-Methoxycarbonylmethyl-	114–115°	142, 431, 457
3-o-Methoxyphenacyl-	188°	265
3-3′-Methoxypropyl-	oil; HCl 182–184°	197
3-2′-Morpholinoethyl-	oil; HCl 228–230°, 225°	197, 264
3-Phenacyl-	135–136°	265

TABLE IV.14.   3-Aryl-3,4-dihydro-2-methyl-4-oxoquinazolines.

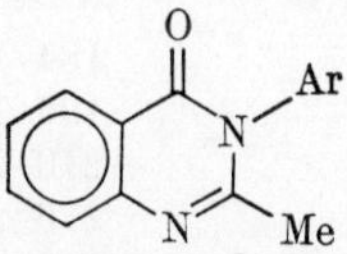

3,4-Dihydro-2-methyl-4-oxoquinazoline	M.p. (°c)	References
3-(3′-Acetamido-2′-methyl)-phenyl-	209–210.5°	131
3-o-Acetamidophenyl-	208–209.5°	131
3-p-Acetamidophenyl-	260°	120, 436
3-(4′-(4-amino-3-methoxy-phenyl)-2′-methoxy)phenyl-	72–73°	117

(*Table continued*)

TABLE IV.14 *(continued)*

3,4-Dihydro-2-methyl-4-oxoquinazoline	M.p. (°c)	References
3-(3′-Amino-2′-methyl)phenyl-	185–188.5°	131
3-(3′-Amino-6′-methyl)phenyl-	180–181.5°	131
3-(4′-Amino-2′-methyl)phenyl-	137–139°; HCl 252–254°	197
3-o-Aminophenyl-	167–170°	131
3-m-Aminophenyl-	210°	117
3-p-Aminophenyl-	220°, 220–223°	117, 120, 422, 436
3-4′-(p-Aminophenyl)phenyl-	282–283°, 284–288°	117, 442
3-o-2′-Benzimidazolylphenyl-	300°	230
3-(4′-Bromo-2′,3′-dimethyl)-phenyl-	168–170°	199
3-(2′-Bromo-4′-methyl)phenyl-	132–133°	184
3-(3′-Bromo-2′-methyl)phenyl-	140–141°	131
3-(4′-Bromo-2′-methyl)phenyl-	150–151°, 173–174°; HCl 134–135°	190, 232, 189
3-(4′-Bromo-1′-naphthyl)-	214–215°	131
3-o-Bromophenyl-	148–150°; HCl 218–220°	197, 199
3-m-Bromophenyl-	134–136°; HCl 261–263°	179, 199
3-p-Bromophenyl-	165–167°, 171–172°; HCl 258–268°	131, 197, 199, 200
3-(4′-Bromo-2′-trifluoromethyl)-phenyl-	161–162°	131
3-o-Carboxyphenyl-	246–247°; HCl 247–248°	87, 146, 181, 200
3-m-Carboxyphenyl-	276°	181
3-p-Carboxyphenyl-	259°, 281°, 283–284°	144, 181, 182
3-(4′-Chloro-2′,5′-dimethoxy)-phenyl-	142–144°	131
3-(2′-Chloro-6′-methoxy)phenyl-	187°	131
3-(3′-Chloro-4′-methoxy)phenyl-	86–88°; HCl 253–255°	197
3-(5′-Chloro-2′-methoxy)phenyl-	179–181°; HCl 252–254°	197
3-(5′-Chloro-2′-methyl-4′-nitro)phenyl-	HCl 240–242°	198
3-(2′-Chloro-6′-methyl)phenyl-	135°, 131°, 106°, 108°; HCl 198–200°	131, 194, 197
3-(3′-Chloro-2′-methyl)phenyl-	151°, 143–145°; HCl 246–248°	131, 133, 197
3-(3′-Chloro-4′-methyl)phenyl-	oil; HCl 271–273°	197
3-(4′-Chloro-2′-methyl)phenyl-	120–121°, 103–105°; HCl 245–247°, 272–273°	131, 189, 197
3-(5′-Chloro-2′-methyl)phenyl-	148°, 142–144°, 114–116°; HCl 258–260°	131, 175, 197

(Table continued)

TABLE IV.14 (continued)

3,4-Dihydro-2-methyl-4-oxoquinazoline	M.p. (°c)	References
3-(4'-Chloro-1'-naphthyl)-	212–213.5°	131
3-(2'-Chloro-4'-nitro)phenyl-	170–171°	175
3-(5'-Chloro-2'-phenoxy)phenyl-	105–106°	131
3-(2'-Chloro-5'-trifluoro-methyl)phenyl-	106–108°; HCl 217–219°	197
3-p-Chloroacetamidophenyl-	206° (dec.)	120, 436
3-o-Chlorophenyl-	126–127°, 130°; HCl 240°	131, 181, 187, 199, 200, 201
3-m-Chlorophenyl-	128–129°, 136°; HCl 248–250°	99, 181, 197, 199, 200
3-p-Chlorophenyl-	155°, 158°; HCl 273–275°	99, 131, 168, 171, 172, 181, 197, 200
3-p-(N-o-Chlorophenyl-sulphamoyl)phenyl-	227°	141
3-p-2'-Chloropropionamido-phenyl-	222°	120
3-(3'-Cyano-2'-methyl)phenyl-	200–201°	131
3-p-Cyanophenyl-	240°	144
3-2',3'-Dichlorophenyl-	189.5–190.5°, 152–154°; HCl 231–233°	131, 197
3-2',4'-Dichlorophenyl-	144–146°, 151–152°; HCl 250° (dec.)	197, 199
3-3',4'-Dichlorophenyl-	163–165°; HCl 258–260°	197
3-p-2'-Diethylaminoethoxy-phenyl-	—	131
3-o-N,N-Diethylcarbamoyl-phenyl-	148–150°	131
3-p-N,N-Diethylsulphamoyl-phenyl-	226–227°	141
3-p-(N-4',6'-Dimethylpyrimidin-2'-ylsulphamoyl)phenyl-	273°	140
3-(2'-Ethoxy-5'-methyl)phenyl-	111–113°	131
3-o-Ethoxycarbonylamino-phenyl-	—	131
3-p-Ethoxycarbonylphenyl-	172–173°, 175–176°	144, 182
3-o-Ethoxyphenyl-	115–116°; HCl 199–200°, 215° (dec.)	172, 197, 199
3-m-Ethoxyphenyl-	130–132°; HCl 225° (dec.)	199

(Table continued)

TABLE IV.14 (continued)

3,4-Dihydro-2-methyl-4-oxoquinazoline	M.p. (°c)	References
3-p-Ethoxyphenyl-	155–156°; HCl 229–231°, 270° (dec.); 1-methiodide 221° (dec.)	131, 144, 168, 172, 197, 200, 253
3-o-Ethylphenyl-	81°; HCl 247°	194
3-(3'-Fluoro-2'-methyl)phenyl-	139–140°	131
3-(3'-Fluoro-4'-methyl)phenyl-	147–148°	188
3-(4'-Fluoro-2'-methyl)phenyl-	114–115°	131
3-o-Fluorophenyl-	116–117°	131
3-m-Fluorophenyl-	130.5–131°, 228–229°	131, 188
3-p-Fluorophenyl-	133–134°; HCl 280° (dec.)	131, 197, 199
3-p-Guanidinosulphonylphenyl-	300°	140
3-p-bis-2'-Hydroxyethylacet-amidophenyl-	220°	120
3-o-Hydroxyphenyl-	198–200°	131, 194
3-p-Hydroxyphenyl-	278–280°, 287°; HCl > 350°	131, 172, 200
3-(3'-Iodo-2'-methyl)phenyl-	147–148.5°	131
3-p-Iodophenyl-	178–180°; HCl 265° (dec.)	199
3-(2'-Methoxy-4'-nitro)phenyl-	135–137°; HCl 246–248°	197, 198
3-(2'-Methoxy-5'-nitro)phenyl-	118–120°; HCl 235–237°	197, 198
3-(4'-Methoxy-2'-nitro)phenyl-	190–200°; HCl 205–207°	197, 198
3-o-Methoxycarbonylphenyl-	140–142°, 120–121°	131, 181, 200
3-m-Methoxycarbonylphenyl-	132°	181
3-o-Methoxyphenyl-	131–132°, 135°; HCl 282° (dec.)	99, 172, 181, 200
3-m-Methoxyphenyl-	117°, 152°	99, 181
3-p-Methoxyphenyl-	171°; HCl 240° (dec.); 1-methiodide 231.5° (dec.)	99, 144, 168, 199, 200, 253
3-(3'-Methyl-4'-(4-amino-2-methylphenyl))phenyl-	80–81°	117
3-(2'-Methyl-3'-nitro)phenyl-	235–236.5°	131
3-(2'-Methyl-4'-nitro)phenyl-	262–264°	198
3-(2'-Methyl-5'-nitro)phenyl-	196–198°; HCl 228–230°, 242–244°	131, 197, 198
3-(2'-Methyl-6'-nitro)phenyl-	133–136°	131
3-(4'-Methyl-2'-nitro)phenyl-	178–180°; HCl 213–215°, 233–235°	197, 198
3-(2'-Methyl-3'-propoxy)phenyl-	96–97°	131
3-p-3',4'-Methylenedioxy-benzylphenyl-	135–138°	190
3-1'-Naphthyl-	361°, 152°, 158–160°; HCl 230–232°; 1-methiodide 235° (dec.)	130, 174, 197, 253

(Table continued)

TABLE IV.14 (continued)

3,4-Dihydro-2-methyl-4-oxoquinazoline	M.p. (°c)	References
3-2′-Naphthyl-	169–170°, 175°; HCl 233–235°; 1-methiodide 238°	130, 157, 168, 179, 197, 200, 253
3-o-Nitrophenyl-	170–171°; HCl 243–245°	131, 168, 197
3-m-Nitrophenyl-	127–129°, 98–100°; HCl 258–260°	168, 197
3-p-Nitrophenyl-	192–193°, 152–154°; HCl 242–244°	130, 131, 168, 197
3-Phenyl-	147–148°; HCl 249–251°, 278°; 1-ethiodide 244°; 1-methiodide 243° (dec.)	98, 100, 157, 168, 170, 180, 181, 200, 215, 253
3-p-N′-Phenylhydrazino-sulphonylphenyl-	239°	141
3-p-Piperidinoacetamidophenyl-	140°	120, 436
3-p-2′-Piperidinopropionamido-phenyl-	200°	120, 436
3-p-2′-Pyridylsulphamoyl-phenyl-	279°	140
3-p-Pyrimidin-2′-ylsulphamoyl-phenyl-	277°	140
3-p-Sulphamoylphenyl-	240°	195
3-o-Tolyl-	111–113°, 120°; HCl 238–240°, 252–254°	99, 131, 173, 180, 181, 190, 197, 201
3-m-Tolyl	125–126°, 129°; HCl 250–252°	99, 173, 180, 181, 200
3-p-Tolyl-	151°; HCl 248–250°; 1-methiodide 234–235° (dec.)	99, 130, 157, 180, 181, 200, 253, 456
3-p-(o-Tolylsulphamoyl)phenyl-	229°	141
3-2′,4′,5′-Trichlorophenyl-	HCl 238–240°	197
3-2′,4′,6′-Trichlorophenyl-	143–145°; HCl 160–162°	197
3-o-Trifluoromethylphenyl-	109–110.5°; HCl 235–236°, 244–246°	131, 185, 197
3-m-Trifluoromethylphenyl-	139–140°, 76–78°; HCl 243–245°	131, 197
3-3′,4′,5′-Trimethoxyphenyl-	150–152°; HCl 250° (dec.)	199
3-2′,3′-Xylyl-	156–158°, 172–173°; HCl 240° (dec.)	131, 197, 199

(Table continued)

TABLE IV.14 *(continued)*

3,4-Dihydro-2-methyl-4-oxoquinazoline	M.p. (°c)	References
3-2′,4′-Xylyl-	100–102°, 135–136°; HCl 243–245°	131, 186, 197, 199, 200
3-2′,5′-Xylyl-	125–127°	199
3-2′,6′-Xylyl-	134–136°, 138°; HCl 216–218°	99, 131, 175, 197, 199
3-3′,4′-Xylyl-	134–136°	199

TABLE IV.15.   3,4-Dihydro-2-methyl-4-oxoquinazolines with a Heterocyclic Group in Position 3.

3,4-Dihydro-2-methyl-4-oxoquinazoline	M.p. (°c)	References
3-(4′-*p*-Chlorophenyl-2′-thiazolyl)-	204°	436
3-(3′,4′-Dihydro-2′-methyl-4′-oxoquinazolin-3′-yl)-	281–286°	192
3-(1′,3′-Dimethyl-5′-oxo-2′-phenylpyrazolin-4′-yl)-	234.5–235°	131
3-(2′,3′-Dimethyl-5′-oxo-1′-phenylpyrazolin-4′-yl)-	229–231°	197
3-(4′,5′-Dimethyl-2′-thiazolyl)-	200°	121, 436
3-(4′-Ethoxycarbonyl-5′-methyl-2′-thiazolyl)-	235°	121, 436
3-(4′-Ethyl-2′-thiazolyl)-	201°	121, 436
3-2′-(*N-o*-Hydroxybenzyl)piperidyl-	214°	436
3-(4′-*p*-Hydroxyphenyl-2′-thiazolyl)-	160°	436
3-(4′-*p*-Methoxyphenyl-2′-thiazolyl)-	160°	121
3-(4′-Methyl-2′-thiazolyl)-	148°	121, 436
3-(4′-Phenyl-2′-thiazolyl)-	144°	121, 436
3-2′-Pyridyl-	145–146°; HCl 222–224°	131, 137, 191, 197
3-3′-Pyridyl-	HCl 225–226°	137
3-4′-Pyridyl-	144–146°	137
3-5′-Quinolinyl-	208–209°	137
3-2′-Thiazolyl-	184°	121
3-Xanthenyl-	300–305°	271

TABLE IV.16.   3-Substituted 2-Ethyl-3,4-dihydro-4-oxoquinazolines.

2-Ethyl-3,4-dihydro-4-oxoquinazoline	M.p. (°c)	References
3-Benzyl-	110°; HCl 196° (dec.)	172
3-p-Bromophenyl-	170–172°	199
3-2'-Carbamoylethyl-	193°	269
3-o-Carboxyphenyl-	241° (dec.)	180
3-m-Carboxyphenyl-	261° (dec.)	180
3-p-Carboxyphenyl-	238° (dec.)	180
3-(3'-Chloro-2'-methyl)phenyl-	134–135°	131
3-(4'-Chloro-2'-methyl)phenyl-	140–141°	131
3-(6'-Chloro-2'-methyl)phenyl-	127–128°	131
3-o-Chlorophenyl-	125–127°; HCl 224–225°	180, 197, 199
3-m-Chlorophenyl-	114°; HCl 234°	172, 180, 197
3-p-Chlorophenyl-	185°; HCl 230°	172, 180, 197
3-p-(o-Chlorophenylsulphamoyl)phenyl-	212°	141
3-2'-Cyanoethyl-	179–180°	269
3-Cyclohexyl-	83°; HCl 215°	128
3-Cyclopentyl-	HCl 219°	128
3-(2',3'-Dimethyl-5'-oxo-1'-phenylpyrazolin-4'-yl)-	221–223°	197
3-p-Ethoxycarbonylphenyl-	213–215°; HCl 249°	180
3-o-Ethoxyphenyl-	117°; HCl 220°	172
3-p-Ethoxyphenyl-	168–170°; HCl 204–206°	172, 197
3-Ethyl-	181°	123
3-β-Hydroxyphenethyl-	144–146°	269a
3-p-Hydroxyphenyl-	261°	172
3-(6'-Methoxy-8'-quinolinyl)-	196–198°	195, 196
3-o-Methoxycarbonylphenyl-	129–131°; HCl 178–180°	180
3-m-Methoxycarbonylphenyl-	148–149°; HCl 229–230°	180
3-o-Methoxyphenyl-	145°; HCl 211° (dec.), 247°	172, 180
3-m-Methoxyphenyl-	115–116°; HCl 232–233°	180
3-p-Methoxyphenyl-	145°; HCl 208–210°, 252° (dec.)	172, 180
3-Methyl-	121°	109, 206
3-1'-Naphthyl-	143–144°; HCl 214–216°	173
3-2'-Naphthyl-	138–139°; HCl 194–195°	173
3-o-Nitrophenyl-	167–168°; HCl 193–195°	173
3-p-Nitrophenyl-	194–195°; HCl 223–224°	173

(*Table continued*)

TABLE IV.16 (*continued*)

2-Ethyl-3,4-dihydro-4 oxoquinazoline	M.p. (°c)	References
3-Phenyl-	128°; HCl 216–218°	86, 173, 180, 236
3-*p*-Phenylsulphamoylphenyl-	244–245°	141
3-*p*-2′-Pyridylsulphamoyl- phenyl-	238°	140
3-*p*-Pyrimid-2′-ylsulphamoyl- phenyl-	257°	140
3-*p*-Sulphamoylphenyl-	235–236°	195
3-*p*-2′-Thiazolylsulphamoyl- phenyl-	271°	140
3-*o*-Tolyl-	94–95°; HCl 195–196°	131, 173, 180
3-*m*-Tolyl-	131–132°; HCl 211–212°	173, 180
3-*p*-Tolyl-	162–163°; HCl 218–220°	173, 180
3-*p*-(*o*-Tolylsulphamoyl)phenyl-	227°	141

TABLE IV.17.   3-Substituted 3,4-Dihydro-4-oxo-2-propyl-(and isopropyl-) quinazolines.

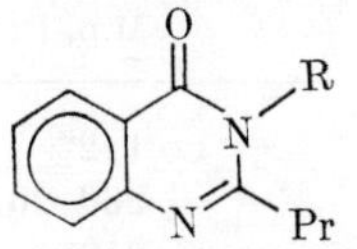

3,4-Dihydro-4-oxo-2- propylquinazoline	M.p. (°c)	References
3-Benzyl-	92°; HCl 184°	172
3-*p*-Bromophenyl-	139–141°	199
3-*p*-Chlorophenyl-	132°; HCl 220° (dec.)	172
3-Cyclohexyl-	55°; HCl 227°	128
3-*o*-Ethoxyphenyl-	102°; HCl 203°	172
3-*p*-Hydroxyphenyl-	221°	172
3-*o*-Methoxyphenyl-	101°; HCl 216° (dec.)	172
3-*p*-Methoxyphenyl-	182°; HCl 308° (dec.)	172
3-Methyl-	77–78°	109
3-1′-Naphthyl-	131–132°	173
3-2′-Naphthyl-	126–127°; HCl 187–188°	173
3-*p*-Nitrophenyl-	159–160°; HCl 191–193°	173
3-Phenyl-	122–123°; HCl 202–203°	86, 173, 280

(*Table continued*)

TABLE IV.17 (continued)

3,4-Dihydro-4-oxo-2-propylquinazoline	M.p. (°c)	References
3-o-Tolyl-	HCl 199–200°	173, 180
3-m-Tolyl-	80–81°; HCl 176–177°	173, 180
3-p-Tolyl-	145°; HCl 176°	173, 180
3-Methyl-[a]	78–79°	109
3-Phenyl-[a]	175–177°	180
3-o-Tolyl-[a]	142–143°; HCl 209–212°	180
3-m-Tolyl-[a]	158°	180
3-p-Tolyl-[a]	127–128°; HCl 204–205°	180

[a] These compounds have an isopropyl group in position 2.

TABLE IV.18.   3-Substituted 2-Ethenyl-3,4-dihydro-4-oxoquinazolines.

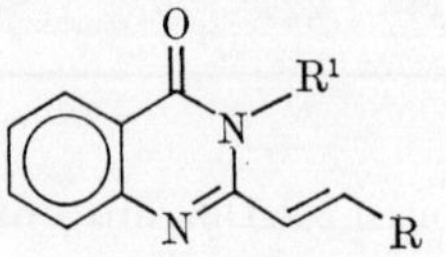

3,4-Dihydro-4-oxoquinazoline	M.p. (°c)	References
3-Benzyl-2-styryl-	142°	144
3-p-Bromophenacyl-2-styryl-	260–261°	265
3-p-Bromophenyl-2-styryl-	219°	274
3-(3'-Chloro-2'-methyl)phenyl-2-2'-pyridylethenyl-	216.5–217.5°	131
3-(4'-Chloro-2'-methyl)phenyl-2-2'-pyridylethenyl-	188.5°	131
3-(3'-Chloro-2'-methyl)phenyl-2-styryl-	183–184°	131
3-(4'-Chloro-2'-methyl)phenyl-2-styryl-	179.5–181.5°	131
3-o-Chlorophenyl-2-2'-pyridylethenyl-	190.5–191.5°	131
2-o-Chlorostyryl-3-2'-diethylaminoethyl-	210°/10⁻³ mm	265
2-p-Chlorostyryl-3-o-tolyl-	154–156°	131
3-2'-Diethylaminoethyl-2-3',4'-dimethoxystyryl-	250°/10⁻³ mm	265
3-2'-Diethylaminoethyl-2-p-methoxystyryl-	220°/10⁻³ mm	265
3-2'-Diethylaminoethyl-2-styryl-	170°/10⁻³mm	265
2-3',4'-Dimethoxystyryl-3-methyl-	208°	122

(Table continued)

TABLE IV.18 *(continued)*

3,4-Dihydro-4-oxoquinazoline	M.p. (°c)	References
3-2′-Dimethylaminoethyl-2-*p*-methoxystyryl-	1-methiodide 149–150°	265
2-*p*-Dimethylaminostyryl-3-methyl-	175°; 1-ethiodide 205.5° and 257–263° (dec.) (*cis* and *trans* forms); 1-methiodide 216° and 263–265° (dec.) (*cis* and *trans* forms)	122, 280
2-*p*-Dimethylaminostyryl-3-*m*-tolyl-	190°	274
3-*p*-Ethoxyphenyl-2-*p*-methoxystyryl-	181°	274
3-*p*-Ethoxyphenyl-2-styryl-	204°	144
3-Ethyl-2-styryl-	125°; HI 217–218°; 1-methidode 212° and 255° (dec.) (*cis* and *trans* forms)	144, 253, 280
2-2′-Furylethenyl-3-*o*-tolyl-	146–147.5°	131
2-(4′-Hydroxy-3′-methoxy)styryl-3-methyl-	280°; HI 223–225°	277, 253
2-2′-Hydroxystyryl-3-phenyl-	270	144
3-*p*-Methoxyphenyl-2-styryl-	223°	144
2-*p*-Methoxystyryl-3-methyl-	146°	122
2-*p*-Methoxystyryl-3-*o*-tolyl-	183–184°	131
3-Methyl-2-3′,4′-methylenedioxystyryl-	185°	122
3-Methyl-2-2′-pyridylethenyl-	170–171°	131
2-(3′-Methyl-2′-pyridyl)ethenyl-3-*o*-tolyl-	152–153.5°	131
3-Methyl-2-styryl-	167°, 170°; HNO₃ 177° (dec.); 1-methiodide 214° (dec.)	122, 153, 253, 277
3-3′,4′-Methylenedioxystyryl-2-*o*-tolyl-	206–207.5°	131
3-1′-Naphthyl-2-styryl-	187°	144
3-2′-Naphthyl-2-styryl-	240°	144
3-*m*-Nitrostyryl-2-*o*-tolyl-	207–207.5°	131
3-Phenyl-2-styryl-	201°	144
3-Phenethyl-2-styryl-	204°	144
2-4′-Phenylbutadienyl-3-methyl-	HI 232.5° (dec.)	253
2-2′-Pyridylethenyl-3-*o*-tolyl-	195–195.5°	131
2-3′-Pyridylethenyl-3-*o*-tolyl-	200–201°	131
2-4′-Pyridylethenyl-3-*o*-tolyl-	170–171°	131
2-2′-Quinolinylethenyl-3-*o*-tolyl-	195–196°	131
2-Styryl-3-*o*-tolyl-	162–163°	131
2-Styryl-3-*p*-tolyl-	197°; 1-methiodide 219.5° (dec.)	144, 253
2-2′-Thienylethenyl-3-*o*-tolyl-	150–151°	131

TABLE IV.19.   2-Alkyl- (other than Methyl, Ethyl, Propyl, or Ethenyl)
3-Substituted 3,4-Dihydro-4-oxoquinazolines.

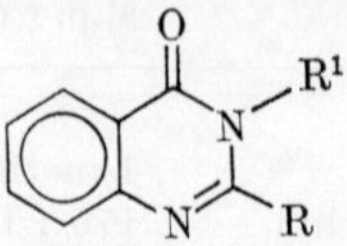

3,4-Dihydro-4-oxoquinazoline	M.p. (°c)	References
2-Acetoxy-3-(4'-chloro-2'-methyl)phenyl-	143°	184
2-Allyl-3-phenyl-	195–197° (dec.); HCl	
	307° (dec.)	180
2-Allyl-3-o-tolyl-	145–146°; HCl	
	316–318° (dec.)	180
2-Allylcarbamoyloxymethyl-3-p-		
chlorophenyl-	117°	184
2-Benzamidomethyl-3-phenyl-	205°	136
2-Benzamidomethyl-3-m-tolyl-	177–178°	136
2-Benzamidomethyl-3-p-tolyl-	195–196°	136
3-Benzoyl-2-p-chlorophenyl-	210°	110
2-Benzyl-3-o-carboxyphenyl-	283°; platinichloride	
	256–258° (dec.)	444
2-Benzyl-3-2'-diethylaminoethyl-	—	131
2-Benzyl-3-N,N-diethylcarbamoylmethyl-	158°	474
3-Benzyl-2-2',4'-dinitrophenylhydrazono-		
methyl-	275–277°	143
3-Benzyl-2-diphenylmethyl-	103–104°	100
2-Benzyl-3-methyl-	86.5–88°, 95°	90, 207
2-Benzyl-3-phenyl-	229°	44
3-(4'-Bromo-2'-methyl)phenyl-2-methyl-		
carbamoyloxymethyl-	153°	184
3-(4'-Bromo-2'-methyl)phenyl-2-		
morpholinocarbonyloxymethyl-	223°	184
2-Carbamoyloxymethyl-3-(4'-chloro-2'-		
methyl)phenyl-	220°	184
3-(4'-Chloro-2'-methyl)phenyl-2-2'-		
diethylaminoethylcarbamoyloxy-		
methyl-	145°	184
3-(4'-Chloro-2'-methyl)phenyl-2-diethyl-		
carbamoyloxymethyl-	211°	184
3-(4'-Chloro-2'-methyl)phenyl-2-2'-		
hydroxyethylcarbamoyloxymethyl-	203°	184
3-(4'-Chloro-2'-methyl)phenyl-2-(4'-(2-		
hydroxyethyl)piperazin-1'-ylcarbonyl-		
oxy)methyl-	HCl 185° (dec.)	184
3-(4'-Chloro-2'-methyl)phenyl-2-		
hydroxymethyl-	120°; HCl 245°	184

(*Table continued*)

TABLE IV.19 (*continued*)

3,4-Dihydro-4-oxoquinazoline	M.p. (°c)	References
3-(4′-Chloro-2′-methyl)phenyl-2-isopropylcarbamoyloxymethyl-	164°	184
3-(4′-Chloro-2′-methyl)phenyl-2-methylcarbamoyloxymethyl-	125°	184
3-(3′-Chloro-2′-methyl)phenyl-2-2′-piperidinoethyl-	120.5°	131
2-Chloromethyl-3-*o*-chloromethylphenyl-	139°	131
2-Chloromethyl-3-methyl-	136–138.5°	131
3-*p*-Chlorophenyl-2-diethylcarbamoyloxymethyl-	215°	184
3-*p*-Chlorophenyl-2-ethylcarbamoyloxymethyl-	136°	184
2-(1′,2′-Dibromo-2′-(2-pyridyl))ethyl-3-*o*-tolyl-	182–183°	131
2-(1′,2′-Dihydro-2′-oxoquinoxalin-3′-yl)methyl-3-methyl-	354°	283
2-Diphenylmethyl-3-phenyl-	122–123°	100
2-Ethoxallylmethyl-3-methyl-	173°; phenylhydrazone 168–169°	283
3-Ethyl-2-(2′-indan-1′,3′-dionyl)-	198.5°	281
3-(3′-Fluoro-4′-methyl)phenyl-2-(3′,3′,3′-trichloro-2′-hydroxy)propyl-	214–215°	188
3-*m*-Fluorophenyl-2-(3′,3′,3′-trichloro-2′-hydroxy)propyl-	104–105°	188
3-*p*-Fluorophenyl-2-(3′,3′,3′-trichloro-2′-hydroxy)propyl-	110–112°	188
2-1′-Hydroxyethyl-3-methyl-	63.5–65.5°	241
2-Hydroxymethyl-3-methyl-	153–154°	241
2,3-1′-Hydroxytrimethylene-	212° (dec.)	88
2-Isobutyl-3-methyl-	68–69°	109
2-Isopentyl-3-methyl-	40–41°	109
2-*p*-Methoxyphenethyl-3-methyl-	118–118.5°	250
3-Methyl-2-3′,4′-methylenedioxyphenethyl-	94–94.5°	250
2-Phenoxymethyl-3-phenyl-	130–132°	100
2-2′-Piperidinoethyl-3-*o*-tolyl-	—	131
2-2′-Pyridylethynyl-3-*o*-tolyl-	151–152°	131
2,3-Tetramethylene-	99°, 100.5°; chloroplatinate 260° (dec.); picrate 196°	235, 446 466
3-*o*-Tolyl-2-(3′,3′,3′-trichloro-2′-hydroxy)propyl-	128°	131
2,3-Trimethylene-	110–111°; 1′-benzylidene deriv. 137–139°	88, 446

TABLE IV.20.   3-Substituted 2-Aryl-3,4-dihydro-4-oxoquinazolines.

3,4-Dihydro-4-oxoquinazoline	M.p. (°c)	References
3-Acetyl-2-phenyl-	233°	208
3-Benzyl-2-phenyl-	146°	456
2-*p*-Bromophenyl-3-ethyl-	122–124°	199
2-*o*-Bromophenyl-3-methyl-	154–156°	199
2-*p*-Bromophenyl-3-methyl-	170–172°	199
3-Butyl-2-phenyl-	116–118°	199
2-*p*-Chlorophenyl-3-methyl-	170–172°	119, 456
2-*p*-Chlorophenyl-3-phenyl-	177°	86, 155
3-*o*-Chlorophenyl-2-phenyl-	164°	139
3-*m*-Chlorophenyl-2-phenyl-	161°	139
3-*p*-Chlorophenyl-2-phenyl-	173°	139
3-Diethylcarbamoylmethyl-2-phenyl-	109–110°	474
3-*m*-(3′,4′-Dihydro-4′-oxo-2′-*m*-nitrophenyl-quinazolin-3′-yl)phenyl-2-*m*-nitrophenyl-	226°	117
3-*m*-(3′,4′-Dihydro-4′-oxo-2′-*p*-nitrophenyl-quinazolin-3′-yl)phenyl-2-*p*-nitrophenyl-	207°	117
3-2′,3′-Dihydroxypropyl-2-phenyl-	179–181°, 176°	199, 264
3-Dimethylcarbamoylmethyl-2-phenyl-	146–147°	474
3-Ethyl-2-*p*-dimethylaminophenyl-	1-ethiodide 212°	447
3-Ethyl-2-phenyl-	130–132°; HCl 205° (dec.)	199
3-*o*-Methoxyphenyl-2-phenyl-	159–160°	155
3-*p*-Methoxyphenyl-2-phenyl-	197°	155
3-Methyl-2-phenyl-	136–138°; HCl 208° (dec.)	79, 199, 206
3-Methyl-2-*o*-tolyl-	107–109°; HCl 205° (dec.)	199
2-1′-Naphthyl-3-phenyl-	180°	155
3-1′-Naphthyl-2-phenyl-	194°	139
3-2′-Naphthyl-2-phenyl-	184°	85, 139, 155
2-*o*-Nitrophenyl-3-phenyl-	224–225°	86
2,3-Diphenyl-	158–159°	85, 86, 100, 155
2-Phenyl-3-*o*-tolyl-	154°	139, 155
2-Phenyl-3-*m*-tolyl-	139, 148°	85, 139, 155
2-Phenyl-3-*p*-tolyl-	168°, 180–181°	139, 155
3-Phenyl-2-*o*-tolyl-	159–180°, 152°	86, 155
3-Phenyl-2-*p*-tolyl-	178°	86
2-Phenyl-3-2′,4′-xylyl-	135–136°	155
2,3-Di-*o*-tolyl-	179–180°	86
2,3-Di-*p*-tolyl-	178°	86

TABLE IV.21.   3-Aryl-3,4-dihydro-4-oxoquinazolines with a Heterocyclic
Group in Position 2.

3,4-Dihydro-4-oxoquinazoline	M.p. (°c)	References
3-p-Bromophenyl-2-2′-furyl-	200°	192
3-p-Bromophenyl-2-(5′-methyl-2′-furyl)-	245°	193
3-o-Carboxyphenyl-2-2′-furyl-	245°	192
3-m-Carboxyphenyl-2-2′-furyl-	249°	192
3-p-Carboxyphenyl-2-2′-furyl-	265°	192
3-o-Carboxyphenyl-2-(5′-methyl-2′-furyl)-	228°	193
3-m-Carboxyphenyl-2-(5′-methyl-2′-furyl)-	268°	193
3-p-Carboxyphenyl-2-(5′-methyl-2′-furyl)-	271°	193
3-p-Chlorophenyl-2-2′-furyl-	205°	192
3-p-Chlorophenyl-2-(5′-methyl-2′-furyl)-	239°	193
3-p-Ethoxyphenyl-2-2′-furyl-	216°	192
3-p-Ethoxyphenyl-2-(5′-methyl-2′-furyl)-	220°	193
2-2′-Furyl-3-phenyl-	215°	192
2-2′-Furyl-3-p-tolyl-	228°	192
3-o-Methoxycarbonylphenyl-2-2′-furyl-	180°	192
3-m-Methoxycarbonylphenyl-2-2′-furyl-	213°	192
3-p-Methoxycarbonylphenyl-2-2′-furyl-	235°	192
3-o-Methoxycarbonylphenyl-2-(5′-methyl-2′-furyl)-	210°	193
3-m-Methoxycarbonylphenyl-2-(5′-methyl-2′-furyl)-	178°	193
3-p-Methoxycarbonylphenyl-2-(5′-methyl-2′-furyl)-	213°	193
3-p-Methoxyphenyl-2-2′-furyl-	204°	192
3-p-Methoxyphenyl-2-(5′-methyl-2′-furyl)-	232°	193
2-(5′-Methyl-2′-furyl)-3-phenyl-	235°	193
2-(5′-Methyl-2′-furyl)-3-p-tolyl-	216°	193
3-Phenyl-2-3′-pyridyl-	175– 176.5°	86

TABLE IV.22.   3-Substituted 3,4-Dihydro-4-oxoquinazolines with Halogeno, Alkoxy, or Aryloxy Substituents in Position 2.

3,4-Dihydro-4-oxoquinazoline	M.p. (°c)	References
2-Chloro-3-2′-chloroethyl-	195.5–196°	359
2-Chloro-3-2′-chloroisopropyl-	98°, 130°/0.1 mm	359
2-Chloro-3-p-chlorophenyl-	161°	455
2-Chloro-3-3′-chloropropyl-	114.5–115°	359
2-Chloro-3-phenyl-	131.5°, 135–136°, 245°/15 mm; HCl 140°	455, 462
2-Chloro-3-o-tolyl-	134°	455
3-2′-Chloroethyl-2-ethoxy-	104–105°	420
2-Ethoxy-3-methyl-	77.5°	311, 312, 453
2-Ethoxy-3-phenyl-	96°	455
2-Fluoro-3-phenyl-	170°	455
2-Methoxy-3-methyl-	93°	453
2-Methoxy-3-phenyl-	134°	462

TABLE IV.23.   3,4-Dihydro-2-methyl-4-oxoquinazolines Substituted in the Benzene Ring.

3,4-Dihydro-2-methyl-4-oxoquinazoline	M.p. (°c)	References
5,6-Benzo-	290–292°, 295°	19, 206
6,7-Benzo-	320° (dec.)	19, 56, 162, 434
7,8-Benzo-	322°	206
6-Bromo-	302°	61, 101, 130
6,8-Dibromo-	> 300° (dec.)	103
5-Chloro-	288–290°	472
6-Chloro-	287°; HCl 281°; picrate 202–203°	119, 165
7-Chloro-	270°	264
6,8-Dichloro-	348°, > 360°; HCl > 360°; picrate 238°	61, 263
7-Chloro-6-sulphamoyl-	> 320°	233
6-Ethoxy-	220°	206
8-Ethoxy-	225°	206
6-Iodo-	345°; HCl > 360°; picrate 256°	61
6,8-Diiodo-	> 360°; HCl > 360°; picrate 274°	61
6-Methoxy-	270°	112, 206, 264
7-Methoxy-	272°, 257°	112, 206
8-Methoxy-	263°, 243°	129, 206, 264
6,7-Dimethoxy-	297–300°	135
7,8-Dimethoxy-	223–224°; HCl 226–228°	467
8-Methoxy-6,7-methylenedioxy-	285–286°	478
6-Methyl-	240°, 250°; picrate 196–198°	206, 210
7-Methyl-	255°	26, 38, 72, 206
8-Methyl-	240°; picrate 164°	206
6,8-Dimethyl-	271.5–272.5°, 266°; picrate 197°	104, 206
6,7-Methylenedioxy-	346°	461
5-Nitro-	277–279°; HCl 276–277°; HNO₃ 205° (dec.)	50, 123
6-Nitro-	280°, 302–304°	75, 78, 130, 132, 291
7-Nitro-	287–290°, 290–295°	49, 74, 123, 165
8-Nitro-	264°	77
6-Sulphamoyl-	> 320°	291

TABLE IV.24.   2-Alkyl-(other than Methyl) 3,4-dihydro-4-oxoquinazolines
with Substituents in the Benzene Ring.

R¹—[benzene ring fused to quinazolinone]

3,4-Dihydro-4-oxoquinazoline	M.p. (°c)	References
5,6 (or 6,7)-Benzo-2-benzyl-	278°	207
6,7-Benzo-2-benzyl-	264° (dec.)	162
7,8-Benzo-2-benzyl-	265°	207
6,7-Benzo-2-2'-cyanoethyl-	290° (dec.)	162
6,7-Benzo-2-cyanomethyl-	290° (dec.)	162
6,7-Benzo-2-3'-cyanopropyl-	282° (dec.)	162
6,7-Benzo-2-ethoxycarbonylmethyl-	235° (dec.)	162
2-Benzyl-6-methoxy-	241°; picrate 198°	207
2-Benzyl-8-methoxy-	257°; picrate 191°	207
2-Benzyl-6,7-dimethoxy-	253°	135
2-Benzyl-6-methyl-	239°; picrate 194°	207
2-Benzyl-7-methyl-	230°; picrate 168°	207
2-Benzyl-8-methyl-	198°; picrate 153°	207
2-Benzyl-7,8-dimethyl-	189°; picrate 165°	207
2-Benzyl-7-nitro-	259–259.5°	165
2-2'-Benzylaminoethyl-6-iodo-	2 HCl 298°; picrate 212°	61
6-Bromo-2-2'-dimethylaminoethyl-	2 HCl 314°; picrate 186°	61
6-Bromo-2-ethyl-	267–268.5°	101
6,8-Dibromo-2-ethyl-	278–280°	103
6-Bromo-2-isobutyl-	253–254°	101
6,8-Dibromo-2-isobutyl-	230–231.5°	103
6-Bromo-2-isopentyl-	235–236°	101
6-Bromo-2-isopropyl-	259–260.5°	101
6,8-Dibromo-2-isopropyl-	259–260°	103
6-Bromo-2-propyl-	255–256°	101
6,8-Dibromo-2-propyl-	238–240°	103
6-Bromo-2-2'-morpholinoethyl-	2 HCl 352° (dec.); picrate 199°	61
6,8-Dichloro-2-2'-cyclohexylamino-ethyl-	2 HCl 315°; picrate 184°	61
6,8-Dichloro-2-2'-diethylaminoethyl-	2 HCl 360° (dec.); picrate 226°	61
6,8-Dichloro-2-2'-dimethylaminoethyl-	2 HCl > 354°; picrate 210°	61
6-Chloro-2-ethyl-	259°	264
7-Chloro-2-ethyl-6-sulphamoyl-	0.5 H₂O 310–312°	233
6,8-Dichloro-2-2'-ethylaminoethyl-	2 HCl 278°; picrate 178°	61

(*Table continued*)

TABLE IV.24 (continued)

3,4-Dihydro-4-oxoquinazoline	M.p. (°c)	References
7-Chloro-2-isopropyl-6-sulphamoyl-	> 280°	233
6,8-Dichloro-2-2′-methylaminoethyl-	2 HCl 288° (dec.);	
	picrate 169°	61
6,8-Dichloro-2-2′-morpholinoethyl-	2 HCl 357° (dec.);	
	picrate 258° (dec.)	61
6,8-Dichloro-2-2′-piperidinoethyl-	2 HCl 360° (dec.);	
	picrate 240°	61
2-2′-Cyclohexylaminoethyl-6-iodo-	2 HCl 320°; picrate 240°	61
2-3′,4′-Diethoxystyryl-8-methoxy-	261°	129
2-2′-Diethylaminoethyl-6-iodo-	2 HCl 298°; picrate	
	260° (dec.)	61
6,8-Diiodo-2-2′-methylaminoethyl-	2 HCl > 360°; picrate	
	209°	61
6,8-Diiodo-2-2′-morpholinoethyl-	2 HCl > 360°; picrate	
	269° (dec.)	61
6,8-Diiodo-2-2′-piperidinoethyl-	2 HCl > 360°; picrate	
	275° (dec.)	61
2-3′,4′-Dimethoxybenzyl-6,7-dimethoxy-	269°	135
2-2′-Dimethylaminoethyl-6-iodo-	2 HCl 345°; picrate 238°	61
2-2′-Dimethylaminoethyl-6,8-iodo-	2 HCl > 360°; picrate	
	232°	61
2-Ethyl-6-methyl-	227°	206
2-Ethyl-7-methyl-	240°	26, 38
2-Ethyl-8-methyl-	215°	206
2-Ethyl-5-nitro-	240°	123
2-2′-Ethylaminoethyl-6-iodo-	2 HCl 340°; picrate 230°	61
2-2′-Indan-1′,3′-dionyl-6-nitro-	> 355°	281
6-Iodo-2-2′-morpholinoethyl-	2 HCl 335° (dec.);	
	picrate 264° (dec.)	61
6-Iodo-2-2′-piperidinoethyl-	2 HCl 330°; picrate 275°	61
2-Isobutyl-7-methyl-	219°	38
2-Isopropyl-7-methyl-	228°	26, 38
7-Methoxy-2-3′,4′-methylenedioxystyryl-	193°	122
8-Methoxy-2-p-methoxystyryl-	249°	129
8-Methoxy-2-styryl-	268°	129
6-Methyl-2-t-butyl-	248–249°	224
6,8-Dimethyl-2-t-butyl-	209°	224
6,7-Methylenedioxy-2-propyl-	280°	461
6-Nitro-2-p-nitrostyryl-	335°	144
6-Nitro-2-styryl-	323–325°	144
6-Nitro-2-trichloromethyl-	240–242°	465

TABLE IV.25.   2-Aryl-3,4-dihydro-4-oxoquinazolines with Substituents in the
Benzene Ring.

3,4-Dihydro-4-oxoquinazoline	M.p. (°c)	References
2-(2'-Amino-5'-nitro)phenyl-6-nitro-	> 360°	106
2-o-Aminophenyl-6-bromo-	264–265°	448
2-o-Aminophenyl-6-fluoro-	266–267°	448
2-o-Aminophenyl-6-methyl-	223–224°; HCl 279–281°	448
2-o-Aminophenyl-8-methyl-	259–260°	448
6,7-Benzo-2-2'-furyl-	270° (dec.)	162
5,6-Benzo-2-phenyl-	295–298°	208
6,7-Benzo-2-phenyl-	300° (dec.)	162
7,8-Benzo-2-phenyl-	300°	208
5-Bromo-7-nitro-2-phenyl	318°	83
6-Bromo-2-o-nitrophenyl-	278–280°	448
6-Bromo-2-phenyl-	> 300°	435
7-Chloro-2-2'-furyl-	276°	161
5-Chloro-7-nitro-2-phenyl-	311°	83
2-(2'-Chloro-5'-nitro)phenyl-6-nitro-	324–325° (dec.)	106
2-o-Chlorophenyl-6-nitro-	278–279°	106
6-Fluoro-2-o-nitrophenyl-	248–249°	448
2-2'-Furyl-6-methyl-	257°	160
5-Iodo-7-nitro-2-phenyl-	321°	83
6-Methyl-2-o-nitrophenyl-	271–273°	448
7-Methyl-2-p-nitrophenyl-	> 370°	38
8-Methyl-2-o-nitrophenyl-	286–288°	448
6-Methyl-2-phenyl-	265–266°	114
7-Methyl-2-phenyl-	243°	38
6-Nitro-2-p-nitrophenyl-	317–318°	106
7-Nitro-2-m-nitrophenyl-	345–346° (dec.)	106
7-Nitro-2-phenyl-	329°	139
8-Nitro-2-phenyl-	> 250°	77

TABLE IV.26.   3,4-Dihydro-3-methyl-4-oxoquinazolines with Substituents in the Benzene Ring.

O
‖
R—⟨benzene ring fused⟩—N—Me
N

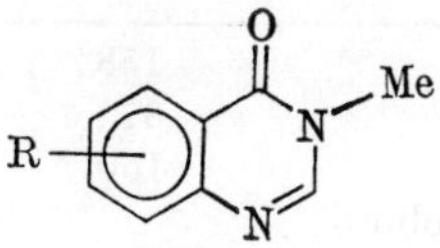

3,4-Dihydro-3-methyl-4-oxoquinazoline	M.p. (°c)	References
6,7-Benzo-	192–193°	249
6-Chloro-8-nitro-	230°	33
7-Chloro-6-sulphamoyl-	H_2O 238–240°	292
8-Hydroxy-	153°	46
8-Hydroxy-7-morpholinomethyl-	164°	305
8-Hydroxy-7-piperidinomethyl-	152°	305
8-Methoxy-	172°	46
6-Nitro-	196°; 1-methiodide 228.5°	130, 253, 452
7-Nitro-	212°	452
8-Nitro-	155°, 157°	33, 452
6,8-Dinitro-	229°	33

TABLE IV.27.   3-Alkyl- (other than Methyl) 3,4-dihydro-4-oxoquinazolines with Substituents in the Benzene Ring.

O
‖
R¹—⟨benzene ring fused⟩—N—R
N

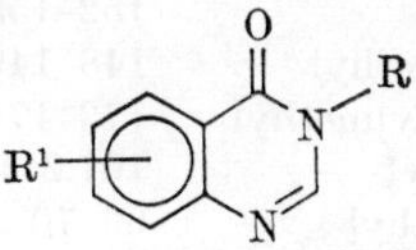

3,4-Dihydro-4-oxoquinazoline	M.p. (°c)	References
6,7-Benzo-3-butyl-	130–131°	249
6,7-Benzo-3-ethyl-	113°	249
6,7-Benzo-3-isobutyl-	112–113°	249
6,7-Benzo-3-isopropyl	129–130°	249
6,7-Benzo-3-propyl-	158°	249
3-Benzyl-6-bromo-	131–132°	100
3-Benzyl-6-chloro-	120°	100
3-Benzyl-8-hydroxy-	160°	46
3-Benzyl-8-methoxy-	118°	46
6,8-Dibromo-3-ethyl-	229–230°	103

(*Table continued*)

TABLE IV.27 (*continued*)

3,4-Dihydro-4-oxoquinazoline	M.p. (°c)	References
3-2'-Bromoethyl-8-hydroxy-	158°	46
3-Butyl-8-hydroxy-	87°	46
3-Butyl-8-hydroxy-7-iodo-	150°	305
3-Butyl-8-hydroxy-7-morpholino- methyl-	111°	305
3-Butyl-8-hydroxy-7-piperidinomethyl-	121°	305
3-Butyl-8-methoxy-	78°	46
3-2'-Carbamoylethyl-7-chloro-	189–190°	69
3-Carbamoylmethyl-6-chloro-	276–277°	263
3-Carbamoylmethyl-6,8-dichloro-	271–274°	263
3-Carboxymethyl-6-chloro-	270–271°	263
3-Carboxymethyl-6,8-dichloro-	278°	263
6-Chloro-3-2'-(N-carbamoyl-N- ethyl)aminoethyl-	187.9–188.1°	454
6-Chloro-3-2'-(4-6'-chloro-3',4'-dihydro- 4'-oxoquinazolin-3'-yl-2''-ethyl- piperazin-1-yl)ethyl-	> 300°; picrate > 300°	449
6-Chloro-3-2'-chloroethyl-	160°	449
7-Chloro-3-2'-chloroethyl-	131°	64
6-Chloro-3-2'-chloropropyl-	115–117°	118
6-Chloro-3-cyclohexyl-	158°; picrate 233°	128
6-Chloro-3-(3'-cyclohexylamino-2'- hydroxy)propyl-	160–162°	118
6-Chloro-3-3'-cyclohexylaminopropyl-	2 HCl·H$_2$O 242–244° (dec.)	118
6-Chloro-3-2'-epoxypropyl-	152–155°	118
6-Chloro-3-ethoxycarbonylmethyl-	148–149°	263
6,8-Dichloro-3-ethoxycarbonylmethyl-	173–174.5°	263
6-Chloro-3-2'-ethylaminoethyl-	107.2–107.9°	454
6-Chloro-3-2'-diethylaminoethyl-	69–70°; 2 HCl 210–214° (dec.)	63
6-Chloro-3-(4'-diethylamino-1'- methyl)butyl-	156–157°	63
6-Chloro-3-2'-(N-ethyl-N- nitroso)aminoethyl-	158.6–158.8°	454
6-Chloro-3-2'-hydroxyethyl-	175°; picrate > 260°	449
6-Chloro-8-methoxy-3-prop-2'-ynyl-	116–116.5°	268
6-Chloro-3-2'-morpholinoethyl-	> 280°	449
3-2'-Chloroethyl-6-iodo-	185°	449
3-2'-Chloroethyl-8-methoxy-	140°	46
3-2'-Chloroethyl-6-methyl-	152°	64
3-2'-Chloroethyl-8-methyl-	168°	64
3-3'-Chloropropyl-6-methyl-	HCl 209–211° (dec.)	118
3-2'-Dibutylaminoethyl-8-hydroxy-	2 HCl 183° (dec.)	46

(*Table continued*)

3,4-Dihydro-4-oxoquinazoline	M.p. (°c)	References
3-2'-Dibutylaminoethyl-8-methoxy-	232°/4 mm	46
3-2'-Diethylaminoethyl-8-hydroxy-	2 HCl 206° (dec.)	46
3-2'-Diethylaminoethyl-8-methoxy-	224°/4 mm	46
3-2'-Diheptylaminoethyl-8-hydroxy-	2 HCl 152° (dec.)	46
3-2'-Diheptylaminoethyl-8-methoxy-	248°/4 mm	46
3-2'-(4-3',4'-Dihydro-6'-iodo-4'-oxo-quinazolin-3'-yl-2''-ethylpiperazin-1-yl)ethyl-6-iodo-	>300°; picrate > 300°	449
3-2'-Dipentylaminoethyl-8-hydroxy-	2 HCl 169° (dec.)	46
3-2'-Dipentylaminoethyl-8-methoxy-	238°/4 mm	46
3-Ethoxycarbonylmethyl-5-methyl-	—	431
3-Ethyl-8-hydroxy-	118°	46
3-Ethyl-8-hydroxy-7-iodo-	182°	305
3-Ethyl-8-hydroxy-7-morpholino-methyl-	128°	305
3-Ethyl-8-hydroxy-7-piperidinomethyl-	134°	305
3-Ethyl-8-methoxy-	108°	46, 417
3-Ethyl-6-nitro-	165°	130
8-Hydroxy-3-2'-hydroxyethyl-	189°	46
8-Hydroxy-7-iodo-3-propyl-	160°	305
8-Hydroxy-7-morpholinomethyl-3-propyl-	86°	305
8-Hydroxy-3-2'-piperidinoethyl-	2 HCl 158° (dec.)	46
8-Hydroxy-7-piperidinomethyl-3-propyl-	131°	305
8-Hydroxy-3-isopropyl-	128°	46
8-Hydroxy-3-propyl-	96°	46
3-2'-Hydroxyethyl-6-iodo-	195°	449
3-2'-Hydroxyethyl-8-methoxy-	150°	46
6-Iodo-3-2'-piperidinoethyl-	>280°	449
3-Isopropyl-8-methoxy-	138°	46
8-Methoxy-3-2'-piperidinomethyl-	228°/9 mm	46
8-Methoxy-3-propyl-	113°	46

TABLE IV.28.   3-Aryl-3,4-dihydro-4-oxoquinazolines with Substituents in the
Benzene Ring.

3,4-Dihydro-4-oxoquinazoline	M.p. (°c)	References
3-*p*-Aminophenyl-6-nitro-	259–260° (dec.)	117
6-Bromo-3-*p*-bromophenyl-	257°	69
6-Bromo-3-phenyl-	150–151°	167
6-Chloro-3-*p*-chlorophenyl-	225°	66, 219
3-*p*-Chlorophenyl-7-methoxy-	315–316°	105
3-*p*-Chlorophenyl-6,7-dimethoxy-	313–314°	105
6-Ethoxy-3-*p*-ethoxyphenyl-	210°	213
6-Fluoro-3-*p*-fluorophenyl-	260°	219
6-Methoxy-3-*p*-methoxyphenyl-	191.5–192.5°	66
6-Methyl-3-*p*-tolyl-	113.5–114.5°	66

TABLE IV.29.   3-Alkyl-3,4-dihydro-2-methyl-4-oxoquinazolines with
Substituents in the Benzene Ring.

3,4-Dihydro-2-methyl-4-oxoquinazoline	M.p. (°c)	References
3-Allyl-5-nitro-	160–161°	116
5,6-Benzo-3-methyl-	295°	206
3-Benzyl-6-iodo-	121–123°	443
3-Benzyl-8-methoxy-	115°	129
3-Benzyl-7-nitro-	131–132°; HCl 229–230°	49
6,8-Dibromo-3-ethyl-	100–105°	103
3-Butyl-6-iodo-	114–116°	443
3-Butyl-8-methoxy-	82°	129
3-2′-Carbamoylethyl-6-chloro-	209–210°	269
3-2′-Carbamoylethyl-7-chloro-	210–211°	269
3-Carbamoylmethyl-6-chloro-	278–279°	263
3-Carbamoylmethyl-6,8-dichloro-	323–324°	263

(*Table continued*)

TABLE IV.29 (continued)

3,4-Dihydro-2-methyl-4-oxoquinazoline	M.p. (°c)	References
3-Carbamoylmethyl-7-nitro-	275°	49
3-2′-Carboxyethyl-6,8-diiodo-	256.4–257.4°	473
3-Carboxymethyl-6-chloro-	258–260°	263
3-Carboxymethyl-6,8-dichloro-	210–211°	263
3-1′-Carboxypentyl-6,8-diiodo-	254° (dec.)	473
3-5′-Carboxypentyl-6,8-diiodo-	187.5–189.5° (dec.)	473
6-Chloro-3-2′-cyanoethyl-	153–154°	269
6-Chloro-3-cyclohexyl-	125°; HCl 249°	128
6-Chloro-3-2′,4′-dihydroxypropyl-	195°	264
6-Chloro-3-(1′-ethylpyrrolidin-3′-yl)methyl-	2 HCl 208–211° (dec.)	149
6-Chloro-3-2′-hydroxyethyl-	190°	264
7-Chloro-3-methyl-6-sulphamoyl-	3 H₂O 245°	292
6-Chloro-3-(1′-methylpyrrolidin-3′-yl)methyl-	2 HCl 244–250°	149
6-Chloro-3-phenethyl-	150–152°	168
3-Cyanomethyl-7-nitro-	207–208°	49
3-Cyclohexyl-8-methoxy-	HCl 255–256°	128
3-Cyclopentyl-6-methoxy-	97°; HCl 227°	128
3-2′,3′-Dihydroxypropyl-6-methoxy-	180°	264
3-2′,3′-Dihydroxypropyl-8-methoxy-	175°	264
6-Ethoxy-3-methyl-	148°	206
3-Ethoxycarbonylmethyl-7-nitro-	139–140°	49
3-Ethyl-8-hydroxy-7-morpholino-methyl-	97°	305
3-Ethyl-8-methoxy-	75°	129
3-Ethyl-6,8-dimethyl-	190°	206
3-Ethyl-5-nitro-	208°	123
3-Ethyl-6-nitro-	166°	130, 132
3-Ethyl-7-nitro-	175°	123
8-Hydroxy-3-methyl-7-morpholino-methyl-	153°	305
8-Hydroxy-3-methyl-7-piperidino-methyl-	125°	305
8-Hydroxy-7-morpholinomethyl-3-propyl-	106°	305
3-2′-Hydroxyethyl-6-iodo-	177–179°	443
6-Iodo-3-isopropyl-	177–178°	443
3-Isobutyl-5-nitro-	202–203°	116
3-Isopentyl-8-methoxy-	93°	129
3-Isopentyl-5-nitro-	213–214°	116
3-Isopentyl-7-nitro-	117–118°	123

(Table continued)

TABLE IV.29 (continued)

3,4-Dihydro-2-methyl-4-oxoquinazoline	M.p (°c)	References
3-Isopropyl-5-nitro-	219–220°	116
6-Methoxy-3-methyl-	133°; H_2O 87°	122, 206
7-Methoxy-3-methyl-	149°; H_2O 80°	122, 206
8-Methoxy-3-methyl-	143°	129
8-Methoxy-3-pentyl-	90°	129
8-Methoxy-3-phenethyl-	167°	129
8-Methoxy-3-propyl-	137°	129
3,8-Dimethyl-	107°	206
3,6,7-Trimethyl-	210–212°	127
3,6,8-Trimethyl-	146°	206
3-Methyl-5-nitro-	203°	116
3-Methyl-6-nitro-	165°	75, 78, 132
3-Methyl-7-nitro-	151–152°, 144–145°	49, 74, 123
3-Methyl-8-nitro-	175°	77
5-Nitro-3-propyl-	204–205°	116
7-Nitro-3-propyl-	140°	49
5-Nitro-3-s-butyl-	209–210°	116

TABLE IV.30.   3-Aryl- (and Heteroaryl-) 3,4-dihydro-2-methyl-4-oxoquinazolines with Substituents in the Benzene Ring.

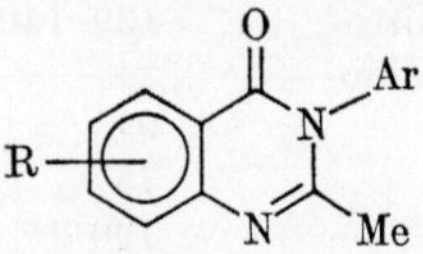

3,4-Dihydro-2-methyl-4-oxoquinazoline	M.p. (°c)	References
3-o-Aminophenyl-6-iodo-	> 290°	443
3-m-Aminophenyl-6-iodo-	> 290°	443
3-p-(p-Aminophenyl)phenyl-6-bromo-	198–199°	117
6-Bromo-3-p-bromophenyl-	165°	195
6,8-Dibromo-3-p-bromophenyl-	224–226°	471
6-Bromo-3-(5′-chloro-2′-methyl)phenyl-	154–156°	34
6-Bromo-3-o-chlorophenyl-	176°; HCl 237° (dec.)	178
6-Bromo-3-m-chlorophenyl-	196°; HCl 255° (dec.)	178
6-Bromo-3-p-chlorophenyl-	145°	195
6,8-Dibromo-3-p-chlorophenyl-	207–209°	471
6-Bromo-3-p-(o-chlorophenylsulphamoyl)phenyl-	221°	141

(Table continued)

TABLE IV.30 (continued)

3,4-Dihydro-2-methyl-4-oxoquinazoline	M.p. (°c)	References
6-Bromo-3-p-diethylaminophenyl-	227°; HCl 247° (dec.)	178
6-Bromo-3-o-ethoxyphenyl-	135°, 136–138°	195, 471
6-Bromo-3-p-ethoxyphenyl-	150°	195
6,8-Dibromo-3-o-ethoxyphenyl-	182–184°	471
6-Bromo-3-(3′-fluoro-4′-methyl)phenyl-	130°	188
6,8-Dibromo-3-(3′-fluoro-4′-methyl)-phenyl-	97°	188
6-Bromo-3-m-fluorophenyl-	192–193°	188
6-Bromo-3-p-fluorophenyl-	99–100°	188
6-Bromo-3-p-guanidinosulphamoyl-phenyl-	308°	140
6-Bromo-3-p-iodophenyl-	204°	195
6-Bromo-3-o-methoxyphenyl-	176°	195, 471
6-Bromo-3-p-methoxyphenyl-	181°; HCl 233° (dec.)	178
6,8-Dibromo-3-o-methoxyphenyl-	209–211°	471
6-Bromo-3-p-nitrophenyl-	255°	178
6-Bromo-3-phenyl-	186°; HCl 246° (dec.)	101, 178
6-Bromo-3-p-2′-pyridylsulphamoyl-phenyl-	272°	140
6-Bromo-3-p-pyrimidin-2′-ylsulphamoyl-phenyl-	284–285°	140
6-Bromo-3-p-2′-thiazolylsulphamoyl-phenyl-	279°	140
6-Bromo-3-o-tolyl-	137–138°, 148°; HCl 241° (dec.)	101, 178
6-Bromo-3-m-tolyl-	165°; HCl 236° (dec.)	178, 471
6-Bromo-3-p-tolyl-	131°; HCl 245° (dec.)	178
6,8-Dibromo-3-o-tolyl-	188–189°	471
6,8-Dibromo-3-m-tolyl-	208–210°	471
6,8-Dibromo-3-p-tolyl-	172–174°	471
6-Bromo-3-p(o-tolylsulphamoyl)phenyl-	240–242°	141
3-p-Bromophenyl-6-chloro-	174°	195
3-p-Bromophenyl-6-iodo-	177–179°	34
3-p-Bromophenyl-6-methyl-	170–171°	195
3-p-Bromophenyl-7-nitro-	300°	440
3-Carbamoylphenyl-7-nitro-	320–321°	49
6-Chloro-3-o-chlorophenyl-	158°; HCl 236° (dec.)	178
6-Chloro-3-m-chlorophenyl-	175°; HCl 254° (dec.)	178
6-Chloro-3-p-chlorophenyl-	152°	195
6-Chloro-3-p-(o-chlorophenyl-sulphamoyl)phenyl-	204°	141
6-Chloro-3-p-diethylaminophenyl-	210°; HCl 234° (dec.)	178

(Table continued)

TABLE IV.30 (*continued*)

3,4-Dihydro-2-methyl-4-oxoquinazoline	M.p. (°c)	References
6-Chloro-3-*p*-*N*,*N*-diethyl- sulphamoylphenyl-	210°	141
6-Chloro-3-*p*-ethoxyphenyl-	149°	195
6-Chloro-3-*m*-fluorophenyl-	> 286° (dec.)	188
6-Chloro-3-*p*-iodophenyl-	204°	195
6-Chloro-3-*o*-methoxyphenyl-	147°	195
6-Chloro-3-*p*-methoxyphenyl-	172°; HCl 237° (dec.)	178
3-(5′-Chloro-2′-methyl)phenyl-6-iodo-	136–138°	34
3-(3′-Chloro-2′-methyl)phenyl-6-nitro-	190–191°	131
3-(4′-Chloro-2′-methyl)phenyl-6-nitro-	205–206°	131
6-Chloro-3-*p*-nitrophenyl-	246°	178
6-Chloro-3-phenyl-	181–182°, 163°; HCl 241° (dec.)	171, 178
6-Chloro-3-*p*-phenylsulphamoylphenyl-	205°	141
6-Chloro-3-*p*-2′-pyridylsulphamoylphenyl-	242°	140
6-Chloro-3-*p*-thiazolylsulphamoylphenyl-	277°	140
6-Chloro-3-*o*-tolyl-	158–159°, 167°; HCl 238°	131, 178
6-Chloro-3-*m*-tolyl-	179°	178
6-Chloro-3-*p*-tolyl-	104°; HCl 235° (dec.)	178
7-Chloro-3-*o*-tolyl-	118–120°	131
6-Chloro-3-*p*-(*o*-tolylsulphamoyl)phenyl-	245°	141
3-*p*-Chlorophenyl-6-iodo-	156–157°	34
3-*p*-Chlorophenyl-6,8-diiodo-	204–206°	179
3-*o*-Chlorophenyl-6-methyl-	175°; HCl 240°	177
3-*o*-Chlorophenyl-8-methyl-	150°	176
3-*m*-Chlorophenyl-6-methyl-	144°; HCl 255–256°	177
3-*p*-Chlorophenyl-6-methyl-	150°; HCl 264–265°	177
3-*p*-Chlorophenyl-8-methyl-	151°	176
3-*o*-Chlorophenyl-7-nitro-	192°	440
3-*p*-Chlorophenyl-6-nitro-	260–262°	179
3-*o*-Cyanophenyl-7-nitro-	234°	49
3-2′,4′-Dichlorophenyl-6-methyl-	152°	195
3-(3′,4′-Diethoxycarbonyl-2′,5′-dimethyl- 1′-pyrrolyl)-7-nitro-	171°	49
3-(3′,4′-Dihydro-2′-methyl-6′-nitro-4′- oxoquinazolin-3′-yl)-6-nitro-	281–285°	132
3-(3′,4′-Dihydro-2′-methyl-7′-nitro-4′- oxoquinazolin-3′-yl)-7-nitro-	337.5°	49
3-*o*-Ethoxyphenyl-6-iodo-	144–146°	34
3-*o*-Ethoxyphenyl-6-methyl-	138–140°	175
3-*p*-Ethoxyphenyl-6-methyl-	175°	195
6-Iodo-3-*o*-methoxyphenyl-	178–180°	34

(*Table continued*)

TABLE IV.30 (continued)

3,4-Dihydro-2-methyl-4-oxoquinazoline	M.p. (°c)	References
6-Iodo-3-m-methoxyphenyl-	175–177°	443
6-Iodo-3-p-methoxyphenyl-	165–166°	34
6,8-Diiodo-3-p-methoxyphenyl-	214–216°	179
6-Iodo-3-(3'-methyl-2'-pyridyl)-	159–161°	443
6-Iodo-3-1'-naphthyl-	155–157°	443
6-Iodo-3-2'-naphthyl-	253–255°	179, 443
6-Iodo-3-o-nitrophenyl-	214–215°	34
6-Iodo-3-m-nitrophenyl-	230–232°	34
6-Iodo-3-p-nitrophenyl-	208–210°	34, 443
6-Iodo-3-phenyl-	151–152°	34, 443
6-Iodo-3-2'-pyridyl-	159–161°	443
6-Iodo-3-o-tolyl-	142–144°	34
6-Iodo-3-m-tolyl-	179–181°	34
6-Iodo-3-p-tolyl-	154–155°	34
6,8-Diiodo-3-2',4',6'-tribromophenyl-	248–250°	179
6-Iodo-3-2',6'-xylyl-	152–154°	34
3-p-Iodophenyl-6-methyl-	190°	195
8-Methoxy-3-phenyl-	155°	129
6,7-Dimethoxy-3-o-tolyl-	218.5–219.5°	131
3-o-Methoxycarbonylphenyl-7-nitro-	175°	49
3-o-Methoxyphenyl-6-methyl-	176–178°	175
3-p-Methoxyphenyl-6-methyl-	148°; HCl 246°	177
3-p-Methoxyphenyl-8-methyl-	135°; HCl 220° (dec.)	176
3-p-Methoxyphenyl-7-nitro-	228°	49
6-Methyl-3-p-guanidinosulphamoyl- phenyl-	305°	140
6-Methyl-3-p-nitrophenyl-	249–250°	195
8-Methyl-3-o-nitrophenyl-	195°	176
8-Methyl-3-p-nitrophenyl-	197°	176
6-Methyl-3-phenyl-	124°; HCl 272°	177
8-Methyl-3-phenyl-	148°; HCl 212° (dec.)	176
6-Methyl-3-p-phenylsulphamoylphenyl-	226°	141
6-Methyl-3-p-2'-pyridylsulphamoyl- phenyl-	245°	140
6-Methyl-3-p-pyrimidin-2'-ylsulphamoyl- phenyl-	255–257°	140
6-Methyl-3-p-2'-thiazolylsulphamoyl- phenyl-	260°	140
6-Methyl-3-o-tolyl-	159–161°, 166°; HCl 248°	175, 177
6-Methyl-3-m-tolyl-	125°; HCl 252°	177
6-Methyl-3-p-tolyl-	136°; HCl 262°	177

(Table continued)

TABLE IV.30 *(continued)*

3,4-Dihydro-2-methyl-4-oxoquinazoline	M.p. (°c)	References
8-Methyl-3-*o*-tolyl-	140°	176
8-Methyl-3-*p*-tolyl-	140°	176
6-Methyl-3-*p*-(*o*-tolylsulphamoyl)phenyl-	235°	141
6,7-Methylenedioxy-3-*o*-tolyl-	159–160°	131
3-2′-Naphthyl-7-nitro-	218–219°	49
6-Nitro-3-*p*-nitrophenyl-	264°	130
7-Nitro-3-*o*-nitrophenyl-	170°	440
7-Nitro-3-*m*-nitrophenyl-	192°	440
7-Nitro-3-*p*-nitrophenyl-	298°	440
5-Nitro-3-phenyl-	233–234°	50
6-Nitro-3-phenyl-	219–220°	132
7-Nitro-3-phenyl-	209°	49
6-Nitro-3-*o*-tolyl-	179–179.5°, 175–177°	131, 183
7-Nitro-3-*o*-tolyl-	154°	440
7-Nitro-3-*p*-tolyl-	223°	440

TABLE IV.31. 2-Ethyl-3,4-dihydro-4-oxoquinazolines with Substituents in the Benzene Ring and in Position 3.

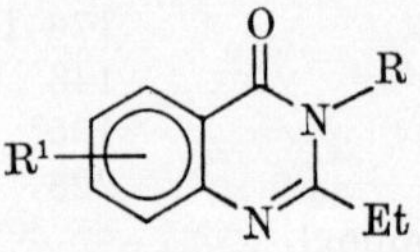

2-Ethyl-3,4-dihydro-4-oxoquinazoline	M.p. (°c)	References
6-Bromo-3-*p*-bromophenyl-	177°	195
6-Bromo-3-*p*-chlorophenyl-	171°	195, 196
6-Bromo-3-2′,4′-dichlorophenyl-	134°	195, 196
6-Bromo-3-*p*-guanidinosulphamoylphenyl-	296°	140
6-Bromo-3-*p*-iodophenyl-	188°	195
6-Bromo-3-*p*-methoxyphenyl-	154°	195
6-Bromo-3-*p*-2′-pyridylsulphamoylphenyl-	298–299°	140
6-Bromo-3-*p*-pyrimidin-2′-ylsulphamoylphenyl-	248°	140
6-Bromo-3-*p*-2′-thiazolylsulphamoylphenyl-	306°	140
3-*p*-Bromophenyl-6-chloro-	192°	195
3-*p*-Bromophenyl-6-methyl-	174°	195
6-Chloro-3-*o*-chlorophenyl-	115°	195
6-Chloro-3-*p*-chlorophenyl-	185°	195, 196
7-Chloro-3-2′-cyanoethyl-	173–174°	269

(Table continued)

TABLE IV.31 *(continued)*

2-Ethyl-3-4-dihydro-4-oxoquinazoline	M.p. (°c)	References
6-Chloro-3-2',4'-dichlorophenyl-	122°	195
6-Chloro-3-o-ethoxyphenyl-	135°	195
6-Chloro-3-p-ethoxyphenyl-	168°	195
6-Chloro-3-p-methoxyphenyl-	128°	195, 196
6-Chloro-3-phenyl-	145°	195
6-Chloro-3-p-2'-pyridylsulphamoylphenyl-	276°	140
6-Chloro-3-p-pyrimidin-2'-ylsulphamoylphenyl-	236–237°	140
6-Chloro-3-p-2'-thiazolylsulphamoylphenyl-	286°	140
6-Chloro-3-p-tolyl-	191°	195
3-o-Chlorophenyl-6-methyl-	88–90°	195, 196
3-p-Chlorophenyl-6-methyl-	178°	195
3-p-Ethoxy-6-methyl-	170°	195, 196
3-o-Ethoxyphenyl-6-methyl-	97°	195
3-Ethyl-5-nitro-	180–181°	123
3-2',4'-Dichlorophenyl-6-methyl-	135°	195, 196
3-p-N,N-Diethylsulphamoylphenyl-6-methyl-	206°	141
3-p-Guanidinosulphamoylphenyl-6-methyl-	295°	140
2-p-Iodophenyl-6-methyl-	204°	195
3-o-Methoxyphenyl-6-methyl-	178°	195
3-p-Methoxyphenyl-6-methyl-	145°	195
3,6-Dimethyl-	111°	206
3-Methyl-5-nitro-	197–198°	123
6-Methyl-3-p-Nitrophenyl-	238–240°	195
6-Methyl-3-phenyl-	152°	195
6-Methyl-3-p-2'-pyridylsulphamoylphenyl-	272°	140
6-Methyl-3-p-pyrimidin-2'-ylsulphamoylphenyl-	282–285°	140
6-Methyl-3-p-tolyl-	179–180°	195

TABLE IV.32. 2-Alkyl- (other than Methyl or Ethyl) 3,4-dihydro-4-oxo-quinazolines with Substituents in the Benzene Ring and in Position 3.

3,4-Dihydro-4-oxoquinazoline	M.p. (°c)	References
2-Benzyl-6-methoxy-3-methyl-	121°	207
2-Benzyl-8-methoxy-3-methyl-	138°	207
2-Benzyl-3,6-dimethyl-	116°	207
6-Bromo-2-p-dimethylaminostyryl-3-o-tolyl-	255°	274
6-Bromo-3-(3'-fluoro-4'-methyl)phenyl-2-(3',3',3'-trichloro-2'-hydroxy)propyl-	98–99°	188
6,8-Dibromo-3-(3'-fluoro-4'-methyl)phenyl-2-(3',3',3'-trichloro-2'-hydroxy)propyl-	218–219°	188
6-Bromo-3-m-fluorophenyl-2-(3',3',3'-trichloro-2'-hydroxy)propyl-	94–95°	188
6-Bromo-3-p-fluorophenyl-2-(3',3',3'-trichloro-2'-hydroxy)propyl-	81–82°	188
6-Bromo-3-p-methoxyphenyl-2-p-methoxystyryl-	235°	274
6-Bromo-3-p-methoxyphenyl-2-styryl-	211°	274
3-p-Bromophenyl-2-p-dimethylaminostyryl-6-methyl-	258°	274
3-2'-Carboxyethyl-6,8-diiodo-2-propyl-	198–199°	473
6-Chloro-3-o-chlorophenyl-2-p-dimethoxystyryl-	237°	274
6-Chloro-3-cyclohexyl-2-propyl-	115°; HCl 187°	128
6-Chloro-3-m-fluorophenyl-2-(3',3',3'-trichloro-2'-hydroxy)propyl-	226°	188
6-Chloro-3-p-methoxyphenyl-2-p-methoxystyryl-	210°	274
6-Chloro-3-phenyl-2-styryl-	236°	274
2-3',4'-Diethoxystyryl-8-methoxy-3-methyl-	176°	129
3-p-Ethoxyphenyl-2-p-methoxystyryl-6-methyl-	191°	274
3-p-Ethoxyphenyl-6-methyl-2-styryl-	205°	274
3-Ethyl-2-3',4'-diethoxystyryl-8-methoxy-	171°	129
3-Ethyl-8-methoxy-2-p-methoxystyryl-	174°	129
3-Ethyl-8-methoxy-2-styryl-	147°	129
8-Methoxy-2-3',4'-diethoxystyryl-3-phenyl-	199°	129
8-Methoxy-2-p-methoxystyryl-3-methyl-	152°	129
8-Methoxy-2-p-methoxystyryl-3-phenyl-	184°	129
8-Methoxy-3-methyl-2-styryl-	188°	129
8-Methoxy-3-phenyl-2-styryl-	205°	129

TABLE IV.33.   3,4-Dihydro-4-oxo-2-phenylquinazolines with Substituents in the Benzene Ring and in Position 3.

$$R^1 \underset{N}{\overset{O}{\underset{\|}{\bigcirc}}} \overset{R}{\underset{Ph}{N}}$$

3,4-Dihydro-4-oxo-2-phenylquinazoline	M.p. (°c)	References
5-Chloro-3-o-chlorophenyl-7-nitro-	170°	83
5-Chloro-3-m-chlorophenyl-7-nitro-	163°	83
5-Chloro-3-p-chlorophenyl-7-nitro-	169°	83
5-Chloro-3-1'-naphthyl-7-nitro-	183°	83
5-Chloro-3-2'-naphthyl-7-nitro-	200°	83
5-Chloro-7-nitro-3-phenyl-	176°	83
5-Chloro-7-nitro-3-o-tolyl-	160°	83
5-Chloro-7-nitro-3-m-tolyl-	161°	83
5-Chloro-7-nitro-3-p-tolyl-	179°	83
3-o-Chlorophenyl-5-iodo-7-nitro-	157°	83
3-m-Chlorophenyl-5-iodo-7-nitro-	160°	83
3-p-Chlorophenyl-5-iodo-7-nitro-	181°	83
5-Bromo-3-o-chlorophenyl-7-nitro-	154°	83
5-Bromo-3-m-chlorophenyl-7-nitro-	160°	83
5-Bromo-3-p-chlorophenyl-7-nitro-	165°	83
3-Bromo-3-1'-naphthyl-7-nitro-	189°	83
5-Bromo-3-2'-naphthyl-7-nitro-	211°	83
5-Bromo-7-nitro-3-phenyl-	184°	83
5-Bromo-7-nitro-3-o-tolyl-	157°	83
5-Bromo-7-nitro-3-m-tolyl-	145°	83
5-Bromo-7-nitro-3-p-tolyl-	162°	83
6-Bromo-3-phenyl-	186°	435
6-Bromo-3-m-tolyl-	145°	435
5-Iodo-3-1'-naphthyl-7-nitro-	193°	83
5-Iodo-3-2'-naphthyl-7-nitro-	209°	83
5-Iodo-7-nitro-3-phenyl-	190°	83
5-Iodo-7-nitro-3-o-tolyl-	162°	83
5-Iodo-7-nitro-3-m-tolyl-	147°	83
5-Iodo-7-nitro-3-p-tolyl-	165°	83
3-Methyl-8-nitro-	138°	77
7-Nitro-3-phenyl-	180°	139

TABLE IV.34.   3,4-Dihydro-3-(3′-(3-hydroxy-2-piperidyl)-2′-oxo)propyl-4-oxo-quinazolines with Substituents in the Benzene Ring.

3,4-Dihydro-3-(3′-(3-hydroxy-2-piperidyl)-2′-oxo)propyl-4-oxoquinazoline	M.p. (°c)	References
Unsubstituted	2 HCl·2 H_2O 204–206° (dec.); 2 HBr 152–160° (dec.); carbamoyl deriv. 216–217°	451, 460
Unsubstituted (*cis*)	O-Phenylcarbamoyl deriv. 226–227° (dec.); O-Phenyl-carbamoyl·2 HCl 234–235° (dec.)	464
Unsubstituted (*trans*)	2 HCl 224–226° (dec.); N-carbamoyl deriv. 193–194°	464
6,7-Benzo-	2 HCl·1.5 H_2O 202°	37
5-Bromo-	2 HCl·H_2O 217° (dec.)	31
6-Bromo-	2 HCl·0.5 H_2O 226°	31
7-Bromo-	2 HCl 215–216°	31
5,7-Dibromo-	2 HCl·2 H_2O 222°	37
5-Chloro-	2 HCl·H_2O 223° (dec.)	31
6-Chloro-	2 HCl·H_2O 255° (dec.)	31
7-Chloro-	2 HCl·2 H_2O 191–192° (dec.)	31
8-Chloro-	2 HCl·2 H_2O 214–217° (dec.)	31
5,6-Dichloro-	2 HCl.H_2O 231°	37
5,8-Dichloro-	2 HCl.H_2O 213°	37
6,7-Dichloro-	2 HCl·H_2O 234°	37
6,8-Dichloro-	2 HCl 240° (dec.)	37
5-Chloro-8-hydroxy-	2 HCl 218–219°	430
5-Chloro-6-methoxy-	2 HCl·2 H_2O 230° (dec.)	43
5-Chloro-8-methoxy-	2 HCl 218–219°	43
7-Chloro-6-methoxy-	2 HCl·H_2O 181° (dec.)	43
5-Chloro-6-methyl-	2 HCl·2 H_2O 235° (dec.)	43, 430, 451
5-Chloro-8-methyl-	2 HCl·H_2O 232° (dec.)	43
6-Chloro-5-methyl-	2 HCl·H_2O 245–250°	43
6-Chloro-7-methyl-	2 HCl·H_2O 232° (dec.)	43

(*Table continued*)

TABLE IV.34 (*continued*)

3,4-Dihydro-3-(3'-(3-hydroxy-2-piperidyl)-2'-oxo)propyl-4-oxoquinazoline	M.p. (°c)	References
6-Chloro-8-methyl-	2 HCl·0.5 H$_2$O 228° (dec.)	43
7-Chloro-6-methyl-	2 HCl·1.5 H$_2$O 229° (dec.)	43
7-Chloro-8-methyl-	2 HCl·0.5 H$_2$O 246° (dec.)	43
8-Chloro-6-methyl-	2 HCl·2 H$_2$O 172° (dec.)	43
5-Ethyl-	2 HCl·H$_2$O 217–219° (dec.)	57
5-Fluoro-	2 HCl·0.5 H$_2$O 216° (dec.)	57, 430, 451
6-Hydroxy-	2 HCl·2 H$_2$O 196–198° (dec.)	430
5-Iodo-	HCl 252° (dec.)	57
5-Methoxy-	2 HCl·2 H$_2$O 224° (dec.)	430, 451
6-Methoxy-	HCl·2 H$_2$O 196–198°	31
7-Methoxy-	2 HCl·1.5 H$_2$O 174°	31
5-Methyl-	2 HCl·H$_2$O 225° (dec.)	31
6-Methyl-	2 HCl·2 H$_2$O 165–167° (dec.)	31
7-Methyl-	2 HCl·H$_2$O 212–213° (dec.)	31
8-Methyl-	HCl·H$_2$O 222–223° (dec.)	31
5,6-Dimethyl-	2 HCl·1.5 H$_2$O 229° (dec.)	37
5,7-Dimethyl-	2 HCl·1.5 H$_2$O 193°	37
5,8-Dimethyl-	2 HCl·H$_2$O 218°	37
6,7-Dimethyl-	2 HCl·2 H$_2$O 189°	37
6,8-Dimethyl-	2 HCl·H$_2$O 222°	37
7,8-Dimethyl-	2 HCl·H$_2$O 223°	37
5-Methylthio-	2 HCl.2 H$_2$O 229° (dec.)	57, 451
5-Methylsulphonyl-	2 HCl.H$_2$O 246–248° (dec.)	57
5-Nitro-	2 HCl 209–210° (dec.)	57, 451
6-Phenyl-	75°	31
7-Phenyl-	2 HCl 188–189°	31
5-Propyl-	2 HCl·1.5 H$_2$O 213° (dec.)	57
5,6-Tetramethylene-	2 HCl·1.5 H$_2$O 207°	37
6,7-Tetramethylene-	2 HCl·1.5 H$_2$O 201°	37
5-Trifluoromethyl-	2 HCl 211° (dec.)	57, 430, 451

TABLE IV.35.   3-(3′-(1-Ethoxycarbonyl-3-methoxy-2-piperidyl)-2′-oxo)-propyl-4-oxoquinazolines with Substituents in the Benzene Ring.

3-(3′-(1-Ethoxycarbonyl-3-methoxy-2-piperidyl)-2′-oxo)propyl-4-oxoquinazoline	M.p. (°c)	References
Unsubstituted	138–140°	451, 460
Unsubstituted (cis)	133–134°	464
6,7-Benzo-	167–168°	37
5-Bromo-	gum	430, 451
5-Chloro-	gum	430
6-Chloro-	124–125°	430, 451
7-Chloro-	125–126°	31, 430
8-Chloro-	153–154°	31, 430
6,7-Dichloro-	129°	37
6,8-Dichloro-	130°	37, 430, 451
5-Chloro-8-methoxy-	145–146°	43, 430
5-Chloro-6-methyl-	gum	430, 451
5-Chloro-8-methyl-	140–142°	43
6-Chloro-5-methyl-	134–136°	43
6-Chloro-7-methyl-	140–141°	43
6-Chloro-8-methyl-	128°	43
7-Chloro-6-methyl-	151–152°	43
8-Chloro-6-methyl-	174–176°	43
5-Fluoro-	gum	430, 451
5-Methoxy-	gum	430, 451
6-Methoxy-	102–103°	31, 430
5-Methyl-	gum	430
6-Methyl-	113–115°	430
7-Methyl-	oil	430
8-Methyl-	143–145°	31, 430, 451
5,6-Dimethyl-	gum	430, 451
6,7-Dimethyl-	140–141°	37
6,8-Dimethyl-	147–148°	37
6-Phenyl-	134–136°	31
7-Phenyl-	114–116°	31
6,7-Tetramethylene-	116–117°	37
5-Trifluoromethyl-	gum	430, 451

TABLE IV.36.   3-(3'-(3-Methoxy-2-piperidyl)-2'-oxo)propyl-4-oxo-
quinazolines with Substituents in the Benzene Ring.

3-(3'-(3-Methoxy-2-piperidyl)-2'-oxo)propyl-4-oxoquinazoline	M.p. (°c)	References
Unsubstituted	202–204°; 2 HCl·H$_2$O 158–160° (dec.)	451, 460
6,7-Benzo-	2 HCl·0.5 H$_2$O 232°	37
5-Bromo-	2 HCl 211° (dec.)	31, 430, 451
6-Bromo-	2 HCl 209°	31
7-Bromo-	2 HCl·H$_2$O 216–217°	31
5,7-Dibromo-	2 HCl·2 H$_2$O 214°	37
5-Chloro-	2 HCl·0.5 H$_2$O 200° (dec.)	31, 430
6-Chloro-	2 HCl·H$_2$O 205–206° (dec.)	31, 430, 451
7-Chloro-	2 HCl·0.5 H$_2$O 209–210° (dec.)	31, 430
8-Chloro-	2 HCl·0.5 H$_2$O 209–211° (dec.)	31, 430
5,6-Dichloro-	2 HCl·0.5 H$_2$O 227–228°	37
5,8-Dichloro-	2 HCl·0.5 H$_2$O 205°	37
6,7-Dichloro-	2 HCl 223–224°	37
6,8-Dichloro-	2 HCl 235° (dec.)	37, 430, 451
5-Chloro-6-methoxy-	2 HCl·0.5 H$_2$O 227° (dec.)	43
5-Chloro-8-methoxy-	2 HCl·H$_2$O 201–202° (dec.)	43, 430
7-Chloro-6-methoxy-	2 HCl·H$_2$O 205° (dec.)	43
5-Chloro-6-methyl-	2 HCl 226° (dec.)	43, 430, 451
5-Chloro-8-methyl-	2 HCl·0.5 H$_2$O 213° (dec.)	43
6-Chloro-5-methyl-	2 HCl·H$_2$O 245–248° (dec.)	43
6-Chloro-7-methyl-	2 HCl·0.5 H$_2$O 222° (dec.)	43
6-Chloro-8-methyl-	2 HCl 240° (dec.)	43
7-Chloro-6-methyl-	2 HCl 222–223° (dec.)	43
7-Chloro-8-methyl-	2 HCl·0.5 H$_2$O 240° (dec.)	43
8-Chloro-6-methyl-	2 HCl·0.5 H$_2$O 211° (dec.)	43
5-Ethyl-	2 HCl·H$_2$O 210° (dec.)	57
5-Fluoro-	2 HCl 206° (dec.)	57, 430, 451
5-Iodo-	2 HCl·1.5 H$_2$O 253° (dec.)	57
5-Methoxy-	2 HCl·H$_2$O 173–174° (dec.)	31, 430, 451
6-Methoxy-	2 HCl·2 H$_2$O 165–168° (dec.)	31
7-Methoxy-	HCl·H$_2$O 221°	31

(*Table continued*)

TABLE IV.36 (*continued*)

3-(3'-(3-Methoxy-2-piperidyl)-2'-oxo)propyl-4-oxoquinazoline	M.p. (°c)	References
5-Methyl-	2 HCl·H$_2$O 223°	31
6-Methyl-	2 HCl·2 H$_2$O 164–166° (dec.)	31, 430
7-Methyl-	2 HCl·0.5 H$_2$O 229° (dec.)	31
8-Methyl-	2 HCl 228–229°	31
5,6-Dimethyl-	2 HCl·0.5 H$_2$O 223° (dec.)	37, 430, 451
5,7-Dimethyl-	2 HCl·1.5 H$_2$O 173°	37
5,8-Dimethyl-	2 HCl·0.5 H$_2$O 227°	37
6,7-Dimethyl-	2 HCl·1.5 H$_2$O 219–220°	37
6,8-Dimethyl-	2 HCl 232°	37
7,8-Dimethyl-	2 HCl·0.5 H$_2$O 231°	37
5-Methylsulphonyl-	2 HCl 217–219° (dec.)	57
5-Methylthio-	2 HCl·H$_2$O 218–219° (dec.)	57
5-Nitro-	2 HCl 212–213° (dec.)	57
6-Phenyl-	2 HCl·H$_2$O 207–208°	31
7-Phenyl-	2 HCl·1.5 H$_2$O 232–233°	31
5-Propyl-	2 HCl 202° (dec.)	57
5,6-Tetramethylene-	2 HCl·2 H$_2$O 226°	37
6,7-Tetramethylene-	2 HCl·0.5 H$_2$O 230°	37
5-Trifluoromethyl-	2 HCl 215° (dec.)	57, 430, 451

TABLE IV.37.   Miscellaneous 3,4-Dihydro-4-oxo-3-(2'-oxo-3'-(2-piperidyl))-propylquinazolines.

3,4-Dihydro-4-oxoquinazoline	M.p. (°c)	References
3-(3'-(1-Benzoyl-4-hydroxy-3-piperidyl)-2'-oxo)propyl-	HCl 190–192° (dec.)	57
3-(3'-(1-Benzoyl-2-piperidyl)-2'-oxo)propyl-	HCl 195–196°	57
3-(3'-(1-2',4'-Dinitrobenzoyl-3'-piperidyl)-2'-oxo)propyl-	231–233° (dec.)	57
3-(3'-(4-Hydroxy-2-piperidyl)-2'-oxo)propyl-	2 HCl 232–233° (dec.); O-Phenylcarbamoyl deriv. 190–191° (dec.)	257
3-(3'-(4-Hydroxy-3-piperidyl)-2'-oxo)propyl-	2 HCl 240–242° (dec.)	256
3-(3'-(5-Hydroxy-2-piperidyl)-2'-oxo)propyl-	130–133°; 2 HCl 225–227° (dec.)	457, 459
3-(3'-(5-Hydroxy-1,4,5,6-tetrahydro-2-pyridyl)-2'-oxo)propyl-	229–230°	457, 459
2-Methyl-3-(2'-oxo-3'-(2-piperidyl))propyl-	2 HCl 187–189° (dec.)	142
2-Methyl-3-(2'-oxo-3'-(1,4,5,6-tetrahydro-2-pyridyl))propyl-	198–198.5°; 2 HCl·2 H₂O 187–189° (dec.)	142, 457
3-(2'-Oxo-3'-(2-piperidyl))propyl-	138–140°; 2 HCl 212–214°	142, 457
3-(2'-Oxo-3'-(3-piperidyl))propyl-	2 HCl 235–237° (dec.)	256
3-(2'-Oxo-3'-(1,4,5,6-tetrahydro-2-pyridyl))propyl-	176–178°	142
3-(3'-(1-Phenylsulphonyl-2-piperidyl)-2'-oxo)propyl-	166–167°	142

TABLE IV.38.   3,4-Dihydro-4-oxo-3-(2'-oxo-3'-(pyrrolidin-2-yl))
propylquinazolines.

3,4-Dihydro-4-oxoquinazoline	M.p. (°c)	References
3-(3'-(1-Benzoylpyrrolidin-2-yl)-2'-oxo)propyl-	HCl 200–202° (dec.)	57
3-(3'-(1-2',4'-Dinitrobenzoyl-pyrrolidin-2-yl)-2'-oxo)propyl-	215–217° (dec.)	57
3-(3'-(1-Ethoxycarbonyl-3-methoxy-methylpyrrolidin-2-yl)-2'-oxo)propyl-	94–96°	57
3-(3'-(1-Ethoxycarbonyl-4-methoxy-methylpyrrolidin-2-yl)-2'-oxo)propyl-	100–102°	57
3-(3'-(1-Ethoxycarbonyl-3-methyl-pyrrolidin-2-yl)-2'-oxo)propyl-	149–150°	57
3-(3'-(1-Ethoxycarbonyl-4-methyl-pyrrolidin-2-yl)-2'-oxo)propyl-	123–124°	450
3-(3'-(4,5-Dihydro-2-pyrrolyl)-2'-oxo)propyl-	207–208°	142
3-(3'-(3-Hydroxymethylpyrrolidin-2-yl)-2'-oxo)propyl-	2 HCl 230° (dec.); O-Phenylcarbamoyl deriv. 185–187°	57
3-(3'-(4-Hydroxymethylpyrrolidin-2-yl)-2'-oxo)propyl-	2 HCl · H₂O 228° (dec.)	57
3-(3'-(3-Methylpyrrolidin-2-yl)-2'-oxo)propyl-	2 HCl 237° (dec.)	57
3-(2'-Oxo-3'-(pyrrolidin-2-yl))propyl-	2 HCl 170° (dec.)	57

TABLE IV.39.   Quinazolines with Hydroxy Groups in the Benzene Ring.

Quinazoline	M.p. (°c)	References
7-Allyl-8-hydroxy-	109.5°	405
2-o-Aminophenyl-8-hydroxy-4,5,7-trimethyl-	211°	407
2-o-(4′,5′-dimethyl-2′-imidazolylazo)-phenyl-8-hydroxy-4,5,7-trimethyl-	175–178°	412
5-Hydroxy-	229–230° (dec.)	403
6-Hydroxy-	238–239° (dec.)	404
7-Hydroxy-	251–252° (dec.)	403
8-Hydroxy-	149–150°; 3-methiodide 192° (dec.)	404, 405
8-Hydroxy-2-o-(2′-hydroxy-5′-methyl-phenylazo)phenyl-4,5,7-trimethyl-	199°	407
8-Hydroxy-4-methyl-	158–159°	405
5-Hydroxy-6,8-dimethyl-	208–209°	406
8-Hydroxy-2,4-dimethyl-	112–113°	8, 411
8-Hydroxy-4,5,7-trimethyl-2-o-nitro-phenyl-	168.5–169°	407
8-Hydroxy-4-methyl-2-phenyl-	110–112°	8
5-Hydroxy-6,8-dimethyl-2-phenyl-	248.5–250°	406
8-Hydroxy-4-propyl-	100°	405

TABLE IV.40.   3,4-Dihydro-4-oxoquinazolines with Hydroxy Groups in the
Benzene Ring.

3,4-Dihydro-4-oxoquinazoline	M.p. (°c)	References
3-Benzyl-8-hydroxy-2-methyl-	109°	129
3-Butyl-8-hydroxy-2-methyl-	109°	129
3-Ethyl-8-hydroxy-	—	417
3-Ethyl-8-hydroxy-7-(4'-(3,4-dihydro-3-ethyl-8-hydroxy-4-oxoquinazolin-7-ylmethyl)pyrazin-1'-yl)methyl-	215°	305
3-Ethyl-8-hydroxy-2-methyl-	112°	129
3-Ethyl-8-hydroxy-2-methyl-7-piperidino-methyl-	91°	305
3-Ethyl-8-hydroxy-2-styryl-	189°	129
8-Hydroxy-	295°	46, 417
8-Hydroxy-7-(4'-(3,4-dihydro-8-hydroxy-4-oxo-3-propylquinazolin-7-ylmethyl)-pyrazin-1'-yl)methyl-3-propyl-	230°	305
8-Hydroxy-3-isopentyl-2-methyl-	103°	129
8-Hydroxy-2-p-methoxystyryl-3-methyl-	219°	129
7-Hydroxy-2-methyl-	310° (dec.); acetyl deriv. 266°	125, 408
8-Hydroxy-2-methyl-	248°	129
8-Hydroxy-2,3-dimethyl-	160°	129
8-Hydroxy-3-methyl-7-(4'-(3,4-dihydro-8-hydroxy-3-methyl-4-oxoquinazolin-7-ylmethyl)pyrazin-1'-yl)methyl-	259°	305
8-Hydroxy-2,3-dimethyl-7-(4'-(3,4-dihydro-8-hydroxy-2,3-dimethyl-4-oxoquinazolin-7-ylmethyl)pyrazin-1'-yl)methyl-	277°	305
8-Hydroxy-2-methyl-3-pentyl-	55°	129
8-Hydroxy-2-methyl-3-phenethyl-	113°	129
8-Hydroxy-2-methyl-3-phenyl-	222°	129
8-Hydroxy-2-methyl-7-piperidinomethyl-3-propyl-	104°	305
8-Hydroxy-2-methyl-3-propyl-	119°	129
8-Hydroxy-3-methyl-2-styryl-	218°	129
6,8-Dihydroxy-2-phenyl-	—	409
8-Hydroxy-3-phenyl-2-styryl-	243°	129
8-Hydroxy-2-styryl-	252°	129

TABLE IV.41.   1-Substituted (and Unsubstituted) 1,2,3,4-Tetrahydro-2,4-dioxoquinazolines.

1,2,3,4-Tetrahydro-2,4-dioxo-quinazoline	M.p. (°c)	References
Unsubstituted	348°, 356°, ~ 360°	308, 309, 310, 317, 318, 326, 329, 337, 341, 428
1-Benzoyl-	206° (dec.)	231
1-Benzyl-	> 360° (dec.)	331
1-Ethyl-	215–217°	347
1-Methyl-	257–259°, 265–266°, 265°	329, 330, 380
1-Phenyl-	306–309°, 360° (dec.)	331, 347a, 380

TABLE IV.42.   3-Substituted 1,2,3,4-Tetrahydro-2,4-dioxoquinazolines.

1,2,3,4-Tetrahydro-2,4-dioxo-quinazoline	M.p. (°c)	References
3-Allyl-	183°, 187–189°	333, 429
3-p-Aminophenyl-	311°	368
3-Benzoyl-	216–217° (dec.)	231
3-Benzyl-	227–228°	317, 357
3-m-Bromophenyl-	295–298°	327
3-Butyl-	156–157°	352, 357
3-Carboxymethyl-	296–298°	366
3-o-Carboxyphenyl-	298–300°, 292–293°, 310°	317, 367, 418
3-2′-Chloroisopropyl-	182–183°	359
3-o-Chlorophenyl-	231°	418
3-m-Chlorophenyl-	260.5–261.5°	376, 418
3-p-Chlorophenyl-	288°	418

(Table continued)

TABLE IV.42 (*continued*)

1,2,3,4-Tetrahydro-2,4-dioxo-quinazoline	M.p. (°c)	References
3-4'-(4-*m*-Chlorophenylpiperazin-1-yl)butyl-	192–193°; HCl 243–245°	421
3-2'-(4-*m*-Chlorophenylpiperazin-1-yl)ethyl-	212.5–214.5°; maleate 210.5–211.5° (dec.)	421
3-5'-(4-*m*-Chlorophenylpiperazin-1-yl)pentyl-	180–184°; HCl 206–208°	421
3-3'-(4-*o*-Chlorophenylpiperazin-1-yl)propyl-	185–186°; HCl > 260°	421
3-3'-(4-*m*-Chlorophenylpiperazin-1-yl)propyl-	195–196°; HCl 240–241°; methyl sulphate 204–206°	421
3-3'-(4-*p*-Chlorophenylpiperazin-1-yl)propyl-	228.5–230°; maleate 195–197° (dec.)	421
3-2'-Chloropropyl-	205.5–206°	359
3-3'-Chloropropyl-	176–177°	359
3-Cyclohexyl-	270–271°	352, 357
3-4'-Diethylaminobut-2'-ynyl-	149–151°	422
3-2'-Diethylaminoethyl-	148–149°; HCl 265–266°; picrate 219–220° (dec.); methiodide 245° (dec.)	420
3-3'-Diethylaminopropyl-	HCl 227–228°	421
3-3',4'-Dimethoxyphenethyl-	202–203°	421
3-2'-Dimethylaminoethyl-	HCl 219–221°	360
3-3'-Dimethylaminopropyl-	HCl 180–182°	360
3-Ethyl-	196–198°	333, 347, 357, 360, 362
3-3'-(4-*p*-Fluorophenyl-piperazin-1-yl)propyl-	194–195°; HCl 259–260°	421
3-2'-Hydroxyethyl-	354°, 246–249°, 257°	359, 360, 366, 420
3-3'-(4-2'-Hydroxyethyl-piperazin-1-yl)propyl-	dimaleate 181–183°	421
3-2'-Hydroxyisopropyl-	214.5°	359
3-3'-(4-Hydroxy-4-phenyl-piperidino)propyl-	HCl 250–250.5° (dec.)	421
3-2'-(3-Indolyl)ethyl-	275–278°	421
3-Isopropyl-	188°	357
3-*m*-Methoxyphenyl-	272°	418
3-*p*-Methoxyphenyl-	229°, 300°	368, 418
3-Methyl-	238°, 241–243°	329, 334, 347, 357, 362, 366, 421

(*Table continued*)

TABLE IV.42 (*continued*)

1,2,3,4-Tetrahydro-2,4-dioxo-quinazoline	M.p. (°c)	References
3-(3'-Methyl-2'-pyridyl)-	236–237°	360
3-2'-(4-Methyl-1,2,3,4-tetrahydro-quinoxalin-1-yl)ethyl-	2 HCl·MeOH 210° (dec.)	421
3-3'-(4-Methyl-1,2,3,4-tetrahydro-quinoxalin-1-yl)propyl-	2 HCl 217–218°	421
3-3'-Morpholinopropyl-	168–169°; HCl 242–243°	421
3-1'-Naphthyl-	273–274°, 268°	352, 368
3-2'-Naphthyl-	291°	418
3-Phenyl-	272°, 280°	126, 328, 333, 335a, 348, 350, 352, 364, 368, 379, 382, 383, 426
3-Phenethyl-	215°, 216°	421
3-3'-(4-Phenethylpiperazin-1-yl)propyl-	166–167°; 2 HCl > 260°	421
3-(4'-Phenylpiperazin-1'-yl)-	307–309° (dec.); 2 HCl > 260°	421
3-4'-(4-Phenylpiperazin-1-yl)butyl-	196.5–197.5°; 2 HCl 276–277°	421
3-2'-(4-Phenylpiperazin-1-yl)-yl)ethyl-	244–245°; HCl > 270°	421
3-5'-(4-Phenylpiperazin-1-yl)-pentyl-	172–173°; 2 HCl 211–213° (dec.)	421
3-3'-(4-Phenylpiperazin-1-yl)-propyl-	202–203°; 2 HCl·H₂O 224–226° (dec.)	421
3-3'-(4-Phenylpiperidino)propyl-	172–176°; maleate 210–212°	421
3-Propyl-	187–188°	252, 257
3-Prop-2'-ynyl-	231–233°	422
3-2'-Pyridyl-	> 260°; 0.25 H₂O 253–255°; HCl 265–267° (dec.)	360, 421
3-3'-Pyridylmethyl-	238–239°; HCl 243–247°	421
3-p-Sulphamoylphenyl-	> 320° (dec.)	355
3-t-Butyl-	198–199°	360
3-o-Tolyl-	254–255°, 241–242°	368, 382
3-m-Tolyl-	254°, 251°	376, 418
3-p-Tolyl-	270°, 265–266°	327, 352, 376, 418
3-3'-(4-m-Trifluoromethylphenyl-piperazin-1-yl)propyl-	maleate 203–204.5° (dec.)	421

202 Chapter IV

TABLE IV.43. 1,2,3,4-Tetrahydro-2,4-dioxoquinazolines with Substituents in the Benzene Ring.

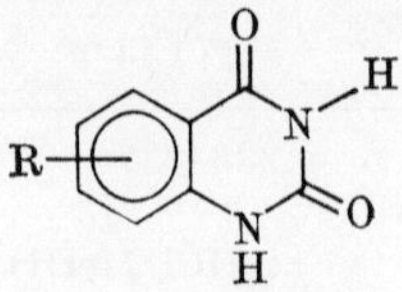

1,2,3,4-Tetrahydro-2,4-dioxoquinazoline	M.p. (°c)	References
6,7-Benzo-	342°, 358–359°	319, 336
7,8-Benzo-	341°	477
5-Diazoacetyl-	157–159°	400
6-Methyl-	316°	39
7-Methyl-	320°, 317°	72, 336, 358
8-Methyl-	283°	342
5-Nitro-	357–358°	322
6-Nitro-	331–332°	48, 322, 425
7-Nitro-	337° (dec.)	322, 336, 385
8-Nitro-	272–273°	322
6,8-Dinitro-	274–275°, 263–265°	48, 321, 322
6-Nitro-7-methyl-	326° (dec.)	358
5-Phenylacetyl-	257–261°	399
7-t-Butyl-	270–271°	320
7-Trifluoromethyl-	315–320°	319

TABLE IV.44. 3-Substituted (and Unsubstituted) 1,2,3,4-Tetrahydro-2,4-dioxoquinazolines with Halogens in the Benzene Ring.

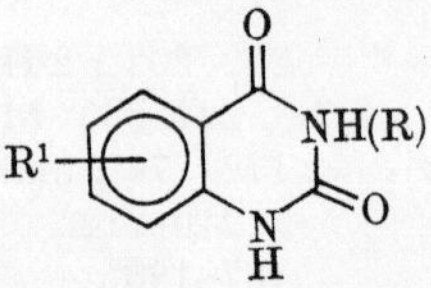

1,2,3,4-Tetrahydro-2,4-dioxoquinazoline	M.p. (°c)	References
3-2′-Aminoethyl-6-bromo-	270–272°	420
6-Bromo-	354°	343, 368
6,8-Dibromo-	299–302°, 305–306°, 291–292°	319, 321, 323
6-Bromo-3-2′-bromoethyl-	287–290°	420
6-Bromo-3-p-bromophenyl-	325.5–328°	375
6-Bromo-3-2′-chloroethyl-	273–274°	420
6,8-Dibromo-3-ethyl-	252.5–253°	321, 323
6-Bromo-3-2′-hydroxyethyl-	269–271°	420

(*Table continued*)

TABLE IV.44 (*continued*)

1,2,3,4-Tetrahydro-2,4-dioxoquinazoline	M.p. (°c)	References
6,8-Dibromo-3-methyl-	268°	321
6-Bromo-3-2'-*N*-methylanilinoethyl-	228–229°	420
6,8-Dibromo-3-phenyl-	282–283°	323
6,8-Dibromo-3-propyl-	225°	321
6-Chloro-	345–348°	336
7-Chloro-	347–348°	336
6,8-Dichloro-	296–297°	323, 324, 325
6-Chloro-3-*p*-chlorophenyl-	325°	373, 375, 379
7-Chloro-3-*m*-chlorophenyl-	312°	373, 375, 376
8-Chloro-3-*o*-chlorophenyl-	223–224°	373, 375
6-Chloro-3-2'-(4-*m*-chlorophenylpiperazin-1-yl)ethyl-	228–230°; maleate 220–222°	421
6-Chloro-3-3'-(4-*m*-chlorophenylpiperazin-1-yl)propyl-	198–199°; maleate 223–225°	421
6-Chloro-3-3'-(4-*p*-chlorophenylpiperazin-1-yl)propyl-	259–262°; maleate 203–205°	421
5,8-Dichloro-3-2',5'-dichlorophenyl-	281.8–283°	373, 375
6,8-Dichloro-3-ethyl-	244.5–253°	323
6-Chloro-1-methyl-3-3'-(4-phenylpiperazin-1-yl)propyl-[a]	2 HCl > 250°	421
6-Chloro-3-3'-(4-phenethylpiperazin-1-yl)-propyl-	dimaleate 233–234°	421
6-Chloro-3-phenyl-	292°, 312°	379, 386
6-Chloro-3-(4'-phenylpiperazin-1'-yl)-	> 250°	421
6-Chloro-3-4'-(4-phenylpiperazin-1-yl)-butyl-	205–210°; maleate 220–222°	421
6-Chloro-3-2'-(4-phenylpiperazin-1-yl)-ethyl-	251–253°; maleate 230–231°	421
6-Chloro-3-5'-(4-phenylpiperazin-1-yl)-pentyl-	185–187°; HCl 226–230°	421
6-Chloro-3-3'-(4-phenylpiperazin-1-yl)-propyl-	227–230°; maleate 213–216°	421
6-Chloro-3-3'-(4-phenylpiperidino)propyl-	198–199.5°; maleate 221.5–222.5° (dec.)	421
7-Chloro-6-sulphamoyl-	0.5 H₂O 275°	292
6,8-Diiodo-	325–327°	323
6,8-Diiodo-3-ethyl-	275–276°	323

[a] This compound is an $N_{(1)}$-substituted derivative.

8+Q.

TABLE IV.45. 3-Substituted (and Unsubstituted) 1,2,3,4-Tetrahydro-2,4-dioxoquinazolines with Hydroxy or Alkoxy Groups in the Benzene Ring.

1,2,3,4-Tetrahydro-2,4-dioxo-quinazoline	M.p. (°c)	References
6-Hydroxy-	> 360° (subl.)	344
5,6,7-Trihydroxy-	261–264° (dec.)	332
5-Methoxy-	308°	336
6-Methoxy-	316–318°	336, 424
7-Methoxy-	299–301°, 300–301°, 312–320°	45, 336, 424
8-Methoxy-	258–259°	336, 344
6,8-Dimethoxy-	323–325°	336
5,6,7-Trimethoxy-	261–264°	332
6-Methoxy-3-p-methoxy-phenyl-	279°	377, 379

TABLE IV.46. 1,3-Disubstituted 1,2,3,4-Tetrahydro-2,4-dioxoquinazolines.

1,2,3,4-Tetrahydro-2,4-dioxo-quinazoline	M.p. (°c)	References
1,3-Dibenzyl-	153–154°	231
1,3-bis-2′-Chloroethyl-	127–128°	359
3-(4′-bis-β-Chloroethylaminobut-2′-ynyl)-1-methyl-	HCl 172–175° (dec.)	422
3-3′-(4-m-Chlorophenylpiperazin-1-yl)propyl-1-methyl-	103–105°; HCl 256–258°	421
3-4′-Diethylaminobutyl-1-methyl-	HCl 184–186°	422

(Table continued)

TABLE IV.46 (*continued*)

1,2,3,4-Tetrahydro-2,4-dioxo-quinazoline	M.p. (°c)	References
1,3-bis-(4′-Diethylaminobut-2′-ynyl)-	66–68°	422
1-(4′-Diethylaminobut-2′-ynyl)-3-methyl-	HCl 195–197°	422
3-(4′-Diethylaminobut-2′-ynyl)-1-methyl-	HCl 190–194°	422
1,3-bis-2′-Diethylaminoethyl-	209–210°/5 mm; 227°/1.5 mm; dipicrate 212° (dec.); dimethiodide 354–355° (dec.)	359, 423
1,3-bis-2′-Dimethylaminoethyl-	202°/1 mm; 2 HBr 124° (dec.); dipicrate 213–214°; dimethiodide 305° (dec.)	359
1,3-Diethyl-	105–106°, 110–111°	12, 347
1-Ethyl-3-methyl-	138–139°	347
3-Ethyl-1-methyl-	133–134°	347
1,3-Dimethyl-	167–168°	48, 255, 329, 334, 380, 397
3-Methyl-1-(4′-morpholinobut-2′-ynyl)-	HCl 238–241° (dec.)	422
1-Methyl-3-phenyl-	233°	351, 387
3-Methyl-1-phenyl-	234°	380
1-Methyl-3-3′-(4-phenylpiperazin-1-yl)propyl-	99–101°; 2 HCl 247–249°	421
1-Methyl-3-3′-(4-phenylpiperidino)-propyl-	maleate 185–188° (dec.)	421
1-Methyl-3-prop-2′-ynyl-	205–207°	422
3-Methyl-1-prop-2′-ynyl-	187–189°	422
3-Methyl-1-(4′-N-pyrrolidinylbut-2′-ynyl)-	HCl 212–216° (dec.)	422
1-Methyl-3-p-tolyl-	254°	351
1,3-bis-Prop-2′-ynyl-	168–170°	422

TABLE IV.47.   3- and 1,3-Substituted 1,2,3,4-Tetrahydro-2,4-dioxo-
quinazolines with Substituents in the Benzene Ring.

1,2,3,4-Tetrahydro-2,4-dioxo- quinazolines	M.p. (°c)	References
7,8-Benzo-3-1'-naphthyl-	333–334°	376
5-Bromoacetyl-3-methyl-	200–201°	400
6-Butyl-3-p-butylphenyl-	—	377
5-Decyl-3-m-decylphenyl-	—	377
5-(1'-Hydroxy-2'-morpholino)ethyl- 3-methyl-	HCl 200° (dec.); picrate 150° (dec.)	400
1,3-Dimethyl-5-nitro-	275–277°	322
1,3-Dimethyl-6-nitro-	213–214°	322
1,3-Dimethyl-7-nitro-	229–230°	322
1,3-Dimethyl-8-nitro-	217–218°	322
5-Methyl-3-phenyl-	256°	379
6-Methyl-3-phenyl-	296°	379, 419
8-Methyl-3-phenyl-	256°	419
6-Methyl-3-p-tolyl	288–290°	373, 375, 377, 379
7-Methyl-3-m-tolyl-	290.5–292.5°	373, 375, 377, 379
8-Methyl-3-o-tolyl-	225–227°	373, 375, 377
5,8-Dimethyl-3-2',5'-xylyl-	—	377
6,8-Dimethyl-3-2',4'-xylyl-	253–254.5°	375
6-Nitro-3-3'-(4-phenylpiperazin-1- yl)propyl-	208–210°	421
5-Octadecyl-3-m-octadecylphenyl-	—	377

6. References

1. *Handbook for Chemical Society Authors*, London Chemical Society, Burlington House, W.1., 1960.
2. Gabriel and Posner, *Ber. Deut. Chem. Ges.*, **28**, 1029 (1895).
3. Gabriel and Stelzner, *Ber. Deut. Chem. Ges.*, **29**, 1300 (1896).
4. Schofield, *J. Chem. Soc.*, **1952**, 1927.
5. Kippenberg, *Ber. Deut. Chem. Ges.*, **30**, 1130 (1897).
6. Hanschke, *Ber. Deut. Chem. Ges.*, **32**, 2021 (1899).
7. Drawert, *Ber. Deut. Chem. Ges.*, **32**, 1259 (1899).

8. Schofield, *J. Chem. Soc.*, **1954**, 4034.

9. Tröger and Bohnekamp, *J. Prakt. Chem.*, **117** (2), 161 (1927).

10. Armarego and Smith, *J. Chem. Soc.* (C), **1966**, 234.

11. Elderfield and Serlin, *J. Org. Chem.*, **16**, 1669 (1951).

12. Bogert and May, *J. Am. Chem. Soc.*, **31**, 507 (1909).

13. Stefanović, Lorenc, and Mihailović, *Rec. Trav. Chim.*, **80**, 149 (1961).

14. Hayashi, Yamanaka, and Higashino, *Chem. Pharm. Bull.* (*Japan*), **7**, 149 (1959).

15. Higashino, *J. Pharm. Soc. Japan*, **79**, 699 (1959).

16. Hayashi and Higashino, *Chem. Pharm. Bull.* (*Japan*), **12**, 43 (1964).

17. Yamanaka, *Chem. Pharm. Bull.* (*Japan*), **7**, 152 (1959).

18. Breukink and Verkade, *Rec. Trav. Chim.*, **79**, 443 (1960).

19. Rosowsky, Protopapa, Burke, and Modest, *J. Org. Chem.*, **29**, 2881 (1964).

20. Albert and Barlin, *J. Chem. Soc.*, **1962**, 3129.

20a. Metlesics, Silverman, Toome, and Sternbach, *J. Org. Chem.*, **31**, 1007 (1966).

21. Albert and Phillips, *J. Chem. Soc.*, **1956**, 1294.

22. Mason, *J. Chem. Soc.*, **1957**, 4874.

23. Culbertson, Decius, and Christensen, *J. Am. Chem. Soc.*, **74**, 4834 (1952).

24. Brown and Mason, *J. Chem. Soc.*, **1956**, 3443.

25. Albert and Howell, *J. Chem. Soc.*, **1962**, 1591.

26. Niementowski, *J. Prakt. Chem.*, **51** (2), 564 (1895).

27. Armarego, *J. Appl. Chem.*, **11**, 70 (1961).

28. Chiang and Li, *Hua Hsüeh Hsüeh Pao*, **22**, 235 (1956); *Chem. Abstr.*, **52**, 10080 (1958).

29. Price, Leonard, and Curtin, *J. Am. Chem. Soc.*, **68**, 1305 (1946).

30. Endicott, Alden, and Sherrill, *J. Am. Chem. Soc.*, **68**, 1303 (1946).

31. Baker, Schaub, Joseph, McEvoy, and Williams, *J. Org. Chem.*, **17**, 141 (1952).

32. Sen and Singh, *J. Indian Chem. Soc.*, **36**, 787 (1959).

33. Tsuda, Fukushima, Ichikawa, Yoshida, and Ishii, *J. Pharm. Soc. Japan*, **62**, 69 (1942); *Chem. Abstr.*, **45**, 1580 (1951).

34. Subbaram, *J. Madras Univ.*, **24B**, 183 (1954); *Chem. Abstr.*, **50**, 352 (1956).

35. Magidson and Golovchinskaya, *Zh. Obshch. Khim.*, **8**, 1797 (1938); *Chem. Abstr.*, **33**, 4993 (1939).

36. Maillard, Morin, Vincent, and Bernard, *U.S. Pat.*, 3,047,462 (1962); *Chem. Abstr.*, **58**, 1474 (1963).

37. Baker, Schaub, Joseph, McEvoy, and Williams, *J. Org. Chem.*, **17**, 149 (1952).

38. Bogert and Hoffman, *J. Am. Chem. Soc.*, **27**, 1293 (1905).

39. Oakes, Rydon, and Undheim, *J. Chem. Soc.*, **1962**, 4678.

40. Ehrlich, *Ber. Deut. Chem. Ges.*, **34**, 3366 (1901).

41. Findeklee, *Ber. Deut. Chem. Ges.*, **38**, 3553 (1905).

42. Gabriel and Thieme, *Ber. Deut. Chem. Ges.*, **52**, 1079 (1919).

43. Baker, Joseph, Schaub, McEvoy, and Williams, *J. Org. Chem.*, **17**, 157 (1952).

44. Smith, Elisberg, and Sherrill, *J. Am. Chem. Soc.*, **68**, 1301 (1946).

45. Chapman, Gibson, and Mann, *J. Chem. Soc.*, **1947**, 890.

46. Iyer, Anand, and Dhar, *J. Sci. Ind. Res. India*, **15C**, 1 (1956).

47. Tsuda, Ishii, Fukushima, and Kagaya, *J. Pharm. Soc. Japan*, **63**, 445 (1943); *Chem. Abstr.*, **45**, 5156 (1951).
48. Bogert and Scatchard, *J. Am. Chem. Soc.*, **41**, 2052 (1919).
49. Bogert and Klaber, *J. Am. Chem. Soc.*, **30**, 807 (1908).
50. Bogert and Chambers, *J. Am. Chem. Soc.*, **27**, 649 (1905).
51. Elderfield, Williamson, Gensler, and Kremer, *J. Org. Chem.*, **12**, 405 (1947).
52. Morley and Simpson, *J. Chem. Soc.*, **1948**, 360.
53. Osborn, Schofield, and Short, *J. Chem. Soc.*, **1956**, 4191.
54. Farbenindustrie, A.-G., *Brit. Pat.*, 327,450 (1929); *Chem. Abstr.*, **24**, 5166 (1930).
55. Dewar, *J. Chem. Soc.*, **1944**, 619.
56. Etienne and Legrand, *Compt. Rend.*, **229**, 1372 (1949).
57. Baker, Schaub, Joseph, McEvoy, and Williams, *J. Org. Chem.*, **17**, 164 (1952).
58. Armarego and Smith, unpublished results (1966).
59. Pawlewski, *Ber. Deut. Chem. Ges.*, **36**, 2384 (1903).
60. Endicott, Wick, Mercury, and Sherrill, *J. Am. Chem. Soc.*, **68**, 1299 (1946).
61. Sen and Gupta, *J. Indian Chem. Soc.*, **39**, 368 (1962).
62. Andrisano and Modena, *Gazz. Chim. Ital.*, **80**, 228 (1950).
63. Chi and Shown, *Hua Hsüeh Hsüeh Pao*, **23**, 112 (1957); *Chem. Abstr.*, **52**, 13735 (1958).
64. Hasspacher, *Ger. Pat.*, 1,107,234 (1959); *Chem. Abstr.*, **56**, 11602 (1962); addition to *Ger. Pat.*, 1,102,755 (1959); *Chem. Abstr.*, **56**, 484 (1962).
65. Kulisch, *Chem. Zentr.*, **I**, 847 (1899).
66. Denney and Rosen, *U.S. Dept. Comm. Office Tech. Service AD.*, 260,401, 11 pp (1960); *Chem. Abstr.*, **59**, 4839 (1963).
67. Meyer and Wagner, *J. Org. Chem.*, **8**, 239 (1943).
68. Bell and Childress, *J. Org. Chem.*, **29**, 506 (1964).
69. Cairncross and Bogert, *Collection Czech. Chem. Commun.*, **7**, 548 (1935).
70. Bogert and Gotthelf, *J. Am. Chem. Soc.*, **22**, 522 (1900).
71. Bischler and Burkart, *Ber. Deut. Chem. Ges.*, **26**, 1349 (1893).
72. Niementowski, *J. Prakt. Chem.*, **40** (2), 1 (1889).
73. Baker, Joseph, Schaub, McEvoy, and Williams, *J. Org. Chem.*, **18**, 138 (1953).
74. Bogert and Steiner, *J. Am. Chem. Soc.*, **27**, 1327 (1905).
75. Thieme, *J. Prakt. Chem.*, **43** (2), 451 (1891).
76. Weddige, *J. Prakt. Chem.*, **36** (2), 141 (1887).
77. Zacharias, *J. Prakt. Chem.*, **43** (2), 432 (1891).
78. Dehoff, *J. Prakt. Chem.*, **42** (2), 346 (1890).
79. Körner, *J. Prakt. Chem.*, **36** (2), 155 (1887).
80. Knape, *J. Prakt. Chem.*, **43** (2), 209 (1891).
81. Weddige, *J. Prakt. Chem.*, **31** (2), 124 (1885).
82. Lesser, *U.S. Pat.*, 2,089,971 (1937); *Chem. Abstr.*, **31**, 7261 (1937).
83. Gambhir and Joshi, *J. Indian Chem. Soc.*, **41**, 47 (1964).
84. de Cat and van Poucke, *Compt. Rend. 27e Congr. Intern. Chim. Ind.*, *Brussels*, 1954, 3; *Ind. Chim. Belge*, **20**, Spec. No. 595 (1955); *Chem. Abstr.*, **50**, 12063 (1956).
85. Deisbach, Jacobi, and Taddei, *Helv. Chim. Acta*, **23**, 469 (1940).

86. Zentmyer and Wagner, *J. Org. Chem.*, **14**, 967 (1949).
87. Lustig and Katscher, *Monatsh. Chem.*, **48**, 96 (1927).
88. Morris, Hanford, and Adams, *J. Am. Chem. Soc.*, **57**, 951 (1935).
89. Hanford, Liang, and Adams, *J. Am. Chem. Soc.*, **56**, 2780 (1934).
90. Lawes and Scarborough, *U.S. Pat.*, 3,127,401 (1964); *Chem. Abstr.*, **60**, 14525 (1964).
91. Ahmed, Narang, and Ray, *J. Indian Chem. Soc.*, **15**, 152 (1938).
92. Partridge and Butler, *J. Chem. Soc.*, **1959**, 2396.
93. Tavernier and de Cat, *Belg. Pat.*, 565,656 (1958); *Chem. Abstr.*, **54**, 15037 (1960).
94. Dass, Vig, Gupta, and Narang, *J. Sci. Ind. Res. India*, **11B**, 461 (1952).
95. Stephen and Wadge, *J. Chem. Soc.*, **1956**, 4420.
96. Tomisek and Christensen, *J. Am. Chem. Soc.*, **70**, 1701 (1948).
97. Beri, Narang, and Ray, *J. Indian Chem. Soc.*, **12**, 395 (1935).
98. Arcoria, *Ann. Chim. (Italy)*, **52**, 149 (1962).
99. Grammaticakis, *Compt. Rend.*, **252**, 4011 (1961).
100. Petyunin and Kozhevnikov, *Zh. Obshch. Khim.*, **30**, 2352 (1960).
101. Bogert and Hand, *J. Am. Chem. Soc.*, **28**, 94 (1906).
102. Bogert and Hand, *J. Am. Chem. Soc.*, **24**, 1031 (1902).
103. Bogert and Hand, *J. Am. Chem. Soc.*, **25**, 935 (1903).
104. Bamberger and Weiler, *J. Prakt. Chem.*, **58** (2), 333 (1898).
105. McKee, McKee, and Bost, *J. Am. Chem. Soc.*, **68**, 1902 (1946).
106. Taylor, Knopf, and Borror, *J. Am. Chem. Soc.*, **82**, 3152 (1960).
107. Hickinbottom, in *Chemistry of Carbon Compounds* (Ed. Rodd), Elsevier (1954), Vol. IIIA, p. 559.
108. Bogert and Gotthelf, *J. Am. Chem. Soc.*, **22**, 129 (1900).
109. Gotthelf, *J. Am. Chem. Soc.*, **23**, 611 (1901).
110. König, *J. Prakt. Chem.*, **69** (2), 1 (1904).
111. Hölljes, Jr. and Wagner, *J. Org. Chem.*, **9**, 31 (1944).
112. Hardman and Partridge, *J. Chem. Soc.*, **1954**, 3878.
113. Cooper and Partridge, *J. Chem. Soc.*, **1954**, 3429.
114. Cooper and Partridge, *J. Chem. Soc.*, **1955**, 991.
115. Patterson and Capell, *The Ring Index*, Reinhold, 1940, p. 143; see also Elderfield, Todd, and Gerber, in *Heterocyclic Compounds* (Ed. Elderfield), 1957, Vol. 6, p. 564, and Capell and Walker, *The Ring Index*, 2nd ed., American Chemical Society, 1960, No. 1560, p. 203.
116. Bogert and Seil, *J. Am. Chem. Soc.*, **27**, 1305 (1905).
117. Bogert, Gortner, and Amend, *J. Am. Chem. Soc.*, **33**, 949 (1911).
118. Baker, Querry, Kadish, and Williams, *J. Org. Chem.*, **17**, 35 (1952).
119. Tomisek and Christensen, *J. Am. Chem. Soc.*, **70**, 2423 (1948).
120. Jain and Narang, *J. Indian Chem. Soc.*, **30**, 701 (1953).
121. Jain and Narang, *J. Indian Chem. Soc.*, **30**, 711 (1953).
122. Heilbron, Kitchen, Parkes, and Sutton, *J. Chem. Soc.*, **1925**, 2167.
123. Bogert and Seil, *J. Am. Chem. Soc.*, **29**, 517 (1907).
124. Anschütz, Schmidt, and Greiffenberg, *Ber. Deut. Chem. Ges.*, **35**, 3480 (1902).
125. Zeitler, *Z. Physiol. Chem.*, **340**, 73 (1965).
126. Taniyama, Yasui, Uchida, and Okuda, *J. Pharm. Soc. Japan*, **81**, 431 (1961).
127. Bogert and Bender, *J. Am. Chem. Soc.*, **36**, 568 (1914).

128. Marchetti, Bergesi, and Mattalia, *Ann. Chim.* (*Italy*), **52**, 836 (1962).
129. Iyer and Dhar, *J. Sci. Ind. Res. India*, **17C**, 193 (1958).
130. Bogert and Geiger, *J. Am. Chem. Soc.*, **34**, 524 (1912).
131. Boltze, Dell, Lehwald, Lorenz, and Rüberg-Schweer, *Arzneimittelforsch.*, **13**, 689 (1963).
132. Bogert and Cook, *J. Am. Chem. Soc.*, **28**, 1449 (1906).
133. Klosa, *Ger. Pat.*, 1,123,332 (1962); *Chem. Abstr.*, **57**, 3458 (1962).
134. Marr and Bogert, *J. Am. Chem. Soc.*, **57**, 729 (1935).
135. Fetscher and Bogert, *J. Org. Chem.*, **4**, 71 (1939).
136. Ghosh, *J. Indian Chem. Soc.*, **14**, 411 (1937).
137. Kischor, Kumar, and Parmar, *J. Med. Chem.*, **7**, 831 (1964).
138. Claesen and Vanderhaeghe, *Bull. Soc. Chim. Belges*, **68**, 220 (1959).
139. Joshi and Gambhir, *J. Org. Chem.*, **26**, 3714 (1961).
140. Dhatt and Bami, *J. Sci. Ind. Res. India*, **18C**, 256 (1959).
141. Dhatt, *Indian J. Chem.*, **2** (1), 36 (1964).
142. Baker, Querry, Schaub, and Williams, *J. Org. Chem.*, **17**, 58 (1952).
143. Anet and Somasekhara, *Can. J. Chem.*, **38**, 746 (1960).
144. Bogert and Beal, *J. Am. Chem. Soc.*, **34**, 516 (1912).
145. Anschütz, Schmidt, and Greiffenberg, *Ber. Deut. Chem. Ges.*, **35**, 3477 (1902).
146. Anschütz and Schmidt, *Ber. Deut. Chem. Ges.*, **35**, 3470 (1902).
147. Kowalski and Niementowski, *Ber. Deut. Chem. Ges.*, **30**, 1186 (1897) (for structure see *Beilstein*, I, **24**, 216).
148. Hickinbottom, in *The Chemistry of Carbon Compounds* (Ed. Rodd), Elsevier, 1954, Vol. IIIA, p. 580.
149. Scarborough, *U.S. Pat.*, 3,073,826 (1963); *Chem. Abstr.*, **59**, 1656 (1963).
150. Wagner, *J. Org. Chem.*, **5**, 133 (1940).
151. Mehta, *Indian Pat.*, 74,226 (1963); *Chem. Abstr.*, **60**, 2980 (1964).
152. Mehta, *Indian Pat.*, 74,424 (1963); *Chem. Abstr.*, **60**, 1773 (1964).
153. Clark and Wagner, *J. Org. Chem.*, **9**, 55 (1944).
154. Mumm and Hesse, *Ber. Deut. Chem. Ges.*, **43**, 2505 (1910).
155. Levy and Stephen, *J. Chem. Soc.*, **1956**, 985.
156. Stephen and Stephen, *J. Chem. Soc.*, **1957**, 490.
157. Stephen and Staskun, *J. Chem. Soc.*, **1956**, 980.
158. Kemp and Stephen, *J. Chem. Soc.*, **1948**, 110.
159. Finger and Schupp, *J. Prakt. Chem.*, **74** (2), 154 (1906).
160. Andrisano and Modena, *Boll. Sci. Fac. Chim. Ind. Bologna*, **8**, 1 (1950); *Chem. Abstr.*, **45**, 1601 (1951).
161. Andrisano and Modena, *Gazz. Chim. Ital.*, **80**, 321 (1950).
162. Ried and Stephan, *Chem. Ber.*, **96**, 1218 (1963).
163. Ried and Stephan, *Chem. Ber.*, **95**, 3042 (1962).
164. Ried and Sinharay, *Chem. Ber.*, **96**, 3306 (1963).
165. Dymek and Berezowski, *Dissertationes Pharm.*, **15**, 23 (1963); *Chem. Abstr.*, **59**, 11491 (1963).
166. Finger, *J. Prakt. Chem.*, **76** (2), 97 (1907).
167. Runti, Nisi, and Sindellari, *Ann. Chim.* (*Italy*), **51**, 719 (1961).
168. Grimmel, Guenther, and Morgan, *J. Am. Chem. Soc.*, **68**, 542 (1946).
169. Gujral, Saxena, and Tiwari, *Indian J. Med. Res.*, **43**, 637 (1955).
170. Guenther and Morgan, *U.S. Pat.*, 2,408,633 (1946); *Chem. Abstr.*, **41**, 1251 (1947).

171. Guenther and Morgan, *U.S. Pat.*, 2,439,386 (1948); *Chem. Abstr.*, **42**, 5056 (1948).
172. Rani, Vig, Gupta, and Narang, *J. Indian Chem. Soc.*, **30**, 331 (1953).
173. Kacker and Zaheer, *J. Indian Chem. Soc.*, **28**, 344 (1951).
174. Sen and Upadhyaya, *J. Indian Chem. Soc.*, **27**, 40 (1950).
175. Subbaram, *Proc. Indian Acad. Sci.*, **40A**, 22 (1954); *Chem. Abstr.*, **49**, 11665 (1955).
176. Mewada, Patel, and Shah, *J. Indian Chem. Soc.*, **32**, 199 (1955).
177. Mewada, Patel, and Shah, *J. Indian Chem. Soc.*, **32**, 483 (1955).
178. Salimath, Patel, and Shah, *J. Indian Chem. Soc.*, **33**, 140 (1956).
179. Subbaram, *J. Sci. Ind. Res. India*, **17B**, 137 (1958).
180. Andrisano and Chiesi, *Ateneo Parmense*, **32**, 671 (1961); *Chem. Abstr.*, **58**, 3428 (1963).
181. Serventi and Marchesi, *Boll. Sci. Fac. Chim. Ind. Bologna*, **15**, 117 (1957); *Chem. Abstr.*, **52**, 9147 (1958).
182. Ecsery, Kosa, Somfai, Tardos, and Leszkovszky, *Hung. Pat.*, 149,813 (1962); *Chem. Abstr.*, **60**, 9291 (1964).
183. Wallace and Tiernan, Inc., *Brit. Pat.*, 916,139 (1963); *Chem. Abstr.*, **59**, 1663 (1963).
184. Merck A.-G., *Fr. Pat.*, M1678 (1963); *Chem. Abstr.*, **59**, 2833 (1963).
185. Wallace and Tiernan, Inc., *Brit. Pat.*, 912,085 (1962); *Chem. Abstr.*, **58**, 10217 (1963).
186. Herbrand and Mehlhose, *Ger. Pat.*, 1,124,504 (1962); *Chem. Abstr.*, **57**, 8591 (1962).
187. S.I.F.A., *Belg. Pat.*, 611,980 (1962); *Chem. Abstr.*, **59**, 1655 (1963).
188. Joshi and Giri, *J. Indian Chem. Soc.*, **39**, 188 (1962).
189. Laubach and McLamore, *U.S. Pat.*, 2,915,521 (1959); *Chem. Abstr.*, **55**, 25998 (1961).
190. Ecsery, Kosa, Somfai, Tardos, and Leszkovszky, *Hung. Pat.*, 149,660 (1962); *Chem. Abstr.*, **58**, 4585 (1963).
191. Shetty, Campanella, and Hays, *U.S. Pat.*, 3,086,910 (1963); *Chem. Abstr.*, **60**, 1772 (1964).
192. Andrisano and Pappalardo, *Ann. Chim. (Italy)*, **43**, 723 (1953).
193. Pappalardo, *Boll. Sedute Accad. Gioenia Sci. Nat. Catania*, **3** (4), 59 (1955); *Chem. Abstr.*, **51**, 7379 (1957).
194. Biersdorf and Co., A.-G., *Belg. Pat.*, 615,282 (1962); *Chem. Abstr.*, **58**, 13971 (1963).
195. Bami and Dhatt, *J. Sci. Ind. Res. India*, **16B**, 558 (1957).
196. Bami and Dhatt, *Current Sci. (India)*, **26**, 85 (1957).
197. Klosa, *J. Prakt. Chem.*, **14**, 84 (1961).
198. Klosa, *Belg. Pat.*, 619,888 (1962); *Chem. Abstr.*, **59**, 11531 (1963).
199. Jackman, Petrow, and Stephenson, *J. Pharm. Pharmacol.*, **12**, 529 (1960).
200. Petyunin and Kozhevnikov, *Zh. Obshch. Khim.*, **34**, 854 (1964).
201. Klosa, *J. Prakt. Chem.*, **20**, 283 (1963).
202. Cohen, du Picard, and Boissier, *Arch. Intern. Pharmacodyn.*, **136**, 271 (1962); *Chem. Abstr.*, **57**, 3965 (1962).
203. De and Ray, *J. Indian Chem. Soc.*, **4**, 541 (1927).
204. Sen and Ray, *J. Chem. Soc.*, **1926**, 646.
205. Young and Clark, *J. Chem. Soc.*, **1898**, 361.

8*

206. Bhattacharyya, Bose, and Ray, *J. Indian Chem. Soc.*, **6**, 279 (1929).
207. Aggarwal, Das, and Ray, *J. Indian Chem. Soc.*, **6**, 717 (1929).
208. Shah and Ichaporia, *J. Chem. Soc.*, **1936**, 431.
209. Gompper, Noppel, and Schaafer, *Angew. Chem.*, **75**, 918 (1963).
210. Bischler and Muntendam, *Ber. Deut. Chem. Ges.*, **28**, 723 (1895).
211. Bischler and Lang, *Ber. Deut. Chem. Ges.*, **28**, 279 (1895).
212. Baumgarten, Creger, and Villars, *J. Am. Chem. Soc.*, **80**, 6609 (1958).
213. Lepetit, Maffei, and Maimeri, *Gazz. Chim. Ital.*, **57**, 862 (1927).
214. Maffei, *Gazz. Chim. Ital.*, **58**, 261 (1928), and Maffei, *Gazz. Chim. Ital.*, **59**, 3 (1929).
215. Paal and Krecke, *Ber. Deut. Chem. Ges.*, **24**, 3049 (1891).
216. Paal and Koch, *J. Prakt. Chem.*, **48** (2), 549 (1893).
217. Paal and Krückeberg, *J. Prakt. Chem.*, **48** (2), 542 (1893).
218. Paal and Busch, *Ber. Deut. Chem. Ges.*, **22**, 2683 (1889).
219. Farrar, *J. Chem. Soc.*, **1954**, 3253.
220. Smith and Stephen, *Tetrahedron*, **1**, 38 (1957).
221. Feldman and Wagner, *J. Org. Chem.*, **7**, 31 (1942).
222. Schöpf and Oechler, *Ann. Chem.*, **523**, 1 (1936).
223. Alessandri, *Atti Accad. Naz. Lincei, Rend. Classe Sci. Fis. Mat. Nat.*, **22**, 150, 227 (1913).
224. Piozzi, Dubini, and Cecere, *Gazz. Chim. Ital.*, **89**, 2342 (1959).
225. Capuano and Giammanco, *Gazz. Chim. Ital.*, **86**, 126 (1956).
226. Capuano and Giammanco, *Gazz. Chim. Ital.*, **86**, 119 (1956).
227. Jacini, *Gazz. Chim. Ital.*, **77**, 295 (1947); cf. de Mayo and Ryan, *Chem. Comm.* **1967**, 88.
228. Noland and Jones, *J. Org. Chem.*, **27**, 341 (1962).
229. Simonov, Martsokha, and Pozharskii, *Zh. Obshch. Khim.*, **32**, 2388 (1962); **33**, 1001 (1963).
230. Davis and Mann, *J. Chem. Soc.*, **1962**, 945.
231. Heller, Buchwaldt, Fuchs, Kleinicke, and Kloss, *J. Prakt. Chem.*, **111** (2), 1 (1925).
232. Ecsery, Kosa, Somfai, Tardos, and Leszkovszky, *Hung. Pat.*, 150,883 (1963); *Chem. Abstr.*, **60**, 6855 (1964).
233. Cohen, Klarberg, and Vaughan, Jr., *J. Am. Chem. Soc.*, **81**, 5508 (1959).
234. Hardman and Partridge, *J. Chem. Soc.*, **1958**, 614.
235. Böhme and Böing, *Arch. Pharm.*, **294**, 556 (1961).
236. Palazzo, Bizzi, and Pozzati, *Ann. Chim. (Italy)*, **49**, 853 (1959).
237. Kassur and Weil, *Roczniki Chem.*, **18**, 163 (1938); *Chem. Abstr.*, **33**, 624 (1939).
238. Leonard and Ruyle, *J. Org. Chem.*, **13**, 903 (1948).
239. Scarborough and Minielli, *U.S. Pat.*, 3,119,824 (1964); *Chem. Abstr.*, **60**, 9292 (1964).
240. Fry, Kendall, and Morgan, *J. Chem. Soc.*, **1960**, 5062.
241. Uskoković, Iacobelli, Toome, and Wenner, *J. Org. Chem.*, **29**, 582 (1964).
242. Blatter, Lukaszewski, and DeStevens, *J. Org. Chem.*, **30**, 1020 (1965).
243. Huang-Hsinmin and Mann, *J. Chem. Soc.*, **1949**, 2903.
244. Heilbron, Holt, and Kitchen, *J. Chem. Soc.*, **1928**, 934.
245. Lora-Tamayo, Madroñero, and Muñoz, *Chem. Ber.*, **94**, 208 (1961).
246. Christensen, Wang, Davies, and Harris, *Anal. Chem.*, **21**, 1573 (1949).

247. Pakrashi, Bhattacharyya, Johnson, and Budzikiewicz, *Tetrahedron*, **19**, 1011 (1963).
248. Hearn, Morton, and Simpson, *J. Chem. Soc.*, **1951**, 3318.
249. Mehta, *Indian Pat.*, 70,727 (1962); *Chem. Abstr.*, **58**, 4583 (1963); *Indian Pat.*, 70, 957 (1960); *Chem. Abstr.*, **56**, 12910 (1962).
250. Papa and Bogert, *J. Am. Chem. Soc.*, **58**, 1701 (1936).
251. Leonard and Curtin, *J. Org. Chem.*, **11**, 341 (1946).
252. Gompper, *Chem. Ber.*, **93**, 198 (1960).
253. Bogert and Geiger, *J. Am. Chem. Soc.*, **34**, 683 (1912).
254. Simpson and Morley, *J. Chem. Soc.*, **1949**, 1354.
255. Vincent, Maillard, and Benard, *Bull. Soc. Chim. France*, **1963**, 119.
256. Baker, Querry, Kadish, and Williams, *J. Org. Chem.*, **17**, 52 (1952).
257. Baker, Schaub, Querry, and Williams, *J. Org. Chem.*, **17**, 97 (1952).
258. Magidson and Yü-hua, *Zh. Obshch. Khim.*, **29**, 2843 (1959).
259. Nikit-skaya, Usovskaya, and Rubtsov, *Zh. Obshch. Khim.*, **29**, 3272 (1959).
260. Nikit-skaya, Usovskaya, and Rubtsov, *Zh. Obshch. Khim.*, **30**, 171 (1960).
261. Ghosh, Das, and Basu, *Indian J. Chem.*, **1**, 407 (1963).
262. Bhaduri, Khanna, and Dhar, *J. Sci. Ind. Res. India*, **21B**, 378 (1962).
263. Lehr-Splawinski, *Zeszyty Nauk Uniw. Jagiel.,Ser. Nauk Mat.-Przyrod., Mat., Fiz., Chem.*, (6), 53 (1959); *Chem. Abstr.*, **55**, 3602 (1961).
264. Buzas and Hoffmann, *Bull. Soc. Chim. France*, **1959**, 1889.
265. Bhaduri, Khanna, and Dhar, *Indian J. Chem.*, **2**, 159 (1964).
266. Magidson and Yü-hua, *Zh. Obshch. Khim.*, **29**, 3299 (1959).
267. Koepfli, Brockman, Jr., and Moffat, *J. Am. Chem. Soc.*, **72**, 3323 (1950).
268. Baker, *U.S. Pat.*, 2,621,162 (1952); *Chem. Abstr.*, **47**, 10012 (1953).
269. Somasekhara, Dighe, and Mukherjee, *Current Sci. (India)*, **33**, 209 (1964).
269a. Klosa, *Monatsh. Chem.*, **31** (4), 34 (1966).
270. Monti, *Gazz. Chim. Ital.*, **72**, 515 (1942).
271. Monti and Delitala, *Gazz. Chim. Ital.*, **72**, 520 (1942).
272. Mirza, *Nature*, **186**, 716 (1960).
273. Bunnett and Bassett, Jr., *J. Org. Chem.*, **27**, 3714 (1962).
274. Dhatt, *Current Sci. (India)*, **30**, 179 (1961).
275. Monti and Simonetti, *Gazz. Chim. Ital.*, **71**, 651 (1941).
276. Mandasescu and Stoicescu-Crivat, *Acad. Rep. Populare Romine, Filiala Iaşi, Studii Cercetări Ştiint., Chim.*, **11**, 75 (1960); *Chem. Abstr.*, **56**, 4764 (1962).
277. Bogert, Beal, and Amend, *J. Am. Chem. Soc.*, **32**, 1654 (1910).
278. Anker and Cook, *J. Chem. Soc.*, **1944**, 489.
279. Mandasescu, Stoicescu-Crivat, and Gabe, *Acad. Rep. Populare Romine, Filiala, Iaşi, Studii Cercetări Ştiint., Chim.*, **11**, 311 (1960); *Chem. Abstr.*, **56**, 11751 (1962).
280. Bogert and Clark, *J. Am. Chem. Soc.*, **46**, 1294 (1924).
281. Bogert and Heidelberger, *J. Am. Chem. Soc.*, **34**, 183 (1912).
282. Kulkarni, *J. Indian Chem. Soc.*, **19**, 180 (1942).
283. Cook and Naylor, *J. Chem. Soc.*, **1943**, 397.
284. Niementowski, *Ber. Deut. Chem. Ges.*, **29**, 1356 (1896).
285. Chiang and Li, *Hua Hsüeh Hsüeh Pao*, **23**, 391 (1957); *Chem. Abstr.*, **52**, 15539 (1958).

286. Monti, *Atti Accad. Naz. Lincei, Rend. Classe Sci. Fis. Mat. Nat.*, **28**, 96 (1938); *Chem. Abstr.*, **33**, 2897 (1939); Vène, *Bull. Soc. Chim. France*, **12**, 506 (1945).

287. Murata and Yamamoto, *Chem. Pharm. Bull. (Japan)*, **12**, 631 (1964).

288. Mirza, *Sci. Cult. (Calcutta)*, **17**, 530 (1952).

289. Osborn and Schofield, *J. Chem. Soc.*, **1956**, 3977.

290. Hutchings, Gordon, Ablondi, Wolf, and Williams, *J. Org. Chem.*, **17**, 19 (1952).

291. Somasekhara and Mukherjee, *Current Sci. (India)*, **32**, 547 (1963).

292. Cohen, Klarberg, and Vaughan, Jr., *J. Am. Chem. Soc.*, **82**, 2731 (1960).

293. Leonard, Ruyle, and Bannister, *J. Org. Chem.*, **13**, 617 (1948).

294. Chun, Li-ho, and Hsiu, *Sci. Sinica (Peking)*, **14**, 141 (1965).

295. Sen and Sidhu, *J. Indian Chem. Soc.*, **25**, 437 (1948).

296. Koelsch, *J. Am. Chem. Soc.*, **67**, 1718 (1945).

297. Zaheer and Kacker, *Current Sci. (India)*, **24**, 12 (1955).

298. Mustafa, Asker, Kamel, Shalaby, and Hassan, *J. Am. Chem. Soc.*, **77**, 1612 (1955).

299. Kacker and Zaheer, *J. Chem. Soc.*, **1956**, 415.

300. Hamer, Heilbron, Reade, and Walls, *J. Chem. Soc.*, **1932**, 251.

301. Monti and Simonetti, *Gazz. Chim. Ital.*, **71**, 658 (1941); *Boll. Sci. Fac. Chim. Ind. Bologna*, 164, 166 (1940); *Chem. Abstr.*, **36**, 5477, 5478 (1942).

302. Monti, Osti, and Piras, *Gazz. Chim. Ital.*, **71**, 654 (1941).

303. Monti, *Boll. Sci. Fac. Chim. Ind. Bologna*, 133 (1940); *Chem. Abstr.*, **34**, 7292 (1940).

304. Monti and Felici, *Gazz. Chim. Ital.*, **70**, 375 (1940).

305. Iyer and Dhar, *J. Sci. Ind. Res. India*, **20C**, 175 (1961).

306. Stephen and Stephen, *J. Chem. Soc.*, **1956**, 4178.

307. Butler, Partridge, and Waite, *J. Chem. Soc.*, **1960**, 4970.

308. Griess, *Ber. Deut. Chem. Ges.*, **2**, 415 (1869).

309. Griess, *J. Prakt. Chem.*, **5** (2), 369 (1872).

310. Griess, *Ber. Deut. Chem. Ges.*, **11**, 1985 (1878).

311. Finger and Günzler, *J. Prakt. Chem.*, **83** (2), 198 (1911).

312. McKee, *J. Prakt. Chem.*, **84** (2), 821 (1911).

313. Finger and Zeh, *J. Prakt. Chem.*, **81** (2), 466 (1910).

314. Finger, *J. Prakt. Chem.*, **81** (2), 470 (1910).

315. Lempert and Doleschall, *Tetrahedron Letters*, **1963**, 781.

316. Doleschall and Lempert, *Monatsh. Chem.*, **95**, 1083 (1964).

317. Doleschall and Lempert, *Monatsh. Chem.*, **95**, 1068 (1964).

318. Lempert and Doleschall, *Monatsh. Chem.*, **95**, 950 (1964).

319. Schuhmacher and Ehrhardt, *Ger. Pat.*, 1,117,130 (1961); *Chem. Abstr.*, **56**, 11602 (1962).

320. Skinner and Zell, *J. Am. Chem. Soc.*, **77**, 5441 (1955).

321. Sheibley and Turner, *J. Am. Chem. Soc.*, **55**, 4918 (1933).

322. Huntress and Gladding, *J. Am. Chem. Soc.*, **64**, 2644 (1942).

323. Sheibley, *J. Org. Chem.*, **12**, 743 (1947).

324. Sheibley, *J. Org. Chem.*, **3**, 414 (1938).

325. Ebel, Rupp, and Trauth, *U.S. Pat.*, 2,697,097 (1954); *Chem. Abstr.*, **49**, 4301 (1955).

326. Diels and Wagner, *Ber. Deut. Chem. Ges.*, **45**, 874 (1912).

327. Kunckell, *Ber. Deut. Chem. Ges.*, **38**, 1212 (1905).
328. Pawlewski, *Ber. Deut. Chem. Ges.*, **38**, 130 (1905).
329. Párkányi, *Collection Czech. Chem. Commun.*, **26**, 998 (1961).
330. Mayeda, *J. Pharm. Soc. Japan*, (417), 17 (1916); *Chem. Abstr.*, **11**, 578 (1917).
331. Wielandt, *J. Prakt. Chem.*, **49** (2), 319 (1894).
332. Pollak and Goldstein, *Ann. Chem.*, **351**, 161 (1907).
333. Stewart, *J. Prakt. Chem.*, **49** (2), 318 (1894).
334. Abt, *J. Prakt. Chem.*, **39** (2), 141 (1889).
335. Toyoshima, Shimada, Hamano, and Ogo, *J. Pharm. Soc. Japan*, **85**, 502 (1965).
336. Curd, Landquist, and Rose, *J. Chem. Soc.*, **1948**, 1759.
337. Gabriel and Colman, *Ber. Deut. Chem. Ges.*, **38**, 3559 (1905).
338. Lange and Sheibley, *Org. Synth.*, **II**, 79 (1943).
339. Bogert and Scatchard, *J. Am. Chem. Soc.*, **38**, 1606 (1916).
340. Libermann, *Fr. Pat.*, 1,107,487 (1956); *Chem. Abstr.*, **53**, 11418 (1959).
341. Jacobs and Heidelberger, *J. Am. Chem. Soc.*, **39**, 2418 (1917).
342. Jürgens, *Ber. Deut. Chem. Ges.*, **40**, 4409 (1907).
343. Scott and Cohen, *J. Chem. Soc.*, **1923**, 3177.
344. Froelicher and Cohen, *J. Chem. Soc.*, **1921**, 1425.
345. Scott and Cohen, *J. Chem. Soc.*, **1921**, 664.
346. Wang, Feng, and Christensen, *J. Am. Chem. Soc.*, **72**, 4887 (1950).
347. Lange and Sheibley, *J. Am. Chem. Soc.*, **55**, 2113 (1933).
347a. Durant, *J. Soc. Chem. Ind. (London)*, **1965**, 1429.
348. Hurd, Buess, and Bauer, *J. Org. Chem.*, **19**, 1140 (1954).
349. Paal, *Ber. Deut. Chem. Ges.*, **27**, 974 (1894).
350. Kizber, *Zh. Obshch. Khim.*, **24**, 2195 (1954).
351. Fortmann, *J. Prakt. Chem.*, **55** (2), 123 (1897).
352. Taub and Hino, *J. Org. Chem.*, **26**, 5238 (1961).
353. Heller, *Ber. Deut. Chem. Ges.*, **49**, 523 (1916).
354. Busch, Blume, and Pungs, *J. Prakt. Chem.*, **79** (2), 513 (1909).
355. Bayer A.-G., *Brit. Pat.*, 753,171 (1956); *Chem. Abstr.*, **51**, 6691 (1957).
355a. Kurihara and Yoda, *Tetrahedron Letters*, **1965**, 2597.
356. Sheibley, *J. Org. Chem.*, **17**, 221 (1952).
357. Staiger and Wagner, *J. Org. Chem.*, **18**, 1427 (1953).
358. Niementowski, *J. Prakt. Chem.*, **51** (2), 510 (1895).
359. Grout and Partridge, *J. Chem. Soc.*, **1960**, 3546.
360. Gadekar, Kotsen, and Cohen, *J. Chem. Soc.*, **1964**, 4666.
361. Hoogewerff and van Dorp, *Rec. Trav. Chim.*, **10**, 4 (1891).
362. Spring and Woods, *J. Chem. Soc.*, **1945**, 625.
363. Braun and Tcherniac, *Ber. Deut. Chem. Ges.*, **40**, 2709 (1907).
364. Darapsky and Gaudian, *J. Prakt. Chem.*, **147** (2), 43 (1937).
365. Kühle and Wegler, *Ger. Pat.*, 1,068,263 (1959); *Chem. Abstr.*, **55**, 12435 (1961).
366. Kühle and Wegler, *Ann. Chem.*, **616**, 183 (1958).
367. Heller, *Ber. Deut. Chem. Ges.*, **49**, 2757 (1916).
368. Jacini, *Gazz. Chim. Ital.*, **73**, 85 (1943). (See also Haslinger, *Ber. Deut. Chem. Ges.*, **41**, 1444 (1908).)
369. Dorsch *J. Prakt. Chem.*, **33** (2), 51 (1886).

370. Jacini, *Gazz. Chim. Ital.*, **71**, 532 (1941).
371. Jacini, *Gazz. Chim. Ital.*, **73**, 306 (1943).
372. Rupe and Guggenbühl, *Helv. Chim. Acta*, **8**, 358 (1925).
373. Dokunikhin and Gaeva, *Zh. Obshch. Khim.*, **23**, 606 (1953); *Chem. Abstr.*, **48**, 7018 (1954).
374. Effenberger and Gleiter, *Chem. Ber.*, **97**, 472 (1964).
375. Dokunikhin, *Organ. Poluprod. i Krasiteli, Nauchn.-Issled. Inst. Organ. Poluprod. Krasitelei, Sb. Statei*, (1), 148 (1959); *Chem. Abstr.*, **55**, 21140 (1961).
376. Kizber and Glagoleva, *Zh. Obshch. Khim.*, **23**, 1028 (1953); *Chem. Abstr.*, **48**, 8790 (1954).
377. Gilbert, *U.S. Pat.*, 2,680,741 (1954); *Chem. Abstr.*, **49**, 6322 (1955).
378. Cairns, Coffman, and Gilbert, *J. Am. Chem. Soc.*, **79**, 4405 (1957).
379. Horiie and Murahashi, *J. Am. Chem. Soc.*, **78**, 4816 (1956); *Bull. Chem. Soc. Japan*, **33**, 88 (1960); *U.S. Pat.*, 2,944,056 (1960); *Chem. Abstr.*, **55**, 1667 (1961); *Japan Pat.*, 9133 (1958); *Chem. Abstr.*, **54**, 5714 (1960) (see also, Prichard, *U.S. Pat.*, 2,769,003 (1956); *Chem. Abstr.*, **51**, 7412 (1957)).
380. Das and Mukherjee, *J. Indian Chem. Soc.*, **40**, 35 (1963).
381. Busch, *J. Prakt. Chem.*, **51** (2), 113 (1895).
382. Busch, *J. Prakt. Chem.*, **51** (2), 257 (1895).
383. Paal and Weil, *Ber. Deut. Chem. Ges.*, **27**, 34 (1894).
384. Söderbaum and Widman, *Ber. Deut. Chem. Ges.*, **22**, 2933 (1889).
385. Ubrański, Serafinowa, and Gacówna, *Roczniki Chem.*, **27**, 167 (1953); *Chem. Abstr.*, **49**, 338 (1955).
386. Sulkowski and Childress, *J. Org. Chem.*, **27**, 4424 (1962).
387. Lee, *J. Heterocyclic Chem.*, **1**, 235 (1964).
388. Sam and Richmond, *J. Heterocyclic Chem.*, **1**, 134 (1964).
389. Bates and Belcher, *Anal. Chim. Acta*, **3**, 412 (1949).
390. Higuchi, Sciarrone, and Haddad, *J. Med. Pharm. Chem.*, **3**, 195 (1961).
391. Haddad, Sciarrone, and Higuchi, *J. Am. Pharm. Assoc. (Sci. Ed.)*, **48**, 588 (1959).
392. Poe and Edson, *Univ. Col. Studies*, **18**, 201 (1931); *Chem. Abstr.*, **26**, 2968 (1932).
393. Yoe and Cogbill, *Mikrochem. Mikrochim. Acta*, **38**, 492 (1951).
394. Gut, Prystaš, Jonáš, and Šorm, *Collection Czech. Chem. Commun.*, **26**, 974 (1961).
395. Horák and Gut, *Collection Czech. Chem. Commun.*, **26**, 1680 (1961).
396. Grammaticakis, *Compt. Rend.* **247**, 2013 (1958).
397. Arndt, Loewe, and Ergener, *Istanbul Univ., Fen. Fac. Mecmuasi*, **13A**, 103 (1948); *Chem. Abstr.*, **43**, 579 (1949).
398. Konz, *U.S. Pat.*, 2,767,182 (1956); *Chem. Abstr.*, **51**, 8150 (1957); *Ger. Pat.*, 944,312 (1956); *Chem. Abstr.*, **52**, 16379 (1958).
399. Lange, Chisholm, and Szabo, *J. Am. Chem. Soc.*, **61**, 2170 (1939).
400. Wang and Christensen, *J. Am. Chem. Soc.*, **71**, 1440 (1949).
401. Hedley and Co., Ltd., *Brit. Pat.* 847,566 (1960); *Chem. Abstr.* **55**, 8438, (1961).
402. Bogert, *Ger. Pat.*, 228,796 (1910); *Chem. Zentr.*, **I**, 51 (1911).
403. Armarego, *J. Chem. Soc.*, **1962**, 561.
404. Albert and Hampton, *J. Chem. Soc.*, **1952**, 4985.
405. Albert and Hampton, *J. Chem. Soc.*, **1954**, 505.

406. Wessely, Zbiral, and Sturm, *Monatsh. Chem.*, **93**, 1211 (1962).
407. Dziomko and Markovich, *Zh. Obshch. Khim.*, **32**, 1622 (1962).
408. Bogert, Amend, and Chambers, *J. Am. Chem. Soc.*, **32**, 1297 (1910).
409. *Beilstein*, I, **25**, 76.
410. Irving and Rossotti, *J. Chem. Soc.*, **1954**, 2910.
411. Crimmin, *Anal. Chim. Acta*, **16**, 501 (1957); *Chem. Abstr.*, **52**, 1736 (1958).
412. Dziomko, Zelichenok, and Markovich, *Zh. Anal. Khim.*, **18**, 937 (1963); *Chem. Abstr.*, **59**, 14569 (1963).
413. Albert, Hampton, Selbie, and Simon, *Brit. J. Exp. Pathol.*, **35**, 75 (1954).
414. Mason, *J. Chem. Soc.*, **1958**, 674.
415. Irving, Rossotti, and Harris, *Analyst*, **80**, 83 (1955).
416. Rossotti and Rossotti, *J. Chem. Soc.*, **1958**, 1304.
417. Singh and Sharma, *Chemotherapy, Proc. Symposium Lucknow*, **1958**, 157; *Chem. Abstr.*, **54**, 4911 (1960).
418. Dave, Mewada, and Amin, *Acta Chim. Acad. Sci. Hung.*, **34**, 101 (1962); *Chem. Abstr.*, **59**, 627 (1963).
419. Murahashi and Horie, *Ann. Rept. Sci. Works, Fac. Sci., Osaka Univ.*, **7**, 89 (1959); *Chem. Abstr.*, **54**, 24785 (1960).
420. Grout and Partridge, *J. Chem. Soc.*, **1960**, 3551.
421. Hayao, Havera, Strycker, Leipzig, Kulp, and Hartzler, *J. Med. Chem.*, **8**, 807 (1965).
422. Danielsson and Skoglund, *Acta Pharm. Suecica*, **2**, 167 (1965).
423. Donleavy and Kise, *J. Am. Chem. Soc.*, **57**, 753 (1935).
424. Mead, Johnson, and Co., *Brit. Pat.*, 920,019 (1963); *Chem. Abstr.*, **59**, 3935 (1963).
425. Suri, Sharma, and Narang, *J. Indian Chem. Soc.*, **41**, 591 (1964).
426. Reissert and Schaaf, *Ber. Deut. Chem. Ges.*, **59**, 2494 (1926).
427. Hauptmann, *Arzneimittelforsch.*, **15**, 610 (1965).
428. Curd, Hoggarth, Landquist, and Rose, *J. Chem. Soc.*, **1948**, 1766.
429. Pawlewski, *Ber. Deut. Chem. Ges.*, **39**, 1732 (1906).
430. Baker and Schaub, *Brit. Pat.*, 713, 767 (1954); *Chem. Abstr.*, **50**, 14002 (1956).
431. Baker and Querry, *U.S. Pat.*, 2,651,633 (1953); *Chem. Abstr.*, **48**, 13731 (1954).
432. Curd, Landquist, and Rose, *J. Chem. Soc.*, **1947**, 775.
433. Gärtner, *Ann. Chem.*, **336**, 229 (1904).
434. Etienne and Legrand, *Compt. Rend.*, **229**, 220 (1949).
435. Hirwe and Kulkarni, *Proc. Indian Acad. Sci.*, **16A**, 294 (1942); *Chem. Abstr.*, **37**, 4061 (1943).
436. Jain and Narang, *Research Bull. East Punjab Univ.*, (29), 51 (1953); *Chem. Abstr.*, **49**, 1063 (1955).
437. Meyer and Bellmann, *J. Prakt. Chem.*, **33** (2), 18 (1886).
438. Lorenz, *Ger. Pat.*, 1,064,072 (1959); *Chem. Abstr.*, **55**, 17664 (1961).
439. Mandasescu, Stoicescu-Crivat, Gabe, Lica, and Stefanescu, *Acad. Rep. Populare Romine, Filiala, Iaşi Studii Cercetări Ştiint., Chim.*, **13**, 115 (1962); *Chem. Abstr.*, **59**, 4069 (1963).
440. Seshavataram and Rao, *Proc. Indian Acad. Sci.*, **49A**, 96 (1959); *Chem. Abstr.*, **53**, 18045 (1959).
441. Martin, Wheeler, Majewski, and Corrigan, *J. Med. Chem.*, **7**, 812 (1964).

442. Ciba Ltd., *Belg. Pat.*, 611,898 (1962); *Chem. Abstr.*, **58**, 9267 (1963).
443. Kishor, Arora, and Parmar, *J. Med. Chem.*, **8**, 550 (1965).
444. Niementowski, *Chem. Zentr.*, **II**, 122 (1902).
445. Tomisek and Christensen, *J. Am. Chem. Soc.*, **70**, 874 (1948).
446. Späth and Platzer, *Ber. Deut. Chem. Ges.*, **68**, 2221 (1935).
447. Dhatt and Bami, *Current Sci.* (*India*), **28**, 367 (1959); *Chem. Abstr.*, **54**, 7055 (1960).
448. Partridge, Vipond, and Waite, *J. Chem. Soc.*, **1962**, 2549.
449. Sen and Singh, *J. Indian Chem. Soc.*, **42**, 409 (1965).
450. Baker, Schaub, and Williams, *J. Org. Chem.*, **17**, 109 (1952).
451. Baker and Schaub, *U.S. Pat.*, 2,694,711 (1954); *Chem. Abstr.*, **49**, 15976 (1955).
452. Tsuda, Ishii, Fukushima, and Yoshida, *J. Pharm. Soc. Japan*, **62**, 335 (1942).
453. Lange and Sheibley, *J. Am. Chem. Soc.*, **56**, 1188 (1933).
454. Sherrill, Ortelt, Duckworth, and Budenstein, *J. Org. Chem.*, **19**, 699 (1954).
455. Pesson and Richer, *Compt. Rend.*, **260**, 603 (1965).
456. Legrand and Lozach, *Bull. Soc. Chim. France*, **1960**, 2088.
457. Baker and Querry, *U.S. Pat.*, 2,625,549 (1953); *Chem. Abstr.*, **48**, 745 (1954).
458. Baker, Schaub, Querry, and Williams, *J. Org. Chem.*, **17**, 77 (1952).
459. Baker, Querry, Pollikoff, Schaub, and Williams, *J. Org. Chem.*, **17**, 68 (1952).
460. Baker, Schaub, McEvoy, and Williams, *J. Org. Chem.*, **17**, 132 (1952).
461. Bedi and Narang, *J. Indian Chem. Soc.*, **13**, 253 (1936).
462. McCoy, *Am. Chem. J.*, **21**, 111 (1899).
463. Lange and Sheibley, *J. Am. Chem. Soc.*, **53**, 3867 (1931).
464. Baker, McEvoy, Schaub, Joseph, and Williams, *J. Org. Chem.*, **18**, 153 (1953).
465. Hepworth, *Brit. Pat.*, 857,362 (1960); *Chem. Abstr.*, **55**, 14487 (1961).
466. Stephen and Stephen, *J. Chem. Soc.*, **1956**, 4694.
467. Rodionow and Fedorowa, *Bull. Soc. Chim. France*, **6**, 478 (1939).
468. Culbertson, Willits, and Christensen, *J. Am. Chem. Soc.*, **76**, 3533 (1954).
469. Stachel, *Arch. Pharm.*, **296**, 337 (1963).
470. Spinks and Young, *Brit. Pat.*, 750,175 (1956); *Chem. Abstr.*, **51**, 1303 (1957); *U.S. Pat.*, 2,794,018 (1957); *Chem. Abstr.*, **51**, 12988 (1957).
471. Subbaram, *J. Madras Univ.*, **24B**, 179 (1954); *Chem. Abstr.*, **50**, 352 (1956).
472. Dighe, Somasekhara, Bagavant, and Mukherjee, *Current Sci.* (*India*), **33**, 78 (1964).
473. Wallingford and Kruty, *U.S. Pat.*, 2,786,055 (1957); *Chem. Abstr.*, **51**, 18014 (1957).
474. Engelbrecht and Lenke, *Ger.* (*East*) *Pat.*, 19,629 (1960); *Chem. Abstr.*, **55**, 22346 (1961).
475. Dymek and Lubimowski, *Dissertationes Pharm.*, **16**, 247 (1964).
476. Shirakawa and Tsujikawa, *Takeda Kenkyusho Nempo*, **22**, 27 (1963); *Chem. Abstr.*, **60**, 12009 (1964).
477. Dymek and Subistowicz, *Monatsh. Chem.*, **96**, 542 (1965).
478. Dallacker, Gohlke, and Lipp, *Monatsh. Chem.*, **91**, 1103 (1960).
479. Mohr and Köhler, *J. Prakt. Chem.*, **80**, 521 (1909).
480. Abezgauz, Sokolov, and Udilov, *Zh. Obshch. Khim.*, **34**, 2965 (1964).

CHAPTER V

Halogenoquinazolines and Quinazolinyl Ethers

1. Halogenoquinazolines

The most extensively studied halogenoquinazolines are the chloro derivatives. A small number of bromo-, iodo-, and fluoroquinazolines are known and the majority of them have the halogen atom in the benzene ring. 2-, 4-, and 2,4-Halogenoquinazolines together with their derivatives are discussed here in detail. Quinazolines with halogen atoms in the benzene ring and on side chains are only briefly described, but appropriate cross references to other chapters of this work are given.

A. Preparation of 2-Halogenoquinazolines

1,2-Dihydro-2-oxoquinazolines are converted to 2-chloroquinazolines (1) by boiling with phosphoryl chloride. The reaction time is usually between 0.25 to 0.75 hours,[1,2] and heating periods of up to 3 hours can be used only when a stable substituent is present on $C_{(4)}$.[3] One mole of phosphorus pentachloride can be added to the mixture to facilitate the reaction particularly when it is found that the oxoquinazoline is reluctant to dissolve in the phosphoryl chloride (Reaction 1).[1,4,5] The yields of substituted 2-chloroquinazolines are usually above 50% although that for 2-chloroquinazoline is at best 40%.[6] This low yield is possibly due to the presence of a reactive 3,4-double bond which may increase side reactions. 4-Methyl-,[7] 4-isopropyl-,[3] 4-phenyl-,[1,2] 4-2′,4′-xylyl-,[4] 6-methyl-4-phenyl-,[5] and 4-2′-pyridyl-[8] 2-chloroquinazolines can be prepared in this way. 4-Ethoxy- and 4-methoxy- 2-chloroquinazolines (2, R = OEt, OMe) have also been prepared from the corresponding 2-oxo compounds with the above reagents (Reaction 2). Great care must be exercised in this preparation because of the

219

lability of the 4-alkoxy group (Sect. 2.E.b.(i)).[9] It is essential to carry out the work-up step of these chlorinations in the minimum possible time in order to obtain maximum yields (Sect. 1.B.). Another means of obtaining 4-alkoxy-2-chloroquinazolines is from the reaction of 4-alkoxy-quinazoline-1-oxides and sulphuryl chloride (Reaction 2)[9] (see Ch. IX, Sect. 1.). 4-Alkoxy-2-chloroquinazolines (2) are most conveniently

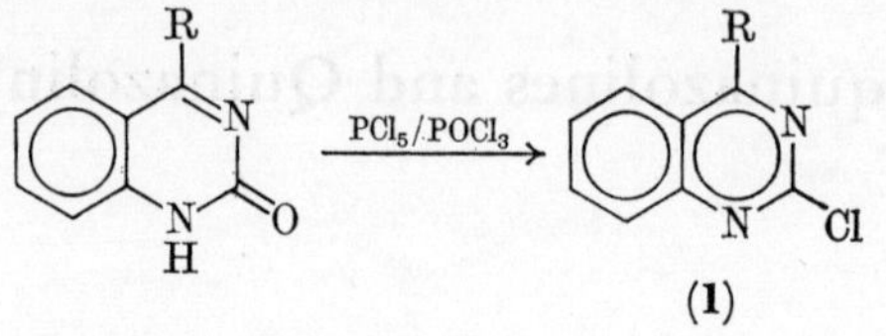

$$\text{(1)} \qquad \xrightarrow{\text{PCl}_5/\text{POCl}_3} \qquad \text{(1)}$$

(1)

obtained from 2,4-dichloroquinazoline by taking advantage of the greater reactivity of the 4-chlorine atom (Sect. 1.E.b.(ii)). These

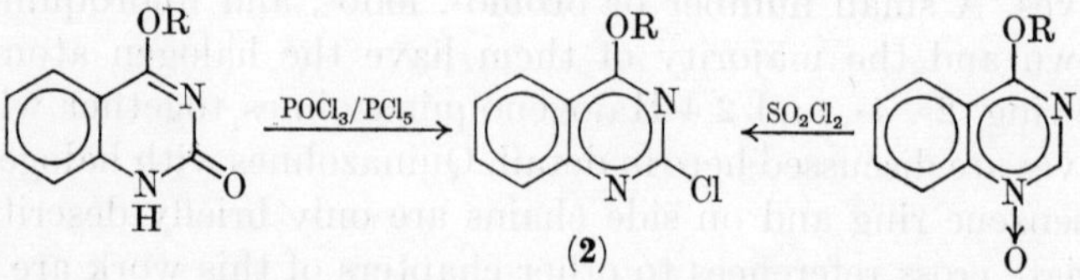

$$\text{(2)} \qquad \xrightarrow{\text{POCl}_3/\text{PCl}_5} \qquad \xleftarrow{\text{SO}_2\text{Cl}_2} \qquad \text{(2)}$$

(2)

compounds are prepared by boiling 2,4-dichloroquinazoline with one equivalent of metal alkoxide in the corresponding alcohol (Eq. 3).[10-15] The reaction also proceeds at low temperature. Thus 4-benzyloxy-2-chloroquinazoline can be obtained in 98% yield by adding 2,4-dichloro-quinazoline to sodium benzyloxide in benzyl alcohol below 10° and storing for 2 hours[12] at 20°. When the alcohol has alkali-sensitive groups, for example in diethyl-2-hydroxyethylmethylammonium iodide, then the condensation can be carried out in acetone in the presence of triethylamine.[12] With chloroalcohols, e.g. ethylene chlorohydrin, the

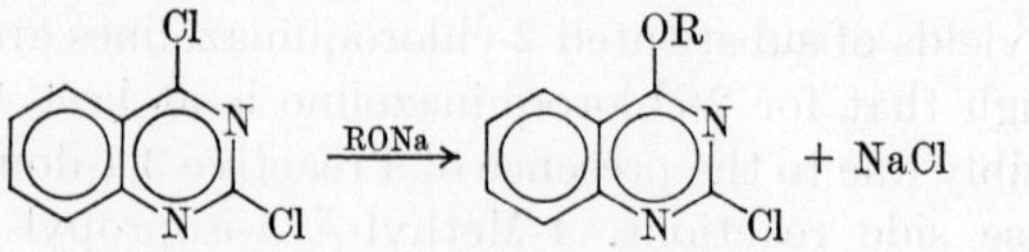

$$\xrightarrow{\text{RONa}} \qquad + \text{NaCl} \qquad \text{(3)}$$

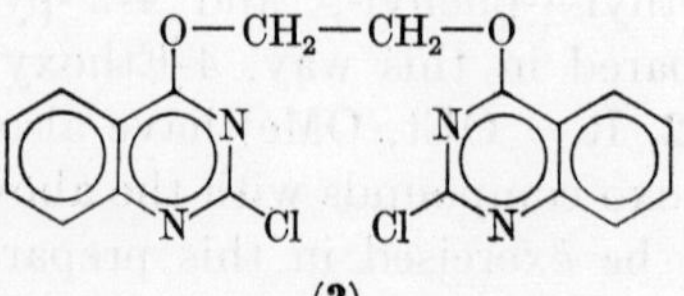

(3)

4-chloroalkoxy-2-chloroquinazolines are formed by refluxing an acetone solution containing potassium carbonate as base. 1,2-Di(2-chloroquinazolin-4-yloxy)ethane (3) is obtained when ethylene glycol is used. Care must be taken in handling some of these ethers because they may rearrange to 3-substituted 2-chloro-3,4-dihydro-4-oxoquinazolines on heating[12] (Sect. 2.E.b.(iv)).

2-Chloro-4-phenoxyquinazoline cannot be prepared from 2,4-dichloroquinazoline and sodium phenoxide in alcohol because this leads to the 4-alkoxy-2-chloroquinazoline. The 4-phenyl ether is best prepared by adding 2,4-dichloroquinazoline to a solution of molten phenol containing an equivalent of sodium.[10] The reason stated for this difference was that phenol reacted as sodium phenate, which liberated sodium chloride from the intermediate. In alcohol, the alkoxide ion was the reacting entity. However, we now know that the alkoxide ion is a stronger nucleophile in displacement reactions than the phenoxide ion.[16] Resorcinol and sodium ethoxide in ethanol react with 2,4-dichloroquinazoline to yield a mixture of 4-ethoxy- and 4-m-hydroxyphenyl- 2-chloroquinazolines.[10]

4-Amino substituted 2-chloroquinazolines are prepared by warming 2,4-dichloroquinazoline with two equivalents of amine. The second equivalent of amine is used to neutralize the acid liberated from the reaction, otherwise the hydrochloride of the amine is isolated (Eq. 4).[17,18] Alternatively equimolar quantities of 2,4-dichloroquinazoline and amine are kept at room temperature for one hour and then sodium hydroxide is added at intervals to keep the pH neutral until one equivalent has been added.[19] This method is particularly useful when the reacting amine is a strong base. Several 4-amino-2-chloroquinazolines have been prepared mainly in connection with biological activity.[19-24] Sodio ethyl cyanoacetate reacts with 2,4-dichloroquinazoline to form 2-chloro-4-(α-cyano-α-ethoxycarbonyl)methylquinazoline.[25]

$$\text{(2,4-dichloroquinazoline)} \xrightarrow{\text{2 RNH}_2} \text{(4-amino-2-chloroquinazoline)} + RNH_3^+Cl^- \qquad (4)$$

(4)

When 2,4-dichloroquinazoline is ground with cold N sodium hydroxide solution until most of it dissolves and the solution filtered then carefully acidified, 2-chloro-3,4-dihydro-4-oxoquinazoline (4) is obtained.[20,26] Hydrolysis of 2-chloro-4-ethoxyquinazoline with alcoholic potassium hydroxide in the cold also yields 4.[26] This is a useful intermediate for the preparation of 2-substituted 3,4-dihydro-4-oxoquinazolines.[20,26]

Chlorine reacts with 2-thioquinazolines in dry chloroform to give the respective 2-chloroquinazolines. 2-Chloro-3,4-dihydro-4-oxo-3-phenyl-quinazoline[27] is prepared in this way. Bromine in glacial acetic acid converts 4-phenyl- and 4-2′,4′-xylyl- 1,2-dihydro-2-thioquinazolines to 4-phenyl- and 4-2′,4′-xylyl-[4] 2-bromo-3,4-dihydroquinazolines respectively. Sulphuryl chloride is another effective reagent to bring about a similar conversion, and on boiling equimolar quantities of the 2-thioquinazoline and sulphuryl chloride in chloroform good yields of 3-phenyl-, 3-o-tolyl-, and 3-p-chlorophenyl- 2-chloro-3,4-dihydro-4-oxoquinazolines are obtained. 2-Fluoro-3,4-dihydro-4-oxo-3-phenyl-quinazoline can be prepared in 95% yield by heating the corresponding 2-chloro compound with potassium fluoride in dimethyl sulphoxide (Reaction 5).[28]

$$\xrightarrow{\quad\quad}\text{(5)}$$

with reagents $\underset{\text{CHCl}_3}{\overset{\text{SO}_2\text{Cl}_2}{\longrightarrow}}$ and $\underset{\text{Me}_2\text{SO}}{\overset{\text{KF}}{\longrightarrow}}$ (5)

B. Preparation of 4-Halogenoquinazolines

4-Chloroquinazolines are most commonly prepared by boiling 3,4-dihydro-4-oxoquinazoline with phosphoryl chloride containing a little more than one equivalent of phosphorus pentachloride. The mixture is heated until all the oxo compound dissolves and then for a further 0.5 to 1 hour in order to complete the reaction. 4-Chloro-quinazoline is prepared in this way on a large scale,[29] and the method can be used to prepare 4-chloroquinazolines substituted in the 2-position with 2′-furyl,[30,31] phenyl,[32,33] o-chlorophenyl,[34] and phenethyl groups with alkoxy or methylenedioxy substituents in the benzene ring;[35,36] also 4-chloroquinazolines substituted in the benzene ring with methyl,[37,38] halogeno,[18,37,39–43] trifluoromethyl,[44] nitro,[18,37,42,45] chloro-nitro,[44] and methoxy[18,37,45,47] groups (Reaction 6). It is interesting to note that in the last named group demethylation does not occur.

The yields in these reactions are usually above 50%. 4-Chloroquinazolines are unstable in the presence of acid so that it is necessary to remove every trace of acid in order to store these compounds for a reasonable period, e.g. 3 months. Thus it is very important, in order to obtain a good yield and a clean product, to carry out the necessary washing with water and base (preferably, saturated aqueous sodium bicarbonate) during the work-up, which should be performed below 15°, and as rapidly as possible (Sect. 1.A.). The last traces of acid or phosphoryl chloride are removed by passing a solution of the crude chloro compound in benzene through an alumina column,[29,37,48] and all solutions must be evaporated below 40° under vacuum.

$$R-\underset{N}{\overset{O}{\underset{\|}{\bigcirc\bigcirc}}} \overset{NH}{\underset{R^1}{}} \xrightarrow{PCl_5/POCl_3} R-\underset{N}{\overset{Cl}{\bigcirc\bigcirc}} \overset{N}{\underset{R^1}{}} \qquad (6)$$

In 1890 Dehoff[49] reported that when 3,4-dihydro-2-methyl-4-oxoquinazoline and a mixture of phosphorus pentachloride and phosphorus trichloride were heated in a sealed tube at 160°, a tetrachloromethylquinazoline was formed. Bogert and May[50] in 1909

$$\underset{(5)}{\overset{Cl}{\bigcirc\bigcirc}\underset{N}{\overset{N}{}}CCl_3} \qquad\qquad \underset{(6)}{\overset{Cl}{\bigcirc\bigcirc}\underset{N}{\overset{N}{}}CCl_2CH_3}$$

repeated the experiment using phosphorus pentachloride-phosphoryl chloride mixture and confirmed the previous results. They showed that one of the chlorine atoms was readily replaced by an ethoxy, amino, or anilino group, and concluded that the product was a 4-chloroquinazoline substituted with three chlorine atoms in the benzene ring. Similarly 2-ethyl-3,4-dihydro-4-oxoquinazoline gave a tetrachloroethylquinazoline, but attempts to prepare the monochloroalkylquinazolines failed.[50] The structure of these tetrachloroquinazolines was elucidated in 1965 by Smith and Kent[51] who showed that the chlorination was successful only with the phosphorus pentachloride-phosphorus trichloride mixture. In the methyl compound the proton magnetic resonance spectrum showed the presence of the four benzene protons but no —CH$_3$ protons, indicating that the product was 4-chloro-2-trichloromethylquinazoline (**5**). The spectrum of chlorinated ethylquinazoline showed the presence of the four benzene protons and a single peak for the —CH$_3$ group, indicating that it was 4-chloro-2-1′,1′-dichloroethylquinazoline (**6**).[51] The recently recorded melting point for the chlorination product of 2-ethyl-3,4-dihydro-4-oxoquinazoline[51] suggested that the substance obtained by Bogert and May must have been impure. The chlorination of 3,4-dihydro-2-methyl-4-oxoquinazoline to 4-chloro-2-methylquinazoline has, however, been effected in 57% yield under milder conditions by using boiling phosphoryl chloride containing N,N-dimethylaniline.[52] It is relevant to point out here that the chlorination of 1,2-dihydro-4-methyl-2-oxoquinazoline proceeds smoothly with phosphorus pentachloride-phosphoryl chloride mixture and is in agreement with the lower reactivity often found for the 4-methyl group with respect to the 2-methyl group in some reactions (Ch. III, Sect. 2.B.a.).

Chlorination of 3,4-dihydro-3-methyl-4-oxoquinazoline with phosphorus pentachloride and phosphoryl chloride gives the 4-chloroquinazoline with elimination of the 3-methyl group[50] probably as chloromethane.

Phosphoryl chloride alone has been used occasionally to effect the chlorinations.[53,54] This is apparently possible when the substituent groups in the 4-oxoquinazoline facilitate the process by increasing the reactivity of the oxo group or the solubility of the compound in the reagent. 6- and 7-Methyl-,[53] 5,6-benzo-,[54] 5-nitro-,[55,56] and 6-methoxy-[57] 4-chloroquinazolines are prepared by boiling with phosphoryl chloride alone. This is particularly useful when a sensitive substituent is present in the molecule, e.g. substituted amino or a thioether group.[58] Sometimes pressure must be applied to the reaction mixture,[59] but invariably the reaction produces fewer by-products if N,N-diethylaniline is added to the mixture in order to remove any free acid formed.[20,52,60] 3,4-Dihydro-4-oxoquinazoline is chlorinated extremely slowly with this reagent alone.

Phosphorus pentachloride alone has been used on one occasion for preparing 4-chloro-5-nitroquinazoline,[61] and 3,4-dihydro-2-o-nitrophenyl-4-oxoquinazoline was chlorinated to 4-chloro-2-o-nitrophenylquinazoline by heating with thionyl chloride in dimethyl formamide.[62] A chlorinating agent which is found useful on an industrial scale is phosgene. When 4-oxoquinazolines in an inert solvent, e.g. trichlorobenzene or nitrobenzene, containing dimethyl formamide, are treated with phosgene, the 4-chloro compounds are readily obtained.[63–65]

N-Phenyl benzimidoyl chloride forms the stannate salt (7) with anhydrous stannic chloride, and heating this salt with one equivalent of cyanogen bromide in nitrobenzene gives a 71% yield of the stannate salt of 4-bromo-2-phenylquinazoline (Reaction 7). The free base can be isolated in 86% yield by making the reaction mixture alkaline, steam distilling the solvent, and collecting the solid.[66,67]

C. Preparation of 2,4-Dihalogenoquinazolines

2,4-Dichloroquinazolines are readily prepared by boiling 1,2,3,4-tetrahydro-2,4-dioxoquinazolines with two equivalents of phosphorus pentachloride in phosphoryl chloride (Reaction 8).[53,68] In this way 2,4-dichloroquinazolines with halogen,[20,69] alkyl,[20,70,71] alkoxy,[20] 5,6-benzo,[20] and nitro[20] groups in the benzene ring are prepared in high yield. Heating in sealed tubes at 150–160° is quite unnecessary.[71] Methyl groups on the nitrogen atoms, as in 1,2,3,4-tetrahydro-3-methyl-2,4-dioxoquinazoline (8), are eliminated in this reaction and the dichloroquinazoline is formed (Reaction 8).[71] Phosphoryl chloride

alone,[72,73] or better in the presence of N,N-dimethylaniline[20,52,74,75] as acid binder, also converts dioxoquinazolines to 2,4-dichloroquinazolines in high yields. Tripropylamine can also be used as acid binder, but with triethylamine, 1,2,3,4-tetrahydro-2,4-dioxoquinazoline gives 4-chloro-2-diethylaminoquinazoline (9).[52] As in the preparation of some 4-chloroquinazolines (Sect. 1.B.), phosgene successfully chlorinates 6,8-dichloro-1,2,3,4-tetrahydro-2,4-dioxoquinazoline to 2,4,6,8-tetra-chloroquinazoline.[63]

D. Preparation of Quinazolines Substituted with Halogen in the Benzene Ring or in the Side Chain

Halogen atoms in the benzene ring have only a small effect on the pyrimidine ring in quinazolines by virtue of the electronic properties. The general methods for preparing alkyl- and aryl- (Ch. III), and oxoquinazolines (Ch. IV) can therefore be applied to the synthesis of benz-substituted halogenoquinazolines. The preparation of benz-substituted halogenooxoquinazolines is described in chapter IV, and the 2-, 4-, and 2,4-halogeno derivatives of these are described in the above sections. 1,2,3,4-Tetrahydro-6-hydroxy-2,4-dioxoquinazoline is the only known example in which a hydroxy group in the benzene ring is converted to a chloro substituent, i.e. to 2,4,6-trichloroquinazoline, by reaction with phosphorus pentachloride in phosphoryl chloride.[76] 5-, 6-, 7-, or 8-Halogenoquinazolines can be prepared by the alkaline decomposition of the corresponding 4-N'-toluene-p-sulphonylhydrazino-quinazoline hydrochloride[37] (Ch. II, Sect. 1. and Ch. III, Sect. 1.D.; see also Sect. 1.E.b.(v)), by Riedel's synthesis[77] (Ch. II, Sect. 1.; Ch. III, Sect. 1.I.), by reaction of N-halogenophenyl imidoyl chlorides or esters with nitriles in the presence of a Lewis acid[66] (Ch. III, Sect. 1.E.), and by reaction of halogenophenyldiazonium borofluorides with nitriles[66] (Ch. III, Sect. 1.F.). By using halogenomethylnitriles in the last two methods 2- and 4-halogenoalkylquinazolines can be prepared.[66] Other preparations that are applicable are the deoxygenation of benz-substituted and side-chain-substituted halogenoquinazoline-N-oxides with phosphorus trichloride[78] (Ch. IX, Sect. 2.C.), the direct chlorination of 3,4-dihydro-2-methyl-4-oxoquinazolines to 3,4-dihydro-4-oxo-2-tri-chloromethylquinazolines followed by treatment with phosphorus pentachloride to give 4-chloro-2-trichloromethylquinazolines,[79] and the direct chlorination of 3,4-dihydro-4-oxoquinazoline to give the 6-chloro derivatives (Ch. IV, Sect. 2.C.b.(iv)). Sodium hypobromite converts a 4-methyl group to a 4-tribromomethyl group[80] (Ch. III, Sect. 2.B.b.). The chlorination of 1,2,3,4-tetrahydro-2,4-dioxoquinazo-line with sodium hypochlorite to 1,3-dichloro-1,2,3,4-tetrahydro-2,4-dioxoquinazoline has been described[81] (Ch. IV, Sect. 3.B.b.).

E. Properties of Halogenoquinazolines

a. *Physical Properties*

Halogenoquinazolines are low-melting solids which are readily crystallized from non-polar solvents, e.g. light petroleum and benzene. They have slightly pungent odours and are irritants to both nose and skin. 4-Chloroquinazolines decompose readily on distillation because traces of acid (formed from partial hydrolysis caused by atmospheric moisture or during the work-up) initiate hydrolysis followed by subsequent condensation which liberates more acid (see Sect. 1.E.b.(iii)). 2,4-Dichloroquinazolines, on the other hand, are best purified by distillation under reduced pressure,[20,73] probably because the 4-chlorine atom in these compounds is less reactive. The effect of the halogen atoms on the ultraviolet[37,82] and infrared spectrum,[83] and ionization constant[37] of quinazoline is described in chapter II, sections 2.B.a. and c., and 2.C.

b. *Chemical Properties*

(i) **Reactivity of halogens in the side chain or in the benzene ring.** Halogen atoms on methyl groups α or γ to the nitrogen atoms are as reactive as in halogenomethyl groups directly attached to an electron-withdrawing group such as carbonyl. 2- or 4-Trihalogenoquinazolines decompose readily with alkali to liberate the respective haloform[66,80] (Ch. III, Sect. 2.B.b.). Halogen atoms at the end of a side chain are not influenced by the quinazoline nucleus as long as they are placed too far away to be able to alkylate the ring. An example of such an alkylation (Reaction 9) is furnished by 6-chloro-4-(*N*-ethyl-*N*-2-chloroethyl)amino-quinazoline (**10**) which readily undergoes self quaternization followed by hydrolysis to 6-chloro-3-2′-ethylaminoethyl-3,4-dihydro-4-oxoquin-azoline (**11**).[84]

Halogen atoms in the benzene ring of quinazoline are much less reactive than those in the pyrimidine ring, but can undergo nucleophilic metathesis. 5-, 6-, and 7-fluoroquinazoline yield the respective methoxy compound with sodium methoxide. Of these, the 6-isomer is the least reactive, but the fluoro compounds are more reactive than the corresponding chloroquinazolines. Similarly 7-fluoroquinazoline and ethylthio anions give 7-ethylthioquinazoline.[44]

(ii) **Reactivity of the 2- and 4-halogen atoms.** 2- and 4-Chloro-and 2,4-dichloroquinazoline are most useful intermediates because the

EtN—CH$_2$CH$_2$Cl

Cl

(10)   (9)

$\longrightarrow$

EtN

Cl   Cl   O

N$^+$ N—CH$_2$CH$_2$NHEt

N   Cl$^-$ N

$\longrightarrow$

(11)

halogen atoms can be displaced by a variety of nucleophiles. The large difference in the reactivity between the 2- and the 4-halogen atoms makes possible the selective replacement of the halogen atoms in the 2,4-dichloro compound.

The kinetics of substitution of the chlorine atom in 2-chloroquinazoline with ethoxide ion and with piperidine have been studied at three different temperatures and it was found to be more reactive towards the former nucleophile. The second order rate constants in ethanol are 29.6×10^{-4} and 4.79×10^{-4}/mole sec at 20° respectively.[85] When compared with 2-chloropyrimidine the reactivity of 2-chloroquinazoline towards ethoxide ion is greater only by a factor of 1.4 instead of the usually fairly large increase observed on annelation.[86] It is suggested that any increase in reactivity due to the fusion of the benzene ring is offset by a reduction in the activating power of N$_{(3)}$ because of bond fixation.[85]

The reactivity of the chlorine atom in 4-chloroquinazoline towards piperidine is so high that the rates were measured at 0.0°, −18.0°, and −30.0° in a conductivity cell by observing the change in conductance due to the piperidine hydrochloride formed.[87] The kinetic data for the 2- and 4-chloroquinazolines are shown in table V.1. The reaction of 4-chloroquinazoline with pyridine in ethanol at 40° was also investigated but was complicated by alcoholysis. The formation of acid in this

TABLE V.1.   Replacement of Chlorine in 2- and 4-Chloroquinazolines by Piperidine in Ethanol.[85]

Compound	k at 20°	E	$\Delta H^{\ddagger}$ (cal/mole)	$\Delta S^{\ddagger}$ (cal/mole deg)
2-Chloroquinazoline	4.79×10^{-4}	11,100	10,500	37.8
4-Chloroquinazoline	3.1	7,000	6,600	37.5

reaction was ascribed to solvolysis of a quaternary salt, which is formed first, with the liberation of a proton.[85] It must be noted that the 4-chlorine atom reacts 6400 times as fast as the 2-chlorine atom, and the effect of annelation in 4-chloroquinazoline, as compared with 4-chloropyrimidine, is to increase the reactivity about 100-fold.[86] The difference in reactivity between the 2- and 4-chloroquinazolines in nucleophilic displacements is explained by the stabilizing influence of the resonance forms 12 and 13 in the transition state in the 4-isomer as compared with 14 and 15 in the 2-isomer, and hence to the greater ease of formation of the former. The contribution from the canonical form 15 in the latter is small because of the less stable o-quinonoid structure.[88,89] Kinetic data on 2,4-dichloroquinazoline is not available.

(12) ⟷ (13)

(14) ⟷ (15)

R = nucleophile

4-Chloroquinazoline reacts spontaneously with methanol to give 4-methoxyquinazoline hydrochloride and it is shown that the alcoholysis is autocatalyzed by the liberated acid. Ethanol reacts similarly, but less rapidly, and if a trace of sodium hydroxide is added to the alcoholic solution, 4-chloroquinazoline can be recrystallized from it without noticeable hydrolysis.[90] 4-Chloroquinazolines can be crystallized from a non-polar solvent, e.g. heptane, containing a small amount of triethylamine.[52] Hydrolysis of 4-chloro-, 4-chloro-6-nitro-, and 4-chloro-7-nitroquinazoline by boiling water is complete in 0.25, 0.5, and 0.5 hours respectively.[91] The effect of substituents on the displacement of the halogen atom in substituted 4-chloroquinazolines is worthy of further investigation. Hydrolysis of 4-chloroquinazoline takes place more rapidly in aqueous acid than in water or dilute alkali, probably because it involves a mechanism which is similar to hydration (Ch. II, Sect. 2.C.) by forming the hydrated intermediate 16 which preferentially loses the halogen atom rather than the hydroxy group (Reaction 10).

Because the chloroquinazolines are readily attacked by water, and liberate hydrogen chloride which autocatalyzes the hydrolysis, they cannot be stored for long periods. The cruder the material the more readily it decomposes. In ethanol, 4-chloroquinazoline gives the

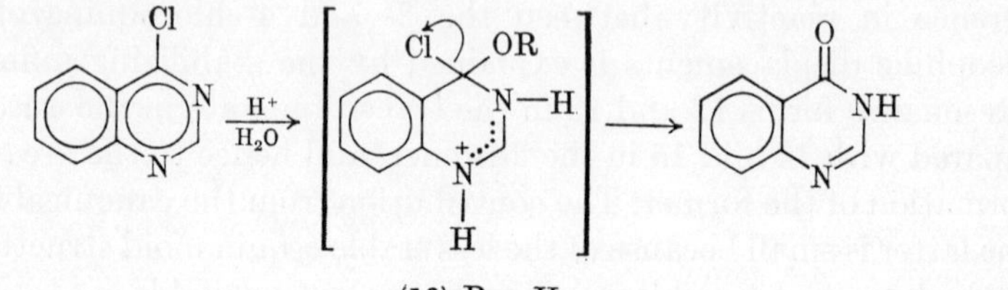

(10)

(16) R = H

intermediate 16 (R = OEt) which decomposes to 4-ethoxyquinazoline. It must be noted, also, that if a solution of 4-chloroquinazoline in ethanol containing sodium cyanide is heated, 4-ethoxy- and not 4-cyanoquinazoline is formed.[10,90] These displacements apply to 2,4-dichloroquinazolines in which the 4-chloro group is displaced first. This preferential exchange provides a useful method for preparing 4-substituted 2-chloroquinazolines (Sect. 1.A.).

(iii) **Metathesis.** The replacement of the 2- and 4-chlorine atoms by alkoxy[10,84] (Sects. 2.A., B., and C.), thio[20] (Ch. VI, Sects. 1.A.,2.B., and 3.), amino[15,20,79,92] (Ch. VII, Sects. 1.A.a., 1.B.a., and 1.C.a.), and azido[93] (Ch. VII, Sect. 1.C.a.) groups is discussed in the relevant chapters. The stepwise replacement of first the 4- and then the 2-chlorine atom in 2,4-dichloroquinazoline by alkoxy,[15] amino,[15,74] and thio groups[74] is useful in preparing a variety of substituted quinazolines (Reaction 11), and is described in the above relevant sections.

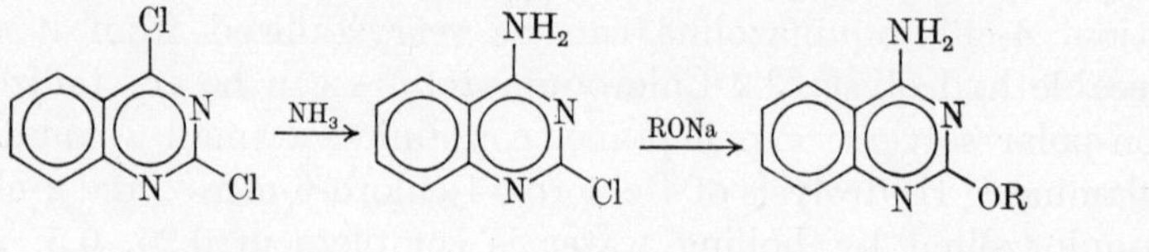

(11)

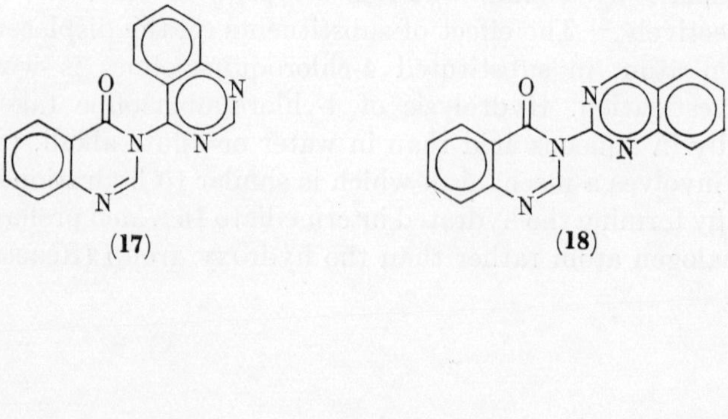

(17)   (18)

4-Chloroquinazoline reacts with an equimolar quantity of 3,4-dihydro-4-oxoquinazoline at 100°, and is rapidly and completely converted to 3,4-dihydro-4-oxo-3-quinazolin-4'-ylquinazoline (17).[94] These authors[94] succeeded in distilling 4-chloroquinazoline under reduced pressure, but distillation invariably leads to the formation of large quantities of 17 unless the crude chloro compound is perfectly dry and free from both acid and the oxo compound. The compound 17 is also formed when the crude chloroquinazoline is not purified over alumina, and when evaporation of solutions is not carried out below 40°.[29] Culbertson, Willits, and Christensen showed that 2-chloroquinazoline also reacts with 3,4-dihydro-4-oxoquinazoline to give 3,4-dihydro-4-oxo-3-quinazolin-2'-ylquinazoline (18), but 1,2-dihydro-2-oxoquinazoline or its potassium salt failed to condense with 2- or 4-chloroquinazoline.[95]

(iv) **Reduction.** Reduction of 2-chloro- and 2-chloro-4-phenyl-quinazoline with red phosphorus and fuming hydriodic acid removes the chlorine atom and reduces the compounds to the corresponding 3,4-dihydroquinazolines. Hydriodic acid in acetic acid reduces 2,4-dichloro-8-methylquinazoline to 3,4-dihydro-8-methylquinazoline.[70] Further examples are found in chapter VIII, section 4.D. In other cases, the same reagent is said to cause only hydrolysis, i.e. 6- and 8-methyl-4-chloroquinazoline yield 3,4-dihydro-6(or 8)-methyl-4-oxoquinazoline respectively. 2,4-Dichloroquinazoline and hydriodic acid containing phosphonium iodide give 3,4-dihydro-4-oxoquinazoline and 3,4-dihydroquinazoline.[53] It is possible that the reason for the formation of these oxoquinazolines is that too weak a hydriodic acid had been used. Reduction of 2-chloro-4-methoxyquinazoline to 4-methoxyquinazoline can be achieved with sodium and ethanol, or zinc and acetic acid in ethanol, but not with sodium in ether or in amyl alcohol, or with zinc and sodium hydroxide in ethanol.[10]

The neatest method for reducing chloroquinazolines is catalytic hydrogenolysis because the progress of the reaction can be followed by measuring the rate of hydrogen uptake. 2-Chloro-4-2'-pyridylquinazoline in methanol is reduced to 4-2'-pyridylquinazoline[8] by 5% palladium on charcoal, but 2-chloro-4-phenylquinazoline yields 3,4-dihydro-4-phenylquinazoline[2] (Ch. III, Sect. 1.J.). The latter example is a reminder that the 3,4-double bond in quinazoline is reactive and may be reduced, unless conditions are carefully devised, i.e. stopping the reduction after the uptake of one molecule of hydrogen. However, this is not a serious drawback because 3,4-dihydroquinazolines are readily oxidized in good yields to the corresponding quinazolines (Ch. II, Sect. 1., Ch. III. Sect. 1.B.). In the catalytic reduction of 4-chloroquinazo-lines hydrogenolysis of the chlorine atom must take place before the 3,4-double bond can be reduced (Reaction 12). The success of these dehalogenations rests on the relative rates of hydrogenolysis of the chlorine atom and the reduction of the 3,4-double bond. The catalytic reduction of 4-chloroquinazoline has been studied in some detail by Elderfield and coworkers.[45] They found that the course of reduction at 30 lbs/in^2 pressure of hydrogen was influenced markedly by the solvent and the catalyst. With palladium on calcium carbonate in hydroxylated solvents, e.g. alcohol or ethylene glycol monomethyl ether, hydrogen absorption proceeded rapidly and 90–93% yields of 3,4-dihydroquinazo-line were obtained. In dioxan, on the other hand, reduction was slow and after absorption of one molecule of hydrogen, reduction practically ceased and quinazoline was isolated in 51% yield. When sodium acetate or potassium hydroxide was added to the latter reaction a second molecule of hydrogen was absorbed but much more slowly than the first, and the product was 3,4-dihydroquinazoline. The reduction in isopropanol and t-butanol proceeded more slowly than in the above examples, but was faster in the secondary than in the tertiary alcohol.[45] Reduction was incomplete with Raney nickel catalyst, in dioxan and in methanol, probably because of inactivation of the catalyst by the acid liberated. The hydrogenation of 4-chloroquinazoline in methanol or ethanol (in the presence of potassium hydroxide, over Raney nickel or palladium on calcium carbonate) resulted in alcoholysis, so that 4-methoxy- and 4-ethoxyquinazoline were formed.[45] Hydrogena-tion over palladium on magnesium oxide at atmospheric pressure of hydrogen can be stopped after the absorption of one molecule of hydrogen to give quinazoline, or after absorption of 2 molecules of hydrogen to give 3,4-dihydroquinazoline.[48] The most satisfactory

$$\text{(12)}$$

conditions for reduction were found to be hydrogenation (at atmos-pheric pressure) of 4-chloroquinazolines in benzene containing 1.5 mol of anhydrous sodium acetate in the minimum volume of methanol (or ethanol) to dissolve this salt, over 5% palladium on charcoal and stopping the reduction after the adsorption of one molecule of hydro-gen.[29,37] The most active palladium–charcoal catalyst for these reductions was prepared by the formaldehyde reduction method,[96] and it is advisable not to use methanol as solvent because it ignites spontaneously with the catalyst prepared in this way. It is also of utmost importance for the success of these reductions that the chloro compound is free from catalyst poisons. The chloroquinazolines should therefore be further purified by passage through an alumina column and a column of charcoal (the same charcoal used in the preparation of the catalyst) in an inert solvent such as benzene.

Nitro groups in the benzene ring of chloroquinazolines are reduced to amino groups in these hydrogenations. The reduction of 4-chloroquinazoline with palladium on charcoal in boiling xylene furnishes 3,4-dihydroquinazoline, but chemical reducing agents only cause substitution of the chlorine atom and not reduction.[97]

The reduction of halogen atoms in the side chain of quinazolines is described in chapter III, section I.J.

(v) **Dehalogenation.** Apart from the above reductions (Sect. 1.E.b.(iv)), non-reductive methods of dehalogenation are known. The methods in this subsection do not suffer from further reduction of the quinazoline nucleus or substituent groups, e.g. nitro, cyano. The most useful way in which a chlorine atom in positions 2 and 4 can be replaced by hydrogen in the quinazoline series is via the decomposition of the toluene-p-sulphonylhydrazino derivatives. This reaction was originated by Escales[98] in 1885 for preparing benzene from N'-phenylbenzene-sulphonylhydrazine, and was first used by Dewar[97] in 1944 on a quinazoline. The usefulness of this reaction in heterocyclic chemistry was clearly demonstrated by Albert and Royer[99] in 1949, who, in the synthesis of acridine derivatives, showed how the reaction conditions should be modified depending on the electronic properties of the substituents.

The method has been used successfully in the quinazoline series[37] as well as in the naphthyridine,[100] cinnoline,[101] phthalazine,[102] and triazanaphthalene[103] series. The chloroquinazoline in chloroform is treated with one equivalent of toluene-p-sulphonylhydrazine in the least possible volume of chloroform and allowed to stand or boiled until the separation of the hydrochloride salt is complete. Bubbling dry hydrogen chloride through the mixture for one or two minutes sometimes assists the reaction but is generally not necessary. The salt is collected, dried and then heated at 100° in aqueous alkali until evolution of nitrogen gas is complete (Eq. 13). The amount of alkali added should be at least 2.2 mols with respect to the tosyl derivative. One mol of

alkali neutralizes the hydrogen chloride from the salt, the second mol
neutralizes the sulphinic acid formed, and the 0.2 mol is excess to keep
the solution alkaline. This reaction is initiated and maintained by
formation of an anion (see Ch. II, Sect. 1.). The most satisfactory
solvent is a water–ethylene glycol mixture (3 : 7, by volume). When
electron-withdrawing groups, e.g. nitro, are present the pH of the
solution must be lower.[37,103] The reaction is catalyzed by powdered
glass.[104] The conditions and yields for substituted quinazolines are
shown in table V.2.

$$\text{(13)}$$

2-Chloro-4-phenylquinazoline is also dehalogenated via the
toluene-p-sulphonylhydrazine derivative, in dioxan with sodium
carbonate, to 4-phenylquinazoline.

Another non-reductive dehalogenation method is the conversion
of the chloro compound to a hydrazinoquinazoline followed by oxidation
of this with copper sulphate. This method was very successful in the
naphthyridine series[105] and proved suitable for the preparation of
4-phenylquinazoline from the 2-chloro derivative.[2] Although 4-chloro-
quinazoline is readily converted to 4-hydrazinoquinazoline, reaction of
this with copper sulphate gave only a trace of quinazoline. If copper
sulphate is replaced by freshly precipitated manganese dioxide (in
acetic acid), the yield of quinazoline is 6%[106] (Ch. II, Sect. 1.).

(vi) **Miscellaneous.** The reactions of chloroquinazolines with
Grignard reagents and with compounds that have a reactive methylene
group are described in chapter III, sections 1.G. and 1.H., respectively.
Chloroquinazolines have been used in the preparation of dyestuffs, and
have been used to modify dyes with hydroxy and amino groups with
which they can react.[69,107,108] Reaction with long chain aliphatic
amines produces surface active compounds which are weaker bases,[109]

TABLE V.2.   Quinazolines Prepared from 4-N'-Toluene-p-sulphonylhydrazino-quinazoline Derivatives in Ethylene Glycol–Water (7 : 3).[37,44]

Quinazoline derivative	Yield (%)	Conditions
5-Me	63	0.5 N NaOH, 100°/2 hr
6-Me	62	0.5 N NaOH, 100°/1 hr
7-Me	67	0.5 N NaOH, 100°/1 hr
8-Me	62	0.5 N NaOH, 100°/1 hr
5-Cl	60	0.5 N NaOH, 100°/2 hr
7-Cl	30	1.0 N NaOH, 100°/2 hr
5-F	48	0.4 N NaOH, 100°/1 hr
6-F	60	0.4 N NaOH, 100°/1 hr
7-F	12.5	0.5 N NaOH, 100°/1 hr
	22	N Na$_2$CO$_3$, 100°/1 hr
5-CF$_3$	34	0.4 N NaOH, 100°/1 hr
6-CF$_3$	50	0.4 N NaOH, 100°/1 hr
7-CF$_3$	62	0.4 N NaOH, 100°/1 hr
8-CF$_3$	33	0.4 N NaOH, 100°/1 hr
7-OMe	65	0.5 N NaOH, 100°/1 hr
5-NO$_2$	25	0.125 N Na$_2$CO$_3$, 100°/2 hr
7-NO$_2$	30	0.125 N Na$_2$CO$_3$, 100°/2 hr
8-NO$_2$	15	0.125 N Na$_2$CO$_3$, 100°/2 hr

and with a variety of amines give biologically active compounds (Ch. XI, Sect. 2.). 1,3-Dichloro-1,2,3,4-tetrahydro-2,4-dioxoquinazoline possesses mild bleaching action by slow elimination of chlorine.[81]

2. Quinazolinyl Ethers

A. Preparation of 2-Quinazolinyl Ethers

2-Ethoxy-3,4-dihydro-4-oxoquinazoline was the second quinazoline to be described (the first being the 2-cyano derivative), and was obtained from anthranilic acid and cyanogen in ethanol (see Ch. I, Sect. 1. and Ch. IV, Sect 3.A.a.).[110] Later it was synthesized from methyl or ethyl anthranilate and ethyl cyanimidocarbonate in the presence of cuprous chloride.[111,112] Similarly by using methyl cyanimidocarbonate, the 2-methoxy derivative was obtained[112] (Ch. IV, Sect. 3.A.a.).

2-Alkoxyquinazolines are commonly prepared by nucleophilic displacement of the halogen atom in 2-chloroquinazolines by sodium

9 + Q.

alkoxide in the appropriate alcohol (Reaction 14).[2,7,27,28,50] Another method (which is limited to the preparation of 3,4-dihydro-4-oxoquinazolines with alkoxy or aryloxy groups in position 2) is the prolonged treatment (4–6 hrs boiling) of the 2,4-diethers of quinazoline with sodium ethoxide in ethanol. Thus 2,4-dimethoxy-, diethoxy-, dipropoxy-, dibutoxy-, and diphenoxyquinazoline yield 2-methoxy-, 2-ethoxy-, 2-propoxy-, 2-butoxy,[15] and 2-phenoxy-[26] 3,4-dihydro-4-oxoquinazolines (Reaction 15). 2-Methoxyquinazoline can be prepared from 4-carboxy-1,2-dihydro-2-oxoquinazoline (Ch. IV, Sect. 1.A.) by methylation with diazomethane and hydrolysis, followed by decarboxylation.[113]

$$\text{(14)}$$

2-Phenoxyquinazoline is prepared by slowly adding 2-chloroquinazoline to phenol containing potassium hydroxide at 100°.[56]

$$\text{(15)}$$

B. Preparation of 4-Quinazolinyl Ethers

a. *Alkylation of 3,4-Dihydro-4-oxoquinazolines*

The direct alkylation of 3,4-dihydro-4-oxoquinazolines almost invariably leads to $N_{(3)}$-alkyl derivatives. Only occasionally, for reasons that are not yet clear, alkylation on oxygen occurs with the formation of 4-quinazolinyl ethers. The alkylation of 3,4-dihydro-4-oxoquinazoline with diazomethane is claimed to give a 20% yield of 4-methoxyquinazoline,[114] and 2-methyl-5-nitro- and 2-ethyl-5-nitro- 3,4-dihydro-4-oxoquinazoline with ethyl iodide give 2-methyl- and 2-ethyl- 4-ethoxy-5-nitroquinazoline.[115] Also 3,4-dihydro-7-nitro-4-oxoquinazoline with ethyl and pentyl iodides yields exclusively 4-ethoxy- and 4-pentyloxy-7-nitroquinazoline respectively[115] (Ch. IV, Sect. 2.C.b.(i)). Because of the danger of alkylation on $N_{(3)}$, which is the normal course for this reaction, the method is not recommended for the preparation of 4-quinazolinyl ethers.

b. *Nucleophilic Displacement at Position 4*

This displacement of the halogen atom in 4-chloroquinazolines by alkoxide ions affords the most convenient method for preparing 4-quinazolinyl alkyl ethers. A large number of 4-alkoxyquinazolines can be obtained by boiling the corresponding 4-chloroquinazolines with sodium alkoxide in the appropriate alcohol for 0.5 to 2 hours (Reaction 16).[30,35,36,38,50,116-118] Heating for longer periods is not advised (see Sect. 2.A.). When 4-ω-aminoalkyloxyquinazolines are to be prepared, sodium in excess of the amino alcohol (which also acts as solvent) is used to displace the 4-chlorine atom.[119,120] 4-Quinazolinyl ethers can also be prepared by heating the 4-chloroquinazoline with the alcohol in dry toluene in the presence of sodium hydride.[52] It must be pointed out

$$X \quad\quad\quad OR$$

$$\xrightarrow{\text{RONa}} \quad\quad\quad (16)$$

$$X = Cl, CN, SMe$$

here that the methoxy-[50] and ethoxyquinazolines[49] obtained from the tetrachloro-2-methylquinazoline which was recently shown to be 4-chloro-2-trichloromethylquinazoline,[51] were 4-methoxy- and 4-ethoxy-2-trichloromethylquinazoline.

4-Phenoxyquinazolines cannot be prepared from 4-chloroquinazolines and phenol in the presence of sodium alkoxide because 4-alkoxyquinazolines are formed (see Sect. 1.A.). Molten phenol containing sodium[10] or potassium hydroxide and a 4-chloroquinazoline gives the 4-phenoxy derivative, but when ammonium carbonate is added, 4-aminoquinazolines are formed[121] (Ch. VII, Sect. 1.B.a.). Phenol and sodium in boiling dioxan forms a useful reagent for preparing 2-2'-furyl-4-phenoxyquinazolines from the corresponding 4-chloro compounds.[30,38,117,118] Twenty-one phenols with chloro, methyl, hydroxy, methoxy, and nitro groups (including α- and β-naphthoxy), however, gave 4-aryloxyquinazolines when boiled with 4-chloroquinazoline in the presence of ethanolic sodium ethoxide.[122] This is probably because these hydroxy compounds are stronger nucleophiles than phenol.

4-Quinazolinyl ethers can also be prepared by the reaction of alkoxide or phenoxide ions with 4-cyanoquinazoline.[123] Many 4-alkoxy-quinazolines have been obtained in yields greater than 60% by boiling the corresponding 4-methylthio- or ethylthioquinazoline with an equivalent of alcoholic sodium alkoxide.[124]

c. *From* o-*Amidobenzonitrile Derivatives*

When o-amidobenzonitriles are boiled with sodium alkoxides in the corresponding alcohols for 3–5 hours, 4-alkoxyquinazolines are formed. The nature of the acyl group determines the substituent on $C_{(2)}$ and the nature of the alkoxide determines the substituent on the oxygen atom (Reaction 17). A serious drawback in this synthesis is deacylation of the starting material but this can be minimized by starting the reaction with 0.05 N alkoxide in the respective alcohol and adding occasionally small volumes of 0.5 N alkoxide to keep the solution alkaline. Yields of over 60% can be obtained in this way. o-Formamido-, o-acetamido-, and o-benzamidobenzonitriles give 4-alkoxy-, 4-alkoxy-2-methyl-, and 4-alkoxy-2-phenyl- quinazolines respectively. For 2-methyl-4-phenoxyquinazolines the reaction is carried out in phenol. The reaction of 1-acetamido-2-cyanonaphthalene and 0.1 N sodium methoxide is slow but gives an 80% yield of 7,8-benzo-4-methoxy-2-methyl-

(17)

quinazoline.[125] When R in **19** is OMe or OEt then the products are 4-alkoxy-1,2-dihydro-2-oxoquinazolines.[126] The latter reaction cannot be brought about without alkoxide ions which suggests that it does not involve a rearrangement.

d. *Miscellaneous*

4-Alkoxy-2-chloroquinazolines can be obtained from 2,4-dichloro-quinazolines and sodium alkoxide[10,12] (Sect. 1.A.). The 2-chlorine atom can be substituted by anilines to give 4-alkoxy-2-anilinoquinazolines.[14,20,127] The preparations of 4-quinazolinyl ethers and their 2-substituted derivatives from quinazoline-N-oxides are described in chapter IX, section 1. The preparation of 4-alkoxyquinazolines by transalkylation is discussed in section 2.E.b.(iii).

C. Preparation of 2,4-Quinazolinyl Diethers

2,4-Dialkoxyquinazolines are readily prepared by boiling 2,4-dichloroquinazolines with 2 equivalents of alkali alkoxides in the appropriate alcohol for about 2 hours,[10,12,15,26,50,68,128] although times of up to 8–9 hours are recorded.[129] 2,4-Diphenoxyquinazoline is obtained from heating 2,4-dichloroquinazoline in molten phenol containing 2 equivalents of sodium.[128] The large enhanced reactivity of the 4- (as compared with the 2-) chlorine atom in 2,4-dichloroquinazoline makes it possible to prepare mixed ethers. Thus 2,4-dichloroquinazoline and one equivalent of sodium ethoxide yield 2-chloro-4-ethoxy-quinazoline which on further treatment with one equivalent of sodium in phenol gives 4-ethoxy-2-phenoxyquinazoline (Reaction 18).[128] Very great care, however, must be taken because of the possibility of transalkylation in position 4. Advantage can be taken of transalkylation in order to prepare mixed ethers. When 2,4-diphenoxyquinazoline is heated with sodium methoxide or ethoxide, 4-methoxy- or 4-ethoxy-2-phenoxyquinazoline (20) is formed. The latter two can be interconverted by using the appropriate alkoxide (Reaction 19). 2,4-Dimethoxy-quinazoline and sodium ethoxide give 4-ethoxy-2-methoxyquinazoline, and 2,4-diethoxyquinazoline and sodium methoxide form 2-ethoxy-4-methoxyquinazoline. The 2-substituent does not undergo this exchange and sodium phenoxide does not exchange with the 4-substituent.[128]

(18)

(20)

2,4-Dialkoxyquinazolines can be prepared from 4-alkoxy-2-cyanoquinazoline by displacement with sodium alkoxides.[9]

OPh   OMe

$$\xrightarrow{\text{NaOMe}} \qquad \xrightarrow{\text{NaOEt}} \mathbf{20} \qquad (19)$$

D. Preparation of Quinazolines with Alkoxy Groups in the Benzene Ring

3,4-Dihydro-4-oxoquinazolines with alkoxy groups in the benzene ring are synthesized by the general methods described in chapter IV. Hence, 6-[18] and 8-methoxy-,[47] and 5-chloro-8-methoxy-[130] 3,4-dihydro-4-oxoquinazolines are prepared by Niementowski's synthesis (Ch. IV, Sect. 2.A.a.); 5-methoxy-,[130] 7-methoxy-,[18] 6,7-methylenedioxy-2-methyl- and 6,7-methylenedioxy-2-propyl- 3,4-dihydro-4-oxoquinazolines are obtained by cyclization of the respective *o*-amidobenzamides with alkali[131] (Ch. IV, Sect. 2.A.b.); 8-methoxy-2-methyl-,[132] 6,7-dimethoxy-2-methyl-,[133,134] 6,7-dimethoxy-2-benzyl-, 6,7-dimethoxy-2-3′,4′-dimethoxybenzyl-,[133] and 7,8-dimethoxy-2-methyl-[135] 3,4-dihydro-4-oxoquinazolines are synthesized from 3,1,4-benzoxazones (Ch. IV, Sect. 2.A.e.); and 6- and 8-methoxy-, 6- and 8-ethoxy- 3,4-dihydro-2-methyl-4-oxoquinazolines[136] are obtained by Sen and Ray's synthesis. (Ch. IV, Sect. 2.A.j.). 2-, 4-, and 2,4-halogeno alkoxy-, or aryloxy-quinazolines with the ether groups in the benzene ring are prepared by methods described in sections 1 and 2.

At this stage attention must be drawn to the alkoxyquinazolines investigated by Dewar[97] and Elderfield and collaborators.[45] The nitration of 2-acetamido-5-methoxytoluene was shown to form 2-acetamido-5-methoxy-4-nitrotoluene (**21**)[137] and not the 3-nitro isomer as postulated by the above authors. Oxidation followed by hydrolysis gave 5-methoxy-4-nitroanthranilic acid (**22**) which was converted to 3,4-dihydro-6-methoxy-7-nitro-4-oxoquinazoline (**23**), and all the 6-methoxy-8-nitroquinazolines described by Dewar[97] and Elderfield and collaborators[45] are 6-methoxy-7-nitroquinazolines, e.g. **24** and **25** (Reaction 20). Compounds derived from these are therefore 7- and not 8-substituted derivatives.

C-Alkyl- and *C*-arylquinazolines with alkoxy groups in the benzene ring are prepared by standard methods discussed in chapter III. 6,7-Dimethoxy-2-methyl-, 6,7-dimethoxy-2-phenyl-,[138] 8-methoxy-, 8-methoxy-2-methyl-, 8-methoxy-2-propyl-, 2-benzyl-8-methoxy-, 8-methoxy-2-phenyl-, 8-methoxy-2-*p*-tolyl-, 2-*o*-chlorophenyl-8-methoxy-, 2-*p*-bromophenyl-8-methoxy-, 2-2′,4′-dichlorophenyl-

(21)   (22)   (20)

(23)   (24)   (25)

8-methoxy-,[139] 2-3',4'-dimethoxybenzyl-6,7-dimethoxy-,[140] 6,7-di-methoxy-2-3',4'-methylenedioxybenzyl-, 6,7-methylenedioxy-2-3',4'-methylenedioxybenzyl-,[141] 6,7-methylenedioxy-2-3',4'-methylenedioxyphenyl-,[142] 6,7-dimethoxy-2-phenyl-,[143] 8-methoxy-4-methyl-, 8-methoxy-4-propyl-[144] 8-methoxy-2,4-dimethyl- and 8-methoxy-4-methyl-2-phenyl- quinazolines are obtained by Bischler's synthesis (Ch. III, Sect. 1.A.). 6,7-Methylenedioxyquinazoline can be prepared by oxidation of the corresponding 3,4-dihydro derivative[143,145] (Ch. III, Sect. 1.B.), 7-methoxyquinazoline is formed from the 4-N'-toluene-p-sulphonylhydrazino hydrochloride derivative[37] (Sect. 1.E.b.(v) and Ch. III, Sect. 1.D.), and 6,7-methylenedioxy-,[146] 6,7-dimethoxy-,[133] and 5-,[37] 6-,[37,77,147] 7-,[77] and 8-methoxy-[147] quinazolines can be obtained by Reidel's synthesis (Ch. III, Sect. 1.I.).

E. Properties of Quinazolinyl Ethers

a. *Physical Properties*

Quinazolinyl ethers are mostly low-melting compounds, some of which are steam volatile[50] and have pleasant odours not unlike phenyl ethers. They are readily soluble in organic solvents and can be distilled or sublimed without decomposition. 2- and 4-alkoxyquinazolines tend to be hygroscopic[125] and take up one or two molecules of water in their crystal structure, but this can easily be removed by distillation or by heating in a vacuum over a drying agent. The effects of alkoxy groups on the ultraviolet and infrared spectra, ionization constants, and covalent addition of water, of quinazoline, are discussed in chapter II.

b. *Chemical Properties*

(i) **Hydrolysis.** Alkoxy groups in the benzene ring are compara-tively stable and are dealkylated by reagents commonly used in the benzene series, i.e. boiling hydrobromic acid[8,132] or anhydrous aluminium chloride[37,147] (Ch. IV, Sect. 4.A.). 2- and 4-Quinazolinyl ethers, on the other hand, are very readily hydrolyzed by hydrochloric acid to the corresponding oxoquinazolines.[10,12,28,50,125] This reaction is very useful to distinguish 2- and 4-quinazolinyl ethers from the isomeric $N_{(1)}$- and $N_{(3)}$-alkyloxoquinazolines. The latter require more drastic hydrolytic treatment (Ch. IV, Sect. 2.C.b.(iii)). 4-Alkoxy groups are more easily hydrolyzed than 2-alkoxy groups, and 2,4-dialkoxyquinazolines, if boiled for long periods with sodium ethoxide, give 2-alkoxy-3,4-dihydro-4-oxoquinazolines[15,90] (see Sect. 2.A.). The formation of 3,4-dihydro-4-oxoquinazoline hydrochloride by boiling 4-chloroquinazoline in methanol under strictly anhydrous conditions is anomalous.[90] 4-Phenoxy-, 6-nitro-4-phenoxy-, and 7-nitro-4-phenoxy- quinazolines are not hydrolyzed by boiling water after 2 to 4 hours, but boiling for one hour in 0.02 N hydrochloric acid converts them completely to the respective 3,4-dihydro-4-oxoquinazolines.[91] As in the hydrolysis of 4-chloroquinazolines (Sect. 1.E.b.(ii)), a hydrated protonated intermediate may be involved in the hydrolysis (Reaction 21).

$$(21)$$

(ii) **Alkylation.** Methylation of 8-methoxy-[144] and 6,7-methylenedioxy-[146] quinazolines proceeds as for quinazoline (Ch. II, Sect. 3.B.) and the corresponding 3-methylquinazolinium salts are formed. The presence of an alkoxy or phenoxy group on $C_{(4)}$ alters the site of alkylation from $N_{(3)}$ to $N_{(1)}$. However the latter reaction is sometimes accompanied by rearrangement.[148,149] Thus 4-methoxyquinazoline and methyl and ethyl iodides yield 3,4-dihydro-1,3-dimethyl- and 3,4-dihydro-1-ethyl-3-methyl-4-oxoquinazolinium iodides respectively (Reaction 22). Methyl toluene-p-sulphonate gives similar products.

$$(22)$$

4-Phenoxyquinazolines form 1,4-dihydro-1-methyl-4-oxoquinazolines without rearrangement but with elimination of phenol. The structure of the products is deduced by alkaline hydrolysis to o-alkylaminobenzoic acids.[121,150]

(iii) **Metathesis.** Substitution reactions involving ether groups in the benzene ring of quinazoline are not known, but the substitution of alkoxy groups on $C_{(2)}$ and $C_{(4)}$ are common. The 4-alkoxy group is displaced more readily than the 2-alkoxy group. 2,4-Dimethoxyquinazolines react with the sodio derivative of sulphanilamides to form 2-methoxy-4-sulphanilamidoquinazolines.[151,152] Transalkylation, or the displacement of the alkoxy or aryloxy group in 4-quinazolinyl ethers, can be effected with comparative ease. When 4-methoxyquinazoline is heated with sodium ethoxide in ethanol or sodium isopropoxide in isopropanol, 4-ethoxy- and 4-isopropoxyquinazoline are formed in 51 and 58% yields (Reaction 23).[153] Generally the alkoxy group in the 4-quinazolinyl ethers can be converted to the higher or lower homologue, a phenoxy group can be converted to an alkoxy or benzyloxy group, but it cannot be formed by this reaction.[118] 4-Butoxy-, 4-pentyloxy-, and 4-benzyloxy-2-anilinoquinazoline can be prepared in good yields from 2-anilino-4-ethoxyquinazoline by boiling with the appropriate alcohol containing the sodium alkoxide.[12,127] 2-Methoxy-quinazoline also undergoes this reaction with sodium ethoxide and sodium isopropoxide to give 2-ethoxy- and 2-isopropoxyquinazoline in 83 and 61% yields.[153] 2,4-Dialkoxyquinazolines undergo these

$$\text{(23)}$$

displacements at $C_{(4)}$ (Sect. 2.C.), and the only example where the two alkoxy groups have been exchanged is the conversion of 2,4-dimethoxyquinazoline to 2,4-bis-2'-methoxyethoxyquinazoline with sodium 2-methoxyethoxide.[152]

The displacement of a 4-alkoxy group, e.g. methoxy, by ammonia takes place very slowly[114] but with alkylamines, e.g. 2-diethylamino-ethylamine[20] or hydrazine,[15] the reaction occurs readily (Ch. VII, Sect. 1.B.a.).

(iv) **Rearrangements.** The first record of rearrangements in the quinazolinyl ether series was that of Bogert and Seil[115] who showed that 4-ethoxy-2-methyl- and 4-ethoxy-2-ethyl-5-nitroquinazoline

9*

rearranged to 3-ethyl-2-methyl- and 2,3-diethyl- 3,4-dihydro-5-nitro-4-oxoquinazolines, respectively, on recrystallization from alcohol (Ch. IV, Sect. 2.C.b.(i)). Grout and Partridge recently showed that 4- and 2,4-quinazolinyl ethers undergo thermal rearrangement. 2,4-Dialkoxyquinazolines rearranged to 1,3-dialkyl-1,2,3,4-tetrahydro-2,4-dioxoquinazolines on distillation (Reaction 24). Also, distillation of 2-chloro-4-2'-chloroethoxyquinazoline yields 2-chloro-3-2'-chloroethyl-3,4-dihydro-4-oxoquinazoline. 2-Chloro-4-2'-hydroxyethoxyquinazoline and the homologous 4-3'-hydroxypropoxy derivative, undergo similar rearrangements when treated with thionyl chloride. In each case the ω-chloroalkyl-oxoquinazoline is formed (Reaction 25). The rearrangement proceeds most likely via an oxazolinium chloride because 2-chloro-4-2'-chloropropoxyquinazoline isomerizes to 2-chloro-3-2'-chloroisopropyl-3,4-dihydro-4-oxoquinazoline (26) on distillation, and not to 2-chloro-3-2'-chloropropyl-3,4-dihydro-4-oxoquinazoline (27) (Reaction 26).[12] Similarly 4-(estra-1',3',5'-trien-17'-on-3'-yl)oxyquinazoline rearranges to the $N_{(3)}$ derivative by heating at 330–335°.[153a] Distillation of

(24)

2-chloro-4-2'-diethylaminoethoxyquinazoline caused elimination of ethyl chloride with the formation of 1-ethyl-1,2,3,5-tetrahydro-5-oxoimidazo(2,1-b)quinazoline (Reaction 27). A similar rearrangement with cyclization occurs with the dimethylaminoethoxy derivative which

(25)

also produces some 1,2,3,4-tetrahydro-3-methyl-2,4-dioxoquinazoline, implying that 2-chloro-3-2'-dimethylaminoethyl-3,4-dihydro-4-oxoquinazoline is an intermediate.[11] 4-Alkoxy-2-chloro-, 4-benzyloxy-2-chloro-, and 2-chloro-4-ethoxyquinazoline did not isomerize on heating, and 2-anilino-4-2'-hydroxyethoxyquinazoline did not undergo rearrangement with thionyl chloride.[12]

2,4-bis-2'-Diethylaminoethoxyquinazoline described by Donleavy and Kise[154] is apparently 1,3-bis-2'-diethylaminoethyl-1,2,3,4-tetrahydro-2,4-dioxoquinazoline.[12]

$$(26)$$

$$(26)$$

$$(27)$$

8-Allyloxyquinazoline undergoes a Claisen rearrangement to 7-allyl-8-hydroxyquinazoline on heating[144] (Ch. IV, Sect. 4.A.).

$$(27)$$

3. Tables

TABLE V.3.   2-Chloroquinazolines.

2-Chloroquinazoline	M.p. (°c)	References
Unsubstituted	108°	1
4-2'-Acetamidoethylamino-	206–207°	20, 21
4-Amino-	239°	24
4-Amino-6-methyl-	272°	73
4-Anilino-7,8-benzo-	184°	162
6,7-Benzo-4-2'-diethylaminoethylamino-	H$_2$O 140–142°	19
4-Benzylamino-6-methyl-	160°	73

(*Table continued*)

TABLE V.3 (*continued*)

2-Chloroquinazoline	M.p. (°c)	References
4-*p*-Chloroanilino-	HCl 210–215°	58
4-(α-Cyano-α-ethoxycarbonyl)methyl-	145.5–147°	25
4-Ethylamino-	169–170°	23
4-(1′-Ethylpyrrolidin-3′-ylmethylamino)-	H₂O 93–97° (dec.)	52
4-Diethylamino-	76.5–77.5°	23, 52
4-4′-Diethylaminobutylamino-	71°	20
4-*p*-2′-Diethylaminoethoxyanilino-	HCl 211–213°	22
4-2′-Diethylaminoethylamino-	85°; H₂O 80–81°, 185°/0.04 mm; HCl 202–203°	18, 20
4-2′-Diethylaminoethylamino-7-methyl-	112°	19
4-2′-Diethylaminoethylamino-6-nitro-	125–126°	19
4-2′-Diethylaminoethylamino-7-nitro-	117°	19
4-*N*-2′-Diethylaminoethylanilino-	239–241°	22
4-2′-(2-Diethylaminoethylthio)ethyl-amino-	102–104°	22
4-(4′-Diethylamino-1′-methyl)butyl-amino-	98°, 200–203°/0.08 mm	18, 20
4-(3′-Diethylamino-1′-methyl)propyl-amino-	HCl 165–167°	22
4-3′-Diethylaminopropylamino-	2 H₂O 66–68°	20, 21
4-Dimethylamino-	67.5°	52
4-2′-Dimethylaminoethylamino-	96–98°	20
4-3′-Dimethylaminopropylamino-	2 H₂O 74°	20
4-Hydrazino-6-methyl-	330–335° (dec.)	73
4-2′-Hydroxyethylamino-	186°	20
4-Isopropyl-	oil	3
4-(1′-Isopropylpyrrolidin-3′-ylmethyl-amino)-	122–123° (dec.)	52
4-Methyl-	112°	7
6-Methyl-4-phenyl-	140–141°	5
4-(1′-Methylpyrrolidin-3′-ylmethyl-amino)-	H₂O 91–96° (dec.)	52
4-Morpholino-	114°	17
4-(1′-Phenethylpyrrolidin-3′-ylmethyl-amino)-	129–131°	52
4-Phenyl-	114–115°	1, 2
4-Piperidino-	71°	17
4-3′-Piperidinopropylamino-	H₂O 141°	20
4-2′-Pyridyl-	171–172°	8
4-*N*-Pyrrolidinyl-	170°	17
4-Sulphanilamido-	360°, ~ 260° rapid heating	152
4-2′,4′-Xylyl-	126°	4

TABLE V.4.   4-Chloroquinazolines.

4-Chloroquinazoline	M.p. (°c)	References
Unsubstituted	96°; picrate 170–170.5°	1, 29, 33, 48, 50, 52
2-2′-Anthraquinonyl-	276–278°	156
6,7-Benzo-	179°	54
6,7-Benzo-x-chloro-	192°	54
2-Benzyl-	74–75.5°	155
2-3′-Butylaminopropylamino-	sesquipicrate 157–159°	58
2-p-Chloroanilino-	177–178°	20, 60
2-p-Chlorocarbonylphenyl-	155–156°	63
2-o-Chlorophenyl-	124–125°	156
2-3′-Dibutylaminopropylamino-	sesquipicrate 157–159°	58
2-1′,1′-Dichloroethyl-	96–96.5°	51
2-2′,4′-Dichlorophenyl-	133–134°	156
2-Diethylamino-	118–120°/5 mm	52
2-2′-Diethylaminoethylamino-	170–175°/0.001 mm; sesquipicrate 205°	58
2-3′-Diethylaminopropylamino-	210–212°/0.2 mm	58
2-3′,4′-Dimethoxyphenethyl-	116–118°	35
2-2′-Furyl-	120°	30
2-2′-Furyl-6-methyl-	144°	38
2-p-Methoxyphenethyl-	125–128°	36
2-o-Methoxyphenyl-	100–101°	156
2-p-Methoxyphenyl-	125.5–126.5°	156
2-Methyl-	81.5–83°	52
5-Methyl-	104.5–105.5°	37, 52
6-Methyl-	105–106°	37, 52, 53
7-Methyl-	88–89°	37
8-Methyl-	130°	37, 53
7-Methyl-6-nitro-	110°	59
5-Nitro-	138.5–139°, 146–147°	55, 56, 61
6-Nitro-	129°	42, 59
7-Nitro-	148°	18, 59
8-Nitro-	197–197.5°	45
6-Nitro-2-phenyl-	193–195°	63
7-Nitro-2-phenyl-	240–250° (dec.)	59
6-Nitro-2-trichloromethyl-	95°	79
2-o-Nitrophenyl-	182–183°	62, 63

(Table continued)

TABLE V.4 (*continued*)

4-Chloroquinazoline	M.p. (°c)	References
2-*p*-Nitrophenyl-	188–190°	63, 64
2-Phenyl-	127.5–128.5°; picrate 191–192°	15, 32, 33, 63
2-3'-Piperidinopropylamino-	190–195°/0.15 mm, 71°	58
2-Trichloromethyl-	124–125°	49, 51
5-Trifluoromethyl-	67°	44
6-Trifluoromethyl-	69°	44
7-Trifluoromethyl-	62°	44
8-Trifluoromethyl-	148°	44
2-*m*-Trifluoromethylphenyl-	86–88°	156

TABLE V.5. 2,4-Dichloroquinazolines.

2,4-Dichloroquinazoline	M.p. (°c)	References
Unsubstituted	116–118°, 120°	10, 20, 52, 68, 71, 72, 74, 75
6,7-Benzo-	184°, 270–300°/10–15 mm	19
6-*N*,*N*-Dimethylsulphamoyl-	161–162°	108
5-Methoxy-	160–162°	19
6-Methoxy-	171°, 250–300°/15 mm	19
7-Methoxy-	121–121.5°, 260–290°/15 mm	18, 19, 151
8-Methoxy-	154–156°, 230–260°/20 mm	19
6,7-Dimethoxy-	158°	19
6-Methyl-	140°	73
7-Methyl-	113°, 220–250°/15–20 mm	19
8-Methyl-	140°	70
6-Nitro-	127–129°, 220–230°/16–20 mm	19
7-Nitro-	148–150°, 250–270°/10 mm	19

TABLE V.6.   Chloroquinazolines with Chloro Substituents in the Benzene Ring

Cl—⬡⬡N—H(R)

Quinazoline	M.p. (°c)	References
2-Acetoxymethyl-6-chloro-4-phenyl-	116–117°	78
4-2′-Aminoethylamino-6-chloro-	140–143°	169
4-Anilino-7-chloro-2-2′-furyl-	170°	117
4-p-Anisidino-7-chloro-2-2′-furyl-	189°	117
4-p-Anisidino-6-chloro-2-methyl-	321° (dec.)	168
2-2′-Benzimidazolylamino-6-chloro-4-2′-diethylaminoethylamino-	196–197°	22
4-Benzyl-6-chloro-2-phenyl-	195°	66
4-Benzyl-6,8-dichloro-2-phenyl-	310°	66
5-Chloro-	87.5–88°	37
6-Chloro-	141–142°	77
7-Chloro-	95–96°	37, 77
8-Chloro-	119–120°	37
6,8-Dichloro-	175–176°	37
6-Chloro-2-chloromethyl-4-phenyl-	126–127°	78
6-Chloro-4-2′-(6-chloroquinazolin-4-ylamino)ethylamino-	381° (dec.)	169
6-Chloro-4-3′-dibutylaminopropylamino-	79–80°; HCl 168.5–169.5°	18
7-Chloro-4-3′-dibutylaminopropylamino-	81–82°	18
7-Chloro-4-3′-(2-diethylaminoethoxy)-propylamino-	69–70°	18
6-Chloro-4-2′-diethylaminoethylamino-	138–138.5°; HCl 242–243°	18
7-Chloro-4-2′-diethylaminoethylamino-	125°	18
6,8-Dichloro-4-2′-diethylaminoethylamino-	98°, 200–210°/0.05 mm; picrate 212°	157
6-Chloro-4-2′-diethylaminoethylamino-2-2′-benzothiazolylamino-	210°; HCl 310–311°	22
6-Chloro-4-2′-diethylaminoethylamino-2-2′-(6-methoxybenzothiazolyl)amino-	197–198°; HCl 299–300°	22
6-Chloro-4-2′-diethylaminoethylamino-2-2′-(6-methylbenzothiazolyl)amino-	226–228°	22

(*Table continued*)

TABLE V.6 (*continued*)

Quinazoline	M.p. (°c)	References
6-Chloro-4-2'-diethylaminoethylamino-2- 2'-thiazolylamino-	180.5–181°; HCl 286– 288°	22
6-Chloro-4-(4'-diethylamino-1'-methyl)- butylamino-	112–113°	18
7-Chloro-4-(4'-diethylamino-1'-methyl)- butylamino-	104–105°, 115–116°; 1.77 H$_2$O 120–121°, 210–215°/4.5 mm; dipicrate 205–206°	18, 40, 172
7-Chloro-4-(4'-diethylamino-1'-methyl)- butylamino-2-2'-furyl-	112°; picrate 199°	117
6-Chloro-4-(4'-diethylamino-1'-methyl)- butylamino-2-*p*-methoxyphenyl-	2 HCl 261–263° (dec.)	170
7-Chloro-4-(4'-diethylamino-1'-methyl)- butylamino-2-*p*-methoxyphenyl-	2 HCl 233–235° (dec.)	170
6,8-Dichloro-4-(3'-diethylamino-1'- methyl)propylamino-	190–210°/0.03 mm; HClO$_4$ 241–243° (dec.)	157
6-Chloro-4-3'-diethylaminopropylamino-	HCl 162.5–163°, 255°; picrate 181–184°	18, 42
7-Chloro-4-3'-diethylaminopropylamino-	105°	18
6-Chloro-4-2',3'-dihydroxypropylamino-	188–189.5°	171
7-Chloro-4-2',3'-dihydroxypropylamino-	210–212°	171
6-Chloro-4-3'-dimethylaminopropyl- amino-	123–124°; HCl 203–204°	18
7-Chloro-4-3'-dimethylaminopropyl- amino-	102°	18
7-Chloro-2-2'-furyl-4-*p*-phenetidino-	180°	117
7-Chloro-2-2'-furyl-4-*p*-toluidino-	201°	117
7-Chloro-4-2'-(2-hydroxyethoxy)ethyl- amino-	127°	171
7-Chloro-4-2'-hydroxyethylamino-	H$_2$O 179°	171
6-Chloro-4-6'-hydroxyhexylamino-	115–117°; H$_2$O 137– 138°; HCl 179°	171
7-Chloro-4-6'-hydroxyhexylamino-	140°; HCl 183.5°	171
6-Chloro-4-(6'-methoxy-1',2',3',4'-tetra- hydro-1'-quinolyl)-	106–108°	158
6-Chloro-2-methyl-4-(1'-methyl- pyrrolidin-3'-ylmethylamino)-	125–127°	52
6-Chloro-2-methyl-4-phenyl-	105–106°	78, 163
6-Chloro-2-methylamino-4-phenyl-	93–95°	167
5-Chloro-4-(1'-methylpyrrolidin-3'- ylmethylamino)-	63–64°	52

(*Table continued*)

TABLE V.6 (*continued*)

Quinazoline	M.p. (°c)	References
6-Chloro-4-(1'-methylpyrrolidin-3'-ylmethylamino)-	145–147°	52
7-Chloro-4-(1'-methylpyrrolidin-3'-ylmethylamino)-	112–115°	52
6-Chloro-4-phenyl-	136–138°	163
6-Chloro-2,4-diphenyl-	184–185°	66
6,8-Dichloro-2,4-diphenyl-	200–201°	66
6-Chloro-4-3'-piperidinopropyl-	117–118°; HCl 209–209.5°	18
7-Chloro-4-3'-piperidinopropyl-	0.5 H$_2$O 130–131°	18

TABLE V.7.   Chloroquinazolines with Chloro Substituents in Both Rings.

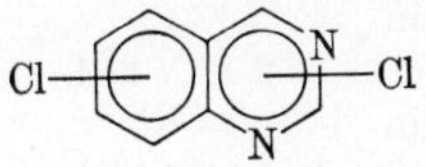

Cl—(structure)—Cl

Quinazoline	M.p. (°c)	References
4,5-Dichloro-	131.5–133°	52
4,6-Dichloro-	155–155.5°; picrate 173°	18, 39, 41, 42, 84
4,7-Dichloro-	135–136°	18, 40, 52
4,8-Dichloro-	175–176°	37
2,4,6-Trichloro-	131°, 230–240°/15 mm	19, 76
2,6,7-Trichloro-	127°	19
4,6,8-Trichloro-	140°; picrate 221–223°	37, 39, 43
2,4,6,8-Tetrachloro-	142–145°, 150–152°	63, 69
2,6-Dichloro-4-2'-diethylamino-ethylamino-	135–136°	19
2,7-Dichloro-4-2'-diethylamino-ethylamino-	119°; 2 H$_2$O 84–85°	19
4,7-Dichloro-2-2'-furyl-	137°	117
4,6-Dichloro-8-nitro-	152–153°	46

TABLE V.8.   Miscellaneous Halogenoquinazolines.

Quinazoline	M.p. (°c)	References
4-Amino-6-bromo-2-*p*-nitrophenyl-	283–285°	165
4-Amino-6-bromo-2-phenyl-	224–226°	165
6-Bromo-	128–130°	77
7-Bromo-	87–88°	77
6-Bromo-4-chloro-	178°, 164–166°; picrate	
	189–190°	39, 52
8-Bromo-4,6-dichloro-	239–240°; picrate 209–211°	39
6-Bromo-4,8-dichloro-	216–217°; picrate 225°	39
6,8-Dibromo-4-chloro-	189–190°; picrate 212°	39
8-Bromo-4-chloro-6-iodo-	222–223°; picrate 211–213°	39
6,8-Dibromo-4-2′-diethylamino-		
ethylamino-	118°	157
6,8-Dibromo-4-(3′-diethylamino-		
1′-methyl)propylamino-	230–245°/0.06 mm; HClO₄	
	240° (dec.)	157
6-Bromo-4-(1′-methylpyrrolidin-		
3′-yl-(*N*-methyl)methylamino)-	2 HCl 251–252.5° (dec.)	52
6-Bromo-4-(1′-methylpyrrolidin-		
3′-ylmethylamino)-	122–126°	52
4-Bromo-2-phenyl-	129°; stannic chloride	
	214–216°	66
4-Chloro-6-iodo-	193–195°; picrate 201–202°	39
4-Chloro-6,8-diiodo-	242–243°; picrate 217–218°	39
4,6-Dichloro-8-iodo-	231–232°; picrate 200–201°	39
4,8-Dichloro-6-iodo-	211°; picrate 221°	39
5-Fluoro-	74°	44
6-Fluoro-	140°	44
7-Fluoro-	130°	44
6-Fluoro-2-methyl-	137°	44

TABLE V.9.   2-Quinazolinyl Ethers.

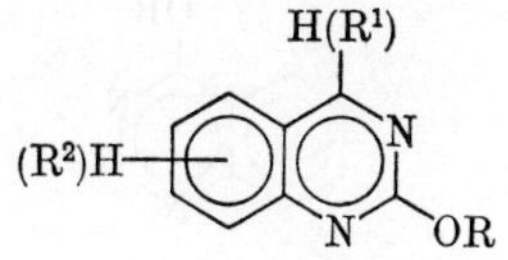

H(R¹)

(R²)H—⟨ ⟩N
          ‖
        N   OR

Quinazoline	M.p. (°c)	References
4-p-Acetamidobenzenesulphonamido-2-methoxy-	240–242°	151
4-p-Acetamidobenzenesulphonamido-2-2′-methoxyethoxy-	210.5–212°	152
4-Amino-2-butoxy-	129–131°	15
4-Amino-2-ethoxy-	136–137°	15
4-Amino-2-methoxy-	203–205°	15
4-Amino-2-propoxy-	154–156°	15
4-Anilino-7,8-benzo-2-2′-diethyl-aminoethoxy-	methiodide 246°	162
4-Anilino-7,8-benzo-2-methoxy-	194°	162
4-Anilino-2-methoxy-	198–200°	166
4-Benzenesulphonamido-2-methoxy-	230–232°	152
4-p-Butyrylamidobenzenesulphon-amido-2-methoxy-	248–250°	151
2-Ethoxy-	65°	50, 153
2-Ethoxy-4-phenyl-	106–107°	2
2-Isopropoxy-	56–58°; picrate 120°	153
4-Isopropyl-2-methoxy-	134° and 151° (isomorphic)	3
2-Methoxy-	55–56°, 58°	50, 113, 153
2,7-Dimethoxy-	230–232°	151
2-Methoxy-4-methyl-	116°/1.0 mm	7
2-Methoxy-6-methyl-	243–244.5°	151
2-Methoxy-4-sulphanilamido-	249–251°, 228.5–230.5° (solidifies at 232° and remelts at 286.5–289°); Na salt 287–289°	151, 152
2-2′-Methoxyethoxy-4-sulphanilamido-	182–185°; anhyd. 182°; H₂O 129.5–138°	151, 152
2-Phenoxy-	124–126°	56
2-Propoxy-4-sulphanilamido-	216–217°	151

TABLE V.10.   4-Quinazolinyl Ethers.

OR

Quinazoline	M.p. (°c)	References
4-*m*-Acetoxyphenoxy-	208°	122
4-*p*-Acetoxyphenoxy-	179°	122
4-2′-Aminoethoxy-	177°	124
4-Benzyloxy-	170–180°/1 mm; picrate	
	159–161°	159, 160
4-Butoxy-	263–265°/760 mm	50
4-*o*-Chlorophenoxy-	123°; picrate 178°; HCl	
	190° (dec.)	122
4-*m*-Chlorophenoxy-	101°; picrate 176°	122
4-*p*-Chlorophenoxy-	113°; picrate 184°; HCl	
	210°	122
4-(2′-Chloro-4′-nitro)phenoxy-	206°; picrate 198°	122
4-(2′,6′-Dichloro-4′-nitro)phenoxy-	243°; picrate 200°	122
4-2′,3′-Dichlorophenoxy-	146°; picrate 174°; HCl	
	200° (dec.)	122
4-2′,4′-Dichlorophenoxy-	173°; picrate 194°; HCl	
	180°	122
4-2′,6′-Dichlorophenoxy-	160°; picrate 184–185°	122
4-3′,4′-Dichlorophenoxy-	130°; picrate 178°	122
4-3′,5′-Dichlorophenoxy-	133°; picrate 163°; HCl	
	196° (dec.)	122
4-2′-Diethylaminoethoxy-	123–125°/0.2 mm	124
4-3′-Diethylaminopropoxy-	citrate 120–121°	119
4-2′-(2-Diisopropylaminoethoxy)-		
ethoxy-	HCl 123–125°	119
4-2′-(2-Dimethylaminoethoxy)-		
ethoxy-	oil; maleate 111–112°	119, 120
4-Ethoxy-	42–43°, 48°, 105°/1 mm;	10, 25, 50,
	picrate 178°	123, 124,
		153
4-*m*-Hydroxyphenoxy-	209°; picrate 185°	122
4-*p*-Hydroxyphenoxy-	196–197°; picrate 179°	122
4-Isopropoxy-	picrate 149–150°	153
4-1′-(Isopropylpyrrolidin-3′-		
ylmethoxy)-	HCl 183–183.5° (dec.)	52
4-Methoxy-	33°, 36°, 127–128°/11 mm;	50, 90, 114,
	137°/13 mm; picrate	123, 124,
	174–175°; HCl 129°	125, 153

(*Table continued*)

TABLE V.10 (*continued*)

Quinazoline	M.p. (°c)	References
4-*o*-Methoxyphenoxy-	155–160°/15 mm; picrate	
	180°	122
4-*m*-Methoxyphenoxy-	145°/6 mm; picrate 185°	122
4-*p*-Methoxyphenoxy-	144°/6 mm; picrate 183°	122
4-(1'-Methylpyrrolidin-3'-		
ylmethoxy)-	HCl 192–194° (dec.)	52
4-1'-Naphthyloxy-	163–165°/10 mm; picrate	
	180–181°	122
4-2'-Naphthyloxy-	165–166°/10 mm; picrate	
	180–181°	122
4-*p*-Nitrophenoxy-	209°; picrate 185°	122
4-(1'-Phenethylpyrrolidin-3'-		
ylmethoxy)-	HCl 171–172° (dec.)	52
4-Phenoxy-	78–79°	123, 150
4-Propoxy-	257–260°/760 mm	50
4-2'-(Quinazolin-4-yloxy)ethoxy-	208°	12
4-*o*-Tolyloxy-	135–140°/15 mm; picrate	
	178°	122
4-*m*-Tolyloxy-	138–140°/15 mm; picrate	
	179°	122
4-*p*-Tolyloxy-	125–127°/10 mm	122

TABLE V.11.   4-Quinazolinyl Ethers with a Substituent in Position 2.

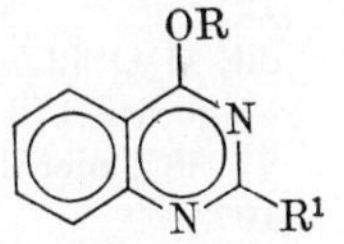

Quinazoline	M.p. (°c)	References
4-2'-Aminoethoxy-2-ethyl-	180°	124
2-Anilino-4-benzyloxy-	118–119°; picrate 215–216°	127
2-Anilino-4-butoxy-	82–83°; picrate 182–183°	127
2-Anilino-4-2'-chloroethoxy-	116–116.5°; picrate 188–188.5°	127
2-Anilino-4-ethoxy-	110–111°; HCl 161° picrate	
	183°	14

(*Table continued*)

TABLE V.11 (*continued*)

Quinazoline	M.p. (°c)	References
2-Anilino-4-methoxy-	113°; HCl 160° (dec.); picrate 210°	14
2-Anilino-4-pentyloxy-	61–62°; picrate 183–185°	127
2-Benzyl-4-ethoxy-	43°	124
2-Benzyl-4-methoxy-	66°	124
4-Benzyloxy-2-2′-furyl-	oil; picrate 171°	118
4-Benzyloxy-2-methyl-	65.5–66°; picrate 147.5–148.5°	125
2-p-Bromophenyl-4-ethoxy-	131°	124
2-p-Bromophenyl-4-methoxy-	119°	124
2-o-Carboxyanilino-4-ethoxy-	200–201°	72
2-o-Carboxyanilino-4-methoxy-	120–121°	72
2-p-Chloroanilino-4-ethoxy-	122°; HCl 175°	20, 60
2-p-Chloroanilino-4-phenoxy-	186–187°	20, 60
2-o-Chlorophenyl-4-ethoxy-	83°	124
2-p-Chlorophenyl-4-ethoxy-	120°	124
2-o-Chlorophenyl-4-methoxy-	132°	124
2-p-Chlorophenyl-4-methoxy-	125.5°	124
4-2′-Diethylaminoethoxy-2-methyl-	128°/0.1 mm	124
4-Ethoxy-2-o-ethoxycarbonyl-anilino-	104–105°	72
4-Ethoxy-2-ethyl-	24°, 120°/1 mm; picrate 168°	124
4-Ethoxy-2-2′-furyl-	83°; picrate 183–184°	118
4-Ethoxy-2-p-methoxyanilino-	98–99°; picrate 179–180°	127
4-Ethoxy-2-o-methoxycarbonyl-anilino-	118–119°; picrate 198° (dec.); HCl 172–173°	72
4-Ethoxy-2-p-methoxyphenyl-	72°	124
4-Ethoxy-2-methyl-	oil; H₂O 39.5–40°, 103°/1 mm; picrate 178–179.5°	124, 125
4-Ethoxy-2-N-methylanilino-	87–88°; picrate 189–190° (dec.)	127
4-Ethoxy-2-1′-naphthyl-	107°	124
4-Ethoxy-2-2′-naphthyl-	100°	124
4-Ethoxy-2-phenyl-	57°	124
4-Ethoxy-2-o-tolyl-	60°	124
4-Ethoxy-2-p-tolyl-	77°	124
4-Ethoxy-2-trichloromethyl-	75–76°	49, 50
2-Ethyl-4-methoxy-	107–109°/1 mm; picrate 188°	124
2-2′-Furyl-4-isopropoxy-	picrate 164°	118
2-2′-Furyl-4-methoxy-	65°, 212°/16 mm; picrate 170°	30, 118
2-2′-Furyl-4-phenoxy-	135°	30, 118
2-2′-Furyl-4-propoxy-	picrate 143.5°	118

(*Table continued*)

TABLE V.11 (*continued*)

Quinazoline	M.p. (°c)	References
4-Methoxy-2-3′,4′-dimethoxy-phenethyl-	96.3–97.3°	35
4-Methoxy-2-o-methoxy-carbonylanilino-	128–129°; picrate 176–178°	72
4-Methoxy-2-p-methoxy-phenethyl-	84.5–85.5°	36
4-Methoxy-2-p-methoxyphenyl-	97°	124
4-Methoxy-2-methyl-	34–35°; 3 H_2O 36–37°, 136–138°/16 mm; picrate 170–171.5°	125
4-Methoxy-2-3′,4′-methylene-dioxyphenethyl-	67–68°	36
4-Methoxy-2-1′-naphthyl-	106°	124
4-Methoxy-2-2′-naphthyl-	146°	124
4-Methoxy-2-phenethyl-	58.5–59.8°	35
4-Methoxy-2-phenyl-	65.5–66°, 189–191°/3 mm; picrate 174–175.5°	124, 125
4-Methoxy-2-o-tolyl-	103°	124
4-Methoxy-2-p-tolyl-	78°	124
4-Methoxy-2-trichloromethyl-	87–88°	50
2-o-Methoxycarbonylanilino-4-isopropoxy-	91–92°; picrate 196–197°	72
2-Methyl-4-phenoxy-	71–71.5°; H_2O 71–83°	125

TABLE V.12.   4-Quinazolinyl Ethers with Substituents in the Benzene Ring.

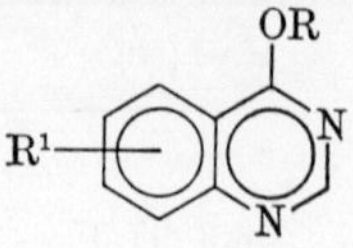

OR

R^1

Quinazoline	M.p. (°c)	References
6-Amino-4-methoxy-	179°	157
7-Amino-4-methoxy-	173°	157
8-Amino-4-methoxy-	153.5–154°	45, 157
7-Amino-4,6-dimethoxy-[a]	149–151°	45
6,7-Benzo-4-methoxy-	120°	54
7,8-Benzo-4-methoxy-2-methyl-	119–120°	126
6-2'-Diethylaminoethylamino-4-methoxy-	210–220°/0.02 mm	157
7-2'-Diethylaminoethylamino-4-methoxy-	200–220°/0.01 mm	157
8-2'-Diethylaminoethylamino-4-methoxy-	210–220°/0.01 mm	157
7-3'-Diethylaminopropylamino-4-methoxy-	230–240°/0.05 mm	157
4-Methoxy-6-nitro-	120°	121, 157
4-Methoxy-7-nitro-	137–138°, 140°	121, 157
4-Methoxy-8-nitro-	132.5–133°, 136°	45, 157
4,6-Dimethoxy-7-nitro-[a]	165–165.5°	45
6-Nitro-4-phenoxy-	148–149°	121
7-Nitro-4-phenoxy-	173.5–174°	121

[a] See Sect. 2.D.

TABLE V.13.   4-Quinazolinyl Ethers with Substituents in Both Rings.

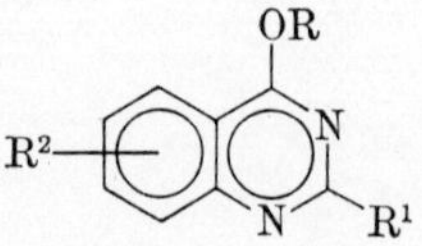

OR

R^2 R^1

Quinazoline	M.p. (°c)	References
4-Ethoxy-2-ethyl-5-nitro-	148–149°	115
4-Ethoxy-2-methyl-5-nitro-	161°	115
4-Ethoxy-2-methyl-7-nitro-	105–106°	115
2-2'-Furyl-4-methoxy-6-methyl-	116°	38
2-2'-Furyl-6-methoxy-4-phenoxy-	141°	38
4-Isopentyloxy-2-methyl-7-nitro-	104°	115

TABLE V.14.   2,4-Quinazolinyl Diethers.

Quinazoline	M.p. (°c)	References
2,4-Di-2′-acetoxyethoxy-	65–66°	128
2,4-Diallyloxy-	38–40°	129
6-Amino-2,4-dibutoxy-	62–64°	129
6-Amino-2,4-di-1′-methylbutoxy-	68–70°	129
6-Amino-2,4-dipentyloxy-	64–65°	129
2,4-Dibutoxy-	154–157°/0.6 mm	15, 129
2,4-Dibutoxy-6-nitro-	50–52°, 200–202°/0.2 mm	129
2,4-Di-1′,4′-dimethylbutoxy-	142–145°/0.5 mm	129
2,4-Di-1′,2′-dimethylpropoxy-	132–133°/0.1 mm	129
2,4-Di-2′,2′-dimethylpropoxy-	59–61°	129
2-Ethoxy-4-methoxy-	61–62°	128
4-Ethoxy-2-methoxy-	57–58°	128
4-Ethoxy-2-phenoxy-	107–108°	128
2,4-Diethoxy-	55°	14, 15, 50, 128
2,4-Di-2′-ethylbutoxy-	170–172°/0.9 mm	129
2,4-Di-1′-ethylpropoxy-	128–130°/0.06 mm	129
2,4-Di-2′-hydroxyethoxy-	153–154°	128
2,4-Di-3′-hydroxypropoxy-	114–115°	129
2,4-Diisobutoxy-	138–142°/0.3 mm	129
2,4-Diisopentyloxy-	167–168°/0.6 mm	129
2,4-Dimethoxy-	66°, 75°	10, 14, 15, 50, 68, 128, 151
2,4,7-Trimethoxy-	102–104°	151
2,4-Dimethoxy-6-methyl-	73–74°	151
4-Methoxy-2-phenoxy-	139.5°	128
2,4-Di-2′-methoxyethoxy-	45–46°	152
2,4-Di-1′-methylbutoxy-	148–150°/0.2 mm	129
2,4-Di-2′-methylbutoxy-	148°/0.1 mm	129
2,4-Di-2′-methylbutoxy-6-nitro-	171°/0.1 mm	129
2,4-Di-2′-methylpentyloxy-	181°/0.8 mm	129
2,4-Dipentyloxy-	150–152°/0.07 mm	129
2,4-Dipentyloxy-6-nitro-	158–162°/0.4 mm	129
2,4-Diphenoxy-	160–161°	128
2,4-Di-2′-phenylethoxy-	82–83°	129
2,4-Dipropoxy-	40–41°, 45°, 47°	15, 50
2,4-Di-s-butoxy-	128–132°/0.4 mm	129
2,4-Di-t-butoxy-	80–82°	129

TABLE V.15.   Quinazolinyl Ethers with Ether Groups in the Benzene Ring.

Quinazoline	M.p. (°c)	References
7-Acetamido-6-methoxy-[a]	215–216°	45
8-Allyloxy-	55°, 98–100°/0.04 mm	144
7-Amino-6-methoxy-[a]	156–156.5°; acetyl deriv.	
	215–216° (dec.)	45
2-Benzyl-8-methoxy-	88°	139
2-p-Bromophenyl-8-methoxy-	127°; picrate 129°	139
4-Butylamino-8-methoxy-	190°	164
4-p-Chlorobenzyl-8-methoxy-	227°	164
2-p-Chlorophenyl-4-(4′-diethyl-amino-1′-methyl)butylamino-7-methoxy-	2 HCl 235–236° (dec.)	173
2-p-Chlorophenyl-4-(4′-diethyl-amino-1′-methyl)butylamino-6,7-dimethoxy-	2 HCl 227–229°	173
2-o-Chlorophenyl-8-methoxy-	118°	139
4-3′-Dibutylaminopropylamino-6-methoxy-	78.5–79.5°; 2 H$_2$SO$_4$ 170–171°	18
4-3′-Dibutylaminopropylamino-7-methoxy-	54–57°; 2 H$_2$SO$_4$ 160–162°	18
2-2′,4′-Dichlorophenyl-8-methoxy-	132°; picrate 105°	139
4-(4′-Diethylamino-1′-methyl)-butylamino-6-methoxy-	151–152°; H$_2$O 144–147°; 2 H$_3$PO$_4$·H$_2$O 219–220°; picrate 138.5–140°	18, 57
4-(4′-Diethylamino-1′-methyl)-butylamino-7-methoxy-	92–93°	18
4-(4′-Diethylamino-1′-methyl)-butylamino-8-methoxy-	158°	164
4-3′-(2-Diethylaminoethoxy)-ethylamino-7-methoxy-	63–65°; H$_2$O 65–67°	18
4-2′-Diethylaminoethylamino-6-methoxy-	119–120°; HCl 213–214°; 2 H$_2$SO$_4$ 162–164°	18
4-2′-Diethylaminoethylamino-7-methoxy-	109–110°	18

(*Table continued*)

TABLE V.15 (*continued*)

Quinazoline	M.p. (°c)	References
4-6'-Diethylaminohexylamino-6-methoxy-	178–180°/0.06 mm; oxalate 101–103°	45
4-3'-Diethylaminopropylamino-6-methoxy-	96–97°; 2 H_2SO_4 187–190°	18
4-3'-Diethylaminopropylamino-7-methoxy-	65–66°; 2 H_2SO_4 186–188°	18
2-3',4'-Dimethoxybenzyl-6,7-dimethoxy-	134–135°	140
4-2'-Dimethylaminoethyl-7-methoxy-	HCl 153–154° (dec.)	161
4-3'-Dimethylaminopropylamino-6-methoxy-	132–133°	18
4-3'-Dimethylaminopropylamino-7-methoxy-	126–127°	18
4-Dodecylamino-8-methoxy-	93°	164
4-Hydrazino-6-methoxy-7-nitro-[a]	202° (dec.)	97
4-Isopentylamino-8-methoxy-	178°	164
5-Methoxy-	84–85°	37
6-Methoxy-	71–72°	37, 77
7-Methoxy-	87°	37, 77
8-Methoxy-	92°	147
6,7-Dimethoxy-	146–147°; HCl 225–227°	133, 143
7-Methoxy-4-methyl-	100–102°; oxalate 193° (dec.); picrate 210° (dec.)	161
8-Methoxy-2-methyl-	128°; picrate 118°; mercurichloride 140°	139
8-Methoxy-4-methyl-	131°	144
8-Methoxy-2,4-dimethyl-	81–83°; 2 H_2O 62–64°	8
6,7-Dimethoxy-2-methyl-	165°; picrate 230° (dec.); mercurichloride 211°	138
7-Methoxy-4-2'-(1-methyl-2,6-dioxocyclohexyl)ethyl-	126–127°; HCl 172° (dec.)	161
6-Methoxy-7-6'-dimethylaminohexylamino-[a]	178–180°/0.06 mm; oxalate 101–103°	45
8-Methoxy-4-methyl-2-phenyl-	132–133°	8
6,8-Dimethoxy-2-3',4'-methylenedioxybenzyl-	148.5–149°	141
6-Methoxy-7-nitro-4-N'-toluene-p-sulphonylhydrazino-[a]	225° (dec.)	97
8-Methoxy-4-octylamino-	144°	164
8-Methoxy-4-pentylamino-	162°	164

(*Table continued*)

TABLE V.15 (continued)

Quinazoline	M.p. (°c)	References
8-Methoxy-2-phenyl-	99°; picrate 178°; chloro-platinate·0.5 H$_2$O 105°	139
6,8-Dimethoxy-2-phenyl-	175–176°; picrate 194°; mercurichloride 214°; chloroplatinate 207°	138, 143
8-Methoxy-4-piperidino-	227°/4 mm	164
6-Methoxy-4-3′-piperidinopropyl-amino-	110–111°; 2 H$_2$SO$_4$ 214–217°	18
7-Methoxy-4-3′-piperidinopropyl-amino-	121–122°	18
8-Methoxy-2-propyl-	60°; picrate 2 H$_2$O 140°; aurichloride 116°	139
8-Methoxy-4-propyl-	38–39°	144
6-Methoxy-4-3′-N-pyrrolidinyl-propylamino-	110–111°; 2 H$_2$SO$_4$ 214–217°	18
8-Methoxy-2-p-tolyl-	70°; picrate 169°	139
6,7-Methylenedioxy-	172–173°; picrate 216°; chloroplatinate 270–275°; methiodide 239–240°; methiodide picrate 185–186°	145, 146
6,7-Methylenedioxy-2-3′,4′-methyl-enedioxybenzyl-	190.5–191°	141
6,7-Methylenedioxy-2-3′,4′-methyl-enedioxyphenyl-	248–249°	142

ᵃ See section 2.D.

TABLE V.16.   Chloroquinazolinyl Ethers with Chloro and Ether Groups in the Pyrimidine Ring.

Quinazoline	M.p. (°c)	References
4-Allyloxy-2-chloro-	76.5–77°, 220°/54 mm	12
4-Benzyloxy-2-chloro-	95–97°, 202°/1.5 mm	12
2-Chloro-4-2′-chloroethoxy-	101–103°	12
2-Chloro-4-2′-chloropropoxy-	64°	12
2-Chloro-4-3′-chloropropoxy-	114.5–115.5°	12
2-Chloro-4-2′-diethylaminoethoxy-	picrate 152°;	
	methiodide 200° (dec.)	11, 12
2-Chloro-4-2′-dimethylaminoethoxy-	picrate 171–172°; HCl	
	186–186.5°	11
2-Chloro-4-ethoxy-	92°	9, 10, 13, 128
2-Chloro-4-m-hydroxyphenoxy-	171–172°	10
2-Chloro-4-3′-hydroxypropoxy-	99–100°	12
2-Chloro-4-isopropoxy-	47–48°	72
2-Chloro-4-methoxy-	99–100°	9, 10, 13, 151
2-Chloro-4-phenoxy-	121°	10

TABLE V.17.   Chloroquinazolinyl Ethers with Chloro and Ether Groups in Separate Rings.

Quinazoline	M.p. (°c)	References
4-p-Acetamidobenzenesulphonamido-6-chloro-2-methoxy-	259–261°	151
6-Chloro-4-2′-diethylaminoethoxy-	116–117°	84
2-Chloro-4-2′-diethylaminoethyl-amino-5-methoxy-	3 H$_2$O 100–102°	19
2-Chloro-4-2′-diethylaminoethyl-amino-6-methoxy-	4 H$_2$O 65–66°	19

(*Table continued*)

TABLE V.17 (continued)

Quinazoline	M.p. (°c)	References
2-Chloro-4-2'-diethylaminoethyl-amino-7-methoxy-	110–111°	18, 19
2-Chloro-4-2'-diethylaminoethyl-amino-8-methoxy-	134–135°	19
2-Chloro-4-2'-diethylaminoethyl-amino-6,7-dimethoxy-	2 H_2O 116–117°	19
6-Chloro-4-ethoxy-	104.5–105.5°	84, 116
6-Chloro-4-ethoxy-2-methyl-	98.5–99.5°, 160–161°/13 mm; picrate 188–189°	125
6-Chloro-4-2'-ethylaminoethoxy-	116–117°	84
7-Chloro-2,2'-furyl-4-methoxy-	130°	117
7-Chloro-2,2'-furyl-4-phenoxy-	140°	117
4-Chloro-6-methoxy-	107.5–108°; picrate 210–210.5°	18, 57
4-Chloro-7-methoxy-	141–142°	18
6-Chloro-2,4-dimethoxy-	116–120°	151
6-Chloro-4-methoxy-2-methyl-	79–80°; 155–156°/12 mm; picrate 168–169.5°	125
4-Chloro-6-methoxy-7-nitro-[a]	148–148.5°	45, 97
6-Chloro-2-methoxy-4-sulphanil-amido-	259–261°	151
6-Chloro-2,4-dipentyloxy-	38–39°; 182–183°/0.5 mm	129

[a] See Sect. 2.D.

4. References

1. Gabriel and Stelzner, Ber. Deut. Chem. Ges., 29, 1300 (1896).
2. Schofield, J. Chem. Soc., 1952, 1927.
3. Hayashi and Higashino, Chem. Pharm. Bull. (Japan), 12, 43 (1964).
4. Drawert, Ber. Deut. Chem. Ges., 32, 1259 (1899).
5. Hanschke, Ber. Deut. Chem. Ges., 32, 2021 (1899).
6. Albert and Barlin, J. Chem. Soc., 1962, 3129.
7. Armarego and Smith, J. Chem. Soc. (C), 1966, 234.
8. Schofield, J. Chem. Soc., 1954, 4034.
9. Higashino, J. Pharm. Soc. Japan, 79, 699 (1959).
10. Lange, Roush, and Asbeck, J. Am. Chem. Soc., 52, 3696 (1930).
11. Grout and Partridge, J. Chem. Soc., 1960, 3551.
12. Grout and Partridge, J. Chem. Soc., 1960, 3546.
13. Lange and Sheibley, J. Am. Chem. Soc., 53, 3867 (1931).
14. Lange and Sheibley, J. Am. Chem. Soc., 54, 1994 (1932).
15. Claesen and Vanderhaeghe, Bull. Soc. Chim. Belges, 68, 220 (1959).

16. Edwards and Pearson, *J. Am. Chem. Soc.*, **84**, 16 (1962); Bunnett and Bassett, Jr., *J. Am. Chem. Soc.*, **81**, 2104 (1959); Bunnett and Zahler, *Chem. Rev.*, **49**, 273 (1951); and Sauer and Huisgen, *Angew. Chem.*, **72**, 294 (1960).

17. Postovskii and Goncharova, *Zh. Obshch. Khim.*, **32**, 3323 (1962).

18. Chapman, Gibson, and Mann, *J. Chem. Soc.*, **1947**, 890.

19. Curd, Landquist, and Rose, *J. Chem. Soc.*, **1948**, 1759.

20. Curd, Landquist, and Rose, *J. Chem. Soc.*, **1947**, 775.

21. Curd, Landquist, Raison, and Rose, *U.S. Pat.*, 2,497,347 (1950); *Chem. Abstr.*, **44**, 4513 (1950).

22. Ciba Ltd., *Brit. Pat.*, 664,262 (1952). *Chem. Abstr.*, **47**, 617 (1953); Isler and Hueni, *U.S. Pat.*, 2,623,878 (1952); *Chem. Abstr.*, **47**, 2217 (1953).

23. Geigy, A.-G., *Brit. Pat.*, 822,069 (1959); *Chem. Abstr.*, **55**, 2005 (1961); Gysin and Knüsli, *Ger. Pat.*, 1,035,398 (1958); *Chem. Abstr.*, **54**, 25543 (1960).

24. Wolf, Beutel, and Stevens, *J. Am. Chem. Soc.*, **70**, 4264 (1948).

25. Elderfield and Serlin, *J. Org. Chem.*, **16**, 1669 (1951).

26. Lange and Sheibley, *J. Am. Chem. Soc.*, **55**, 1188 (1933).

27. McCoy, *Ber. Deut. Chem. Ges.*, **30**, 1682 (1897); McCoy, *Am. Chem. J.*, **21**, 111 (1899).

28. Pesson and Richer, *Compt. Rend.*, **260**, 603 (1965).

29. Armarego, *J. Appl. Chem.*, **11**, 70 (1961).

30. Andrisano and Modena, *Gazz. Chim. Ital.*, **80**, 228 (1950).

31. Andrisano, *Boll. Sci. Fac. Chim. Ind. Bologna*, **7**, 58 (1949); *Chem. Abstr.*, **44**, 9404 (1950).

32. Noland and Jones, *J. Org. Chem.*, **27**, 341 (1962).

33. Endicott, Wick, Mercury, and Sherrill, *J. Am. Chem. Soc.*, **68**, 1299 (1946).

34. Dass, Vig, Gupta, and Narang, *J. Sci. Ind. Res. India*, **11B**, 461 (1952).

35. Marr and Bogert, *J. Am. Chem. Soc.*, **57**, 729 (1935).

36. Papa and Bogert, *J. Am. Chem. Soc.*, **58**, 1701 (1936).

37. Armarego, *J. Chem. Soc.*, **1962**, 561.

38. Andrisano and Modena, *Boll. Sci. Fac. Chim. Ind. Bologna*, **8**, 1 (1950); *Chem. Abstr.*, **45**, 1601 (1951).

39. Sen and Singh, *J. Indian Chem. Soc.*, **36**, 787 (1959).

40. Price, Leonard, and Curtin, *J. Am. Chem. Soc.*, **68**, 1305 (1946).

41. Christensen, Graham, and Tomisek, *J. Am. Chem. Soc.*, **68**, 1306 (1946).

42. Magidson and Golovchinskaya, *Zh. Obshch. Khim.*, **8**, 1797 (1938); *Chem. Abstr.*, **33**, 4993 (1939).

43. Tsuda, Fukushima, Ichikawa, Yoshida, and Ishii, *J. Pharm. Soc. Japan*, **62**, 69 (1942).

44. Armarego and Smith, unpublished results (1966).

45. Elderfield, Williamson, Gensler, and Kremer, *J. Org. Chem.*, **12**, 405 (1947).

46. Spinks and Young, *Brit. Pat.*, 750,175 (1956); *Chem. Abstr.*, **51**, 1303 (1957); *U.S. Pat.*, 2,794,018 (1957); *Chem. Abstr.*, **51**, 12988 (1957).

47. Iyer, Anand, and Dhar, *J. Sci. Ind. Res. India*, **13B**, 451 (1954).

48. Higashino, *J. Pharm. Soc. Japan*, **80**, 245 (1960).

49. Dehoff, *J. Prakt. Chem.*, **42** (2), 346 (1890).

50. Bogert and May, *J. Am. Chem. Soc.*, **31**, 507 (1909).

51. Smith and Kent, *J. Org. Chem.*, **30**, 1312 (1965).

52. Scarborough, Lawes, Minielli, and Compton, *J. Org. Chem.*, **27**, 957 (1962).

53. Gabriel and Colman, *Ber. Deut. Chem. Ges.*, **38**, 3559 (1905).
54. Etienne and Legrand, *Compt. Rend.*, **229**, 1372 (1949).
55. Naff and Christensen, *J. Am. Chem. Soc.*, **73**, 1372 (1951).
56. Osborn, Schofield, and Short, *J. Chem. Soc.*, **1956**, 4191.
57. Smith, Elisberg, and Sherrill, *J. Am. Chem. Soc.*, **68**, 1301 (1946).
58. Curd, Hoggarth, Landquist, and Rose, *J. Chem. Soc.*, **1948**, 1766.
59. Hentrich and Hardtmann, *U.S. Pat.*, 1,880,447 (1933); *Chem. Abstr.*, **27**, 998 (1933).
60. Curd, Landquist, Raison, and Rose, *Brit. Pat.*, 585,363 (1947); *Chem. Abstr.*, **41**, 4173 (1947).
61. Taylor, Knopf, Cogliano, Barton, and Pfleiderer, *J. Am. Chem. Soc.*, **82**, 6058 (1960).
62. Partridge, Vipond, and Waite, *J. Chem. Soc.*, **1962**, 2549.
63. Weidinger and Wellenreuther, *Brit. Pat.*, 927,974 (1963); *Chem. Abstr.*, **60**, 2987 (1964).
64. Weidinger, Lange, and Wellenreuther, *Belg. Pat.*, 618,973 (1962); *Chem. Abstr.*, **59**, 11701 (1963).
65. I. G. Farbenindustrie, A.-G., *Brit. Pat.*, 330,583 (1929); *Chem. Abstr.*, **24**, 5939 (1930).
66. Meerwein, Laasch, Mersch, and Nentwig, *Chem. Ber.*, **89**, 224 (1956).
67. Meerwein, *Ger. Pat.*, 1,074,047 (1960); *Chem. Abstr.*, **55**, 21152 (1961).
68. Bogert and Scatchard, *J. Am. Chem. Soc.*, **41**, 2052 (1919).
69. Ebel, Rupp, and Trauth, *U.S. Pat.*, 2,697,097 (1954); *Chem. Abstr.*, **49**, 4301 (1955).
70. Jürgens, *Ber. Deut. Chem. Ges.*, **40**, 4409 (1907).
71. Abt, *J. Prakt. Chem.*, **39** (2), 140 (1889).
72. Butler and Partridge, *J. Chem. Soc.*, **1959**, 1512.
73. Oakes, Rydon, and Undheim, *J. Chem. Soc.*, **1962**, 4678.
74. Libermann and Rouaix, *Bull. Soc. Chim. France*, **1959**, 1793.
75. Libermann, *Fr. Pat.*, 1,107,487 (1956); *Chem. Abstr.*, **53**, 11418 (1959).
76. Chiang and Li, *Hua Hsüeh Hsüeh Pao*, **23**, 391 (1957); *Chem. Abstr.*, **52**, 15539 (1958).
77. Sidhu, Thyagarajan, and Rao, *Indian J. Chem.*, **1**, 346 (1963).
78. Sternbach, Kaiser, and Reeder, *J. Am. Chem. Soc.*, **82**, 475 (1960).
79. Hepworth, *Brit. Pat.*, 857,362 (1960); *Chem. Abstr.*, **55**, 14487 (1961).
80. Siegle and Christensen, *J. Am. Chem. Soc.*, **73**, 5777 (1951).
81. Scott and Cohen, *J. Chem. Soc.*, **1921**, 664; Thomas Hedley and Co., Ltd., *Brit. Pat.*, 847,566 (1960); *Chem. Abstr.*, **55**, 8438 (1961).
82. Favini and Simonetta, *Gazz. Chim. Ital.*, **90**, 369 (1960).
83. Armarego, Katritzky, and Ridgewell, *Spectrochim. Acta*, **20**, 593 (1964).
84. Sherrill, Ortelt, Duckworth, and Budenstein, *J. Org. Chem.*, **19**, 699 (1954).
85. Chapman and Russell-Hill, *J. Chem. Soc.*, **1956**, 1563.
86. Illuminati, *Advan. Heterocyclic Chem.*, Academic Press, **3**, 345 (1964).
87. Brower, Samuels, Way, and Amstutz, *J. Org. Chem.*, **19**, 1830 (1954).
88. Armarego, *Advan. Heterocyclic Chem.*, Academic Press, **1**, 270 (1963).
89. Williamson, in *Heterocyclic Compounds* (Ed. Elderfield), Wiley, New York, 1957, Vol. 6, p. 358.
90. Tomisek and Christensen, *J. Am. Chem. Soc.*, **67**, 2112 (1945).
91. Keneford, Morley, Simpson, and Wright, *J. Chem. Soc.*, **1950**, 1104.

92. Chapman and Taylor, *J. Chem. Soc.*, **1961**, 1908.
93. Goncharova and Postovskii, *Zh. Obshch. Khim.*, **33**, 2475 (1963).
94. Stephen and Stephen, *J. Chem. Soc.*, **1956**, 4178.
95. Culbertson, Willits, and Christensen, *J. Am. Chem. Soc.*, **76**, 3533 (1954).
96. Mozingo, *Org. Syn.*, **26**, 77 (1946).
97. Dewar, *J. Chem. Soc.*, **1944**, 619.
98. Escales, *Ber. Deut. Chem. Ges.*, **18**, 893 (1885); see also McFadyen and Stevens, *J. Chem. Soc.*, **1936**, 584.
99. Albert and Royer, *J. Chem. Soc.*, **1949**, 1148.
100. Albert and Armarego, *J. Chem. Soc.*, **1963**, 4237.
101. Alford and Schofield, *J. Chem. Soc.*, **1953**, 609; Osborn and Schofield, *J. Chem. Soc.*, **1955**, 2100.
102. Atkinson and Sharpe, *J. Chem. Soc.*, **1959**, 3040.
103. Armarego, *J. Chem. Soc.*, **1962**, 4094; Armarego, *J. Chem. Soc.*, **1963**, 6073.
104. Armarego and Smith, *J. Chem. Soc.*, **1965**, 5360.
105. Albert, *J. Chem. Soc.*, **1960**, 1790.
106. Armarego, unpublished results (1966).
107. Saftien, Eisele, and Graser, *Ger. Pat.*, 942,507 (1956); *Chem. Abstr.*, **53**, 1759 (1959).
108. Ciba Ltd., *Brit. Pat.*, 649,656 (1951); *Chem. Abstr.*, **45**, 6850 (1951); Ciba Ltd., *Swiss Pat.*, 276,911 (1951); *Chem. Abstr.*, **46**, 8863 (1952); Ciba Ltd., *Brit. Pat.*, 675,800 (1952); *Chem. Abstr.*, **46**, 10632 (1952); I. G. Farbenindustrie, *Brit. Pat.*, 719,282 (1954); *Chem. Abstr.*, **49**, 6615 (1955); Ciba Ltd., *Swiss Pat.*, 294,227 (1954); *Chem. Abstr.*, **50**, 4212 (1956); Badische Aniline & Soda Fabric, *Brit. Pat.*, 771,347 (1957); *Chem. Abstr.*, **51**, 14280 (1957); Brassel, Fasciati, and Buehler, *U.S. Pat.*, 2,773,871 (1956); *Chem. Abstr.*, **51**, 5439 (1957); Moser, *U.S. Pat.*, 2,399,477 (1946); *Chem. Abstr.*, **40**, 4223 (1946); Jirou, Brouard, and Bouvet, *Fr. Pat.*, 1,308,044 (1962); *Chem. Abstr.*, **59**, 4075 (1963).
109. Hentrich and Schirm, *U.S. Pat.*, 2,394,306 (1946); *Chem. Abstr.*, **40**, 2328 (1946).
110. Griess, *Ber. Deut. Chem. Ges.*, **2**, 415 (1869).
111. Finger and Günzler, *J. Prakt. Chem.*, **83** (2), 198 (1911).
112. McKee, *J. Prakt. Chem.*, **84** (2), 821 (1911).
113. Stefanović, Lorenc, and Mihailović, *Rec. Trav. Chim.*, **80**, 149 (1961).
114. Leonard and Curtin, *J. Org. Chem.*, **11**, 341 (1946).
115. Bogert and Seil, *J. Am. Chem. Soc.*, **29**, 517 (1907).
116. Endicott, Alden, and Sherrill, *J. Am. Chem. Soc.*, **68**, 1303 (1946).
117. Andrisano and Modena, *Gazz. Chim. Ital.*, **80**, 321 (1950).
118. Andrisano and Modena, *Boll. Sci. Fac. Chim. Ind. Bologna*, **8**, 7 (1950); *Chem. Abstr.*, **45**, 3852 (1951).
119. Winthrop, Sybulski, Gaudry, and Grant, *Can. J. Chem.*, **34**, 1557 (1956).
120. Grant and Winthrop, *U.S. Pat.*, 2,830,055 (1958); *Chem. Abstr.*, **53**, 3254 (1959).
121. Morley and Simpson, *J. Chem. Soc.*, **1948**, 360.
122. Badiger and Nargund, *J. Karnatak Univ.*, **5**, 10 (1960); *Chem. Abstr.*, **58**, 4563 (1963).
123. Higashino, *J. Pharm. Soc. Japan*, **80**, 1404 (1960).
124. Legrand and Lozach, *Bull. Soc. Chim. France*, **1963**, 1161.

10 + Q.

268 Chapter V

125. Breukink, Krol, Verkade, and Wepster, *Rec. Trav. Chim.*, **76**, 401 (1957).
126. Breukink and Verkade, *Rec. Trav. Chim.*, **79**, 443 (1960).
127. Grout and Partridge, *J. Chem. Soc.*, **1960**, 3540.
128. Lange and Sheibley, *J. Am. Chem. Soc.*, **54**, 4305 (1932).
129. Ed. Geistlich Soehne A.-G., *Fr.M. Pat.*, 1672 (1963); *Chem. Abstr.*, **59**, 6422 (1963).
130. Baker and Schaub, *Brit. Pat.*, 713,767 (1954); *Chem. Abstr.*, **50**, 14002 (1956).
131. Bedi and Narang, *J. Indian Chem. Soc.*, **13**, 253 (1936).
132. Iyer and Dhar, *J. Sci. Ind. Res. India*, **17C**, 193 (1958).
133. Fetscher and Bogert, *J. Org. Chem.*, **4**, 71 (1939).
134. Walker, *J. Am. Chem. Soc.*, **77**, 6698 (1955).
135. Rodionov and Fedorova, *Bull. Soc. Chim. France*, **6**, 478 (1939).
136. Bhattacharyya, Bose, and Ray, *J. Indian Chem. Soc.*, **6**, 279 (1929).
137. McMillan, *J. Chem. Soc.*, **1952**, 4019.
138. Rilliet, *Helv. Chim. Acta*, **5**, 547 (1922).
139. Tröger and Sabewa, *J. Prakt. Chem.*, **117** (2), 117 (1927).
140. Marr and Bogert, *J. Am. Chem. Soc.*, **57**, 1329 (1935).
141. Shamshurin, *Zh. Obshch. Khim.*, **13**, 573 (1943); *Chem. Abstr.*, **39**, 704 (1945).
142. Wilson, *J. Am. Chem. Soc.*, **70**, 1901 (1948).
143. Downes and Lions, *J. Am. Chem. Soc.*, **72**, 3053 (1950).
144. Albert and Hampton, *J. Chem. Soc.*, **1954**, 505.
145. Wilkendorf, *Ber. Deut. Chem. Ges.*, **52**, 606 (1919).
146. Reynolds and Robinson, *J. Chem. Soc.*, **1936**, 196.
147. Albert and Hampton, *J. Chem. Soc.*, **1952**, 4985.
148. Bogert and Geiger, *J. Am. Chem. Soc.*, **34**, 683 (1912).
149. Vincent, Maillard, and Benard, *Bull. Soc. Chim. France*, **1963**, 119.
150. Morley and Simpson, *J. Chem. Soc.*, **1949**, 1354.
151. Mead, Johnson, and Co., *Brit. Pat.*, 920,019 (1963); *Chem. Abstr.*, **59**, 3935 (1963).
152. Martin, Wheeler, Mejewski, and Corrigan, *J. Med. Chem.*, **7**, 812 (1964).
153. Adachi, *J. Pharm. Soc. Japan*, **75**, 1426 (1955).
153a. Morrow and Hofer, *J. Med. Chem.*, **9**, 249 (1966).
154. Donleavy and Kise, *J. Am. Chem. Soc.*, **57**, 753 (1935).
155. Lawes and Scarborough, *U.S. Pat.*, 3,127,401 (1964); *Chem. Abstr.*, **60**, 14526 (1964).
156. Ebel, Schuhmacher, and Kling, *Ger. Pat.*, 1,046,565 (1956); *Chem. Abstr.*, **55**, 1009 (1961).
157. Tsuda, Ishii, Fukushima, and Yoshida, *J. Pharm. Soc. Japan*, **62**, 335 (1942).
158. Goodale and McKee, *J. Am. Chem. Soc.*, **71**, 1893 (1949).
159. Yamanaka, *Chem. Pharm. Bull. (Japan)*, **7**, 152 (1959).
160. Higashino, *J. Pharm. Soc. Japan*, **79**, 831 (1959).
161. Jones, *J. Chem. Soc.*, **1964**, 5911.
162. Dymek and Sybistowicz, *Monatsh. Chem.*, **96**, 542 (1965).
163. Bell and Wei, *J. Org. Chem.*, **30**, 3576 (1965).
164. Iyer, Anand, and Dhar, *J. Sci. Ind. Res. India*, **15C**, 1 (1956).
165. Taylor and Borror, *J. Org. Chem.*, **26**, 4967 (1961).

166. Dymek, Brzozowska, and Brzozowski, *Ann. Univ. Mariae Curie-Sklodowska, Lublin Polonia Sect. AA*, **9**, 35 (1954); *Chem. Abstr.*, **51**, 5095 (1957).
167. Sternbach, Reeder, Stempel, and Rachlin, *J. Org. Chem.*, **29**, 332 (1964).
168. Tomisek and Christensen, *J. Am. Chem. Soc.*, **70**, 2423 (1948).
169. Goodale and McKee, *J. Am. Chem. Soc.*, **71**, 1871 (1949).
170. McKee, McKee, and Bost, *J. Am. Chem. Soc.*, **69**, 940 (1947).
171. Christensen, Graham, and Tomisek, *J. Am. Chem. Soc.*, **68**, 1306 (1946).
172. McKee, McKee, and Bost, *J. Am. Chem. Soc.*, **69**, 184 (1947).
173. McKee, McKee, and Bost, *J. Am. Chem. Soc.*, **68**, 1902 (1946).

CHAPTER VI

Thio- and Oxothioquinazolines

The nomenclature of quinazolines containing sulphur atoms is similar to the one used for the corresponding oxoquinazolines (Ch. IV). The possibility of tautomerism in this class of compounds also makes the naming not strictly correct when the tautomeric structure is not fixed, i.e. by having a substituent on the nitrogen or sulphur atom. However, in these examples the name for the presumed predominant tautomer will be used. Hence 2- and 4-thio-, and 2,4-dithioquinazoline will be called 1,2-dihydro-2-thio-, 3,4-dihydro-4-thio-, and 1,2,3,4-tetrahydro-2,4-dithioquinazoline. Similarly 4-oxo-2-thioquinazoline will be called 1,2,3,4-tetrahydro-4-oxo-2-thioquinazoline. Quinazolines with sulphur substituents in the benzene ring will have the usual name, e.g. thiol for —SH and alkylthio for —S-Alk. The thiazoloquinazolines have been included in this chapter because of their close relationship with thioquinazolines. Aminothioquinazolines are described in chapter VII, section 2.A., and the 5,6,7,8-tetrahydro thio- and oxothioquinazolines are in chapter VIII, section 8.

1. 2-Thioquinazolines

A. 1,2-Dihydro-2-thioquinazolines

1,2-Dihydro-2-thioquinazoline is prepared from 2-chloroquinazoline by reaction with alcoholic potassium hydrogen sulphide (Reaction 1).[1,2] Attempts to prepare 1,2-dihydro-1-methyl- and 2,3-dihydro-3-methyl-2-thioquinazolines by a variety of methods were unsuccessful.[1] It is apparently difficult to convert an oxygen atom on a carbon atom between two nitrogen atoms to a sulphur atom by reaction with phosphorus pentasulphide. 1,2-Dihydro-4-methyl-2-thioquinazoline is

270

prepared by reaction of 2-chloro-4-methylquinazoline with thiourea followed by alkaline decomposition of the intermediate S-thiouronium salt with alkali.[3]

2-Thioquinazoline can exist in three tautomeric forms **1**, **2**, and **3** like 2-oxoquinazoline (Ch. IV, Sect. 1.B.). Derivatives of structures **2** and **3** are known but derivatives of **1** have not yet been prepared. There is a body of evidence[1,4] that in related heterocyclic compounds

$$(1)$$

(1)

(2)   **(3)**

a thio group on a carbon atom α or γ to a nitrogen atom exists in the thione rather than the thiol form. Also that the tautomeric ratio of thiol to thione is more in favour of the latter than is the tautomeric ratio of hydroxy to oxo in favour of the oxo form in related oxoquinazolines. The predominant tautomer in 2-thioquinazoline is most probably **1** because the *ortho* quinonoid structure in **3** would make it less favoured. 1,2-Dihydro-2-thioquinazoline is a weak base (pK_a 0.26) and a weak acid (pK_a 8.14), and the ultraviolet spectrum of the cation, anion, and neutral species in aqueous solution is recorded.[1] Methylation in aqueous alkaline solution gives 2-methylthioquinazoline.[1] This is typical of thio compounds, in which, unlike in the oxoquinazolines (Ch. IV, Sects. 2.C.b.(i) and 3.B.b.), alkylation takes place on the sulphur atom and not the nitrogen atom. This is possibly due to the stronger nucleophilic nature of sulphur as compared with oxygen. 2-Methylthioquinazoline (pK_a 1.60) is a stronger base than 1,2-dihydro-2-thioquinazoline and its cation is partially hydrated (covalent) in aqueous acid[1,4] (Ch. II, Sect. 2.C.b.(ii)). 4-Methyl-2-methylthioquinazoline, prepared by a similar alkylation of the corresponding 2-thio compound, is also a weak base (pK_a 1.86).

B. 3-Substituted 2,3-Dihydro- and 1,2,3,4-Tetrahydro-2-thioquinazolines

3-Substituted 2,3-dihydro-2-thioquinazolines and their derivatives were first described by Reissert and Schaaf[5] in 1926 and were later

studied by Gheorghiu and collaborators in great detail. When sodium
isatinate (4) is boiled with phenyl isothiocyanate in 0.5 N sodium
hydroxide, condensation takes place to give 4-carboxy-1,2,3,4-tetra-
hydro-4-hydroxy-3-phenyl-2-thioquinazoline (5). The acid can be
esterified with alcoholic hydrogen chloride, or decarboxylated in boiling benzene, toluene, or xylene to 1,2,3,4-tetrahydro-4-hydroxy-3-
phenyl-2-thioquinazoline (6). On further heating 6 loses the elements
of water to form 2,3-dihydro-3-phenyl-2-thioquinazoline (7) (Reaction
2). The latter, and related compounds (see below), add alcohol to produce 4-ethoxy-1,2,3,4-tetrahydro-3-phenyl-2-thioquinazoline (8).[5] The

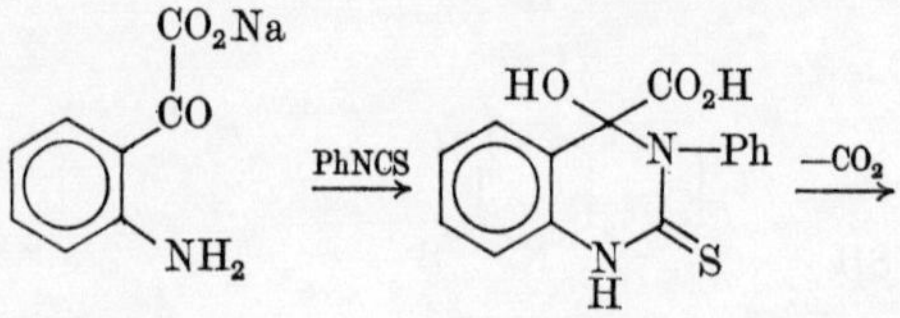

$$\text{(4)} \qquad \xrightarrow{\text{PhNCS}} \qquad \text{(5)} \qquad \xrightarrow{-CO_2}$$

$$\text{(6)} \qquad \xrightarrow{-H_2O} \qquad \text{(7)} \qquad\qquad (2)$$

4-ethoxy group in 8 can be readily replaced by a methoxy, hydroxy,[5]
acetoxy,[6] phenacyl,[7] 4-methylphenacyl, α,α-diethoxycarbonylmethyl,
α-acetyl-α-ethoxycarbonylmethyl, α-benzoylbenzyl, and a phthali-

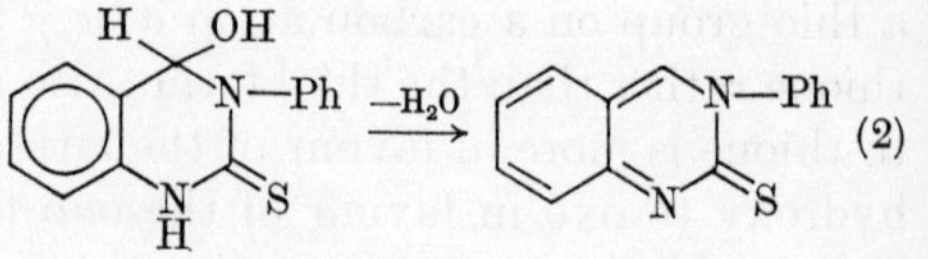

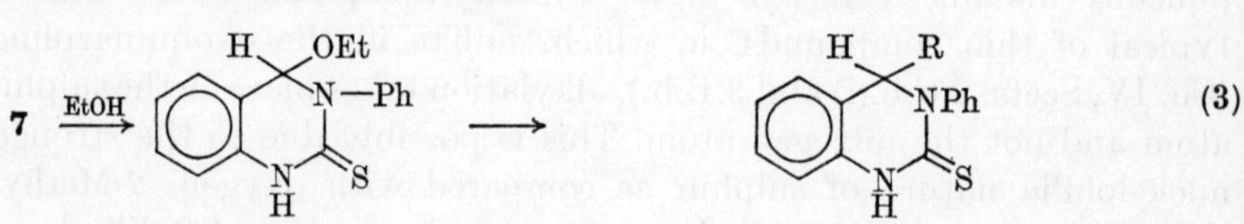

$$7 \xrightarrow{\text{EtOH}} \text{(8)} \longrightarrow \text{(9)} \qquad\qquad (3)$$

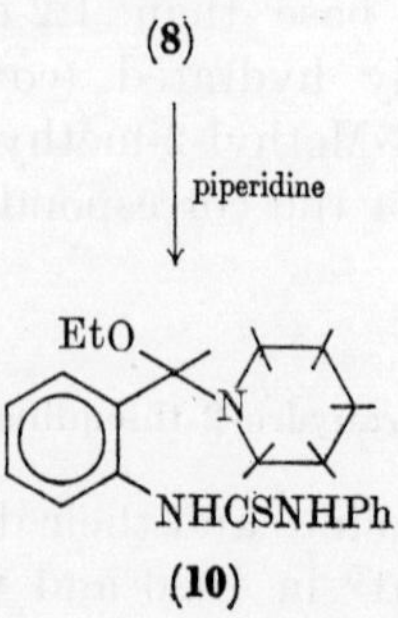

$$R = OH, OAc, PhCOCH_2, p\text{-}CH_3C_6H_4COCH_2,$$
$$CH(CO_2Et)_2, CH(COCH_3)CO_2Et, CHPh(COPh),$$

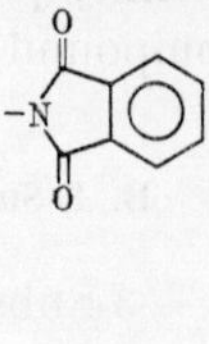

piperidine ↓

(10)

mido[8,9] group (9). With piperidine, ring opening occurs, apparently with the formation of (α-piperidino-o-N'-phenylthioureido)benzyl ethyl ether (10) (Reaction 3).[8] Similarly by using 5-bromoisatin, the 6-bromo derivatives of 2,3-dihydro-2-thioquinazoline are prepared.[10] Also by using o-tolyl and allyl isothiocyanates the respective 3-o-tolyl-[11] and 3-allyl-4-carboxy-1,2,3,4-tetrahydro-4-hydroxy-2-thioquinazoline[12,13] are formed, and from these, derivatives related to 6 and 8 can be readily obtained. The isatinate (4) can be replaced by an o-aminobenzaldehyde, e.g. 2-amino-4,5-methylenedioxybenzaldehyde, which on reaction with phenyl, o- or p-tolyl isothiocyanates finally gives the respective 3-aryl-2,3-dihydro-6,7-methylenedioxy-2-thioquinazolines.[12] o-Aminobenzaldehyde oximes also give the same reaction but the isothiocyanate must be in excess because it consumes the hydroxylamine which may be liberated in the reaction.[11,12] o-Aminobenzophenones react with methyl, allyl, phenyl, α- and β-naphthyl isothiocyanates to produce 3-methyl-,[13a] 3-allyl-, 3-phenyl-, 3-1'- and 3-2'-naphthyl- 1,2,3,4-tetrahydro-4-hydroxy-4-phenyl-2-thioquinazolines (11) (Reaction 4).[14]

$$(4)$$

$$(11)$$

$$(12)$$

Compounds having structures 6 or 8 undergo colour changes on heating in inert solvents such as xylene, bromobenzene, α-bromonaphthalene, nitrobenzene and pyridine.[7,9] The colour changes to violet or red and disappears on cooling.[7,10,15,16] The depth of colour depends on the concentration of the solution,[12] it is not sensitive to oxygen,[17] and is not affected by the dielectric constant of the medium,[12,15] although it may vary from one solvent to another. Thus 3-aryl-4-alkoxy- (or hydroxy-) 1,2,3,4-tetrahydro-2-thioquinazolines are violet in hot benzene and red in hot xylene.[17] The derivatives 9 with R = PhCOCH$_2$—, p-CH$_3$C$_6$H$_4$COCH$_2$—, $-$CH(CO$_2$Et)$_2$, $-$CH(COCH$_3$)-CO$_2$Et, and —CHPh(COPh), do not show these colour changes on heating in nitrobenzene, but **9** (R = phthalimido) becomes violet.[9,15] The violet colour of a solution of **9** (R = OH) in boiling xylene containing acetophenone disappears due to the formation of **9** (R = PhCOCH$_2$).[18] A phenyl group in position 4 assists this thermochromic change and the derivatives of **11** with R^1 = allyl, phenyl, α- or β-naphthyl all show these colour changes in bromo- or nitrobenzene, although with the compounds that have larger groups, e.g. α-naphthyl, the colour persists for comparatively longer periods after heating is stopped.[14] These colour changes do not take place with 4-ethoxy-2-ethylthio-3,4-dihydro-3-phenylquinazoline (**12**),[12,16] and are similar to those observed in spiropyranes.[19] Gheorghiu[12,16] concluded that the colour was due to dissociation with the formation of ionic structures such as **13** and **14**.

(13)   (14)

R = H or Et

Deep colours are also formed when these compounds are melted or dissolved in strong sulphuric or perchloric acid.[12] These compounds also give a variety of coloured mercury salts which have been assigned structures such as **15**, **16**, **17**, and **18**.[6,20,21,22] Silver nitrate forms colourless silver salts or complexes, e.g. **19** and **20**, which give yellow salts, e.g. **21**, on further treatment with acid.[22,23] The latter together with the mercury salts are considered to be dissociated in a similar manner to the free bases in hot inert solvents.[21,23] The structures of some of these mercury salts should be taken with some reserve because they rest on the mercury analyses alone.

These 2-thioquinazolines are generally high melting and their colour turns to red or violet on heating. The sulphur atom can be replaced by oxygen by heating with red mercuric oxide to give the oxygen analogues, e.g. 4-carboxy-1,2,3,4-tetrahydro-4-hydroxy-2-oxo-3-phenylquinazoline[5] and 4-ethoxy-1,2,3,4-tetrahydro-6,7-methylenedioxy-2-oxo-3-phenylquinazoline.[12] Hydrogen peroxide, on the other hand, oxidizes them to the 3-substituted 1,2,3,4-tetrahydro-2,4-dioxoquinazolines,[5] and hydroxylamine yields 3-substituted 1,2,3,4-tetrahydro-4-hydroxy-2-hydroxyiminoquinazolines with loss of hydrogen sulphide.[8] The constant for the equilibrium **21a** $\rightleftharpoons$ **21b** was 0.3 $\pm$ 1. The infrared

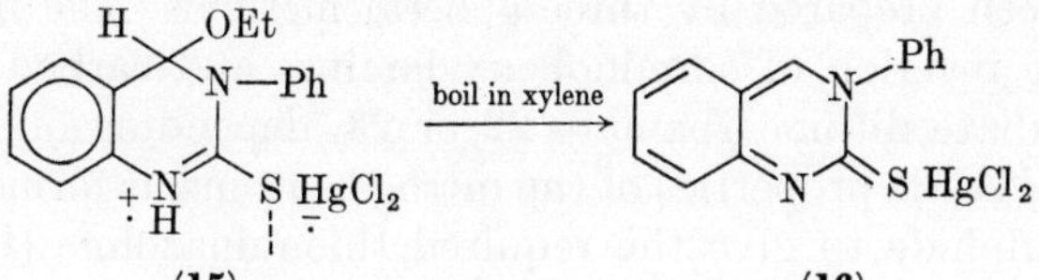

(15) (16)

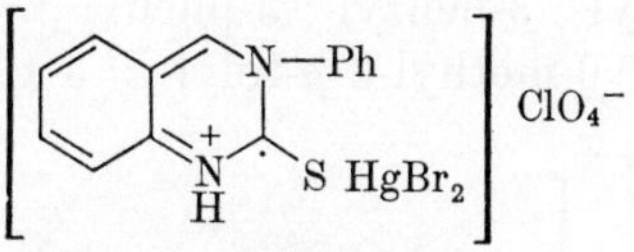

(17)

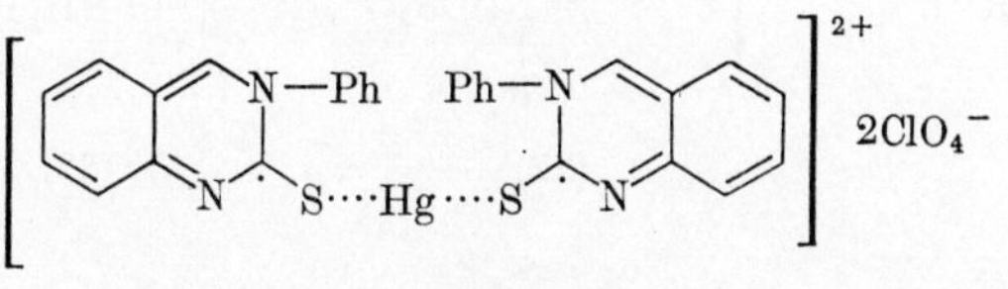

(18)

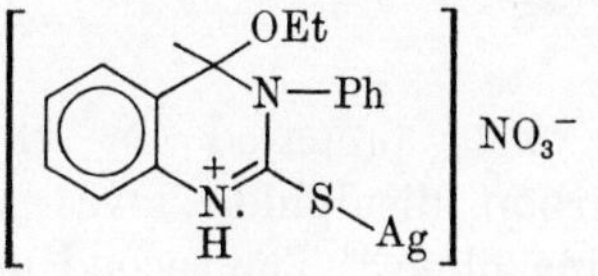

(19) 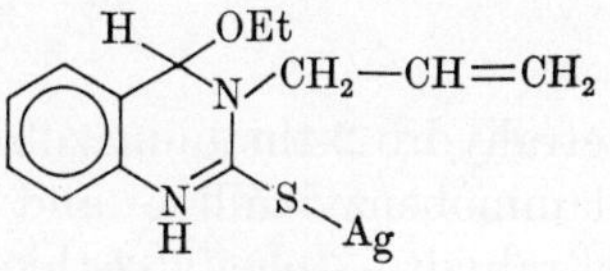 (20)

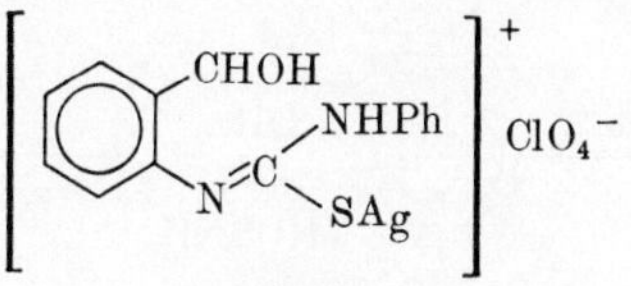

(21)

spectrum of the anhydrous hydrochloride supported the $N_{(1)}$-protonated structure **21b** because it had a band at 1880 cm^{-1} which was attributed to the —C=N$^+$H— group.[13a]

Several 3,4-dihydro derivatives of 2-thioquinazoline are known

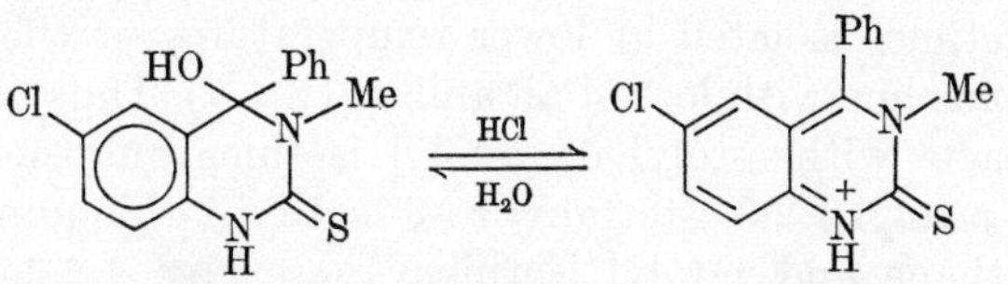

(21a) (21b)

10*

and have been prepared by three general methods. The first method
involves the reaction of o-aminobenzylamines and carbon disulphide.
An intermediate dithiocarbamate **22** or **23**, depending on the nucleo-
philicity and steric properties of the nitrogen atoms, is formed and loses
hydrogen sulphide to give the required thioquinazoline (Reaction 5).
3-Methyl-, 3-ethyl-,[24,25] 3-propyl-, 3-isopropyl-, 3-allyl-, 3-isobutyl-,
3-t-butyl-, 3-cyclohexyl-, 3-benzyl-, 3-phenyl-,[25] 3-o-tolyl-,[26] 6-chloro-
3-methyl-4-phenyl-,[13a] 6-methyl-3-p-tolyl-,[27] 3-1′- and 3-2′-naphthyl-[28]

(5)

1,2,3,4-tetrahydro-2-thioquinazolines are prepared in this way.
o-Benzylaminobenzylaniline and carbon disulphide gives 1-benzyl-
1,2,3,4-tetrahydro-3-phenyl-2-thioquinazoline.[29] The second method is
from o-aminobenzhydrols with hydrothiocyanic acid. The intermediate

(6)

in this case is the o-thioureido derivative **24** which cyclizes to give the
tetrahydrothioquinazoline, e.g. 4-phenyl-,[30] 4-p-tolyl-,[31] 4-2′,4′-xylyl-,[32]
and 6-methyl-4-phenyl-[33] 1,2,3,4-tetrahydro-2-thioquinazolines (Reaction 6). In the third method a dianilinomethane is heated with an
aryl isothiocyanate above 200°. The thiourea is initially formed and
can be sometimes isolated at lower temperatures; it then cyclizes to
the thioquinazoline with loss of an aniline (Eq. 7). Thus di-p-toluidino-
methane reacts with o-tolyl or p-tolyl isothiocyanates to form 3-o-
tolyl- or 3-p-tolyl-1,2,3,4-tetrahydro-6-methyl-2-thioquinazoline, and
dianilinomethane and p-tolyl isothiocyanate give 1,2,3,4-tetrahydro-
6-methyl-3-phenyl-2-thioquinazoline.[34]

$$R-\bigcirc-\underset{\underset{H}{\mid}}{N}-CH_2-\underset{\underset{R}{\mid}}{N}-\bigcirc \xrightarrow{ArNCS} R-\bigcirc-\underset{\underset{H}{\mid}}{N}-CH_2-\underset{\underset{\mid}{N}}{\overset{\overset{\displaystyle S=C}{\mid}}{}}\bigcirc-R \longrightarrow$$

$$R-\bigcirc\underset{\underset{H}{N}}{\overset{N-Ar}{\underset{S}{}}} + R\diagdown\bigcirc\diagup NH_2 \qquad (7)$$

o-Aminoacetophenone and methyl isothiocyanate react to give what the authors believe to be 1,2,3,4-tetrahydro-3-methyl-4-methylene-2-thioquinazoline (25).[35]

$$\bigcirc\underset{\underset{H}{N}}{\overset{\overset{CH_2}{\parallel}}{\underset{}{N}}} \overset{Me}{\underset{S}{}}$$

(25)

1,2,3,4-Tetrahydro-2-thioquinazolines are high-melting solids which can be oxidized with potassium permanganate to 1,2,3,4-tetrahydro-2,4-dioxoquinazolines,[24] and can be reduced with sodium and alcohol to 1,2,3,4-tetrahydroquinazolines.[24,30] Bromine in acetic acid converts them to 2-bromo-3,4-dihydroquinazolines,[30,32] methylation takes place on the sulphur atom to give 3,4-dihydro-2-methylthioquinazolines, and reduction of these with zinc and dilute sulphuric acid produces the respective 1,2,3,4-tetrahydroquinazoline with loss of the methylthio group.[27]

2. 4-Thioquinazolines

A. 1,4- and 3,4-Dihydro-4-thioquinazolines

The earlier methods for the preparation of 2-alkyl-3,4-dihydro-4-thioquinazolines involve heating a mixture of o-aminobenzonitrile and aliphatic acid anhydrides with sodium sulphide in a sealed tube at temperatures above 100°, or in an open vessel depending on the boiling point of the anhydride (Reaction 8). 2-Methyl-, 2-ethyl-, 2-propyl-, and 2-isopropyl- 3,4-dihydro-4-thioquinazolines are prepared in this way, and heating o-amidobenzonitriles with alcoholic hydrogen sulphide and ammonia in a sealed tube is a modification of this.[36] By using hydrogen selenide instead of hydrogen sulphide 3,4-dihydro-2-methyl-4-selenoquinazoline is formed.[37] 3,4-Dihydro-2-methyl-4-thioquinazolines are also obtained by heating the nitrile with dithioacetic acid in a sealed tube.[38,39] The reaction probably goes through the intermediate thioamide, and when o-aminothiobenzamide is boiled with acetic anhydride, 3,4-dihydro-2-methyl-4-thioquinazoline (**26**, R = Me) is produced[36] (Reaction 8).

$$(8)$$

(**26**)

The accessibility of 3,4-dihydro-4-oxoquinazolines (Ch. IV, Sect. 2.A.) makes them very useful intermediates for preparing the corresponding 4-thio analogues. They can be converted to 4-chloroquinazolines and reacted with alcoholic potassium hydrogen sulphide (Reaction 9),[40] or more conveniently by direct thiation with a little

$$(9)$$

more than one molecule of phosphorus pentasulphide in boiling xylene or pyridine (Reaction 10).[1,40-45] If necessary phosphorus pentasulphide can be purified by extraction with carbon disulphide in a Soxhlet.

$$(10)$$

2-Methyl-, 6-chloro-2-methyl-,[41] 2-methyl-6-nitro-,[44] 2-benzyl-3-methyl-,[45] 2-phenyl-,[43] 3-methyl-,[1,40] 2-methyl-3-o-tolyl-, 3-o-, 3-m-, and 3-p-bromophenyl-2-methyl-, 3-p-chlorophenyl-2-methyl-, 3-p-fluorophenyl-2-methyl-,[46] 3-2'-diethylaminoethyl-, 3-2'-dipropyl-aminoethyl- and 3-2'-dibutylaminoethyl-, and 3-3'-diethylamino-propyl-[47] 3,4-dihydro-4-thioquinazolines, and 1-methyl-,[1,40] 1-ethyl-,[40] 1,2-diphenyl-, and 1-p-fluorophenyl-2-phenyl-[48] 1,4-dihydro-4-thioquinazolines (**27**) are prepared from the respective 4-oxo compounds by direct thiation.[40] Although 6-, 7-, and 8-nitro-3,4-dihydro-4-thioquinazoline can be obtained with this reagent, the reaction fails with 3,4-dihydro-5-nitro-4-oxoquinazoline. This can, however, be obtained from 4-chloro-5-nitroquinazoline by reaction with potassium hydrogen sulphide.[49] Phosphorus pentasulphide and 3,4-dihydro-1,3-dimethyl-4-oxoquinazolinium iodide (28) at 145°, in the absence of a solvent, gives 3,4-dihydro-1,3-dimethyl-4-thioquinazolinium iodide (29) (Reaction 11). 1,4-Dihydro-1-methyl-4-thioquinazoline was obtained from 1-methyl-4-methylthioquinazolinium iodide by reaction with aqueous sodium sulphide solution at 20°.[40]

(27)   (28)   (29)   (11)

R = Ph or p-F-C$_6$H$_4$

A large variety of 2-, 3-, and 2,3-substituted 3,4-dihydro-4-thioquinazolines with 2-isopropyl-3-phenyl, 3-2'-diethylaminoethyl-2-methyl, 2-phenyl-3-o-tolyl, and 2-1'-naphthyl-3-phenyl substituents can be prepared by heating benzothiazine-3,1,4-thiones (30) with the appropriate amine until evolution of hydrogen sulphide ceases (Eq. 12).[50-52]

(30) $+ H_2S$ (12)

Imidoyl isothiocyanates or their dimers give 2- and benz-substituted 3,4-dihydro-4-thioquinazolines on heating.[53] The cyclization of N-phenyl benzimidoyl isothiocyanates to 3,4-dihydro-2-phenyl-4-thioquinazolines takes place at temperatures as low as 80°, and occurs regardless of the presence of electron-releasing, e.g. methoxy, or electron-withdrawing, e.g. nitro substituents in either benzene ring (Eq. 13). Cyclizations of this type (multicentre processes) have been designated as 'no mechanism reactions' because of the difficulty in describing precisely the transition state or states.[53a]

$$\text{(13)}$$

B. 4-Alkylthio- and Arylthioquinazolines

Alkylation of 1,4-dihydro- and 3,4-dihydro-4-thioquinazolines with alkyl iodides[1,38,40] or dialkyl sulphate[1,40,42,44] in aqueous alkaline medium gives high yields of 4-alkylthioquinazolines as is the case with all thio compounds (Reaction 14) (Sects. 1.A. and B.). Alkyl iodides in alcoholic solution containing one mol of sodium alkoxide also produce

$$\text{(14)}$$

4-alkylthioquinazolines, but if two mols of sodium alkoxide are used the product is the respective 4-alkoxyquinazoline.[54] Methylation of 1-methyl- and 1-ethyl- 1,4-dihydro-4-thioquinazolines yields 1-methyl- and 1-ethyl-4-methylthioquinazolinium iodide, and ethylation of 1,4-dihydro-1-methyl-4-thioquinazoline yields 4-ethylthio-1-methylquinazolinium iodide (Eq. 15). 3,4-Dihydro-3-methyl-4-thioquinazoline is

$$\text{(15)}$$

the only known exception which is alkylated on nitrogen, and with methyl iodide it gives 1,3-dimethyl-4-thioquinazolinium iodide (**29**).[40] This may perhaps be always the case with 3-substituted 3,4-dihydro-4-thioquinazolines.

4-Arylthioquinazolines cannot be prepared by the above methods because the halogen atom in benzenes is not very reactive. They are obtained in good yields by a nucleophilic displacement of the chlorine atom in 4-chloroquinazolines by thiophenols in the presence of an equivalent of sodium alkoxide in alcohol (Reaction 14).[55-57] 2-Chloro-4-p-chlorophenylthioquinazoline is prepared by forming sodium p-chloro-thiophenate in ethanol, evaporating, and then heating with one mol of 2,4-dichloroquinazoline in ether. This is because the arylthio compound formed can disproportionate to give 2,4-di-p-chlorophenylthio-quinazoline in boiling alcoholic sodium hydroxide.[58] The stannic chlorides of N-phenyl benzimidoyl chloride or trichloroacetimidoyl chloride react with methyl isothiocyanate in nitrobenzene at 100-120° to give 2-phenyl- or 2-trichloromethyl-4-methylthioquinazoline (Reaction 16).[59,60] This is an interesting case because the methyl group in methyl isothiocyanate which is on the nitrogen atom ends up on the sulphur atoms in the quinazoline, inferring that a rearrangement must have taken place during the reaction.

$$(16)$$

C. 1,2,3,4-Tetrahydro-4-thioquinazolines

2,2-Dimethyl-[61,62] and 2-methyl-[62] 1,2,3,4-tetrahydro-4-thio-quinazolines are the only two compounds known in this series. They are prepared by condensation of o-aminothiobenzamide with acetone and acetaldehyde, respectively, in the presence of hydrogen chloride. The former reacts with methyl iodide to give 1,2-dihydro-2,2-dimethyl-4-methylthioquinazoline (Reaction 17).[61]

$$(17)$$

D. Properties of 4-Thioquinazolines

1,2-, 1,4-, and 3,4-Dihydro-4-thioquinazolines are high-melting pale-yellow solids which sublime very slowly at high temperature and in high vacuum. Like 4-oxoquinazoline (Ch. IV, Sect. 2.C.a.) 3,4-dihydro-4-thioquinazoline can exist in the three tautomeric structures **31**, **32**, and **33**. It is soluble in dilute alkali presumably through the participation of the structure **32**, and has a basic and an acidic pK_a of 1.51 and 8.47 respectively.[1] In 4-thioquinazoline the equilibrium is more in favour of the thione structure (Sect. 1.A.) and the tautomeric ratio of **31** to **33** in aqueous solution is 30 to 1 (cf. in 4-oxoquinazoline it is ~ 10; Ch. IV, Sect. 2.C.a.). This ratio is calculated from the

(31)   (32)   (33)

ionization constants of 4-thioquinazoline, 1,4-dihydro-1-methyl-, and 3,4-dihydro-3-methyl- 4-thioquinazolines on the assumption that the third form **32** present in aqueous solution is comparatively small. The infrared spectrum of 4-thioquinazoline (Nujol mull) has a band at ~ 1500 cm^{-1} assigned to the thioureido stretching vibration, and Culbertson, Decius, and Christensen were unable to find a thiol band at about 2500 cm^{-1} in their measurements using a lithium fluoride prism.[63] 3-Substituted 3,4-dihydro-4-thioquinazolines have a thione band at ~ 1360–1363 cm^{-1}.[50]

3,4-Dihydro-4-thioquinazolines react with amines to give 4-amino-quinazolines[42] (Ch. VII, Sect. 1.B.a.), the sodium salt of the parent substance can be oxidized with persulphate to form 4,4'-diquinazolinyl disulphide,[57] and when a substituent is absent on the nitrogen atoms alkylation usually takes place on the sulphur atom to yield the 4-alkylthioquinazolines (Sect. 2.B.). Desulphurization of 3-substituted 3,4-dihydro-4-thioquinazolines with Raney nickel gives 3-substituted 3,4-dihydroquinazolines.[45]

4-Alkylthioquinazolines are pale-yellow solids which are more volatile and lower melting than the respective dihydrothio compounds, and can be easily sublimed. The alkylthio group in 4-alkylthio-quinazolines can be readily eliminated, with degradation of the quina-zoline, by alkali only when a substituent in positions 6 or 8 can stabilize

OH$^-$ attack on $C_{(2)}$ in order to overcome the energy barrier, for example **34** (Reaction 18). Thus 6- and 8-nitro-, but not 5- and 7-nitro-4-alkylthioquinazolines react with potassium hydroxide in dioxan to give 3- and 5-nitro-2-aminobenzonitriles.[49] Methylation of 4-methyl-

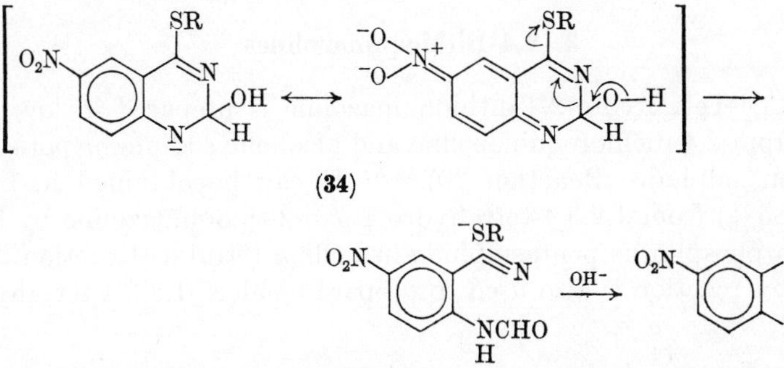

(34)

(18)

thioquinazoline takes place on $N_{(1)}$ because it gives the same 1-methyl-4-methylthioquinazolinium iodide as does the methylation of 1,4-dihydro-1-methyl-4-thioquinazoline (see Ch. III, Sect. 2.B.d.). The quaternary salt condenses with 2-methylbenzothiazole to give a cyanine dye, and with one equivalent of sodium hydroxide it is degraded to o-N-methylformamidobenzonitrile (**35**) with loss of methylthiol

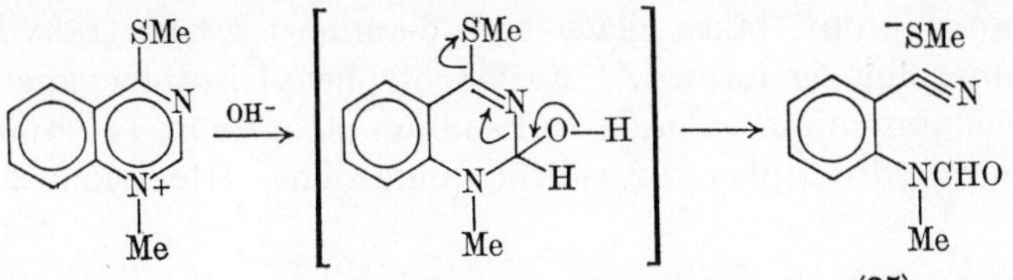

(19)

(35)

(Reaction 19).[40] 4-Methylthioquinazoline can be converted to 4-3'-diethylaminopropylquinazoline by heating with 3-diethylaminopropylamine but in poorer yields than with 3,4-dihydro-4-thioquinazoline.[42] 4-Arylthioquinazolines are oxidized to 4-arylsulphonylquinazolines with hydrogen peroxide in acetic acid.[55]

The 4-thio group in 6-amino- and 6-chloro-1,2,3,4-tetrahydro-2,4-dithioquinazoline, and in the parent dithio compound, is more reactive than the 2-thio group, and the respective 4-amino-1,2-dihydro-2-thioquinazolines are formed with ammonia.[64–66] Also the 4-methylthio group in 2,4-bismethylthioquinazoline is more reactive than the 2-methylthio group, and with alcoholic ammonia at 150°, aniline, sodium ethoxide, and 10% aqueous potassium hydroxide, it yields

4-amino-, 4-anilino-, 4-methoxy-, and 4-oxo-3,4-dihydro- 2-methyl-thioquinazolines respectively. Alcoholic ammonia at 250°, on the other hand, displaces the two methylthio groups to give 2,4-diaminoquinazoline.[59]

3. 2,4-Dithioquinazolines

1,2,3,4-Tetrahydro-2,4-dithioquinazoline is prepared in low yield (44%) from 2,4-dichloroquinazoline and alcoholic sodium or potassium hydrogen sulphide (Reaction 20).[39,67] It can be obtained in better yields (85%) from 1,2,3,4-tetrahydro-4-oxo-2-thioquinazoline by heating with phosphorus pentasulphide in boiling tetralin (Reaction 20).[68] The latter reaction is also used to prepare 6-chloro-1,2,3,4-tetrahydro-

$$(20)$$

2,4-dithioquinazoline,[64] and several 3-aryl substituted derivatives are similarly prepared in boiling xylene.[65] On heating 1,2,3,4-tetrahydro-2,4-dioxo-6-nitroquinazoline with phosphorus pentasulphide, reduction of the nitro group takes place and 6-amino-1,2,3,4-tetrahydro-2,4-dithioquinazoline is formed.[69] Fusion of phenyl isothiocyanate with anhydrous aluminium chloride and sodium chloride at 140–160° gives 1,2,3,4-tetrahydro-3-phenyl-2,4-dithioquinazoline (Reaction 21) to-

$$2PhNCS + AlCl_3 \xrightarrow[140-160°]{NaCl}$$

$$(21)$$

gether with a small quantity of benzothiazole-2-thiol.[70] Phenyl or p-tolyldiazonium borofluoride or hexachlorostannate reacts with methyl isothiocyanate to form 2,4-dimethylthioquinazoline[59,71] or its 6-methyl[68] derivative (Reaction 22). Both these syntheses can be profit-

$$+ 2MeNCS \longrightarrow$$

$$(22)$$

ably explored. Alkylation of 3-substituted 1,2,3,4-tetrahydro-2,4-dithioquinazolines gives 3-substituted 2-alkylthio-3,4-dihydro-4-thioquinazolines,[65] and 2,4-diarylthioquinazolines are formed from 2,4-dichloroquinazoline and 2 equivalents of the thiophenol.[58] The preferential displacement of the 4-thio group in 2,4-dithioquinazolines by nucleophiles is described in Section 2.D.

4. 1,2,3,4-Tetrahydro-4-oxo-2-thioquinazolines

Only 1,2,3,4-tetrahydro-4-oxo-2-thioquinazolines are described in this chapter because the isomeric 1,2,3,4-tetrahydro-2-oxo-4-thioquinazolines are not known. When anthranilic acid is heated with ammonium thiocyanate 1,2,3,4-tetrahydro-4-oxo-2-thioquinazoline is formed.[72] The reaction is smoother if anthranilic esters are used.[73,74] Under very mild conditions the thiocyanate salt of the anthranilic ester is formed but is exothermic when heated at 100° in xylene to give the oxothioquinazoline.[75] o-Alkylaminobenzoic acids or esters react with potassium thiocyanate to give, for example, 1-2'-hydroxyethyl-,[76,77] 1-phenacyl-,[78] and 1-allyl-[79] 1,2,3,4-tetrahydro-4-oxo-2-thioquinazolines. The reaction most probably goes via o-thioureidobenzoic acids or esters because these readily cyclize to oxothioquinazolines on heating (Reaction 23).[73,77] 3-Alkyl- or 3-aryl-1,2,3,4-

$$R = H, Me, Et$$

(23)

tetrahydro-4-oxo-2-thioquinazoline are obtained from alkyl or aryl isothiocyanates and anthranilic acid in acetic acid in a sealed tube at temperatures above 150°.[80,81] o-Allylaminobenzoic acids give 1,3-substituted derivatives (Reaction 23).[81,82] The reaction can also be carried out by boiling in ethanol for a few hours.[83-87] The substituent of the isothiocyanate always ends up on $N_{(3)}$ and although Pawlewski[88] stated that allyl isothiocyanate and anthranilic acid give some of the 1-allyl derivative, it was later disproved.[89] By using the appropriate anthranilic acids, 3-substituted 1,2,3,4-tetrahydro-4-oxo-2-thioquinazolines with halogen,[84,90,91] methyl,[87,92] halogen and methyl,[93] and hydroxy[94] groups in the benzene ring of the quinazoline are prepared.

Anthranilic acid and thiourea at 180–200° give 1,2,3,4-tetrahydro-4-oxo-2-thioquinazoline.[95] 3-Aryl derivatives are obtained by fusion of mono-N-arylthioureas[96,97] and anthranilic acid; and with derivatives of the latter, benzene-substituted 3-aryl-1,2,3,4-tetrahydro-4-oxo-2-thioquinazolines are formed.[98] o-Aminophenylarylamides and urea also give 3-aryl derivatives.[99] This reaction can be also carried out in boiling alcohol (Eq. 24).[85] N-Allyl-N'-phenyl- and N-phenylthiourea react with anthranilic acid to give the same 1,2,3,4-tetrahydro-4-oxo-3-phenyl-2-thioquinazoline.[88] o-N-Benzoylthioureidobenzoic acid or ester cyclizes in basic media, e.g. pyridine, to 1,2,3,4-tetrahydro-4-oxo-2-thioquinazoline,[100] but in acid media, e.g. sulphuric acid, the 3-benzoyl derivative is obtained.[101] 1,2,3,4-Tetrahydro-3-2'-hydroxyethyl-4-oxo-

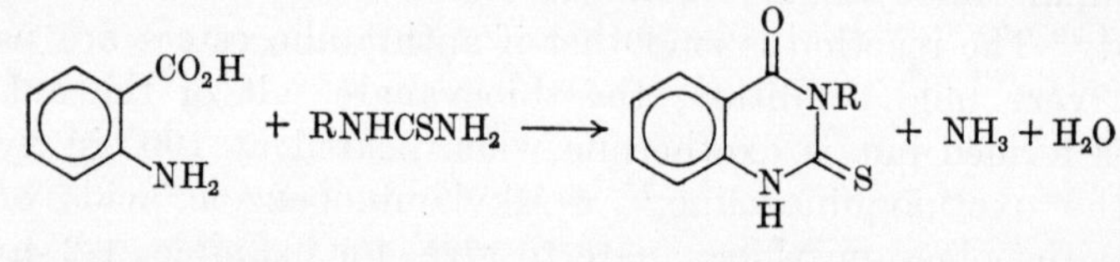

$$\text{(24)}$$

2-thioquinazolines (**36**) with substituents on the 3-ethyl side chain and in the benzene ring are prepared from the corresponding substituted o-aminobenzamides and carbon disulphide by boiling in alcoholic sodium hydroxide (Reaction 25).[77,102] Alkaline hydrolysis of 1,2,3,4-tetrahydro-4-imino-3-phenyl-2-thioquinazoline leads to 1,2,3,4-tetrahydro-4-oxo-3-phenyl-2-thioquinazoline.[103] Alkylation of 1-substituted and 3-substituted (or unsubstituted) 1,2,3,4-tetrahydro-4-oxo-2-thioquinazolines takes place on the sulphur atom to give 1-substituted 1,4-dihydro- (**37**)[100] and 3-substituted (or unsubstituted) 3,4-dihydro-4-

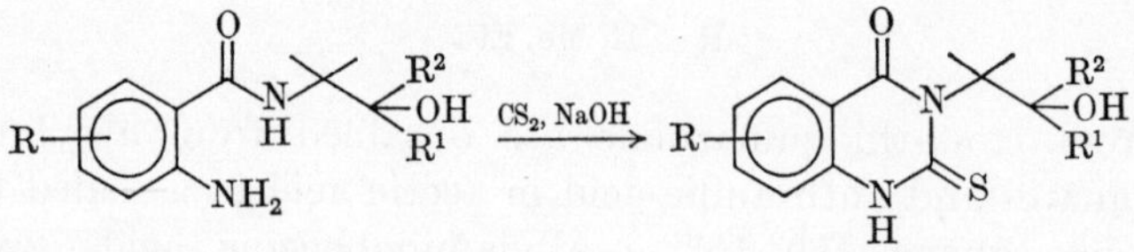

(36)

$$\text{(25)}$$

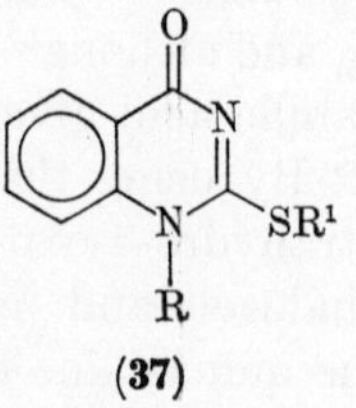

(37) 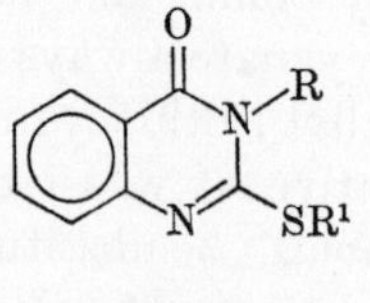   **(38)**

oxo-2-alkylthioquinazolines (38).[77,83,104-112] The reaction condition should not be too drastic because it may lead to loss of the sulphur atom, for example when 1,2,3,4-tetrahydro-4-oxo-2-thioquinazoline is boiled with dimethyl sulphate in potassium hydroxide solution 1,2,3,4-tetrahydro-3-methyl-2,4-dioxoquinazoline is formed.[101] 2-p-Chlorophenylthio-3,4-dihydro-4-oxoquinazoline can be obtained from 2-chloro-3,4-dihydro-4-oxoquinazoline and p-chlorophenylthiol at 100°.[58] 2-Ethoxycarbonylthio-3,4-dihydro-4-oxoquinazolines with substituents in the benzene ring are prepared by reaction of S-ethoxycarbonylthiocyanate, formed in situ, with the required anthranilic acid hydrochloride[112] or its ethyl ester.[113]

Oxothioquinazolines are high-melting solids with a pale-yellow colour. The polarographic behaviour of some derivatives is described.[114] Concentrated sulphuric acid at 125–130° rearranges 1,2,3,4-tetrahydro-4-oxo-3-phenyl-2-thioquinazoline to 2-anilino-4,5-benzo-4-oxo-1,3-thiazine (Eq. 26). The 3-allyl and p-tolyl derivatives behave similarly, except that the former requires hydrochloric acid.[114a]

$$ (26) $$

Potassium permanganate oxidizes 1,2,3,4-tetrahydro-4-oxo-2-thioquinazolines to 1,2,3,4-tetrahydro-2,4-dioxoquinazolines,[88,108-115] and sulphuryl chloride converts 1,2,3,4-tetrahydro-4-oxo-3-phenyl-2-thioquinazoline to 2-chloro-3,4-dihydro-3-phenylquinazoline.[116] Desulphurization of 3-substituted 1,2,3,4-tetrahydro-4-oxo-2-thioquinazolines[106] and 2-alkylthio-3,4-dihydro-4-oxoquinazolines[104] with Raney nickel W-6 takes place in boiling ethanol.

5. Quinazolines Substituted with Thio Groups in the Benzene Ring

Few benzene-substituted thioquinazolines are known. 5-Methylthio- and 5-phenylthio-3,4-dihydro-4-oxoquinazoline are prepared from 5-amino-3,4-dihydro-4-oxoquinazoline by diazotization and reaction with methylthiol and phenylthiol respectively. Oxidation of the former with potassium permanganate yields 3,4-dihydro-5-methylsulphonyl-4-oxoquinazoline.[117] 4-Chloro-6-methoxy-7-nitroquinazoline reacts with excess of phenylthiol in alkaline medium to give 6-methoxy-4,7-bisphenylthioquinazoline (Scheme 1).[118] This is the first example of the nucleophilic displacement of a substituent in the benzene ring of quinazoline (see Ch. V, Sect. 1.E.b.(i)), because the displacement of a sulphonic acid group in the benzene ring of quinazoline by bromine is probably an electrophilic reaction (Ch. IV, Sect. 2.C.b.(iv)). The bisphenylthio derivative hydrolyzes to 3,4-dihydro-6-methoxy-4-oxo-7-phenylthioquinazoline, and is oxidized by hydrogen peroxide in acetic acid to 3,4-dihydro-6-methoxy-4-oxo-7-phenylsulphonylquinazoline. These compounds are incorrectly described as 6-methoxy-8-phenylthio derivatives[118] (Ch. V, Sect. 2.D.).

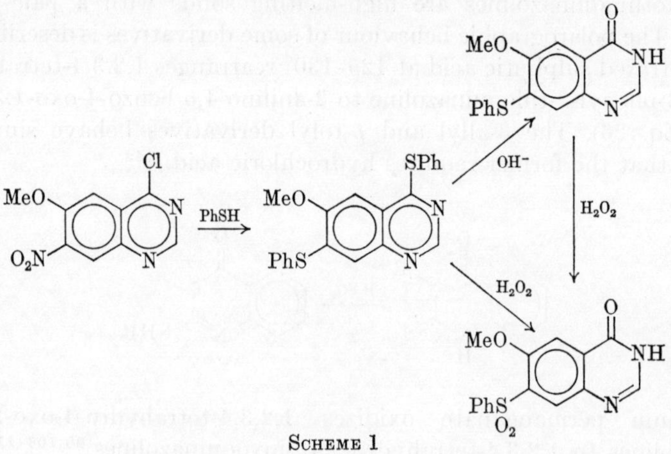

SCHEME 1

6. Thiazoloquinazolines (Thiopegenes)

Thiazoloquinazolines were investigated by Narang and coworkers who gave them the name thiopegenes because of the close structural relationship with the alkaloid peganine (Ch. XI, Sect. 1.B.). The main ring systems studied were thiazolo(2,3-b)quinazolin-5-one (10,11-thiopegen-9,4-one) (RRI 2691)[119] (39), thiazolo(3,2-a)quinazolin-5-one (9,10-thiopegen-10,4-one) (RRI 2694)[119] (40), and 11-*H*-thiazolo(3,2-c)-quinazoline (4,11-thiopegene) (41). Derivatives of 39 and 40 are closely related to the oxothioquinazolines from which many of them are prepared.

Several derivatives of 2,3-dihydrothiazolo(2,3-b)quinazolin-5-one (39) are obtained by condensation of allyl isothiocyanate with anthranilic acid, or its 3-, 4-, 5-, or 6-substituted derivatives, to give the respec-

(39)   (40)   (41)

tive 3-allyl-1,2,3,4-tetrahydro-4-oxo-2-thioquinazolines followed by cylization with dry hydrogen chloride in glacial acetic acid. These undergo the sequence of reactions shown in (27) to give 2-alkylthiazolo(2,3-b)quinazolin-5-ones.[87,90-93] By replacing anthranilic acid with isatinic acid 3-allyl-4-carboxy-1,2,3,4-tetrahydro-4-hydroxy-2-thioquinazoline is formed and leads to 5-carboxy-5-hydroxy derivatives of **39**. Decarboxylation of the thio derivative in boiling benzene yields 3-allyl-1,2,3,4-tetrahydro-4-hydroxy-2-thioquinazoline (**42**) which can be converted, reversibly, to *N*-allyl-*N'*-*o*-formylphenylthiourea (**43**) (Reaction 28). The former gives the 5-hydroxy in place of the 5-oxo deriva-

(27)

tives in reaction (27).[13] The starting materials for the 5-imino derivatives of the compounds in reaction (27) are o-aminobenzonitriles.[90] Another

$$\text{(42)} \quad \xrightleftharpoons[\text{AcOH}]{\text{dil. EtOH}} \quad \text{(43)} \tag{28}$$

attractive synthesis for thiazolo(2,3-b)quinazolin-5-ones is the condensation of anthranilic acid or its derivatives with 2-chlorobenzothiazoles (Eq. 29).[120-122] 4,5-Dihydrothiazol-2-thiol condenses with anthranilic acids to give 2,3-dihydrothiazolo(2,3-b)quinazolin-5-ones which are also formed by cyclization of 1,2,3,4-tetrahydro-3-2'-hydroxyethyl-4-oxo-2-thioquinazolines (36).[77,102] 2,3-Dihydrothiazolo(2,3-b)quinazolin-5-one can also be obtained from o-ethoxycarbonylphenyl isothiocyanate and ethylenimine.[75]

$$R\text{—} \underset{NH_2}{\overset{CO_2H}{\bigcirc}} + \underset{Cl}{\overset{R^2}{\underset{S}{\langle\rangle}}}R^1 \xrightarrow{165-180°} R\text{—}\underset{N}{\overset{O}{\bigcirc}}\overset{R^2}{\underset{S}{\langle\rangle}}R^1 + H_2O + HCl \tag{29}$$

3-Methyl-5H-thiazolo(2,3-b)quinazoline is formed when 1,2,3,4-tetrahydro-2-thioquinazoline is heated with chloroacetone in acetone.[123] Nitration and bromination of 3-phenylthiazolo(2,3-b)quinazolin-5-one, or the 3-substituted phenyl derivatives, takes place in the benzene ring of the quinazoline moiety, i.e. position 7. The substitution products were unambiguously synthesized from 5-nitro- and 5-bromoanthranilic acid and 2-chlorothiazoles.[124]

$$R\text{—}\underset{NH_2}{\overset{CO_2Et}{\bigcirc}} + \overset{R^1}{\underset{SCN}{\overset{|}{\underset{|}{\overset{CO}{\underset{CHR^2}{|}}}}}} \longrightarrow R\text{—}\overset{O}{\underset{N}{\bigcirc}}\overset{5N}{\underset{S}{\langle\rangle}}\underset{R^1R^2}{} + EtOH + H_2O \tag{30}$$

$$\text{(44)}$$

Thiazolo(3,2-a)quinazolin-5-ones (**40**) are the major products from the reaction of ethyl anthranilates and α-thiocyanoketones (Eq. 30).[121,122,125,126] Occasionally a mixture of two isomers is obtained, for example with ethyl 5-chloroanthranilate and thiocyanoacetone; and by the unambiguous synthesis (Eq. 29) it is shown that the higher-

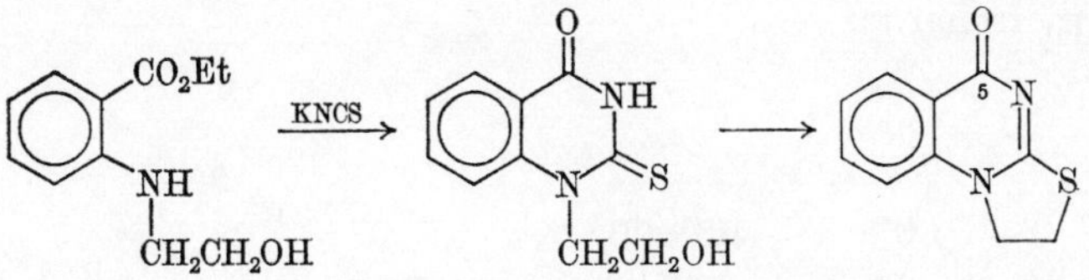

(31)

melting isomer is the angular compound.[122,126] The 2,3-dihydrothiazolo(2,3-b)quinazolin-5-ones obtained by condensation of ethyl o-thioureidobenzoates with ethylene bromide[127] are apparently the angular isomers, i.e. 2,3-dihydrothiazolo(3,2-a)quinazolin-5-ones.[77,127] The last named are best prepared from ethyl N-β-hydroxyethylaminobenzoates and potassium thiocyanate followed by ring closure (Reaction 31).[76,77] o-Phenacylamino- and o-4'-chlorophenacylaminobenzoic acid reacts with potassium thiocyanate to give 1-phenacyl- and 1-p-chlorophenacyl-1,2,3,4-tetrahydro-4-oxo-2-thioquinazoline which cyclize to 2-phenyl- and 2-p-chlorophenylthiazolo(3,2-a)quinazolin-5-one

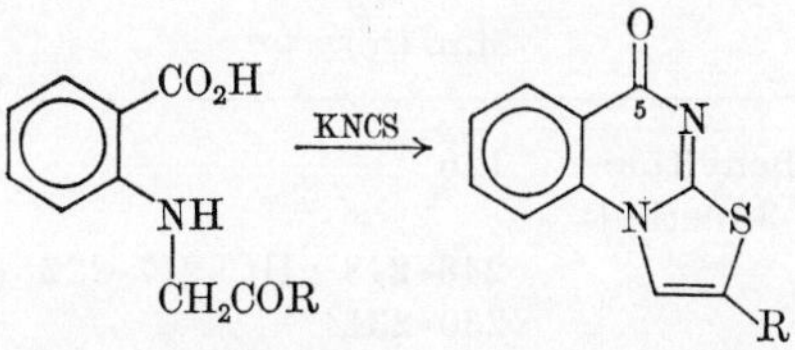

(32)

(Reaction 32).[78] α-Thiocyanoketones and o-aminobenzonitriles form the 5-imino derivatives of **44**.[128] 1-β-Chloroallyl-1,2,3,4-tetrahydro-4-oxo-2-thioquinazoline cyclizes to 2-methylthiazolo(3,2-a)quinazolin-5-one with hydrogen chloride in boiling ethanol.[79] Anthranilic acids and

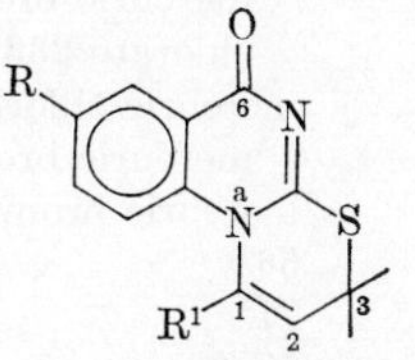

(**45**)

β-thiocyanoketones give 3-H-1,3-thiazino(3,2-a)quinazolin-6-ones (45).[129]

2,3-Dihydro-11-H-thiazolo(3,2-c)quinazolines (46) are prepared by condensation of o-amidobenzaldehydes or N-acyl derivatives of isatinic acids with β-aminoethylthiol compounds (Eq. 33) where R = H or Me, R^1 = H or CO$_2$H, R^2 = H, Me, Ph, or OEt, and R^3 = H, CO$_2$Me, or CO$_2$Et.[130,131,132]

$$ (33) $$

7. Tables

TABLE VI.1.   1,2- and 2,3-Dihydro-2-thioquinazolines, and 2-Alkylthio- and 2-Arylthioquinazolines.

Quinazoline	M.p. (°c)	References
4-Chloro-2-p-chlorophenylthio-	126°	58
6-Chloro-2,3-dihydro-3-methyl-		
4-phenyl-2-thio-	246–248°; HCl 217–222° (dec.)	13a
1,2-Dihydro-2-thio-	230–231°	1, 2
2,3-Dihydro-3-phenyl-2-thio-	252–255°	5
	mercuric chloride 290–292°;	20, 21
	mercuric bromide 296°;	20, 21
	mercuric iodide 252–253°;	20, 21
	mercuric perchlorate 279–282°;	21
	mercuric bromide perchlorate 233°	20
2,3-Dihydro-2-thio-3-o-tolyl-	mercuric chloride 268°;	20
	mercuric bromide 268°	20
2,3-Dihydro-2-thio-3-p-tolyl-	mercuric bromide 276°	20
4-Methoxy-2-methylthio-	56°	59
4-Methyl-2-methylthio-	71°	3
2-Methylthio-	59–60°	1

TABLE VI.2. 1,2,3,4-Tetrahydro-2-thioquinazolines.

$(R^2)H$ —[ring]— NR^1, S, N, H, (R)

1,2,3,4-Tetrahydro-2-thio-quinazoline	M.p. (°c)	References
Unsubstituted	210–212°	24, 25
3-Allyl-	HCl 168–170° (dec.)	25
3-Benzyl-	112°; HCl 225°	25
1-Benzyl-3-phenyl-	93°; HCl 240°; HNO$_3$ 126° (dec.)	29
3-Cyclohexyl-	147° (dec.); HCl 250–252° (dec.)	25
3-Ethyl-	185°; HCl 223–225° (dec.)	24, 25
1-Ethyl-3-methyl-	65°	24
3-Isobutyl-	HCl 189° (dec.)	25
3-Isopropyl-	110°; HCl 255° (dec.)	25
3-Methyl-	181° (dec.); HCl 185–187° (dec.)	24, 25
1-Methyl-3-1'-naphthyl-	HI 212°	28
1-Methyl-3-2'-naphthyl-	140°; HI 249°	28
1-Methyl-3-phenyl-	92°	26
6-Methyl-3-phenyl-	242–250° (dec.)	34
6-Methyl-3-o-tolyl-	255–262° (dec.)	34
6-Methyl-3-p-tolyl-[a]	258–260°; HCl 220–225°; H$_2$SO$_4$ 275°; oxalate 247–252°; platini-chloride 250° (dec.); picrate 240°	27, 34
3-1'-Naphthyl-	255°	28
3-2'-Naphthyl-	280°	28
3-Phenyl-	212° (dec.); HCl 182–184° (dec.)	25
3-Propyl-	HCl 138°	25
3-t-Butyl-	HCl 173–174° (dec.)	25
3-o-Tolyl-	202°	26

[a] The methyl derivative: 3,4-dihydro-6-methyl-2-methylthio-3-p-tolylquinazoline has m.p. 87°; HCl 258°; HI 260° (dec.); H$_2$SO$_4$ 208°; platinichloride 222°; and picrate 168°.[27]

TABLE VI.3.   4-Substituted 1,2,3,4-Tetrahydro-2-thioquinazolines.

$$R^2 \quad H(R^1)$$

$$(R^3)H \quad NH(R)$$

$$N \quad S$$

$$H$$

1,2,3,4-Tetrahydro-2-thio-quinazoline	M.p. (°c)	References
3-Allyl-4-allyloxycarbonyl-4-hydroxy-	160°	13
3-Allyl-4-carboxy-	105° (solidifies and remelts at 160°)	13
3-Allyl-4-ethoxy-	125°; perchlorate 138–145°; silver complex 140° (dec.)	12, 20, 23
3-Allyl-4-ethoxycarbonyl-4-hydroxy-	173–174°	13
3-Allyl-4-hydroxy-	164°, 142°	12, 13
3-Allyl-4-hydroxy-4-methoxy-carbonyl-	198°	13
3-Allyl-4-hydroxy-4-phenyl-	175–180°	14
3-Allyl-4-hydroxy-4-propoxy-carbonyl-	162–163°	13
6-Bromo-4-carboxy-4-hydroxy-3-phenyl-	156–161°	10
6-Bromo-4-ethoxy-4-phenyl-	197–204°; silver nitrate 180° (dec.)	10, 20, 23
4-Carboxy-4-hydroxy-3-phenyl-	159–160°	5
4-Carboxy-4-hydroxy-3-o-tolyl-	138–145° (dec.)	11
4-Carboxy-4-hydroxy-3-p-tolyl-	153–155° (dec.)	11
3-2′,3′-Dibromopropyl-4-ethoxycarbonyl-4-hydroxy-	184–185°	13
3-2′,3′-Dibromopropyl-4-hydroxy-	162°	13
3-2′,3′-Dibromopropyl-4-hydroxy-4-methoxycarbonyl-	172°	13
4-α,α-Diethoxycarbonylmethyl-3-phenyl-	172°	8, 9
4-Ethoxy-4-ethoxycarbonyl-3-phenyl-	192–194°	5
4-Ethoxy-6,7-methylenedioxy-3-o-tolyl-	233–235°	12
4-Ethoxy-6,7-methylenedioxy-3-p-tolyl-	215°	12

(*Table continued*)

TABLE VI.3 (*continued*)

1,2,3,4-Tetrahydro-2-thio-quinazoline	M.p. (°c)	References
4-Ethoxy-3-phenyl-[a]	196°; HCl 175–177°; HBr 161–162°; HI 165–166°; AgNO$_3$ 183° (dec.); AgClO$_4$ 227° (dec.); AgCl 175–177°; AgBr 161–162°; mercuric chloride 121–126°; mercuric bromide 116–121°; mercuric iodide 137–138°	5, 11, 20, 21, 23
4-Ethoxy-3-*o*-tolyl-	228–230°; Ag complex 173° (dec.); mercuric chloride 163–165°; mercuric bromide 168°	11, 20, 23
4-Ethoxy-3-*p*-tolyl-	180–182° (dec.); mercuric chloride 245°; mercuric bromide 173–175°	11, 20, 23
4-Ethoxycarbonyl-4-hydroxy-3-phenyl-	184°	5
4-α-Ethoxycarbonylacetonyl-3-phenyl-	165°; mercuric chloride 215°	8, 9
4-Hydroxy-4-methoxycarbonyl-3-phenyl-	166–167°	5
4-Hydroxy-3-1′-naphthyl-4-phenyl-	171–174°	14
4-Hydroxy-3-2′-naphthyl-4-phenyl-	219°	14
4-Hydroxy-3-phenyl-	212°; HCl 225–226°; HI 193–194°; HClO$_4$ 234°; mercuric chloride perchlorate 252–257°; mercuric bromide perchlorate 190–191°; mercuric iodide perchlorate 207–208°	5, 6, 11, 12 20, 21 20, 21 20, 21
4-Hydroxy-3,4-diphenyl-	181–183°	14
4-Hydroxy-3-*o*-tolyl-	252°	12
4-Methoxy-4-methoxycarbonyl-3-phenyl-	178–180°	5
4-Methoxy-3-phenyl-	190–192°	5
3-Methyl-4-methylene-	223–225°	35
6-Methyl-4-phenyl-	265–270°	33
4-*p*-Methylphenacyl-3-phenyl-	222°	8, 9, 18
4-Phenacyl-3-phenyl-	237°, 238–240°; mercuric chloride 198°	7, 8, 18

(*Table continued*)

TABLE VI.3 *(continued)*

1,2,3,4-Tetrahydro-2-thio-quinazoline	M.p. (°c)	References
4-Phenyl-	230°	30
3-Phenyl-4-α-phenylacetonyl-	222°	8, 9
3-Phenyl-4-α-phenylphenacyl-	222°; mercuric chloride 246°	8
3-Phenyl-4-phthalimido-	285–290°	8
4-p-Tolyl-	224°	31
4-2′,4′-Xylyl-	222–223°	32

a The ethyl derivative: 4-ethoxy-2-ethylthio-3,4-dihydro-3-phenylquinazoline had m.p. 162°; HClO₄ 210°.[12]

TABLE VI.4.   3,4-Dihydro-4-thioquinazolines without Substituents on N(3).

3,4-Dihydro-4-thioquinazoline	M.p. (°c)	References
Unsubstituted	312–314°, 318–323°, 320°, 324–325°	1, 42, 43, 51
2-Benzyl-	215–216°, 221°	45, 51
6,8-Dibromo-2-methyl-	~ 305° (dec.)	38
2-p-Bromophenyl-	280°	51
6-Chloro-2-methyl-	276–278° (dec.)	41
6-Chloro-2-phenyl-	243°, 238°	51, 53
2-o-Chlorophenyl-	206°	51
2-p-Chlorophenyl-	285°	51
2-Ethyl-	203–204° (dec.), 205°	36, 51, 139
2-Isopropyl-	203–204°	36
2-α-Methoxybenzyl-	107–109°	45
2-o-Methoxybenzyl-	174–176°	45
2-p-Methoxyphenyl-	203°, 226°	51, 53
2-Methyl-	218–219°; picrate 198.5–199.5°	36, 39, 41, 51
2-Methyl-6-nitro-	246–249° (dec.)	44
2-1′-Naphthyl-	261°	51
6-Nitro-	261–263° (dec.)	49
7-Nitro-	270–271° (dec.)	49
8-Nitro-	266–267° (dec.)	49
2-Phenyl-	221°, 227°	43, 51, 53
2-Propyl-	182–183°	36
2-t-Butyl-	162°	51
2-o-Tolyl-	192°	51
2-p-Tolyl-	221.5°	51

TABLE VI.5. 3,4-Dihydro-4-thioquinazolines Substituted on $N_{(3)}$.

3,4-Dihydro-4-thioquinazoline	M.p. (°c)	References
3-*p*-Aminophenyl-2-methyl-	212°	50
3-Benzyl-	110°	50
3-Benzyl-2-*o*-chlorophenyl-	114°	50
3-Benzyl-2-*p*-chlorophenyl-	143°	50
2-Benzyl-3-ethyl-	129°	50
2-Benzyl-3-methyl-	88–91°, 96°	45, 50
3-Benzyl-2-methyl-	94.5°	50
2-Benzyl-3-phenyl-	156°	50
3-Benzyl-2-phenyl-	165°	50
3-Benzyl-2-*p*-tolyl-	126°	50
3-*p*-Bromophenyl-2-ethyl-	168–170°	46
2-*p*-Bromophenyl-3-methyl-	167–169°	46
3-*o*-Bromophenyl-2-methyl-	174–176°	46
3-*p*-Bromophenyl-2-methyl-	190–192°	46
3-Butyl-	61°	50
3-Butyl-2-*p*-methoxyphenyl-	104°	50
3-Butyl-2-methyl-	65°	50
3-Butyl-2-phenyl-	146°	50
3-Butyl-2-*p*-tolyl-	135°	50
3-(3'-Chloro-2'-methyl)phenyl-2-methyl-	137–138.5°	133
3-*o*-Chlorophenyl-2-methyl-	134–135.5°	133
3-*p*-Chlorophenyl-2-methyl-	183–185°	46
2-*p*-Chlorophenyl-3-phenyl-	231°	50
3-2'-Dibutylaminoethyl-	222–225°/4 mm	47
3-2'-Diethylaminoethyl-	200–202°/3 mm	47
3-2'-Diethylaminoethyl-2-methyl-	oil	50
3-3'-Diethylaminopropyl-	210–214°/3 mm	47
3-2'-Dipropylaminoethyl-	190–191°	47
3-Ethyl-	132°	50
2,3-Diethyl-	94°	50
3-Ethyl-2-isopropyl-	56°	50
2-Ethyl-3-methyl-	110°	50
3-Ethyl-2-methyl-	109°	50
2-Ethyl-3-phenyl-	123°	50
3-Ethyl-2-phenyl-	116°	50

(Table continued)

TABLE VI.5 (*continued*)

3,4-Dihydro-4-thioquinazoline	M.p. (°c)	References
2-Ethyl-3-*o*-tolyl-	122°	50
3-*p*-Fluorophenyl-2-methyl-	128–130°	46
2-Isopropyl-3-phenyl-	173°	50
3-*p*-Methoxyphenyl-	124.5°	50
3-*p*-Methoxyphenyl-2-methyl-	153°	50
2-*p*-Methoxyphenyl-3-phenyl-	231°	50
3-*p*-Methoxyphenyl-2-phenyl-	215°	50
3-Methyl-	141–142.5°, 144–147°; 1-methiodide 230–231.5° (dec.)	1, 40
2,3-Dimethyl-	100°	50
2-Methyl-3-phenyl-	186°	50
3-Methyl-2-phenyl-	149°	50
2-Methyl-3-*p*-sulphamoylphenyl-	267°	50
2-Methyl-3-*o*-tolyl-	121–123°, 128°; HCl 228–230°	46, 50, 133
2-1'-Naphthyl-3-phenyl-	180°	50
3-Phenyl-	125°	50
2,3-Diphenyl-	208°	50
2-Phenyl-3-*p*-sulphamoylphenyl-	285°	50
2-Phenyl-3-*p*-tolyl-	228°	50
3-*p*-Sulphamoylphenyl-	256.5°	50
3-*p*-Tolyl-	121°	50

TABLE VI.6. 4-Alkylthio- and 4-Arylthioquinazolines.

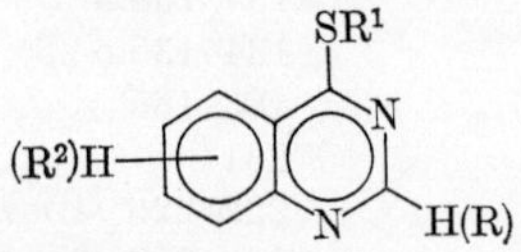

Quinazoline	M.p. (°c)	References
4-(4'-Acetoxy-2'-chloro)phenyl-thio-	127°	55
4-(4'-Acetoxy-3'-chloro)phenyl-thio-	72°; picrate 206°	55
4-(4'-Acetoxy-2',5'-dichloro)-phenylthio-	86–87°	55
4-(4'-Acetoxy-3',5'-dichloro)-phenylthio-	110°	55

(*Table continued*)

TABLE VI.6 (*continued*)

Quinazoline	M.p. (°c)	References
2-Benzyl-4-ethylthio-	57°	54
2-Benzyl-4-methylthio-	65°	54
6,8-Dibromo-4-ethylthio-2-methyl-	> 305° (dec.)	38
2-*p*-Bromophenyl-4-ethylthio-	138°	54
2-*p*-Bromophenyl-4-methylthio-	136°	54
2-Chloro-4-*p*-chlorophenylthio-	156–157°	58
4-(2′-Chloro-4′-hydroxy)phenylthio-	265°	55
4-(3′-Chloro-4′-hydroxy)phenylthio-	296°	55
2-Chloro-4-methylthio-	122°	135
2-*o*-Chlorophenyl-4-ethylthio-	81°	54
2-*p*-Chlorophenyl-4-ethylthio-	141°	54
2-*o*-Chlorophenyl-4-methylthio-	135°	54
2-*p*-Chlorophenyl-4-methylthio-	133°	54
4-*o*-Chlorophenylthio-	130°; picrate 178°	55
4-*m*-Chlorophenylthio-	50–51°; picrate 182°	55
4-*p*-Chlorophenylthio-	139°; picrate 188°	55
4-(2′,5′-Dichloro-4′-hydroxy)phenylthio-	228°	55
4-(3′,5′-Dichloro-4′-hydroxy)phenylthio-	223–224°	55
4-2′,4′-Dichlorophenylthio-	146°; picrate 228°	55
4-2′,5′-Dichlorophenylthio-	158°; picrate 165°	55
4-3′,4′-Dichlorophenylthio-	162°; picrate 212°	55
4-3′,5′-Dichlorophenylthio-	150°; picrate 191°	55
4-2′,4′-Dinitrophenylthio-	191°	57
2-Ethyl-4-ethylthio-	22°, 145°/2 mm; picrate 168°	54
2-Ethyl-4-methylthio-	30–35°, 37°, 135–137°/1.5 mm; picrate 213°	54, 139
4-Ethylthio-	33–35°, 37°, 133°/1 mm, 136–138°/5 mm, 174°/16 mm; picrate 178–181°, 190°; 1-ethiodide 152–156°; 1-methiodide 156.5–157.5°	40, 54, 136 40
4-Ethylthio-2-*p*-methoxyphenyl-	85°	54
4-Ethylthio-2-methyl-	33°, 143°/2 mm	54
4-Ethylthio-2-1′-naphthyl-	93°	54
4-Ethylthio-2-2′-naphthyl-	107°	54
4-Ethylthio-2-phenyl-	62°	54
4-Ethylthio-2-*o*-tolyl-	35°	54

(*Table continued*)

11 + Q.

TABLE VI.6 (*continued*)

Quinazoline	M.p. (°c)	References
4-Ethylthio-2-*p*-tolyl-	113°	54
6-Methoxy-4,7-bisphenylthio-[a]	186–187°	118
2-*p*-Methoxyphenyl-4-methyl-		
thio-	122°	54
2-Methyl-4-methylthio-	52°, 120°/1 mm	54
2-Methyl-4-methylthio-6-nitro-	178–179°	44
4-Methylthio-	64–65°, 113°/1 mm;	1, 40, 42, 54
	1-ethiodide 198–199°;	
	1-methiodide 219–220° (dec.)	40
4-Methylthio-2-1′-naphthyl-	129°	54
4-Methylthio-2-2′-naphthyl-	138°	54
4-Methylthio-5-nitro-	146–147°	49
4-Methylthio-6-nitro-	162–163°	49
4-Methylthio-2-phenyl-	94°; hexachlorostannate	
	278–281°	54, 59
4-Methylthio-2-*o*-tolyl-	82°	54
4-Methylthio-2-*p*-tolyl-	109°	54
4-Methylthio-2-trichloromethyl-	138°	59
4-Quinazolin-4′-yldithio-	192–195°	57
4-*m*-Trimethylsilylphenylthio-	181–182°	56

[a] See Sect. 5.

TABLE VI.7.   4-Arylsulphonylquinazolines and 1,2- and 1,4-Dihydro-4-
thioquinazolines.

Quinazoline	M.p. (°c)	References
4-(2′-Chloro-4′-hydroxy)phenyl-sulphonyl-	243°; picrate 201°	55
4-(3′-Chloro-4′-hydroxy)phenyl-sulphonyl-	picrate 204°	55
4-o-Chlorophenylsulphonyl-	picrate 201°	55
4-m-Chlorophenylsulphonyl-	219°; picrate 210°	55
4-p-Chlorophenylsulphonyl-	275–276°; picrate 210°	55
1-p-Fluorophenyl-1,4-dihydro-2-phenyl-4-thio-	294–296°	48
4-(2′,5′-Dichloro-4′-hydroxy)-phenylsulphonyl-	226° (dec.); picrate 204°	55
4-(3′,5′-Dichloro-4′-hydroxy)-phenylsulphonyl-	236–237°; picrate 205–206°	55
4-2′,4′-Dichlorophenylsulphonyl-	215°; picrate 228°	55
4-2′,5′-Dichlorophenylsulphonyl-	194°; picrate 203°	55
4-3′,4′-Dichlorophenylsulphonyl-	250°; picrate 210°	55
4-3′,5′-Dichlorophenylsulphonyl-	221°; picrate 200°	55
1-Ethyl-1,4-dihydro-4-thio-	146–149°	40
3,4-Dihydro-2-methyl-4-seleno-[a]	213.5°	37
1,4-Dihydro-1-methyl-4-thio-	192–194°, 198–199°	1, 40
1,2-Dihydro-2-methyl-4-thio-	153°	62
1,2-Dihydro-2,2-dimethyl-4-methyl-thio-	62–64°	61
1,2-Dihydro-2,2-dimethyl-4-thio-	151–152°, 163°	61, 62
1,4-Dihydro-1,2-diphenyl-4-thio-	305–307°	48

[a] This is not a thio compound.

TABLE VI.8.   2,4-Dithioquinazolines.

Quinazoline	M.p. (°c)	References
2-Allylthio-3,4-dihydro-3-phenyl-4-thio-	130–131°	65
2-Allylthio-3,4-dihydro-4-thio-3-o-tolyl-	100–101°	65
6-Amino-1,2,3,4-tetrahydro-2,4-dithio-	> 390°	69
2-Benzylthio-3,4-dihydro-3-phenyl-4-thio-	158–159°	65
2-Benzylthio-3,4-dihydro-4-thio-3-o-tolyl-	115–116°	65
2-p-Bromophenacylthio-3,4-dihydro-4-thio-3-p-tolyl-	139–140°	65
2-Butylthio-3,4-dihydro-3-phenyl-4-thio-	74–75°	65
2-Butylthio-3,4-dihydro-4-thio-3-o-tolyl-	98–99°	65
2-Carboxymethylthio-3,4-dihydro-4-thio-3-o-tolyl-	187–188°	65
6-Chloro-1,2,3,4-tetrahydro-2,4-dithio-	300–350° (subl.)	64
3-p-Chlorophenyl-3,4-dihydro-2-ethylthio-4-thio-	147–148°	65
3-p-Chlorophenyl-3,4-dihydro-2-methylthio-4-thio-	190–191°	65
3-p-Chlorophenyl-1,2,3,4-tetrahydro-2,4-dithio-	H₂O 240–241°	65
2,4-Di-p-chlorophenylthio-	135–136°	58
2-2′-Diethylaminoethylthio-3,4-dihydro-3-phenyl-4-thio-	HCl 217–218°	65
2-Ethylthio-3,4-dihydro-3-phenyl-4-thio-	135–136°	65
2-Ethylthio-3,4-dihydro-4-thio-3-o-tolyl-	102–103°	65
1,2,3,4-Tetrahydro-3-phenyl-2,4-dithio-	248–250°, 280–294° (dec.)	65
1,2,3,4-Tetrahydro-2,4-dithio-	308–309° (dec.), 313° (dec.)	39, 67, 68
1,2,3,4-Tetrahydro-2,4-dithio-3-o-tolyl-	197–198°	65
6-Methyl-2,4-dimethylthio-	104–105°	59
2,4-Dimethylthio-	67–68°; fluoroborate 205° (dec.); picrate 171°	59
2-Methylthio-3,4-dihydro-3-phenyl-4-thio-	175–176°	65

(Table continued)

TABLE VI.8 *(continued)*

Quinazoline	M.p. (°c)	References
2-Methylthio-3,4-dihydro-4-thio-3-o-tolyl-	146–147°	65
2-p-Nitrobenzylthio-3,4-dihydro-3-phenyl-4-thio-	174–175°	65
2-Pentylthio-3,4-dihydro-3-phenyl-4-thio-	63–64°	65
2-Pentylthio-3,4-dihydro-4-thio-3-o-tolyl-	69–70°	65
2-Phenethylthio-3,4-dihydro-3-phenyl-4-thio-	88–90°	65
2-Phenethylthio-3,4-dihydro-4-thio-3-p-tolyl-	103–104°	65
2-Propylthio-3,4-dihydro-3-phenyl-4-thio-	79–80°	65
2-Propylthio-3,4-dihydro-4-thio-3-o-tolyl-	82–83°	65

TABLE VI.9. 2-Alkylthio-3,4-dihydro-4-oxoquinazolines.

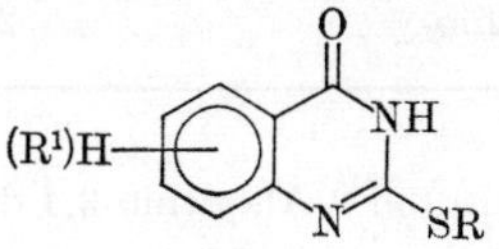

$(R^1)H$

3,4-Dihydro-4-oxoquinazoline	M.p. (°c)	References
2-Allylthio-	168°	102
2-p-Bromophenacylthio-8-methyl-	218–220°	113
2-Carboxymethylthio-	223°	105, 110
6-Chloro-2-p-chlorophenacylthio-	265°	112
6-Chloro-2-α,α-diethoxycarbonylmethylthio-	215°	112
6-Chloro-2-p-methoxyphenacylthio-	210–211°	112
6-Chloro-2-p-methylphenacylthio-	210°	112
6-Chloro-2-phenacylthio-	215°	112
2-p-Chlorophenacylthio-	212°	105
2-p-Chlorophenacylthio-6-methyl-	225–226°	105
2-p-Chlorophenacylthio-8-methyl-	213°	113
2-p-Chlorophenylcarbamoylmethylthio-	265°	107
2-p-Chlorophenylcarbamoylmethylthio-6-methyl-	270°	107

(Table continued)

TABLE VI.9 (continued)

3,4-Dihydro-4-oxoquinazoline	M.p. (°c)	References
2-p-Chlorophenylthio-	246°	58
2-Ethoxycarbonylmethylthio-	149°	109
2-α-α-Diethoxycarbonylmethylthio-	134–135°	105
2-α,α-Diethoxycarbonylmethylthio-6-methyl-	141°	105
2-2'-Hydroxyethylthio-	95°	77
2-p-Methoxyphenacylthio-	201°	105
2-p-Methoxyphenacylthio-6-methyl-	225°	105
2-p-Methoxyphenacylthio-8-methyl-	218°	113
2-p-Methoxyphenylcarbamoylmethylthio-	262–263°	107
6-Methyl-2-p-methylphenacylthio-	220°	105
8-Methyl-2-p-methylphenacylthio-	218–219°	113
6-Methyl-2-phenacylthio-	206–207°	105
8-Methyl-2-phenacylthio-	215°	113
6-Methyl-2-phenylcarbamoylmethylthio-	272°	107
6-Methyl-2-o-tolylcarbamoylmethylthio-	259–260°	107
6-Methyl-2-p-tolylcarbamoylmethylthio-	260°	107
2-p-Methylphenacylthio-	199°	105
2-Methylthio-	210–213°, 219°	59, 101, 111
2-Phenacylthio-	206–207°	105
2-o-Tolylcarbamoylmethylthio-	249–250°	107
2-p-Tolylcarbamoylmethylthio-	263–264°	107

TABLE VI.10.   3-Substituted 2-Alkylthio-3,4-dihydro-4-oxoquinazolines.

3,4-Dihydro-4-oxoquinazoline	M.p. (°c)	References
3-Allyl-2-o-chlorobenzyl-	75.5–76°	104
3-Allyl-2-p-methoxybenzyl-	85–86°	104
3-Allyl-6-methyl-2-p-methylphenacylthio-	135°	92
2-Allylthio-3-benzyl-	93°	83
2-Allylthio-3-p-bromophenyl-	148°	83
2-Allylthio-3-m-chlorophenyl-	178°	83
2-Allylthio-3-p-chlorophenyl-	137°	83
2-Allylthio-3-p-ethoxyphenyl-	152°	83
2-Allylthio-3-o-methoxyphenyl-	98°	83
2-Allylthio-3-p-methoxyphenyl-	160°	83

(Table continued)

TABLE VI.10 (*continued*)

3,4-Dihydro-4-oxoquinazoline	M.p. (°c)	References
3-Benzyl-2-ethylthio-	83°	83
3-Benzyl-2-methylthio-	94°	83
2-Benzylthio-3-*p*-bromophenyl-	182°	83
2-Benzylthio-3-*m*-chlorophenyl-	106°	83
2-Benzylthio-3-*p*-chlorophenyl-	183°	83
2-Benzylthio-3-*p*-ethoxyphenyl-	241°	83
2-Benzylthio-3-*p*-methoxyphenyl-	153°	83
2-Benzylthio-3-phenyl-	176.5–177°, 169.5°	104, 106
3-*p*-Bromophenyl-2-butylthio-	121°	83
3-*p*-Bromophenyl-2-carboxymethylthio-	214°	83
3-*p*-Bromophenyl-2-ethylthio-	146°	83
3-*p*-Bromophenyl-2-1′-methylallylthio-	131°	83
3-*p*-Bromophenyl-2-methylthio-	208°	83
3-*p*-Bromophenyl-2-*p*-nitrobenzylthio-	230°	83
2-Butylthio-3-*m*-chlorophenyl-	88°	83
2-Butylthio-3-*p*-chlorophenyl-	113°	83
2-Butylthio-3-*p*-ethoxyphenyl-	140°	83
2-Butylthio-3-*o*-methoxyphenyl-	141°	83
2-Butylthio-3-*p*-methoxyphenyl-	122°	83
2-Butylthio-3-phenyl-	131–133°	104
3-Carbamoylmethyl-2-methylthio-	245–246°	138
3-Carboxymethyl-2-methylthio-	107–108°	138
2-Carboxymethylthio-3-*m*-chlorophenyl-	180°	83
2-Carboxymethylthio-3-*p*-chlorophenyl-	218°	83
2-Carboxymethylthio-3-*p*-ethoxyphenyl-	202°	83
2-Carboxymethylthio-3-*p*-methoxy- phenyl-	182°	83
3-*m*-Chlorophenyl-2-ethylthio-	124°	83
3-*p*-Chlorophenyl-2-ethylthio-	150°	83
3-*p*-Chlorophenyl-2-isopropylthio-	152°	83
3-*m*-Chlorophenyl-2-1′-methylallylthio-	94°	83
3-*p*-Chlorophenyl-2-1′-methylallylthio-	134°	83
3-*m*-Chlorophenyl-2-methylthio-	156°	83
3-*p*-Chlorophenyl-2-methylthio-	178°	83
3-*m*-Chlorophenyl-2-*p*-nitrobenzylthio-	162°	83
3-*p*-Chlorophenyl-2-*p*-nitrobenzylthio-	218°	83
3-*p*-Chlorophenyl-2-pentylthio-	102°	83
2-2′-Diethylaminoethylthio-3-phenyl-	84.5–85°	104
2-(3′,4′-Dihydro-4′-oxo-3′-phenylquinazo- lin-2′-yldithio)-3-phenyl-	250–252°	114a
2-(3′,4′-Dihydro-4′-oxo-3′-*o*-tolylquin- azolin-2′-yldithio)-3-*o*-tolyl-	215°	114a
2-2′-Dimethylaminoethylthio-3-phenyl-	109–109.5°	104

(*Table continued*)

TABLE VI.10 (*continued*)

3,4-Dihydro-4-oxoquinazoline	M.p. (°c)	References
2-2′-Dimethylaminopropylthio-3-phenyl-	159.5–160.5°	104
3-*p*-Ethoxyphenyl-2-ethylthio-	139°	83
3-*p*-Ethoxyphenyl-2-1′-methylallylthio-	134°	83
3-*p*-Ethoxyphenyl-2-methylthio-	158°	83
3-*p*-Ethoxyphenyl-2-*p*-nitrobenzylthio-	186°	83
3-Ethyl-2-methylthio-	65°	24
2-Ethylthio-3-*o*-methoxyphenyl-	114°	83
2-Ethylthio-3-*p*-methoxyphenyl-	170°	83
2-Ethylthio-3-phenyl-	114°, 117–118°	104, 108
2-Isopropylthio-3-phenyl-	129–129.5°	104
3-*p*-Methoxyphenyl-2-1′-methylallylthio-	113°	83
3-*o*-Methoxyphenyl-2-methylthio-	134°	83
3-*p*-Methoxyphenyl-2-methylthio-	148°	83
3-*p*-Methoxyphenyl-2-*p*-nitrobenzylthio-	188°	83
2-Methylthio-3-phenyl-	125°, 130–130.5°	103, 104, 106, 108
2-Propylthio-3-phenyl-	133–135.5°	104

TABLE VI.11.   3-Substituted (and 3-Unsubstituted) 1,2,3,4-Tetrahydro-4-oxo-2-thioquinazolines.

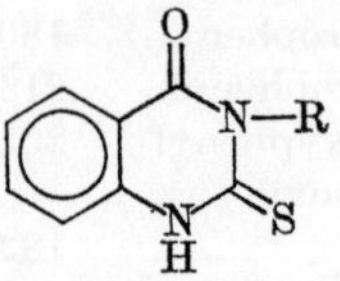

1,2,3,4-Tetrahydro-4-oxo-2-thio-quinazoline	M.p. (°c)	References
Unsubstituted	290–293°, 298°, 306°, 313–314°, 315–316°	69, 75, 101, 103, 105, 106, 112
3-Allyl-	206–207°, 208–210°, 210–210.5°	86, 88, 104, 114a
3-Benzoyl-	157–158°	101
3-Benzyl-	246–247°, 248°	83, 106
3-2′-Bromoallyl-	198°	87
3-*p*-Bromophenyl-	314–315°, 320°	83, 99
3-Carboxymethyl-	216–217°	138
3-*o*-Carboxyphenyl-	288°	85, 96
3-2′-Chloroallyl-	191°	87

(*Table continued*)

TABLE VI.11 *(continued)*

1,2,3,4-Tetrahydro-4-oxo-2-thio-quinazoline	M.p. (°c)	References
3-o-Chlorophenyl-	268°	85, 96
3-m-Chlorophenyl-	289°, 291°, 292°	83, 85, 96, 99
3-p-Chlorophenyl-	253°, 317–319°, 320°	83, 85, 96, 99
3-3'-(4-m-Chlorophenyl-piperazin-1-yl)propyl-	maleate 212–213°	140
3-p-Ethoxyphenyl-	335°	83
3-(3'-Fluoro-4'-methyl)-phenyl-	115°	98
3-p-Fluorophenyl-	90–91°	98
3-2'-Hydroxyethyl-	240°	77
3-o-Methoxyphenyl-	265°, 253°	83, 85
3-m-Methoxyphenyl-	253°	96
3-p-Methoxyphenyl-	275°, 284°	83, 85, 96
3-Methyl-	260–261°, 257–258°	80, 115
3-1'-Naphthyl-	266°, 258°	83, 96
3-2'-Naphthyl-	304°	96
3-o-Nitrophenyl-	234°	85
3-m-Nitrophenyl-	262°	85
3-p-Nitrophenyl-	287°	85
3-Phenyl-	299°, 304–305°, 310–311°	88, 96, 99, 104, 106
3-5'-(4-Phenylpiperazin-1-yl)-pentyl-	2 HCl 262–264°	140
3-p-Sulphamoylbenzyl-	286–287°	137
3-p-Sulphamoylphenyl-	> 350°	137
3-p-Sulphophenyl-	291°	85
3-p-1',2',3',4'-Tetrahydro-4'-oxo-2'-thioquinazolin-3'-ylphenyl-p-sulphonyl-phenyl-	> 350°	137
3-o-Tolyl-	265°, 270–271°	86, 88, 96, 99, 114a
3-m-Tolyl-	276°	96, 99
3-p-Tolyl-	302°, 310°	96, 99, 114a
3-2',4'-Xylyl-	259–260°	114a

11*

TABLE VI.12.   1- and 1,3-Substituted 1,2,3,4-Tetrahydro-4-oxo-2-thioquinazolines.

1,2,3,4-Tetrahydro-4-oxo-2-thioquinazoline	M.p. (°c)	References
1-Allyl-[a]	168°	79
1-Carbamoylmethyl-[b]	304–305°	100
1-2′-Chloroallyl-	189–192°	79
1-p-Chlorophenacyl-	166°	78
1-2′-Hydroxyethyl-	280°	76
1,3-Dimethyl-	186°, 181.5–183°	81, 115
1-Methyl-3-phenyl-	288–289°, 278°, 302–303°	81, 82, 103
1-Phenacyl-	173°	78

[a] The phenacyl derivative: 1-allyl-1,4-dihydro-4-oxo-2-phenacylthioquinazoline has m.p. 197–198°.[79]

[b] The methyl derivative: 1-carbamoylmethyl-1,4-dihydro-2-methylthio-4-oxoquinazoline has m.p. 335–338° (dec.).[100]

TABLE VI.13.   3-Substituted (and 3-Unsubstituted) 1,2,3,4-Tetrahydro-4-oxo-2-thioquinazolines with Substituents in the Benzene Ring.

1,2,3,4-Tetrahydro-4-oxo-2-thioquinazoline	M.p. (°c)	References
3-Allyl-6-chloro-	237°	87
3-Allyl-7-chloro-	217°	90
3-Allyl-8-chloro-	147°	91
3-Allyl-6-chloro-8-methyl-	195°	93
3-Allyl-6-methyl-	231–232°	92
3-Allyl-7-methyl-	233°	87
3-Allyl-8-methyl-	151°	91
3-Allyl-6,7-methylenedioxy-	262°	93
6-Bromo-3-p-fluorophenyl-	102°	98
6,8-Dibromo-3-p-fluorophenyl-	116°	98
3-3′-Bromopropyl-6-methyl-	129°; HBr 322–323° (dec.)	92
6-Chloro-	335°, 353–354°	64, 112
6-Chloro-3-o-carboxyphenyl-	305°	84
6-Chloro-3-2′-chloroallyl-	222°	87
6-Chloro-3-o-chlorophenyl-	287°	84
6-Chloro-3-m-chlorophenyl-	285°	84
6-Chloro-3-p-chlorophenyl-	320°	84
6-Chloro-3-(3′-fluoro-4′-methyl)-phenyl-	95°	98
6-Chloro-3-p-fluorophenyl-	119°	98
6-Chloro-3-o-methoxyphenyl-	287°	84
6-Chloro-3-p-methoxyphenyl-	323°	84
6-Chloro-3-phenyl-	324°	84
6-Chloro-3-3′-(4-phenylpiperazin-1-yl)propyl-	213–215°; HCl > 280°	140
6-Chloro-3-o-tolyl-	302°	84
6-Chloro-3-m-tolyl-	294°	84
6-Chloro-3-p-tolyl-	322°	84
6-Hydroxy-	308–313°	134
5-Hydroxy-3-phenyl-	308–313°	134
6-Hydroxy-3-phenyl-	293–294°	94
8-Hydroxy-3-phenyl-	302–303°	94
3-2′-Hydroxyethyl-6-methyl-	203°	102
6-Methyl-	322°	105
8-Methyl-	262°	113

TABLE VI.14.   3,4-Dihydro-4-oxoquinazolines with Thio or Sulphonyl
Groups in the Benzene Ring.

3,4-Dihydro-4-oxoquinazoline	M.p. (°c)	References
6-Methoxy-7-phenylsulphonyl-[a]	301–303°	118
6-Methoxy-7-phenylthio-[a]	260–261°	118
5-Methylsulphonyl-	275–276°	117
5-Methylthio-	271–272°	117
5-Phenylthio-	250–252°	117

[a] See section 5.

TABLE VI.15.   Aminothioquinazolines.

Quinazolines	M.p. (°c)	References
2-Allyl-1,2,3,4-tetrahydro-4-imino-2-thio-	187°	90
4-Amino-1,2-dihydro-2-thio-	290–293°	66
4-Amino-6-chloro-1,2-dihydro-2-thio-	300–305° (dec.)	64
4-Amino-2-methylthio-	233–234°	59
4-Anilino-1,2-dihydro-1-methyl-2-thio-	184–186°	103
4-Anilino-1,2-dihydro-2-thio-	240–242°	103
4-Anilino-2-methylthio-	179°	59
2-p-Chloroanilino-4-methylthio-	176°	135
2-p-Chlorophenylthio-4-2'-diethyl-aminoethylamino-	123°	58
4-p-Chlorophenylthio-2-2'-diethyl-aminoethylamino-	92°	58
2-p-Chlorophenylthio-4-3'-diethyl-aminopropylamino-	123–124°	58
4-p-Chlorophenylthio-2-3'-diethyl-aminopropylamino-	100°	58
4-3'-Diethylaminopropylamino-2-p-tolylthio-	96°	58
1,2,3,4-Tetrahydro-4-imino-1-methyl-3-phenyl-2-thio-	215–217°	103
1,2,3,4-Tetrahydro-4-imino-3-phenyl-2-thio-	195–198°	103
3,4-Dihydro-4-methylimino-2-methylthio-3-phenyl-	135–136°	103

TABLE VI.16. Thiazolo(2,3-b)quinazolin-5-ones.

Thiazolo(2,3-b)quinazolin-5-one[a]	M.p. (°c)	References
7-Bromo-3-*p*-bromophenyl-	270°	124
7-Bromo-3-*p*-chlorophenyl-	246°	124
7-Bromo-2,3-dimethyl-	209°	124
7-Bromo-3-phenyl-	203–204°	124
2-Bromomethyl-	210°; HBr 295°	87
2-Bromomethyl-7-chloro-	202°; HBr 272° (dec.)	87
2-Bromomethyl-8-chloro-	252°	90
2-Bromomethyl-9-chloro-	204–205°; HBr 302–303° (dec.)	91
2-Bromomethyl-7-methyl-	250°; HBr 320–321° (dec.)	92
2-Bromomethyl-8-methyl-	210°; HBr 311–312° (dec.)	87
2-Bromomethyl-9-methyl-	202°; HBr 280° (dec.)	91
3-*p*-Bromophenyl-	239–240°	120
3-*p*-Bromophenyl-7-chloro-	255°	112
3-*p*-Bromophenyl-7-chloro-9-methyl-	170°	93
2-*p*-Bromophenyl-3-methyl-	266°	125
3-*p*-Bromophenyl-7-methyl-	228–229° (dec.)	120
3-*p*-Bromophenyl-7,8-methylenedioxy-	252°	93
3-*p*-Bromophenyl-2-nitro-	230°	124
3-*p*-Bromophenyl-7-nitro-	357°	124
7-Chloro-3-*p*-chlorophenyl-	240°	112
7-Chloro-3-*p*-chlorophenyl-9-methyl-	160°	93
7-Chloro-2-diethylaminomethyl-	316°	87
9-Chloro-2-diethylaminomethyl-	83°	91
7-Chloro-2-ethoxycarbonyl-3-methyl-	168–169°	112
7-Chloro-3-*p*-methoxyphenyl-	180°	112
7-Chloro-2-methyl-	206°	87
7-Chloro-3-methyl-	160°	126
8-Chloro-2-methyl-	211°	90
9-Chloro-2-methyl-	200°	91
7-Chloro-2,3-dimethyl-	155°	112
7-Chloro-2,9-dimethyl-	225°	93
7-Chloro-9-methyl-3-phenyl-	162°	93

(Table continued)

TABLE VI.16 *(continued)*

Thiazolo(2,3-b)quinazolin-5-one[a]	M.p. (°c)	References
7-Chloro-9-methyl-2-piperidino-methyl-	182°	93
7-Chloro-9-methyl-3-*p*-tolyl-	200°	93
7-Chloro-3-phenyl-	180°	112
7-Chloro-2-piperidinomethyl-	193°	87
8-Chloro-2-piperidinomethyl-	173°	90
9-Chloro-2-piperidinomethyl-	176°	91
7-Chloro-3-*p*-tolyl-	211–212°	112
3-*p*-Chlorophenyl-	235–236°	120
2-*p*-Chlorophenyl-3-methyl-	287°	125
2-*p*-Chlorophenyl-7-methyl-[b]	326°	127
3-*p*-Chlorophenyl-7-methyl-	219°	120
3-*p*-Chlorophenyl-8-methyl-	254°	122
3-*p*-Chlorophenyl-9-methyl-	220–221°	113
3-*p*-Chlorophenyl-7,8-methylene-dioxy-	213°	93
3-*p*-Chlorophenyl-2-nitro-	243°	124
3-*p*-Chlorophenyl-7-nitro-	340°	124
2-Diethylaminomethyl-7-methyl-	145°; HCl 250°	92
2-Diethylaminomethyl-8-methyl-	125°	87
2-Diethylaminomethyl-9-methyl-	94°	91
2-3′,4′-Dimethoxyphenyl-	275°	125
2-Ethoxycarbonyl-3-methyl-	132°	121
2-Ethoxycarbonyl-3,9-dimethyl-	173°	43
2-Ethyl-7,8-methylenedioxy-	210°	93
2-*p*-Ethylphenyl-	213°	125
2-*p*-Ethylphenyl-3-methyl-	194°	125
2-(2′-Hydroxy-6′-methoxy)-phenyl-	285°	125
2-*p*-Methoxyphenyl-7-methyl-[b]	244°	127
3-*p*-Methoxyphenyl-7-methyl-	165°	120
3-*p*-Methoxyphenyl-8-methyl-	159°	122
2-Methyl-	183°	87
3-Methyl-	179°	121
2,3-Dimethyl-	172°	121
2,6-Dimethyl-	225°	122
2,7-Dimethyl-	180°, 168°	92, 127
2,8-Dimethyl-	200°, 192°	87, 122
2,9-Dimethyl-	165°	91
3,7-Dimethyl-	180–181°	120

(Table continued)

TABLE VI.16 (*continued*)

Thiazolo(2,3-b)quinazoline-5-one[a]	M.p. (°c)	References
3,9-Dimethyl-	174–175°	113
2,3,8-Trimethyl-	198°	122
2,3,9-Trimethyl-	175–176°	113
2-Methyl-7,8-methylenedioxy-	235°	93
3-Methyl-2-phenyl-	290°	125
7-Methyl-2-phenyl-[b]	264°	127
7-Methyl-3-phenyl-	197–198°	120
8-Methyl-3-phenyl-	198°	122
7-Methyl-2-piperidinomethyl-	165°; HCl 215° (dec.)	92
9-Methyl-2-piperidinomethyl-	138°	91
3-Methyl-2-*p*-tolyl-	185°	125
7-Methyl-2-*p*-tolyl-[b]	254°	127
7-Methyl-3-*p*-tolyl-	194–195°	120
8-Methyl-3-*p*-tolyl-	218°	122
9-Methyl-3-*p*-tolyl-	161°	113
7,8-Methylenedioxy-3-phenyl-	184°	93
7,8-Methylenedioxy-2-piperidinomethyl-	206°	93
7,8-Methylenedioxy-3-*p*-tolyl-	285°	93
7-Nitro-3-phenyl-	291°	124
7-Nitro-3-*p*-tolyl-	328°	124
3-Phenyl-	214–215°	120
3-*p*-Tolyl-	195–196°	120

[a] 2-Bromomethyl-5-iminothiazolo(2,3-b)quinazoline, m.p. 275° (dec.)[90] and 5-imino-2-piperidinomethylthiazolo(2,3-b)quinazoline, m.p. 146°,[90] are related to the above compounds.

[b] These compounds may have the alternative thiazolo(3,2-a)quinazolin-5-one structure.

TABLE VI.17.   2,3-Dihydrothiazolo(2,3-b)quinazolin-5-ones.

$$(R^1)H \underset{\substack{6 \\ \hspace{2mm}}}{\fbox{}} \overset{O}{\underset{N}{\overset{5}{\fbox{}}}} \overset{N}{\underset{S}{\overset{3}{\fbox{}}}} \overset{2}{H(R)}$$

2,3-Dihydrothiazolo(2,3-b)quinazolin-5-one[a]	M.p. (°c)	References
Unsubstituted	154°	77, 75, 102
7-Bromo-	195°	102
2-Bromomethyl-7-chloro-	144°; HBr 288°	87
2-Bromomethyl-8-chloro-	165°	90
2-Bromomethyl-9-chloro-	123°; HBr 307° (dec.)	91
2-Bromomethyl-7-chloro-9-methyl-	159°; HBr 270° (dec.)	93
2-Bromomethyl-8-methyl-	125°; HBr 320° (dec.)	87
2-Bromomethyl-7,8-methylenedioxy-	192°; HBr 267° (dec.)	93
7-Chloro-	152°	102
8-Chloro-	217°	102
7-Chloro-2-methyl-	146°; HCl 228°	87
8-Chloro-2-methyl-	130°; HCl 191°	90
9-Chloro-2-methyl-	130°	91
7-Chloro-3,3-dimethyl-	204°	102
7-Chloro-2,9-dimethyl-	126°	93
7-Chloro-9-methyl-2-methylene-	203°	93
7-Chloro-2-methylene-	193°	87
8-Chloro-2-methylene-	167°	90
9-Chloro-2-methylene-	175°	91
3-Ethyl-	197°	102
7-Methyl-	198°	102
3,3-Dimethyl-	280°	102
2,7-Dimethyl-	117–118°; HCl 250°	92
2,9-Dimethyl-	102–103°	91
3,3,7-Trimethyl-	307°	102
7-Methyl-2-methylene-	150°; HBr 323–324°	92
8-Methyl-2-methylene-	189°	87
9-Methyl-2-methylene-	199°	91
2-Methyl-7,8-methylenedioxy-	189°	93
2-Methylene-7,8-methylenedioxy-	215°	93

[a] The following related derivatives have the melting points cited: 2-bromomethyl-5-ethoxycarbonyl-5-hydroxythiazolo(2,3-b)quinazoline, m.p. 134°;[13] 2-bromomethyl-5-hydroxy-5-methoxycarbonylthiazolo(2,3-b)quinazoline, m.p. 162°;[13] 3-methyl-5-H-thiazolo(2,3-b)quinazoline, m.p. 174° (dec.), HCl 282° (dec.);[123]also: 2-bromomethyl-2,3-dihydro-5-iminothiazolo(2,3-b)quinazoline, m.p. 320°;[90] 2,3-dihydro-5-imino-2-methylthiazolo(2,3-b)quinazoline, m.p. 255° (dec.); and 2,3-dihydro-5-imino-2-methylenethiazolo(2,3-b)quinazoline, m.p. 126°.[90]

TABLE VI.18. Thiazolo(3,2-a)quinazolin-5-ones.

Thiazolo(3,2-a)quinazolin-5-ones[a]	M.p. (°c)	References
2-Bromomethyl-	230°; HBr 335°	79
2-Bromomethyl-1,2-dihydro-	180°; HBr 360°	79
1-p-Bromophenyl-	263°	126
1-p-Bromophenyl-7-chloro-	352°	126
1-p-Bromophenyl-8-methyl-	284°	122
7-Chloro-1-p-methoxyphenyl-	310°	126
7-Chloro-1-p-chlorophenyl-	340°	126
7-Chloro-1-methyl-	315°	126
7-Chloro-1,2-dimethyl-	227–228°	126
7-Chloro-1-phenyl-	320°	126
7-Chloro-1-p-tolyl-	315°	126
2-p-Chlorophenyl-	228°	78
1-p-Chlorophenyl-6-methyl-	272°	122
1-p-Chlorophenyl-8-methyl-	299–300° (dec.)	122
1-3′,4′-Dihydroxyphenyl-	315°	126
1-p-Ethylphenyl-6-methyl-	175°	122
1,2-Dihydro-	240°	77
1,2-Dihydro-2-methyl-	220°	79
1-p-Methoxyphenyl-6-methyl-	216°	122
1-p-Methoxyphenyl-8-methyl-	249°	122
1-Methyl-	302°	121
2-Methyl-	206°	79
1,7-Dimethyl-	307–308°	120
1,2,8-Trimethyl-	285°	122
6-Methyl-1-phenyl-	260°	122
8-Methyl-1-phenyl-	254°	122
6-Methyl-1-p-tolyl-	205°	122
8-Methyl-1-p-tolyl-	223°	122
6-Methyl-1-2′,4′-xylyl-	217°	122
2-Morpholinomethyl-	160°	79
2-Phenyl-	122°	126
1,2-Diphenyl-	176–177°	126
2-Piperidinomethyl-	220°	79

[a] The hydrochlorides of the following related compounds have the decomposition points in brackets: 1-p-bromophenyl-(326°), 1-p-bromophenyl-8-chloro-(400°), 8-chloro-1-p-methoxyphenyl-(350°), 8-chloro-1-phenyl-(345°), 1-p-chlorophenyl-(305°), 1-p-methoxyphenyl-(300°), 1-phenyl-(345°), 1-p-tolyl-(287–288°) 5-iminothiazolo(3,2-a)quinazolines.[128]

TABLE VI.19. 3-*H*-1,3-Thiazino(3,2-a)quinazolin-6-ones.

3-*H*-1,3-Thiazino(3,2-a)quinazo- lin-6-one	M.p. (°c)	References
8-Bromo-1-ethyl-	218°	129
8-Bromo-1-methyl-	254°	129
1-*p*-Bromophenyl-	214°	129
8-Chloro-1-ethyl-	212°	129
8-Chloro-1-methyl-	252°	129
1-*p*-Chlorophenyl-	226°	129
1-Ethyl-	182°	129
1-Ethyl-8-methyl-	212°	129
1-Methyl-	215°	129
1,8-Dimethyl-	249°	129
1-Phenyl-	193°	129

TABLE VI.20.   11-H-Thiazolo(3,2-c)quinazolines.

Thiazolo(3,2-c)quinazoline	M.p. (°c)	References
11-Carboxy-3-ethoxycarbonyl-2,3-dihydro-5-phenyl-	170–171°	130
11-Carboxy-2,3-dihydro-3-methoxycarbonyl-5-methyl-	220°	130
11-Carboxy-2,3-dihydro-3-methoxycarbonyl-9-methyl-5-phenyl-	160°	130
11-Carboxy-2,3-dihydro-5-methyl-	183°	130
11-Carboxy-2,3-dihydro-9-methyl-5-phenyl-	190°	130
3,11-Dicarboxy-2,3-dihydro-9-methyl-5-phenyl-	205°	130
11-Carboxy-2,3-dihydro-5-phenyl-	170°	130
3,11-Dicarboxy-2,3-dihydro-5-phenyl-	210°	130
3-Ethoxycarbonyl-2,3-dihydro-5-methyl-8,9-methylenedioxy-11-H-	156°	131
2,3-Dihydro-3-methoxycarbonyl-5-methyl-8,9-methylenedioxy-11-H-	168–170°	131
2,3-Dihydro-5-methyl-8,9-methylenedioxy-11-H-	178°	131
2,3-Dihydro-8,9-methylenedioxy-5-phenyl-11-H-	187°	131

8. References

1. Albert and Barlin, *J. Chem. Soc.*, **1962**, 3129.
2. Gabriel, *Ber. Deut. Chem. Ges.*, **36**, 800 (1903).
3. Armarego and Smith, *J. Chem. Soc.* (C), **1966**, 234.
4. Albert and Barlin, *J. Chem. Soc.*, **1959**, 2384.
5. Reissert and Schaaf, *Ber. Deut. Chem. Ges.* 59, 2494 (1926).
6. Gheorghiu and Manolescu, *Bull. Soc. Chim. France*, **3**, 1830 (1936).
7. Cisman and Gheorghiu, *Ann. Sci. Univ. Jassy*, **25**, 424 (1939); *Chem. Abstr.*, **34**, 436 (1940).
8. Crivetz, *Ann. Sci. Univ. Jassy*, **29**, 140 (1943); *Chem. Abstr.*, **42**, 1595 (1948).
9. Gheorghiu and Stoicescu, *Ann. Sci. Univ. Jassy*, **28**, 154 (1942); *Chem. Abstr.*, **43**, 1047 (1949).
10. Gheorghiu and Manolescu, *Bull. Soc. Chim. France*, **3**, 321 (1936).
11. Gheorghiu, *J. Prakt. Chem.*, **130** (2), 49 (1931).
12. Gheorghiu, *Bull. Soc. Chim. France*, **2**, 223 (1935).
13. Sharma, Soni, and Narang, *Tetrahedron*, **18**, 1019 (1962).
13a. Metlesics, Silverman, Toome, and Sternbach, *J. Org. Chem.*, **31**, 1007 (1966).

14. Gheorghiu and Arventi, *Bull. Soc. Chim. France*, **5**, 38 (1938).
15. Gheorghiu and Stoicescu, *Ber. Deut. Chem. Ges.*, **76**, 994 (1943).
16. Gheorghiu, *Compt. Rend.*, **199**, 68 (1934).
17. Gheorghiu, *Compt. Rend.*, **197**, 622 (1933).
18. Sadoveanu, *Ann. Sci. Univ. Jassy*, **26**, 531 (1940); *Chem. Abstr.*, **35**, 3260 (1941).
19. Dickinson and Heilbron, *J. Chem. Soc.*, **1927**, 1699.
20. Manolescu-Pavelescu, *Ann. Sci. Univ. Jassy*, **25**, 223 (1939); *Chem. Abstr.*, **33**, 4994 (1939).
21. Gheorghiu and Manolescu, *Bull. Soc. Chim. France*, **3**, 1353 (1936).
22. Gheorghiu and Manolescu, *Compt. Rend.*, **201**, 78 (1935).
23. Manolescu, *Bull. Soc. Chim. France*, **4**, 1126 (1937).
24. Busch, *J. Prakt. Chem.*, **51** (2), 113 (1895).
25. Orth and Jones, *J. Pharm. Sci.*, **50**, 866 (1961).
26. Busch, *J. Prakt. Chem.*, **51** (2), 257 (1895).
27. Walther and Bamberg, *J. Prakt. Chem.*, **73** (2), 209 (1906).
28. Busch and Brand, *J. Prakt. Chem.*, **52** (2), 410 (1895).
29. Busch and Roegglen, *Ber. Deut. Chem. Ges.*, **27**, 3239 (1894).
30. Gabriel and Stelzner, *Ber. Deut. Chem. Ges.* **29**, 1300 (1896).
31. Kippenberg, *Ber. Deut. Chem. Ges.*, **30**, 1130 (1897).
32. Drawert, *Ber. Deut. Chem. Ges.*, **32**, 1259 (1899).
33. Hanschke, *Ber. Deut. Chem. Ges.*, **32**, 2021 (1899).
34. Senier and Shepheard, *J. Chem. Soc.*, **1909**, 494.
35. Doub, Richardson, Herbst, Black, Stevenson, Bambas, Youmans, and Youmans, *J. Am. Chem. Soc.*, **80**, 2205 (1958); see also Smith, *J. Heterocyclic Chem.*, **3**, 535 (1966).
36. Bogert, Breneman, and Hand, *J. Am. Chem. Soc.*, **25**, 372 (1903).
37. Bogert and Chen, *J. Am. Chem. Soc.*, **44**, 2352 (1922).
38. Bogert and Hand, *J. Am. Chem. Soc.*, **25**, 935 (1903).
39. Yale, *J. Am. Chem. Soc.*, **75**, 675 (1953).
40. Fry, Kendall, and Morgan, *J. Chem. Soc.*, **1960**, 5062.
41. Tomisek and Christensen, *J. Am. Chem. Soc.*, **70**, 2423 (1948).
42. Leonard and Curtin, *J. Org. Chem.*, **11**, 349 (1946).
43. Libermann and Rouaix, *Bull. Soc. Chim. France*, **1959**, 1793.
44. Berg, *J. Chem. Soc.*, **1961**, 4041.
45. Lawes and Scarborough, *U.S. Pat.*, 3,127,401 (1964); *Chem. Abstr.*, **60**, 14525 (1964).
46. Jackman, Petrow, and Stephenson, *J. Pharm. Pharmacol.*, **12**, 529 (1960).
47. Bhaduri, Khanna, and Dhar, *J. Sci. Ind. Res. India*, **21B**, 378 (1962).
48. Blatter, Lukaskewski, and DeStevens, *J. Org. Chem.*, **30**, 1020 (1965).
49. Taylor, Knopf, Cogliano, Barton, and Pfleiderer, *J. Am. Chem. Soc.*, **82**, 6085 (1960).
50. Legrand and Lozach, *Bull. Soc. Chim. France*, **1960**, 2088.
51. Legrand and Lozach, *Bull. Soc. Chim. France*, **1961**, 618.
52. Legrand and Lozach, *Bull. Soc. Chim. France*, **1961**, 1400.
53. Goerdeler and Weber, *Tetrahedron Letters*, **1964**, 799.
53a. DeStevens, Blatter, and Carney, *Angew. Chem.* (English Translation), **5**, 35 (1966).
54. Legrand and Lozach, *Bull. Soc. Chim. France*, **1963**, 1161.

55. Badiger and Nargund, J. Karnatak Univ., 5, 18 (1960); Chem. Abstr., 58, 4563 (1963).
56. Sakata and Hashimoto, J. Pharm. Soc. Japan, 79, 872 (1959).
57. Beber, U.S. Pat., 2,594,381 (1952); Chem. Abstr., 47, 616 (1953).
58. Curd, Hoggarth, Landquist, and Rose, J. Chem. Soc., 1948, 1766.
59. Meerwein, Laasch, Mersch, and Nentwig, Chem. Ber., 89, 224 (1956).
60. Meerwein, Ger. Pat., 1,074,047 (1960); Chem. Abstr., 55, 21152 (1961).
61. Carrington, J. Chem. Soc., 1955, 2527.
62. Böhme and Böing, Arch. Pharm., 293, 1011 (1960).
63. Culbertson, Decius, and Christensen, J. Am. Chem. Soc., 74, 4834 (1952).
64. Falco, Russell, and Hitchings, J. Am. Chem. Soc., 73, 4466 (1951).
65. Bhaduri, Khanna, and Dhar, Indian J. Chem., 2, 159 (1964).
66. Hitchings and Russell, U.S. Pat., 2,682,542 (1954); Chem. Abstr., 49, 7606 (1955); Brit. Pat., 671,927 (1952); Chem. Abstr., 47, 5457 (1953).
67. Kötz, J. Prakt. Chem., 47, 303 (1893).
68. Elion and Hitchings, J. Am. Chem. Soc., 69, 2138 (1947).
69. Russell, Elion, Falco, and Hitchings, J. Am. Chem. Soc., 71, 2279 (1949).
70. Dokunikhin and Gaeva, Zh. Obshch. Khim., 24, 1871 (1954); Dokunikhin, Organ. Poluprod. i Krasiteli, Nauchn-Issled. Inst. Organ. Poluprod i Krasitelei Sb. Statei, (1), 148 (1959); Chem. Abstr., 55, 21140 (1961).
71. Meerwein, Ger. Pat., 1,109,180 (1953); Chem. Abstr., 56, 8726 (1962).
72. Rahlan and Sachev, J. Sci. Ind. Res. India, 19B, 215 (1960).
73. Rupe, Ber. Deut. Chem. Ges., 30, 1097 (1897).
74. Veltman, Ukr. Khim. Zh., 21, 347 (1955); Chem. Abstr., 49, 14738 (1955).
75. Howard and Klein, J. Org. Chem., 27, 3701 (1962).
76. Sharma, Gupta, and Narang, Res. Bull. Punjab Univ., (87), 49 (1956); Chem. Abstr., 51, 7379 (1957).
77. Singh and Narang, J. Indian Chem. Soc., 40, 545 (1963).
78. Singh, Kaur, and Narang, J. Indian Chem. Soc., 41, 855 (1964).
79. Singh, Bhandari, and Narang, J. Indian Chem. Soc., 41, 715 (1964).
80. Butler and Partridge, J. Chem. Soc., 1959, 1512.
81. Fortmann, J. Prakt. Chem., 55 (2), 123 (1897).
82. Párkányi and Vystrčil, Chem. Listy, 50, 666 (1956); Chem. Abstr., 50, 8657 (1956).
83. Bhargava and Ram, Bull. Chem. Soc. Japan, 38, 342 (1965).
84. Mewada, Dave, and Amin, J. Sci. Ind. Res. India, 20B, 299 (1961).
85. Dave, Mewada, and Amin, J. Indian Chem. Soc., 37, 595 (1960).
86. Bereshchagina and Postovskii, Zh. Obshch. Khim., 34, 1745 (1964).
87. Sachdev, Dhami, and Atwal, Tetrahedron, 14, 304 (1961).
88. Pawlewski, Ber. Deut. Chem. Ges., 39, 1732 (1906).
89. Rossi, Gazz. Chim. Ital., 57, 625 (1927).
90. Puar, Sachdev, and Ralhan, Indian J. Chem., 2, 285 (1964).
91. Singh, Dhami, Sharma, and Narang, J. Sci. Ind. Res. India, 17B, 120 (1958).
92. Dhami, Sachdev, and Narang, J. Sci. Ind. Res. India, 16B, 311 (1957).
93. Sharma and Singh, J. Sci. Ind. Res. India, 20C, 178 (1961).
94. Lavenstein and Altman, Biochim. Biophys. Acta, 21, 587 (1956).
95. Stewart, J. Prakt. Chem., 44, 415 (1891).
96. Dave, Mewada, and Amin, Acta Chim. Acad. Sci. Hung., 34, 101 (1962); Chem. Abstr., 59, 627 (1963).

97. Pawlewski, *Ber. Deut. Chem. Ges.*, **38**, 130 (1905).
98. Joshi and Giri, *J. Indian Chem. Soc.*, **39**, 188 (1962).
99. Toyoshima, Shimada, Hamano, and Ogo, *J. Pharm. Soc. Japan*, **85**, 502 (1965).
100. Lempert and Doleschall, *Chem. Ber.*, **96**, 1271 (1963).
101. Douglas and Dains, *J. Am. Chem. Soc.*, **56**, 719 (1934).
102. Kaur, Singh, and Singh, *Indian J. Chem.*, **1**, 308 (1963).
103. Taylor and Ravindranathan, *J. Org. Chem.*, **27**, 2622 (1962).
104. McCarty, Haines, and Vanderwerf, *J. Am. Chem. Soc.*, **82**, 964 (1960).
105. Dhatt and Narang, *J. Indian Chem. Soc.*, **31**, 787 (1954).
106. Párkányi and Vystrcïl, *Chem. Listy*, **50**, 106 (1956); *Chem. Abstr.*, **50**, 8656 (1956).
107. Dhatt and Narang, *J. Indian Chem. Soc.*, **31**, 865 (1954).
108. McCoy, *Am. Chem. J.*, **21**, 111 (1899); McCoy, *Ber. Deut. Chem. Ges.*, **30**, 1682 (1897).
109. Stephen and Wilson, *J. Chem. Soc.*, **1928**, 1415.
110. Kendall and Duffin, *Brit. Pat.*, 634,951 (1950); *Chem. Abstr.*, **44**, 9287 (1950).
111. Lempert and Breuer, *Magy. Kém. Folyóirat*, **68**, 452 (1962); *Chem. Abstr.*, **58**, 11355 (1963).
112. Bariana, Sachdev, and Narang, *J. Indian Chem. Soc.*, **32**, 647 (1955).
113. Sharma, Sachdev, and Narang, *J. Sci. Ind. Res. India*, **15B**, 687 (1956).
114. Párkányi and Vystrcïl, *Chem. Listy*, **50**, 62 (1956); *Chem. Abstr.*, **50**, 4675 (1956); *Collection Czech. Chem. Commun.*, **21**, 689 (1956).
114a. Ghosh, *J. Indian. Chem. Soc.*, **7**, 981 (1930).
115. Párkányi, *Collection Czech. Chem. Commun.*, **26**, 998 (1961).
116. Pesson and Richer, *Compt. Rend.*, **260**, 603 (1965).
117. Baker, Schaub, Joseph, McEvoy, and Williams, *J. Org. Chem.*, **17**, 164 (1952).
118. Elderfield, Williamson, Gensler, and Kremer, *J. Org. Chem.*, **12**, 405 (1947).
119. Patterson, Capell, and Walker, *The Ring Index*, 2nd ed., American Chemical Society, 1960.
120. Sachdev and Narang, *J. Indian Chem. Soc.*, **32**, 631 (1955).
121. Sharma, Gupta, and Narang, *J. Indian Chem. Soc.*, **32**, 589 (1955).
122. Sachdev, Ralhan, Atwal, Garg, and Narang, *J. Sci. Ind. Res. India*, **19B**, 217 (1960).
123. Sykes, *J. Chem. Soc.*, **1955**, 2390.
124. Suri, Sharma, and Narang, *J. Indian Chem. Soc.*, **41**, 591 (1964).
125. Dhami, Arora, and Narang, *J. Med. Chem.*, **6**, 450 (1963).
126. Bariana, Sachdev, and Narang, *J. Indian Chem. Soc.*, **32**, 644 (1955).
127. Dhatt and Narang, *J. Org. Chem.*, **20**, 302 (1955).
128. Sachdev and Ralhan, *J. Sci. Ind. Res. India*, **19C**, 109 (1960).
129. Gakhar, *Indian J. Chem.*, **3**, 44 (1965).
130. Narang and Singh, *J. Indian Chem. Soc.*, **42**, 155 (1965).
131. Narang, Singh, Sharma, and Narang, *J. Indian Chem. Soc.*, **42**, 220 (1965).
132. Narang and Narang, *Indian J. Chem.*, **1**, 318 (1963).
133. Boltze, Dell, Lehwald, Lorenz, and Rüberg-Schweer, *Arzneimittelforsch.*, **13**, 688 (1963).
134. Zeitler, *Z. Physiol. Chem.*, **340**, 73 (1965).

135. Curd, Landquist, and Rose, *J. Chem. Soc.*, **1947**, 775.
136. Asano and Asai, *J. Pharm. Soc. Japan*, **78**, 450 (1958).
137. Martin, Rieche, and Iyer, *Arch. Pharm.*, **296**, 641 (1963).
138. Lempert and Doleschall, *Experientia*, **18**, 402 (1962).
139. Mead, Johnson, and Co., *Brit. Pat.*, 920,019 (1963); *Chem. Abstr.*, **59**, 3935 (1963).
140. Hayao, Havera, Strycker, Leipzig, Kulp, and Hartzler, *J. Med. Chem.*, **8**, 807 (1965).

CHAPTER VII

Aminoquinazolines (including Aminooxo-
and Aminothioquinazolines)

Many aminoquinazolines were prepared in recent years for biological testing, particularly in the field of antimalarials (Ch. XI, Sect. 2.). The term 'aminoquinazoline' in this chapter is used in a generic sense and includes primary and secondary amines, hydrazines, guanidines, and azides. All the compounds described have the amino group attached directly to the quinazoline ring. Reduced amino-, aminooxo-, and aminothioquinazolines are in chapter VIII.

1. 2- and 4-Amino- and 2,4-Diaminoquinazolines

A. Preparation of 2-Aminoquinazolines and 2-Amino-3,4-
dihydro-4-oxoquinazolines

a. By Nucleophilic Displacement with Amines

2-Chloroquinazolines react with alcoholic ammonia,[1,2,3] alkylamines,[3] and hydrazine[4] to give the corresponding 2-amino derivatives (Eq. 1). Thus 2-amino-,[1,2] 2-amino-4-methyl-, 2-methylamino-4-methyl-, 2-dimethylamino-4-methyl-[3], and 2-hydrazino-4-phenylquinazolines[4] were prepared in this manner. Reaction of 2-chloro-4-methylquinazoline with trimethylamine, on the other hand, gave 2-dimethylamino-4-methylquinazoline instead of the quaternary salt, presumably with loss of chloromethane (Eq. 2).[3] 1,2,3,4-Tetrahydro-2,4-dioxoquinazoline reacts with phosphoryl chloride in the presence of triethylamine to form 4-chloro-2-diethylaminoquinazoline, also with loss of chloroethane.[5] Although 4-alkoxy-2-chloroquinazolines react with primary alkylamines with displacement of the alkoxy group, they react smoothly with anilines to form the respective 4-alkoxy-2-anilino-quinazolines.[6] 2-Chloro-4-phenoxyquinazolines behave in a similar way.[7,8] The stronger the nucleophilic properties of the amine, the milder are the conditions necessary to effect this reaction. It is advisable to use two equivalents of amine in order to avoid the formation of the hydrochloride of the aminoquinazoline formed and/or of the reacting amine.

$$\text{(quinazoline-Cl)} \xrightarrow{RNH_2} \text{(quinazoline-NHR)} \quad + \text{HCl} \tag{1}$$

The preparation of many 2-alkylamino-[9,10,11] and 2-arylamino-3,4-dihydro-4-oxoquinazolines[7,8,12,13] from 2-chloro-3,4-dihydro-4-oxo-quinazoline and the respective amines was recorded. The reactivity of the chlorine atom in 2-chloro-3,4-dihydro-4-oxoquinazoline towards aliphatic amines, however, was low.[10,14] Anilines also reacted slowly, and it was found that the displacement of a 2-methylthio group was more satisfactory.[14] 2-Amino-, 2-morpholino-,[15] 2-N-methylanilino-,[13]

$$\text{(4-Me-quinazoline-Cl)} \xrightarrow{Me_3N} \text{(4-Me-quinazoline-NMe_2)} \quad + \text{MeCl} \tag{2}$$

2-2'-diethylaminoethylamino-,[14] and 2-carboxymethylamino-3,4-di-hydro-4-oxoquinazolines[16] were prepared by the reaction of the corresponding amines with 3,4-dihydro-2-methylthio-4-oxoquinazoline. 2-Alkoxy-[17,18] and 2-cyano-3,4-dihydro-4-oxoquinazolines[19] reacted

$$\text{(quinazolinone-R^1)} \xrightarrow{R^2NH_2} \text{(quinazolinone-NHR^2)} \tag{3}$$

$$R^1 = \text{Cl, SMe, OMe, CN}$$

with amines to furnish 2-amino-3,4-dihydro-4-oxoquinazolines (Reaction 3).

2-Aminoquinazoline was also formed by the fusion of 2-phenoxy-quinazoline with ammonium acetate at 170–180°.[20]

b. *Syntheses involving Guanidines, Cyanamides, Ureas, and Related Compounds*

The most satisfactory synthesis of 2-aminoquinazoline is by the reaction of guanidine carbonate with o-aminobenzaldehyde in boiling decalin.[21] This synthesis was used to prepare 5-, 6-, 7-, and 8-methoxy-, 8-methoxy-5-methyl-, 8-methoxy-6-methyl-, 8-methoxy-7-methyl-,[22] and 6-hydroxymethyl-8-methoxy-[23] 2-aminoquinazolines in connection with the structure of Tetrodotoxin (Ch. XI, Sect. 1.E.). Cyanamide can be used instead of guanidine carbonate in this reaction and it was used in the preparation of 4-methyl-,[24] 6-chloro-4-methyl-,[24,25] and 6-hydroxy-4-methyl-[26] 2-aminoquinazolines from o-aminoaceto-phenones (Reaction 4). o-Aminoacetophenone and sodium dicyanamide

$$R^1 \underset{NH_2}{\overset{R}{\diagup\!\!\!\!\diagdown}} C{=}O \quad \xrightarrow[\text{cyanamide}]{\text{guanidine carbonate or}} \quad R^1 \underset{N}{\overset{R}{\diagup\!\!\!\!\diagdown}} NH_2 \qquad (4)$$

gave 2-cyanamino-4-methylquinazoline, and with *N*-cyano-1,2,3,4-tetrahydro-6-methoxyquinoline it gave 2-(1′,2′,3′,4′-tetrahydro-6′-methoxy-1′-quinolyl)-4-methylquinazoline.[24] Dicyandiamide and its

$$R^1 \underset{\underset{H}{N}}{\overset{R}{\diagup\!\!\!\!\diagdown}} \overset{Me}{\underset{Me}{\diagdown}} \quad + \quad NC{-}NH{-}C\underset{NH_2}{\overset{NH}{\diagup}} \quad \longrightarrow$$

(1)

$$R^1 \underset{N}{\overset{R}{\diagup\!\!\!\!\diagdown}} NH{-}C\underset{NH_2}{\overset{NH}{\|}} \quad + \quad CH_2{=}CMe_2 \qquad (5)$$

monosubstituted derivatives react with o-acylanilines in the same way, but the products are the respective 2-guanidino derivatives.[24,25] These can be degraded by alkali to 2-aminoquinazolines, or condensed with β-diketones to form 2-pyrimidin-2′-ylquinazolines.[27] Derivatives of 'acetone anil', now known to be 1,2-dihydro-2,2,4-trimethylquinoline (1), have been used instead of o-acylanilines in the reaction with dicyandiamide and gave a variety of substituted 2-guanidinoquina-zolines together with butylene (Eq. 5). This reaction failed when hydrogen cyanide, cyanamide, or methylnitrile was used instead of dicyandiamide. 1,2,3,4-Tetrahydro-2,2,4-trimethylquinoline did not react under these conditions which suggested that the initial reaction was not biguanide formation at the heterocyclic nitrogen atom.[27-31] The synthesis of 5,6-benzo-4-methyl-[32] and 4,6,7-trimethyl-2-guanidino-quinazoline hydrochloride[33] from the reaction of dicyandiamide with β-naphthylamine and 3,4-xylidine, respectively, in acetone was shown to proceed via the intermediate acetone anils.

The condensation of guanidine and its alkyl derivatives with 2-acetoxy-6-acylcyclohexa-3,5-dien-1-ones (2) yields 2-amino-5-hydroxy-quinazolines (Reaction 6)[34,35] (Ch. IV, Sect. 4.a.).

Anthranilic acid, or its methyl ester, reacts with guanidine carbonate,[36] dicyandiamide,[37] and S-methyl-N-substituted thioureas[12,38,39] to form 2-amino-, 2-guanidino-, and substituted 2-amino-3,4-di-hydro-4-oxoquinazolines. Chloro derivatives of carboimides (3) also condense with methyl anthranilate or anthranilamide to form 2-amino-3,4-dihydro-4-oxoquinazolines (Reaction 7).[40] o-Ureidoanthranilamides can be converted to imidoyl chlorides, e.g. **4**, with phosphoryl chloride and then cyclized to aminooxoquinazolines.[41] o-N'-Phenylureidobenzonitriles and aniline, in benzene containing sodamide, form N-phenyl-C-(o-N'-phenylureidophenyl)formamidine which loses aniline at 200–210° to give 2-anilino-3,4-dihydro-4-oxoquinazoline.[41] 3-Substituted 2-amino-3,4-dihydro-4-oxoquinazolines are formed together with diaza-azulenes in the reaction of 2-bromo-7-methoxytropones with substituted guanidines. The formation of aminooxoquinazolines in this reaction probably follows the course shown in reaction (8).[42]

$$(8)$$

2-Amino-3,4-dihydro-4-oxoquinazolines were conveniently obtained by condensation of methyl anthranilate with cyanamides. The cyanamides were prepared, without isolation, by the reaction of N-substituted ureas with benzenesulphonyl chloride in pyridine.[14] 3-Alkyl- and 3-aryl- 2-amino-3,4-dihydro-4-oxoquinazolines (**5**) undergo a Dimroth rearrangement (Sect. 1.E.c.) to 2-alkylamino- and 2-aryl-amino- 3,4-dihydro-4-oxoquinazolines (**6**) in basic media, hence a mixture of products was sometimes obtained in the reaction (9). The derivatives **6** can be readily separated from **5** by their solubility in dilute alkali. When R in reaction (9) was cyclohexyl, isopropyl,

$$(9)$$

(5)   **(6)**

o- or *p*-tolyl, the method afforded only the derivatives of **6**. Similarly methylphenylcyanamide gave 3,4-dihydro-2-*N*-methylanilino-4-oxo-quinazoline, but 2-diethylaminoethyl-*p*-methoxyphenylcyanamide gave intractable products.[14]

c. *Miscellaneous*

2-Aminoquinazoline was obtained from 2-amino-4-carboxyquinazoline by sublimation[43] (Ch. X, Sect.2.B.), and from 2-amino-5,6,7,8-tetrahydroquinazoline by dehydrogenation with 5% palladium charcoal in boiling decalin[44] (Ch. VIII, Sect. 8.B.) or by bromination followed by treatment with sodium ethoxide.[45] Reduction of 2-aminoquinazoline-3-oxide[46] and 2-amino-3,4-dihydro-4-oxoquinazoline-1-oxide[47] furnished the corresponding 2-aminoquinazolines (Ch. IX, Sects. 2.A. and 4.). 2-Chloro-3,4-dihydro-4-oxoquinazoline reacted with sodium azide but gave tetrazolo(4,5-a)quinazolin-5-one instead of 2-azido-3,4-dihydro-4-oxoquinazoline.[48]

B. Preparation of 4-Aminoquinazolines, 4-Amino-1,2-dihydro-2-oxo- and 4-Amino-1,2-dihydro-2-thioquinazolines

a. *By Nucleophilic Displacement with Amines*

A large number of 4-aminoquinazolines were prepared from 4-chloroquinazolines by reaction with amines (Reaction 10).[1,5,49–71] The conditions for reaction depended on the nucleophilic nature of the amine and on its volatility. The condensations were carried out in boiling alcoholic,[5] alcoholic benzene,[71] or methylnitrile[53] solutions, or by heating alcoholic solutions in a sealed tube,[52,68] or by heating in the absence of a solvent.[53] Several 4-anilinoquinazolines were obtained from this reaction in boiling acetone containing concentrated hydrochloric acid.[51,72] Ethylenediamine and biguanidines condense readily[73] but they need to have a substituent on one of the 'end' nitrogen atoms to avoid the reaction involving two chloroquinazoline molecules.[69,73] 4-Amino-2-trichloromethylquinazolines were also prepared from the corresponding 4-chloro compounds.[74] 4-Amino-2-phenylquinazoline was obtained when 4-bromo-2-phenylquinazoline was heated with alcoholic ammonia.[75]

4-Aminoquinazoline was formed in low yield when 3,4-dihydro-4-oxoquinazoline was heated with methanolic ammonia.[76] 4-Methoxy-quinazoline reacted more readily with alcoholic ammonia than the oxoquinazoline.[76] Fusion of 4-phenoxyquinazolines with ammonium acetate at 160°,[77] or heating 4-chloroquinazolines in phenol containing ammonium carbonate,[78] was used to prepare several 4-aminoquinazolines. 2-Methoxy-4-p-acetamidophenylsulphonamidoquinazoline was formed from 2,4-methoxyquinazoline and sodium acetylsulphanilamide.[79]

$$R = Cl, OMe, SMe, CN \tag{10}$$

Primary alkylamines reacted with 3,4-dihydro-4-thioquinazoline (which was more reactive than 4-methylthioquinazoline[80]) to give 4-alkylaminoquinazolines,[80,81] but with secondary amines, and aniline, the yields were poor.[80] In a modification of this reaction, 4-ethylamino-, 4-methylamino-, and 4-dimethylamino- 2-methyl-6-nitroquinazolines were prepared by bubbling a slow stream of the alkylamine through a solution of the respective 4-methylthio compound in dimethylformamide at 140°.[82] 2,4-Bismethylthioquinazoline and alcoholic ammonia at 150° yield 4-amino-2-methylthioquinazoline with loss of one thio group[75] (compare Sect. 1.C.a.). Similarly 6-chloro-1,2,3,4-tetrahydro-2,4-dithioquinazoline gave 4-amino-6-chloro-1,2-dihydro-2-thioquinazoline.[83]

4-Anilino-, 4-butylamino-, and 4-morpholinoquinazoline were prepared from 4-cyanoquinazoline by reaction with aniline, butylamine, and morpholine respectively.[84]

b. *From o-Aminobenzonitriles*

o-Ureidobenzonitriles, prepared from o-aminobenzonitriles and isocyanates, cyclize to 4-amino-1,2-dihydro-2-oxoquinazolines on heating, or by reaction with sodium alkoxides.[85,86] Thioureas give the corresponding 2-thioquinazolines.[87] These reactions can also be carried out in one step by heating the aminonitrile with the isocyanate or isothiocyanate. When a mixture of o-aminobenzonitrile was heated with phenyl isothiocyanate in boiling methanol, 1,2,3,4-tetrahydro-4-imino-3-phenyl-2-thioquinazoline (**7**, X = S) was formed, which on further heating, or boiling in dimethyl formamide, rearranged to 4-anilino-1,2-dihydro-2-thioquinazoline (**8**, X = S) (Reaction 11). At elevated temperatures 8 was formed directly and in quantitative yield.[88] Alkaline hydrogen peroxide oxidized the latter to 4-anilino-1,2-dihydro-2-oxoquinazoline (8, X = O),[88] which was also obtained from o-aminobenzonitrile and phenyl isocyanate.[85]

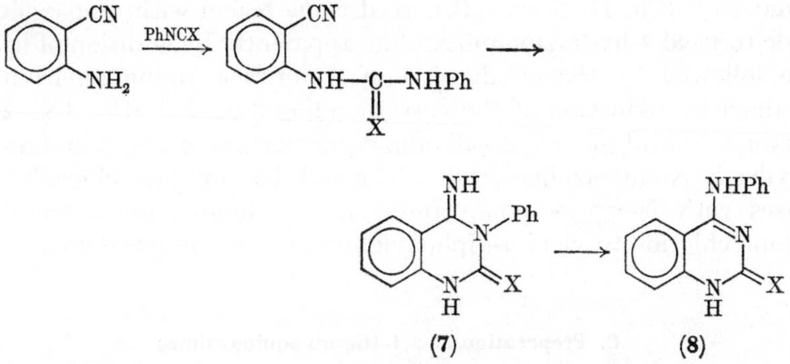

(11)

(7)   (8)

X = O or S

2-Amino-5-nitrobenzonitrile dimerized readily when heated in alcoholic ammonia at 180°, and formed 4-amino-2-(2'-amino-5'-nitro)-phenyl-6-nitroquinazoline.[89] o-Aminobenzonitrile and its 5-bromo derivative failed to dimerize under basic conditions, but reacted with p-nitrobenzonitrile to yield 4-amino-2-p-nitrophenyl- and 4-amino-6-bromo-2-p-nitrophenylquinazolines respectively. Similarly 4-amino-2-methyl- and 4-amino-2-phenylquinazoline were obtained from o-aminobenzonitrile by reaction with methylnitrile and phenylnitrile respectively.[90] 2-Amino-5-nitrobenzonitrile and p-nitrobenzonitrile yielded exclusively 4-amino-6-nitro-2-p-nitrophenylquinazoline without dimerization taking place (Reaction 12). p-Methoxy-, p-amino- and o-nitro-benzonitriles failed to react under these conditions.[90] It was concluded that the course of the reaction was governed by the ability of the cyano group to undergo nucleophilic attack rather than by the basicity of the amino group.[90]

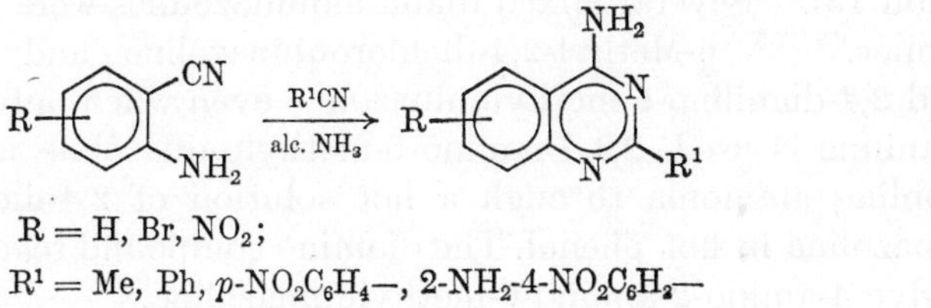

(12)

R = H, Br, NO$_2$;

R^1 = Me, Ph, p-NO$_2$C$_6$H$_4$—, 2-NH$_2$-4-NO$_2$C$_6$H$_4$—

c. *Miscellaneous*

The formation of 4-amino- or 4-hydrazinoquinazoline by the reaction of sodamide or hydrazine on quinazoline probably involves addition of the nucleophile across the 3,4-double bond followed by oxidation[91] (Ch. II, Sect. 3.B.). Hydrazine reacts with quinazoline-3-oxide to yield 4-hydrazinoquinazoline apparently by addition of hydrazine followed by the elimination of water.[92] 4-Aminoquinazoline is obtained by reduction of the corresponding 3-oxide[46] (Ch. IX, 2.A.). Alkaline hydrolysis of 2,4-dianilinoquinazolines gives 4-anilino-1,2-dihydro-2-oxoquinazolines.[93-97] N-Phenyl benzimidoyl chloride condenses with N-cyanodiphenylamine in o-dichlorobenzene containing stannic chloride to yield 4-diphenylamino-2-phenylquinazoline.[98]

C. Preparation of 2,4-Diaminoquinazolines

a. *By Nucleophilic Displacement with Amines*

The 2- and 4-chlorine atoms in 2,4-dichloroquinazolines can be displaced by amines to form 2,4-diaminoquinazolines. 2,4-Diamino-,[99-102] 2,4-bismethylamino-,[100] 2,4-dihydrazino-,[58,103] 2,4-dianilino-, 2,4-biscarboxyanilino-,[104] 2,4-diamino-6-ethyl-, 2,4-diamino-5-isopropyl-8-methyl-, 2,4-diamino-6-methyl-, 2,4-diamino-6,7-dimethyl-, and 2,4-diamino-6,8-dimethyl-[102] quinazolines were thus prepared using excess of amine. The reaction with volatile amines was carried out in a solvent, e.g. ethanol, in a sealed tube at temperatures above 130°, but with non-volatile amines the mixture was fused. The large difference in reactivity between the 2- and 4-chlorine atoms in 2,4-dichloroquinazolines (Ch. V, Sect. 1.E.b.(iii)) made possible the synthesis of quinazolines with amino groups in the 2- and 4-positions that are different. Thus under mild conditions 2,4-dichloroquinazoline reacts with ammonia to form 4-amino-2-chloroquinazoline which then reacts with hydrazine to give 4-amino-2-hydrazinoquinazoline (Reaction 13).[57] Several mixed diaminoquinazolines were prepared in this manner.[48,105] 6-Methyl-2,4-dichloroquinazoline and aniline always yield 2,4-dianilino-6-methylquinazoline even when only one equivalent of aniline is used. 2,4-Diamino-6-methylquinazoline was prepared by bubbling ammonia through a hot solution of 2,4-dichloro-6-methylquinazoline in hot phenol. The diamino compound reacted with aniline to give 4-amino-2-anilino-6-methylquinazoline.[106]

(13)

(9)

Several 4-alkylamino-2-arylaminoquinazolines were prepared by the reaction of 2-arylamino-4-chloroquinazolines (obtained from the chlorination of 2-arylamino-3,4-dihydro-4-oxoquinazolines) with alkylamines.[7,8,9,107] Many 4-alkylamino-2-2'-thiazolylaminoquinazolines were obtained in one step by heating together 2,4-dichloroquinazoline, an alkylamine, and a 2-thiazolylamine in nitrobenzene at 170–175°.[108,109] 4-Ethoxy-, 4-phenoxy-, and 4-methylthio-2-p-chloroanilinoquinazolines gave 2-p-chloroanilino-4-2'-diethylaminoethylaminoquinazoline when heated with 2-diethylaminoethylamine.[7] 2,4-Bismethylthioquinazoline and alcoholic ammonia at 230° yielded 2,4-diaminoquinazoline.[75]

2,4-Dichloroquinazoline and sodium azide did not give 2,4-diazidoquinazoline because the 2-azido group reacted further with the quinazoline nucleus to form 4-azidotetrazolo(4,5-a)quinazoline (9).[110]

b. From Guanidines

The fusion of N,N'-diarylguanidines with aryl isothiocyanates at 220° is a convenient method for preparing 2,4-diarylaminoquinazolines. 2,4-Dianilinoquinazoline was formed from N,N'-diphenylguanidine and phenyl isothiocyanate.[93,94] 8-Methyl-2,4-di-o-toluidino-,[96] 7-methyl-2,4-di-m-toluidino-, and 6-methyl-2,4-di-p-toluidinoquinazoline[97] were obtained in this manner. The aryl isothiocyanate becomes the 4-substituent because N,N'-di-o-tolylguanidine and phenyl isothiocyanate yield 4-anilino-8-methyl-2-o-toluidinoquinazoline (Eq. 14).[96] The product from N-phenyl-N'-1-naphthylguanidine and p-chlorophenyl isothiocyanate was 2-anilino-7,8-benzo-4-p-chloroanilinoquinazoline.[95]

$$(14)$$

c. *From* o-*Aminobenzonitriles*

6-Butyl-,[102] 5-ethyl-,[111] 5-methyl-,[102,111] 5,6,8-trimethyl-,[102] 5,6-trimethylene-,[102,111] 5,6-tetramethylene- and 6-propyl-[102] 2,4-diaminoquinazolines were obtained by heating the o-aminobenzonitrile hydrochlorides with dicyandiamide at 150–160° for a short period (Reaction 15). o-Aminobenzonitrile and dicyandiamide or cyanamide furnishes 2,4-diaminoquinazoline.[112]

$$(15)$$

D. Properties of 2- and 4-Amino-, and 2,4-Diaminoquinazolines

The aminoquinazolines are high-melting solids and the melting points are lowered with increase in the size of the substituent on the amino group. They form salts and are insoluble in aqueous alkaline solution unless they are aminooxoquinazolines which are unsubstituted on the ring nitrogen atoms. They crystallize from alcohols.

The pK_a values of 2- and 4-aminoquinazolines in water are 4.82 and 5.85.[20] The ring nitrogen atom is protonated and the higher basicity of the 4-isomer as compared with the 2-isomer is attributed to the larger contribution of the resonance form **10** in the cation, which has a *p*-quinonoid structure. A similar resonance stabilization in the 2-aminoquinazoline cation would involve a less stable *o*-quinonoid structure. The pK_a values of 4-amino-, 4-anilino-, and 4-amino-6-nitro- quinazolines in 50% aqueous ethanol are 5.17, 4.65, and 3.71 respectively.[113] The two basic ionization constants of several 4-2′-aminoethylaminoquinazolines were measured and the pK_a values were of the order ~ 8.7 and ~ 4.9. The rather large pK_{a_1} values (~ 8.7) could not be explained

(10)

(11)

by the $-\mathrm{I}$ effect of the quinazoline ring and the structure **11** was postulated for the stability, and hence higher basicity, of the protonated species.[53] This is only possible because of the proximity of the 2'-alkylamino group, in the side chain, to $\mathrm{N}_{(3)}$. The first and second pK_a values of 2,4-diamino-6-methylquinazoline in 5% aqueous ethanol are ~ 8.02 and ~ 2.5.[106]

The similarity of the ultraviolet spectra of 4-aminoquinazolines with those of 4-methoxyquinazoline suggested that the amino groups were not in the imino form.[114] The ultraviolet spectrum of 2-amino-3,4-dihydro-4-oxoquinazoline, unlike the spectrum of 1,2,3,4-tetrahydro-4-oxo-2-thio- and 1,2,3,4-tetrahydro-2,4-dioxoquinazoline,[115] was similar to that of 3,4-dihydro-2,3-dimethyl-4-oxoquinazoline[116] and of 3,4-dihydro-4-oxoquinazoline (Ch. IV, Sect. 2.C.a.) indicating that the amino group in this compound also was not in the imino form.

E. Reactions of 2- and 4-Amino- and 2,4-Diaminoquinazolines

a. *Hydrolysis*

Amino- and aminooxoquinazolines decompose slowly in dilute aqueous acid, but hydrolysis to the oxoquinazolines is rapid when the solutions are boiled.[37,85,88] A study of the hydrolysis of several 4-amino- and 4-substituted-aminoquinazolines in boiling dilute hydrochloric acid showed that hydrolysis was complete in 2–3 hours.[117] The rates of hydrolysis were in the order 4-(1',3'-dihydroxy-2'-methyl)-propylamino- > 4-anilino- > 4-amino- > 4-butylaminoquinazoline, and these were 10 to 50 times slower than the secondary amines: 4-diethylamino-, 4-morpholino-, and 4-piperidinoquinazoline.[63]

Hydrolysis of 2,4-dianilinoquinazolines with alcoholic potassium hydroxide at 140° afforded 4-anilino-1,2-dihydro-2-oxoquinazolines, but at 160–180° 1,2,3,4-tetrahydro-2,4-dioxoquinazolines were formed.[93,95,96] Dilute hydrochloric acid, however, converts 2,4-dianilinoquinazoline to 2-anilino-3,4-dihydro-4-oxoquinazoline.[88]

b. *Acylation, Methylation, and Chlorination*

Acetylation of 4-aminoquinazoline was said to proceed with difficulty[1] but later workers have succeeded in preparing 4-acetamidoquinazoline[21,63] by conventional methods. 6- and 7-Nitro-4-acetamidoquinazolines were obtained by acetylation of the corresponding 4-aminoquinazolines with acetic anhydride.[78] 2-Acetamido-,[21] 2,4-bisacetamido-,[94,100] and 2,4-bis-N-acetylanilinoquinazolines[93] were similarly prepared. 2- and 4-p-Sulphanilamidoquinazoline and their acetyl derivatives were prepared by direct treatment of the aminoquinazoline with the required p-aminobenzenesulphonyl chloride.[21,118] Benzoylation of 2,4-diamino-6-methylquinazoline with benzoyl chloride in boiling dioxan required triethylamine to give 2,4-bisbenzamido-6-methylquinazoline. The reaction was unsatisfactory when pyridine was used.[106]

Methylation of 6- and 7-nitro-4-aminoquinazoline with methyl iodide did not give well-defined products, and methylation of the acetyl derivatives with methyl toluene-p-sulphonate gave the respective 1,4-dihydro-1-methyl-4-oxoquinazolines, indicating that alkylation preceded hydrolysis. 6-Nitro- and 7-nitro- 4-anilino-1-methylquinazolinium toluene-p-sulphonates were isolated from alkylation of the 4-anilino compounds. These salts were reduced with iron and water (containing a small quantity of acid) to the corresponding 6- and 7-aminoquinazolinium salts.[79] Berg found that 4-amino-6-nitroquinazolines gave unstable products when treated with dimethyl sulphate, but succeeded in preparing several 1-methylquinazolinium compounds by fusion of 4-amino-6-nitroquinazolines with methyl toluene-p-sulphonate at 140°, or by heating these in nitrobenzene at 170°. He found that the free bases, i.e. 4-imino compounds, liberated from the quinazolinium salts with ammonia, were fairly stable.[82] Methylation of 2-amino- and 2-anilino- 3,4-dihydro-4-oxoquinazolines with methyl iodide or dimethyl sulphate gave 2-amino-[18] and 2-anilino-[88] 3,4-dihydro-3-methyl-4-oxoquinazolines; and 2-anilino-3,4-dihydro-4-oxo-3-phenylquinazoline gave 1,2,3,4-tetrahydro-1-methyl-4-oxo-3-phenyl-2-phenyliminoquinazoline because the product was different from 3,4-dihydro-2-N-methylanilino-4-oxo-3-phenylquinazoline.[13] 6-Chloro-4-N-ethyl-2′-chloroethylaminoquinazoline readily undergoes intramolecular alkylation to give 9-chloro-1-ethyl-2,3-dihydroimidazo(3,2-c)quinazolinium chloride (12).[119]

Phosphoryl chloride chlorinates 2-alkylamino- and 2-arylamino-3,4-dihydro-4-oxoquinazolines to 2-alkylamino- and 2-arylamino-4-chloroquinazoline.[7,9]

(12)

c. Transamination and Molecular Rearrangements

The 4-amino group in 2,4-diaminoquinazolines undergoes displacement reactions with other amines. 2,4-Bis-p-chloroanilino- and 2-p-chloroanilino-4-2′-hydroxyethylaminoquinazoline are converted to 2-p-chloroanilino-4-2′-diethylaminoethylaminoquinazoline on heating with diethylaminoethylamine at 130–140°.[9]

The first example of a Dimroth rearrangement in the quinazoline series was described by Wheeler, Johnson, and McFarland. They found that when 2-amino-3,4-dihydro-4-oxo-3-phenylquinazoline was heated with aqueous alkali it rearranged to the more stable 2-anilino-3,4-dihydro-4-oxoquinazoline[12] (Reaction 16). Grout and Partridge later

(16)

showed that 3-methyl-, 3-ethyl-, 3-propyl-, 3-phenyl- and 3-p-methoxyphenyl- 2-amino-3,4-dihydro-4-oxoquinazolines isomerized almost quantitatively with dilute alkali, but not with dilute acid, to 2-methylamino-, 2-ethylamino-, 2-propylamino-, 2-anilino-, and 2-p-anisidino-3,4-dihydro-4-oxoquinazolines respectively. The 3-benzyl analogue, however, afforded only a low yield of its isomer.[14] Rearrangements of this type involving the 4-position are also known. Thus when 1,2,3,4-tetrahydro-4-imino-3-phenyl-2-thioquinazoline (13, X = S) was heated, or treated with alkali, it isomerized to 4-anilino-1,2-dihydro-2-thioquinazoline (Reaction 17). The 2-oxo analogue (13, X = O) behaved

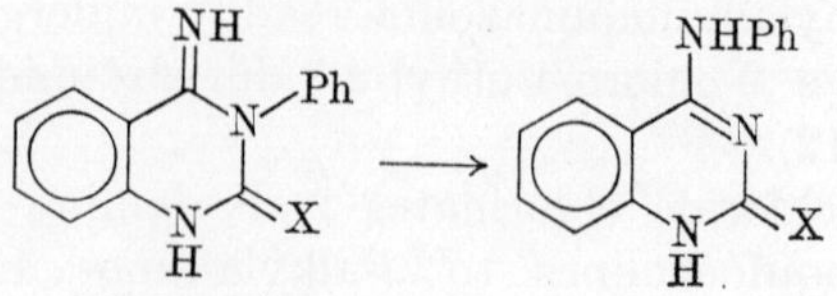

(13)   (17)

X = S or O

similarly.[88] For details of the mechanism of the Dimroth rearrangement the reader is referred to the work of Brown and his collaborators.[120]

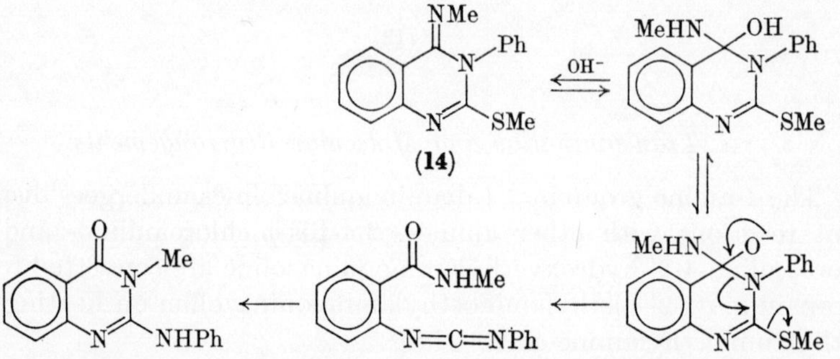

(14)

(18)

(15)

An unusual and facile rearrangement occurred when 3,4-dihydro-4-methylimino-2-methylthio-3-phenylquinazoline (14) was heated with weak aqueous methanolic sodium hydroxide. It gave 2-anilino-3,4-dihydro-3-methyl-4-oxoquinazoline (15). Methyl mercaptan was eliminated in the process and the mechanism in reaction (18) was suggested.[88]

d. Reactions of Hydrazinoquinazolines

The hydrazino group in hydrazinoquinazolines exhibits many of its typical reactions. 4-Hydrazinoquinazoline can be benzoylated and tosylated to form 4-N'-benzoylhydrazino-[121] and 4-N'-tosylhydrazinoquinazoline,[1] and reacts with a variety of aldehydes.[91,92,122,123] 2-Hydrazino-3,4-dihydro-4-oxoquinazoline condenses with β-dicarbonyl compounds to yield 3,4-dihydro-4-oxo-2-pyrazolylquinazolines.[124]

The reaction of 4-hydrazinoquinazoline with copper sulphate gave an oil which was not quinazoline,[125] but with manganese dioxide (Ch. V, Sect. 1.E.b.(v)), and with alcoholic sodium hydroxide (Ch. II, Sect. 1.) quinazoline was formed with elimination of nitrogen. Under the influence of phosphoryl chloride, 4-N'-benzoylhydrazinoquinazoline cyclized to 3-phenyl-1,2,4-triazolo(4,5-c)quinazoline (**16**).[121] 2,4-Dihydrazinoquinazoline reacts with nitrous acid to give 4-azidotetrazolo(4,5-a)quinazoline (**9**).[110] Hydrolytic cleavage of the pyrimidine ring occurs when 2-methyl-, 2-phenyl-, and 2-4'-pyridyl- 4-N'-phenylthiosemicarbazidoquinazolines are heated with hydrochloric acid, and give the same 3-o-aminophenyl-4,5-dihydro-4-phenyl-5-thio-1,2,4(1-H)-triazine.[125a]

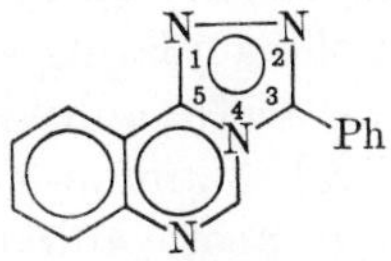

(16)

2. 3-Aminooxo- and 3-Aminothioquinazolines

A. Preparation of 3-Amino-3,4-dihydro-4-oxo- (and 4-thio-) and 3-Amino-1,2,3,4-tetrahydro-2,4-dioxoquinazolines

The general methods for the preparation of 3-aminooxoquinazolines are similar to the corresponding syntheses of 3-substituted oxoquinazolines in which the 3-substituents were introduced by procedures other than by alkylation (Ch. IV, Sects. 2. and 3.).

a. *Syntheses from Anthranilic Acid Derivatives*

3-Amino-3,4-dihydro-4-oxoquinazolines are formed in high yields when methyl or ethyl o-amidobenzoates are heated with hydrazine in a suitable solvent, e.g. ethanol, propanol. The amido group determines the nature of the 2-substituent (Reaction 19).[126-132] The reaction most

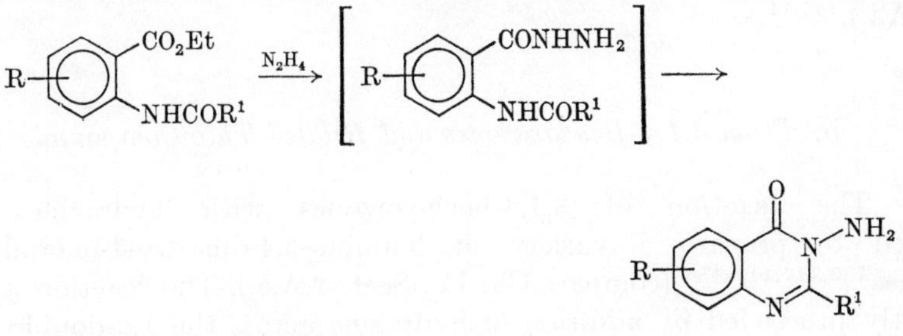

(19)

probably goes via the intermediate hydrazide which then cyclizes, because 2-acetamido-4,5-dimethylbenzoylhydrazine cyclizes to 3-amino-3,4-dihydro-2,6,7-trimethyl-4-oxoquinazoline on heating in alkaline medium.[133]

This cyclization can be accomplished by dilute acid,[132] or more conveniently by heating the hydrazide above 200°.[132,134-138] Ring closure by the action of heat alone was used to prepare several derivatives, substituted on the 3-amino group, directly from the substituted hydrazides.[132,134-136,138] Acylation and cyclization of o-aminobenzoylhydrazines by boiling with the acylating agent, e.g. anhydrous formic acid, ethyl orthoformate, or acetic anhydride, was performed in one operation to produce several 3-amino-3,4-dihydro-4-oxoquinazolines (Reaction 20).[139-144] Excess of acetic anhydride also caused acetylation of the unsubstituted 3-amino group.[132]

$$(20)$$

The action of heat on o-alkoxy- (or benzyloxy-)carbonylamino-benzoylhydrazides,[135] or a mixture of anthranilic esters and semicarbazones[145] furnished 3-amino- and 3-substituted-amino- 1,2,3,4-tetrahydro-2,4-dioxoquinazolines (Reaction 21).

$$(21)$$

Grimmel, Guenther, and Morgan's synthesis involving o-amido-benzoic acids, a hydrazine, and phosphoryl chloride was used to prepare 3-amino-3,4-dihydro-4-oxoquinazolines (compare Ch. IV, Sect. 2.A.i.).[146,147]

b. From 3,1,4-Benzoxazones and Related Thio Compounds

The reaction of 3,1,4-benzoxazones with hydrazines was used to prepare a variety of 3-amino-3,4-dihydro-4-oxoquinazolines[138,147,148-154] (compare Ch. IV, Sect. 2.A.e.). The reaction apparently proceeded by addition of hydrazine across the 1,2-double bond because hydrazine adducts were isolated. This was followed by ring opening and then cyclization with elimination of water. The latter step was promoted by acetic acid or dilute mineral acid (Reaction 22).[155,156] 3,1,4-Benzothiazones and hydrazines similarly yielded 3-amino-3,4-dihydro-4-oxoquinazolines, but 3,1,4-benzothiazathiones gave 3-amino-3,4-dihydro-4-thioquinazolines, while hydrogen sulphide was liberated from both reactions.[150]

$$(22)$$

c. From 3,4-Dihydro-4-oxoquinazolines and Hydrazines

4-Hydrazono-3,4-dihydro-3-phenylquinazoline was said to be formed from 3,4-dihydro-4-oxo-3-phenylquinazoline and hydrazine,[157] but this was later found to be incorrect.[158] The product was shown to be 3-amino-3,4-dihydro-4-oxoquinazoline.[158] This method (where $N_{(3)}$ in oxoquinazolines was displaced by hydrazine) was found to be a general one (Reaction 23).[159,160] 1,2,3,4-Tetrahydro-1-methyl-2,4-dioxoquinazoline reacts similarly with hydrazine to form 3-amino-1,2,3,4-tetrahydro-1-methyl-2,4-dioxoquinazoline.[161] 3-Acetamido-3,4-dihydro-2-methyl-7-nitro-4-oxoquinazoline, however, condenses with phenylhydrazine to yield 3-acetamido-3,4-dihydro-4-phenylhydrazono-2-methyl-7-nitro-4-oxoquinazoline.[149]

$$(23)$$

d. Miscellaneous

Treatment of N-methylsulphonylphthalimide with hydrazine, phenylsulphonylhydrazine, nicotinic acid hydrazide and α-picolinic acid hydrazide gave 3-amino-, 3-phenylsulphonamido-, 3-3'-pyridylcarbonylamino-, and 3-2'-pyridylcarbonylamino- 1,2,3,4-tetrahydro-2,4-dioxoquinazolines respectively (compare Ch. IV, Sect. 3.A.e.).[162,163]

12*

Isatoic acid diazide and hydrazine in ethereal solution yielded 3-amino-1,2,3,4-tetrahydro-2,4-dioxoquinazoline.[164] 4,1-Benzoxazepin-2,5-diones reacted with hydrazine to form 3-amino-3,4-dihydro-2-1'-hydroxy-alkyl-4-oxoquinazolines.[165]

B. Reactions of 3-Aminooxoquinazolines

In addition to having properties typical of 3-substituted oxoquinazolines, 3-aminooxoquinazolines show most of the reactions which are consistent with their having an amino group. Thus the amino group can be diazotized and coupled with β-naphthol to give coloured compounds,[158] it can be acetylated and formylated to give 3-amido derivatives,[148,156,166] and forms 3-ureido and 3-thioureido derivatives with isocyanates and isothiocyanates respectively.[148,160] The 3-amino group condenses with aldehydes and ketones to form azomethenes (Reaction 24).[148,159,160,164,167,168] These bases are more stable than benzylidene anilines and are more like hydrazones. The 3-amino group is more reactive towards aldehydes than a 2-methyl group which is known to react with benzaldehydes to form 2-styryl derivatives

$$\text{(24)}$$

(Ch. IV, Sect. 2.C.b.(ii)).[166,169] Reduction of 3-benzamido-3,4-dihydro-4-oxo-2-phenylquinazoline with zinc and acetic acid furnishes 3,4-dihydro-4-oxo-2-phenylquinazoline.[167] Deamination of 3-aminooxoquinazolines to the corresponding oxoquinazoline takes place in boiling ethanol or isopropanol in the presence of Raney nickel.[127-130] This deamination can be effected also with nitrous acid.[148,164]

3. Aminoquinazolines with Amino Groups in the Benzene Ring

A. Preparation of 5-,6-,7-, and 8-Amino- and Aminooxoquinazolines

Many 5-,6-,7-, and 8-amino-3,4-dihydro-4-oxoquinazolines were prepared by reduction of the respective nitro compounds with stannous chloride and hydrochloric acid,[149,170-172] or catalytically with Raney nickel[172] or palladium charcoal.[173-175] 5-,6-,7-, and 8-Amino-1,2,3,4-tetrahydro-2,4-dioxoquinazolines were obtained by similar reductions of the corresponding nitro compounds.[176-178] 4-Aminoquinazolines with nitro groups in the benzene ring were reduced to the diamino compounds with iron and water containing a little hydrochloric acid,[179] sodium sulphide,[180] or catalytically using Raney nickel[181] or platinum oxide catalysts.[82,182]

6- and 7-Acetamido-3,4-dihydro-4-oxoquinazolines were readily formed by heating the respective 6- and 7-acetamido-3,1,4-benzoxazones with ammonia or amines, and were then hydrolyzed to the aminooxoquinazolines (compare Ch. IV, Sect. 2.A.e.).[170,183–185]

5-,6-,7-, and 8-Aminoquinazolines were obtained by catalytic reduction of the 4-chloronitroquinazolines, with palladium on calcium carbonate, to the amino-3,4-dihydroquinazolines which were successfully oxidized with alkaline potassium ferricyanide (Reaction 25).[20,55,186] 4-Chloro-5-nitroquinazoline was reduced to 5-aminoquinazoline catalytically with Raney nickel in methyl cellosolve.[186] 7-Amino-6-methoxyquinazoline and some of its derivatives were described as the 8-amino-6-methoxy compounds in the literature (Ch. V, Sect. 2.D., and Ch. VI, Sect. 5.).[1,55]

(25)

6-Dimethylamino-1,2,3,4-tetrahydro-2,4-dioxoquinazoline was formed when p-dimethylaminophenylazobenzene and carbon monoxide were heated at 230° in the presence of cobalt carbonyl (compare Ch. IV, Sect. 3.A.g.).[187]

B. Properties of 5-,6-,7-, and 8-Amino- and Aminooxoquinazolines

These aminoquinazolines show the typical reactions of anilines. The ultraviolet spectra and ionization constants of 5-,6-,7-, and 8-aminoquinazolines were measured[20] and their cations were partially hydrated (covalent hydration) across the 3,4-double bond (Ch. II, Sect. 2.C.c.).[20,188] The amino groups in amino- and aminooxoquinazolines can be acylated,[55,70,170,183,186] alkylated,[55] and form azomethenes with aldehydes.[169] They can be diazotized and hence substituted by a chloro,[189] cyano,[63,183] fluoro,[174] hydroxy,[183] iodo, methylthio, phenylthio,[174] or an arsono[190] group. They also condense with phenyl diazonium salts to form aminoazoquinazolines.[82,191]

4. Tables

TABLE VII.1.   2-Amino- and 2-Substituted-aminoquinazolines.

$$H(R^2)$$

$$(R^3)H \quad \underset{N}{\overset{N}{\bigcirc}} \quad NH_2(RR^1)$$

Quinazoline	M.p. (°c)	References
2-Acetamido-	177°	21
2-Acetamido-6-acetoxy-	198°	26
2-Acetamido-5-hydroxy-6-isopropyl-8-methyl-	196–200°	35
2-Acetylsulphanilamido-	271–272°	1, 209, 118
2-Amino-	204–206°	1, 2, 21, 22, 43, 44, 209
2-Amino-4-benzoyloxy-6-methyl-	235°	106
2-Amino-6-chloro-4-methyl-	224–224.5°	24
2-Amino-6-chloro-4-phenyl-	HCl 283°	25
2-Amino-6-hydroxy-	HCl > 250°	26
2-Amino-8-hydroxy-6-hydroxy-methyl-	201°	228
2-Amino-6-hydroxy-4-methyl-	HCl > 250°	26
2-Amino-6-hydroxymethyl-8-methoxy-	223–224°	23
2-Amino-5-methoxy-	240°	22
2-Amino-6-methoxy-	193–194°	22
2-Amino-7-methoxy-	218–220°	22
2-Amino-8-methoxy-	150–152°	22, 198
2-Amino-8-methoxy-5-methyl-	235–237°	22
2-Amino-8-methoxy-6-methyl-	176.5–178°	22, 198
2-Amino-8-methoxy-7-methyl-	263°	22
2-Amino-4-methyl-	155°, 159–159.8°; HCl 239–240° (dec.)	3, 24, 28
2-Amino-6-methyl-	234–235°	45, 228
2-Cyanamino-4-methyl-	237.5–238.5°	24
2-(3′,4′-Dihydro-6′-methyl-4′-oxopyrimidin-2′-ylamino)-4-methyl-	285–290°	28
2-Dimethylamino-	86°	3
2-Dimethylamino-4-methyl-	124°/1.0 mm	3
2-(4′,6′-Dimethylpyrimidin-2′-ylamino)-6-ethoxy-4-methyl-	212–213°	28
2-(4′,6′-Dimethylpyrimidin-2′-ylamino)-4-methyl-	134–135°	28

(*Table continued*)

TABLE VII.1 (*continued*)

Quinazoline	M.p. (°c)	References
2-(6'-Methoxy-1',2',3',4'-tetra-hydroquinolin-1'-yl)-4-methyl-	86.5–88°	24
4-Methyl-2-methylamino-	103°	3
2-Methylamino-	92°	3
2-p-Nitrophenylsulphonamido-	234–238°	21
2-Sulphanilamido-	286°	21

TABLE VII.2.   2-Guanidinoquinazolines.

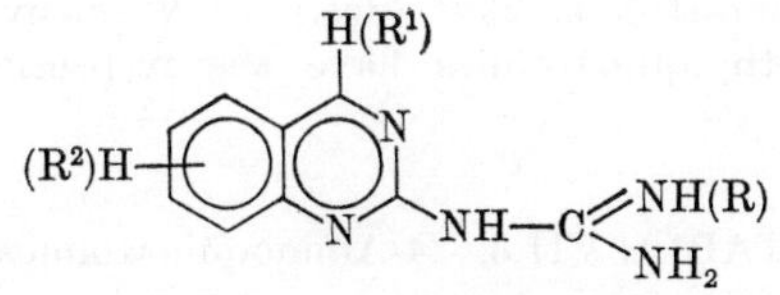

2-Guanidinoquinazoline[a]	M.p. (°c)	References
Unsubstituted	265°; HCl 249°	28
6-Allyloxy-4-methyl-	HCl 238–239°	28
5,6-Benzo-4-methyl-	244–245°; HCl 313–314°	32
6-Benzyloxy-4-methyl-	206–207°; HCl 273° (dec.)	28
6-Bromo-4-methyl-	263–264°; HCl 293–295° (dec.)	27
6-Butyl-4-methyl-	198–199°; HCl 202–203°	28, 31
7-Chloro-6-ethoxy-4-methyl-	HCl 315° (dec.)	28
7-Chloro-4-methyl-	HCl 299–300° (dec.), 310°; HNO₃ 301–302° (dec.); N'-ethyl deriv. HCl H₂O 200° (remelts at 258–259° (dec.)); N'-methyl deriv. HNO₃ 225° (dec.)	24, 28, 31
6-Chloro-4-phenyl-	309–310°	25
6-Decyloxy-4-methyl-	204–205°; HCl 181–182°	28
6-Ethoxy-4-methyl-	263–264°; HCl 268–269° (dec.)	28, 29, 31
8-Ethoxy-4-methyl-	219–221°; HCl 301–302°	28, 31
6-Ethyl-4-methyl-	248–249° (dec.); HCl 239–240°	28, 31
6-2'-(2-Guanidino-4-methyl-quinazolin-6-yl)ethyl-4-methyl-	178–180°; HCl 259–261°	28
6-Hexyloxy-4-methyl-	226–229°; HCl 234–235°	28
6-Isopropyl-4-methyl-	HCl 233–234°	28, 31

(*Table continued*)

TABLE VII.2 (*continued*)

2-Guanidinoquinazoline[a]	M.p. (°c)	References
6-Methoxy-4-methyl-	HCl 326–328°	28
4-Methyl-	243–245°; HCl 330–332° (dec.); HNO₃ 300–301° (dec.)	24, 28, 29, 31
4,6-Dimethyl-	256–258°; HCl 303–304° (dec.)	28, 31
4,7-Dimethyl-	HCl 342°	28
4,6,7-Trimethyl-	259–260°; HCl 316–317°	33
4-Methyl-2-*t*-butyl-	233–235°; HCl 302–303°	28, 31

[a] 2-N'-p-Chlorophenylguanidino-(HCl 261–262.5° (dec.)), 2-N',N'-dimethyl-guanidino-(HNO₃·H₂O 260.5–261°), 2-N'-ethylguanidino-(HNO₃ 205° (dec.)), 2-N'-isopropylguanidino-(HNO₃ 239° (dec.)), 2-N'-phenylguanidino-(HCl 288° (dec.)) 6-chloro-4-methylquinazolines have the respective melting points in brackets.[24]

TABLE VII.3.   4-Aminoquinazolines.

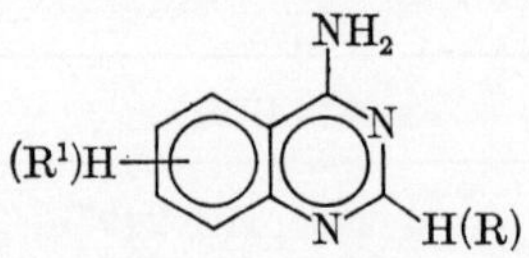

4-Aminoquinazoline	M.p. (°c)	References
Unsubstituted	198°, 267–268°, 272–273°; HBr 292° (dec.); picrate 292°; acetyl deriv. 171°, 174–175°	1, 21, 63, 77, 91, 118, 209
2-Acetonylthio-	168°	87
2-(2'-Amino-5'-nitro)phenyl-6-nitro-	>360°	89
2-p-Aminophenyl-	220–221°	89
2-p-Bromophenacylthio-	HBr 189°	87
6-Chloro-8-nitro-	284–285°	179
2-2'-Furyl-	225°	52
2-Methyl-	228–229°	90
6-Methyl-	275°	106
2-Methyl-6-nitro-	331–333°; 1-methyl tosylate 301° (dec.); 1-methyl chloride.H₂O 266–267° (dec.)	82
2-p-Methylphenacylthio-	HCl 235°	87

(*Table continued*)

TABLE VII.3 (*continued*)

4-Aminoquinazoline	M.p. (°c)	References
2-Methylthio-	233–234°	75
6-Nitro-	320–320.5°; 1-methyl tosylate 335° (dec.); 1-methyl chloride 307–309° (dec.)	78, 82
7-Nitro-	303–305°	78
8-Nitro-	284–286° (dec.)	179
6-Nitro-2-*m*-nitrophenyl-	315° (dec.)	89
6-Nitro-2-*p*-nitrophenyl-	303–304°	90
2-Phenacylthio-	HCl 240°	87
2-Phenyl-	145.5–146.5°	75, 90
2-Trichloromethyl-	183–184° (dec.)	204

TABLE VII.4.   4-Substituted-aminoquinazolines.

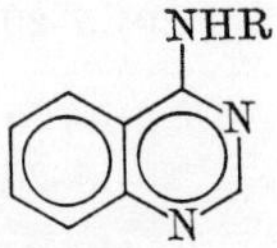

Quinazoline	M.p. (°c)	References
4-Acetylsulphanilamido-	255.5°, 260°	118, 209
4-(4'-Amino-3'-chloro-6'-methoxy)anilino-	210–212°	70
4-(4'-Amino-2',5'-diethoxy)-anilino-	133–136°	70
4-(4'-Amino-2',5'-dimethoxy)-anilino-	98–100°	70
4-(4'-Amino-2'-methoxy-5'-methyl)anilino-	181–184°	70
4-(4'-Amino-2'-methoxy)-anilino-	161–163°	70
4-(3'-Amino-6'-methyl)anilino-	174–178°	70
4-*m*-Aminoanilino-	242–245°	70
4-*p*-Aminoanilino-	213–215°	70
4-Anilino-	216–217°, 220–221°; HCl 271°; picrate 233°	80, 84, 88, 104, 117
4-*p*-Arsonoanilino-	> 320°	190
4-(1'-Benzylpyrrolidin-3'-ylmethylamino)-	105–107°	5

(*Table continued*)

TABLE VII.4 *(continued)*

Quinazoline	M.p. (°c)	References
4-Butylamino-	116–117°; picrate 189.5–190.5°	62, 80, 84
4-3'-Butylaminopropylamino-	oil	50
4-3'-Dibutylaminopropylamino-	70–72°	50
4-(2',5'-Diethoxy-4'-nitro)-anilino-	209–212°	70
4-2',5'-Diethoxyanilino-	104–106°	70
4-Diethylamino-	118°/0.1 mm	210
4-(4'-Diethylamino-1'-methyl)-butylamino-	98°, 101–101.5°; picrate·H_2O 185–187°; 2 H_3PO_4·H_2O 141–142°	50, 61
4-N-2'-Diethylaminoethyl-p-anisidino-	184–188°/0.007 mm; dipicrate 173–174°	53
4-N-2'-Diethylaminoethyl-p-bromoanilino-	200–204°/0.01 mm; dipicrate 201.5–203°	53
4-N-2'-Diethylaminoethyl-p-chloroanilino-	192–196°/0.005 mm; dipicrate 201.5–202°	53
4-N-2'-Diethylaminoethyl-p-fluoroanilino-	178–180°/0.008 mm; dipicrate 201.5–202°	53
4-N-2'-Diethylaminoethyl-p-toluidino-	174–176°/0.005 mm; dipicrate 201–202°	53
2-2'-(2-Diethylaminoethoxy)-ethylamino-	40°, 196–200°/0.01 mm; dimethiodide·H_2O 129–131°	50
4-2'-Diethylaminoethylamino-	124°	7, 50, 54
4-N-2'-Diethylaminoethyl-anilino-	200–205°/0.3 mm; HCl 142.5–143.5°; 2 HCl 231–233°; dipicrate 169–170°	53
4-3'-Diethylaminopropylamino-	69–70°; picrate 197–200°	80, 180
4-2',3'-Dihydroxypropylamino-	187–188°; HCl 209–210°	62
4-N-2'-Dimethylaminoethyl-p-anisidino-	186–190°/0.008 mm; dipicrate 193–194°	53
4-N-2'-Dimethylaminoethyl-p-bromoanilino-	176–180°/0.005 mm; dipicrate 222.5–224°	53
4-N-2'-Dimethylaminoethyl-p-chloroanilino-	170–174°/0.003 mm; dipicrate 209.5–211°	53

(Table continued)

TABLE VII.4 (*continued*)

Quinazoline	M.p. (°c)	References
4-N-2'-Dimethylaminoethyl-N-ethylamino-	130–135°/0.02 mm; picrate 226–228° (dec.)	195
4-N-2'-Dimethylaminoethyl-p-fluoroanilino-	172–176°/0.01 mm; dipicrate 217–218°	53
4-N-2'-Dimethylaminoethyl-N-isopropylamino-	138–142°/0.03 mm; picrate 218–221° (dec.)	195
4-N-2'-Dimethylaminoethyl-N-methylamino-	125–128°/0.001 mm; picrate 207–209°	195
4-N-2'-Dimethylaminoethyl-N-propylamino-	136–138°/0.03 mm; picrate 190–192°	195
4-N-2'-Dimethylaminoethyl-p-toluidino-	HCl 201–202°; dipicrate 199–200.5°	53
4-N-2'-Dimethylaminoethyl-anilino-	200–204°/0.8 mm; HCl 194–194.5°; 2 HCl 215–216°; dipicrate 216°	53
4-3'-Dimethylaminopropyl-amino-	64–65°; dipicrate 215–217°	50
4-p-Ethoxycarbonylanilino-	HCl 253°	200
4-Ethylamino-	148–149°	210
4-(1'-Ethylpyrrolidin-3'-ylmethylamino)-	79–81°	5
4-(2'-Hydroxy-1'-hydroxy-methyl-1'-methyl)ethyl-amino-	213–215° (dec.) (allotrope 197°)	62
4-2'-Hydroxyethylamino-	174–175°	62
4-(1'-β-Hydroxyethylpyrrolidin-3'-ylmethylamino)-	139–141°	5
4-(2'-Methyl-5'-nitro)anilino-	210–215°	70
4-N-(1'-Methylpyrrolidin-3'-ylmethyl)-N-methylamino-	170–180°/0.25 mm	5
4-(1'-Methylpyrrolidin-3'-ylmethylamino)-	110.5–111.5°	5
4-Morpholino-	95–96°; picrate 204–205°	62, 80
4-p-Nitrophenlsulphonamido-	214–219°	21
4-Phenethylamino-	167–171°; HCl 183–186°; picrate 192–194°	201

(*Table continued*)

TABLE VII.4 (*continued*)

Quinazoline	M.p. (°c)	References
4-(1'-Phenethylpyrrolidin-3'-ylmethylamino)-	107–108.5°	5
4-*p*-Phenetidino-	HCl 235°	200
4-Piperidino-	139–140°/5 mm; HCl 230°; picrate 193–194°	62, 84
4-3'-Piperidinopropylamino-	H₂O 106°	50
4-Sulphanilamido-	253–255°	21
4-1'-(1,2,3,4-Tetrahydroquinolinyl)-	130.5–131.5°	56

TABLE VII.5.   4-Substituted-aminoquinazolines with a Substituent in Position 2.

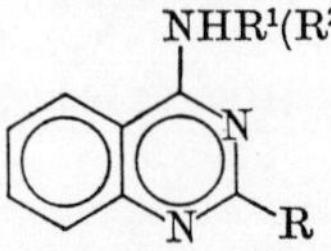

$$NHR^1(R^2R^3)$$

Quinazoline	M.p. (°c)	References
2-*o*-Aminophenyl-4-(2'-cyano-5'-methoxy)anilino-	201–203°	51
2-*o*-Aminophenyl-4-(2'-cyano-5'-methyl)anilino-	195–196° (dec.)	51
2-*o*-Aminophenyl-4-(2'-methoxycarbonyl-3'-methyl)anilino-	152–153°	51
2-*o*-Aminophenyl-4-(2'-methoxycarbonyl-5'-methyl)anilino-	182–183°	51
2-*o*-Aminophenyl-4-*o*-methoxycarbonylanilino-	192–193°; HCl 176–178°	51
4-Anilino-2-2'-furyl-	115°	52
4-Anilino-2-trichloromethyl-	151–153°	204
4-*o*-Anisidino-2-*o*-chlorophenyl-	HCl 156°	49
4-*o*-Anisidino-2-*p*-chlorophenyl-	HCl 270°	49
4-*p*-Anisidino-2-*o*-chlorophenyl-	148°	49
4-*p*-Anisidino-2-*p*-chlorophenyl-	158°	49
4-*p*-Anisidino-2-2'-furyl-	110°	52
4-Benzylamino-2-*o*-chlorophenyl-	188°	49
4-*p*-Benzylanilino-2-*p*-chlorophenyl-	HCl 300°	49

(Table continued)

TABLE VII.5 *(continued)*

Quinazoline	M.p. (°c)	References
4-*p*-Bromoanilino-2-*o*-chloro-phenyl-	197°	49
4-*p*-Bromoanilino-2-*p*-chloro-phenyl-	200°	49
4-Butylamino-2-*N*-butylamino-formamidino-	186–187°	222
4-*o*-Carboxyanilino-2-*o*-nitro-phenyl-	309–311°; HCl 253–255°	51
4-*o*-Carboxyanilino-2-phenyl-	255° (dec.)	221
4-*p*-Chloroanilino-2-*o*-chloro-phenyl-	HCl 257°	49
4-*p*-Chloroanilino-2-*p*-chloro-phenyl-	197°	49
2-*o*-Chlorophenyl-4-*N*-ethyl-*o*-anisidino-	HCl 174°	49
2-*o*-Chlorophenyl-4-*N*-ethyl-*p*-anisidino-	HCl 282–284°	49
2-*p*-Chlorophenyl-4-*N*-ethyl-*p*-anisidino-	124°	49
2-*o*-Chlorophenyl-4-*N*-ethyl-*o*-toluidino-	120°	49
2-*o*-Chlorophenyl-4-*N*-ethyl-*p*-toluidino-	HCl 168.5°	49
2-*p*-Chlorophenyl-4-*N*-ethyl-*p*-toluidino-	181°	49
2-*o*-Chlorophenyl-4-*p*-hydroxy-anilino-	HCl 258°	49
2-*p*-Chlorophenyl-4-*p*-hydroxy-anilino-	HCl 296°	49
2-*o*-Chlorophenyl-4-*N*-methyl-*o*-toluidino-	HCl 163°	49
2-*p*-Chlorophenyl-4-*N*-methyl-*o*-toluidino-	168°	49
2-*o*-Chlorophenyl-4-*o*-phenetidino-	146°	49
2-*o*-Chlorophenyl-4-*p*-phenetidino-	HCl 234–236°	49
2-*p*-Chlorophenyl-4-*o*-phenetidino-	177°	49
2-*p*-Chlorophenyl-4-*p*-phenetidino-	105°	49
2-*o*-Chlorophenyl-4-*o*-toluidino-	HCl 174°	49
2-*o*-Chlorophenyl-4-*p*-toluidino-	170°	49
2-*p*-Chlorophenyl-4-*o*-toluidino-	145°	49
2-*p*-Chlorophenyl-4-*p*-toluidino-	148°	49
4-*o*-Cyanoanilino-2-*o*-nitrophenyl-	186–187°	51

(Table continued)

TABLE VII.5 (*continued*)

Quinazoline	M.p. (°c)	References
4-(2′-Cyano-5′-methoxy)anilino-2-*o*-nitrophenyl-	197–198°; HCl 161–162° (dec.)	51
4-(2′-Cyano-5′-methyl)anilino-2-*o*-nitrophenyl-	197–199°; HCl 192–193° (dec.)	51
4-(Di-2-hydroxyethyl)amino-2-trichloromethyl-	148–150°	74
4-(4′-Diethylamino-1′-methyl)-butylamino-2-2′-furyl-	picrate 179°	59
4-(4′-Diethylamino-1′-methyl)-butylamino-2-phenyl-	187–188°/0.05–0.06 mm; 2 H₃PO₄·H₂O 221–224° (dec.); dipicrate 163–163.5°	61
4-Dimethylamino-6-nitro-2-trichloromethyl-	117–118°	74
4-Diphenylamino-2-phenyl-	156°; hexachlorostannate 276–279°	98
2-2′-Furyl-4-*p*-phenetidino-	105°	52
2-2′-Furyl-4-*p*-toluidino-	133°	52
4-2′-Hydroxyethylamino-2-methyl-	164–166° (remelts at 174.5–176°)	81
4-(2′-Methoxycarbonyl-3′-methyl)-anilino-2-*o*-nitrophenyl-	196–197°; HCl 173–175° (dec.)	51
4-(2′-Methoxycarbonyl-5′-methyl)-anilino-2-*o*-nitrophenyl-	214–215°; HCl 217–219° (dec.)	51
4-*o*-Methoxycarbonylanilino-2-*o*-nitrophenyl-	187–188°; HCl 232–233°	51
2-Methyl-4-(1′-methylpyrrolidin-3′-ylmethylamino)-	123.5–125°	5
2-Methyl-4-sulphanilamido-	282–284°	79
4-Methylamino-2-*o*-nitrophenyl-	169–171°; picrate 279–281°	68
4-Methylamino-2-trichloromethyl-	155°	204
4-Morpholino-6-nitro-2-trichloromethyl-	214°	74

TABLE VII.6.   4-Substituted-aminoquinazolines with Substituents in the
Benzene Ring.

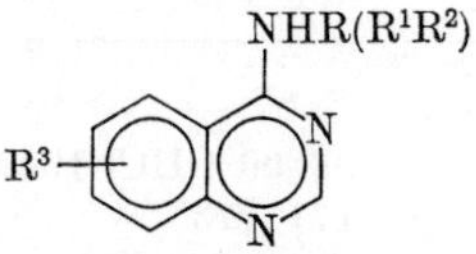

$$NHR(R^1R^2)$$

R³ ⟨structure⟩

Quinazoline	M.p. (°c)	References
4-Acetamido-6-nitro-	262–263° (dec.)	78
4-Acetamido-7-nitro-	240–242° (dec.)	78
4-(4′-Amino-2′,6′-dihydroxy-pyrimidin-5′-ylamino)-7-nitro-	$\frac{1}{2}H_2O > 340°$	194
4-Anilino-6-methyl-	217°	106
4-Anilino-6-nitro-	236–237.5° (dec.); 1-methiodide 247–248° (dec.) and 254–256° (dec.) (two forms); 1-methyl tosylate 249–250°	78
4-Anilino-7-nitro-	251–252° (dec.); 1-methiodide 256–257° (dec.); 1-methyl tosylate 257–258° (dec.)	78
4-p-Anisidino-6-nitro-	203–205°	194
4-p-Anisidino-7-nitro-	236–238°	194
4-Benzylamino-8-hydroxy-	155°	192, 193
4-Butylamino-8-hydroxy-	127°	192, 193
4-Butylamino-7-nitro-	142–144°	179
4-p-Chlorobenzylamino-8-hydroxy-	220°	192, 193
4-3′-Dibutylaminopropylamino-7-nitro-	78–80°; HCl 180.5–182°	50
4-(4′-Diethylamino-1′-methyl)-butylamino-8-hydroxy-	picrate 127°	193
4-(4′-Diethylamino-1′-methyl)-butylamino-6-nitro-	126–127°	215
4-(4′-Diethylamino-1′-methyl)-butylamino-7-nitro-	107–109°; HCl 176–177°	50
4-3′-(2-Diethylaminoethoxy)-propylamino-7-nitro-	69–71°; H₂O 70–71°; HCl 142–143°	50
4-2′-Diethylaminoethylamino-7-nitro-	151–151.5°; HCl 213–214° (dec.)	50

(*Table continued*)

TABLE VII.6 *(continued)*

Quinazoline	M.p. (°c)	References
4-3′-Diethylaminopropylamino-7-nitro-	98–99°; HCl 194.5–195.5°	50
4-Dimethylamino-7-nitro-	171–173°	179
4-3′-Dimethylaminopropyl-amino-7-nitro-	132–132.5°; 2 HCl 238–239°	50
4-Dodecylamino-8-hydroxy-	78–79°	193
4-Ethylamino-7-nitro-	195–197°	179
4-Heptylamino-8-hydroxy-	137°	192, 193
4-Hexylamino-8-hydroxy-	142°	192, 193
8-Hydroxy-4-isopentylamino-	112°	193
8-Hydroxy-4-*p*-methoxybenzyl-amino-	162°	192, 193
8-Hydroxy-4-morpholino-	141°	193
8-Hydroxy-4-octylamino-	119°	192, 193
8-Hydroxy-4-pentylamino-	112°	193
4-Isopropylamino-7-nitro-	161–163°	179
6-Methyl-4-(1′-methylpyrrolidin-3′-ylmethylamino)-	116–117.5°	5
4-(6′-Methyl-3′-quinolylamino)-6-nitro-	294–295°	194
4-(6′-Methyl-3′-quinolylamino)-7-nitro-	337–338°	194
4-Methylamino-7-nitro-	245–246°	179
6-Nitro-4-*m*-nitroanilino-	270–271°	194
6-Nitro-4-*p*-nitroanilino-	319–320° (dec.)	194
7-Nitro-4-*m*-nitroanilino-	H_2O 284–285°	194
7-Nitro-4-*p*-nitroanilino-	291–292° (dec.)	194
7-Nitro-4-3′-piperidinopropyl-amino-	139–140°; HCl 200–201°	50
6-Nitro-4-5′-quinolylamino-	H_2O 282–283° (dec.)	194
6-Nitro-4-6′-quinolylamino-	333–335° (dec.)	194
7-Nitro-4-5′-quinolylamino-	301–302° (dec.)	194
7-Nitro-4-6′-quinolylamino-	2 HCl 319–320° (dec.)	194

TABLE VII.7.   4-Substituted-aminoquinazolines with Substituents in
Both Rings.

$$NHR^1(R^2R^3)$$

R⁴ ─ [quinazoline structure] N
N ─ R

Quinazoline	M.p. (°c)	References
4-Anilino-7-chloro-2-2′-furyl-	170°	214
4-Anilino-2-2′-furyl-6-methyl-	180°	59
4-p-Anisidino-2-2′-furyl-6-methyl-	156°	59
4-(4′-Diethylamino-1′-methyl)-butylamino-2-2′-furyl-6-methyl-	144°, 280°/9 mm; picrate 180°	59
4-Dimethylamino-2-methyl-6-nitro-	188–189°	82
4-Dimethylamino-6-nitro-2-trichloromethyl-	117–118°	74
4-Ethylamino-2-methyl-6-nitro-	222–223°; 1-methiodide 259–260° (dec.); 1-methyl tosylate 245–255° (dec.)	82
4-Furfurylamino-6-nitro-2-trichloromethyl-	140°	74
2-2′-Furyl-6-methyl-4-p-phenetidino-	126°	59
2-2′-Furyl-6-methyl-4-p-toluidino-	140°	59
4-2′-Hydroxyethylamino-6-nitro-2-trichloromethyl-	208–210°	74
4-(bis-2-Hydroxyethyl)amino-6-nitro-2-trichloromethyl-	148–150°	74
2-Methyl-4-methylamino-6-nitro-	226–227°; 1-methyl chloride 289–290° (dec.); 1-methyl tosylate 266–268° (dec.)	82
4-Morpholino-6-nitro-2-trichloromethyl-	214°	74

TABLE VII.8.   2,4-Diaminoquinazolines with Substituents in the
Benzene Ring.

2,4-Diaminoquinazoline	M.p. (°c)	References
Unsubstituted	249–250°; 2 HCl 308°; H_2SO_4 330°; HNO_3 280°; acetate 208°; oxalate 274°; picrate 304° (dec.); diacetyl deriv. 230°	94, 95, 100
6-Bromo-	191–192°	102
6-p-Carboxyanilinomethyl-	1.5 H_2O 283° (dec.)	106
6-p-Ethoxycarbonylanilino- methyl-	162–164° (dec.)	106
5-Ethyl-	165–190°	111
6-Ethyl-	214–215°	101, 102
5-Isopropyl-8-methyl-	223–224°	102
5-Methyl-	212–213°	102, 111
6-Methyl-	256°; HNO_3 293°	102, 106
8-Methyl-	209°	101
6,7-Dimethyl-	191°	101, 102
6,8-Dimethyl-	291°	102
5,6,8-Trimethyl-	198–200°	102
6-Propyl-	194–195°	102
5,6-Tetramethylene-	230°, 240°	102, 111
5,6-Trimethylene-	288°	102

TABLE VII.9.   2,4-Bis Substituted-aminoquinazolines.

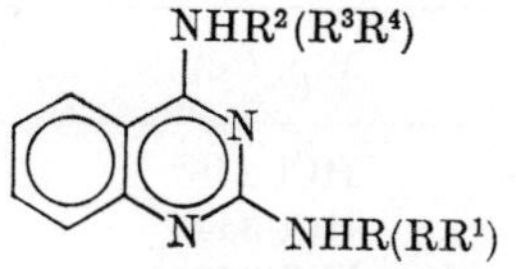

NHR²(R³R⁴)

NHR(RR¹)

Quinazoline	M.p. (°c)	References
2-(6'-Acetamido-2'-benzothiazol-ylamino)-4-p-2'-diethylamino-ethoxyanilino-	166–170°; HCl 292–297°	109
2-(6'-Acetamido-2'-benzo-thiazolylamino)-4-2'-diethyl-aminoethylamino-	252–257°; HCl 317–319°	109
2-(6'-Acetoxy-2'-benzo-thiazolylamino)-4-2'-diethyl-aminoethylamino-	168–169°; HCl 273–275°	109
2,4-Dianilino-	125°, 152°; H_2O 65°; HCl 317°; H_2SO_4 295°; HNO_3 223°; acetate 148°; oxalate 253°; picrate 275°; diacetyl deriv. 148–150°, 152°	93, 94, 104
2-Anilino-4-3'-diethylamino-propylamino-	112–114°	7, 107
2-Anilino-3,4-dihydro-3-phenyl-4-phenylimino-	α form 171°; β form 184°	13
2-p-Anisidino-4-3'-diethyl-aminopropylamino-	114–115°	7,8,107,197
4-p-Anisidino-2-3'-diethyl-aminopropylamino-	2 HCl 228–230°	9
2-2'-Benzimidazolylamino-4-2'-diethylaminoethylamino-	224–225°	109
2-2'-Benzothiazolylamino-4-2'-diethylaminoethylamino-	216–217°; HCl 305–307°	109
3-2'-Benzothiazolylamino-4-N-2'-diethylaminoethylanilino-	168–169°; HCl 278–280°	109
2-(6'-Benzyl-2'-benzothiazolyl-amino)-4-2'-diethylamino-ethylamino-	216–218°	108
2-(6'-Bromo-2'-naphthylamino)-4-2'-diethylaminoethylamino-	2 HCl 284–285°	7, 107
2-(4'-p-Bromophenyl-2'-thiazolylamino)-4-(3'-diethyl-amino-1'-methyl)propyl-amino-	219–221°; HCl 312–314°	109

(*Table continued*)

TABLE VII.9 *(continued)*

Quinazoline	M.p. (°c)	References
2,4-Bis-o-carboxyanilino-	HCl 278°	104
2,4-Bis-m-carboxyanilino-	HCl 344°	104
2,4-Bis-p-carboxyanilino-	HCl 347°	104
4-p-Chloroanilino-2-3'-dibutyl- aminopropylamino-	2 HCl·2 H$_2$O 125–126°	9
4-p-Chloroanilino-2-2'-diethyl- aminoethylamino-	dipicrate 230–232°	9
4-p-Chloroanilino-2-3'-diethyl- aminopropylamino-	107–108°	9
4-p-Chloroanilino-2-3'-piperi- dinopropylamino-	129°; 2 HCl 238–240°; picrate 228–229°	9
2-(6'-Chloro-2'-benzothiazolyl- amino)-4-2'-diethylamino- ethylamino-	210–211°; HCl 310–311°; Me$_2$SO$_4$ 302–304°	109
2-(6'-Cyano-2'-benzothiazolyl- amino)-4-2'-diethylamino- ethylamino-	289–290°; HCl 305–307°; Me$_2$SO$_4$ 299–300°	109
2-(1',5'-Dichloro-3'-naphthyl- amino)-4-2'-diethylamino- ethylamino-	2 HCl 284°	7, 107
2,4-Bisdiethylamino-	123–125°	210
2,4-Bis-2'-diethylaminoethyl- amino-	230–232°/0.1 mm; 3 HCl·H$_2$O 191–192°; tripicrate 193–194° and 213–214° (dimorphic)	9
4-2'-Diethylaminoethylamino- 2-3'-diethylaminopropyl- amino-	206.8°/0.02 mm; tripicrate 180°	7
4-2'-Diethylaminoethylamino- 2-(4',6'-dimethyl-2'- benzothiazolylamino)-	210–213°	108, 223
4-2'-Diethylaminoethylamino- 2-(4',7'-dimethyl-2'- benzothiazolylamino)-	205–207°; HCl 339–342°	109
4-2'-Diethylaminoethylamino- 2-(4',5'-diphenyl-2'- thiazolylamino)-	198–202°	108, 109
4-2'-Diethylaminoethylamino- 2-N-ethylanilino-	110°	7, 107, 197

(Table continued)

TABLE VII.9 (*continued*)

Quinazoline	M.p. (°c)	References
4-2′-Diethylaminoethylamino-2-(6′-methoxy-2′-benzothiazolylamino)-	186–187°; HCl 293–295°	109
4-2′-Diethylaminoethylamino-2-(5′-methyl-2′-benzimidazolylamino)-	225–227°	109
4-2′-Diethylaminoethylamino-2-(4′-methyl-2′-benzothiazolylamino)-	189–191°; HCl 296–298°	109
4-2′-Diethylaminoethylamino-4-(6′-methyl-2′-benzothiazolylamino)-	239–241°	109
4-2′-Diethylaminoethylamino-2-(6′-methylsulphonyl-2′-benzothiazolylamino)-	167–169°	108
4-2′-Diethylaminoethylamino-2-p-methylthioanilino-	HCl 130–131°	7, 107, 197
4-2′-Diethylaminoethylamino-2-2′-naphthylamino-	126°	7, 107, 108, 197
4-2′-Diethylaminoethylamino-2-p-nitroanilino-	2 HCl·4 H$_2$O 286–287°	7, 107, 197
4-2′-Diethylaminoethylamino-2-(6′-nitro-2′-benzothiazolylamino)-	304–306°	109
4-2′-Diethylaminoethylamino-2-(6′-phenoxy-2′-benzothiazolylamino)-	197.5–198°	108
4-2′-Diethylaminoethylamino-2-(4′-phenyl-2′-benzothiazolylamino)-	172–174°	109
2-2′-Diethylaminoethylamino-4-3′-piperidinopropyl-	2 HCl 267–268°	197
4-2′-Diethylaminoethylamino-2-(6′-sulphamoyl-2′-benzothiazolylamino)-	267–269°	108
4-2′-Diethylaminoethylamino-2-2′-thiazolylamino-	142–143°; HCl 297–298°	109
4-2′-Diethylaminoethylamino-2-(4′-p-tolyl-2′-thiazolylamino)-	181–183°	108, 109
4-N-2′-Diethylaminoethylanilino-2-(6′-methyl-2′-benzothiazolylamino)-	180–182°	109

(*Table continued*)

TABLE VII.9 *(continued)*

Quinazoline	M.p. (°c)	References
4-2'-β-Diethylaminoethylthio-ethylamino-2-(6'-methyl-2'-thiazolylamino)-	191–193°	108, 109
4-(3'-Diethylamino-1'-methyl)-propylamino-2-(6'-methyl-2'-benzothiazolylamino)-	142–143°; HCl 295–296°	109
2,4-Bis-3'-diethylaminopropyl-amino-	206–208°/0.2 mm; tripicrate 180°	7
4-3'-Diethylaminopropylamino-2-(6'-methyl-2'-benzothiazolylamino)-	202–204°	109
4-3'-Diethylaminopropylamino-2-2'-naphthylamino-	141°	7, 107, 108, 197
4-3'-Diethylaminopropylamino-2-*p*-toluidino-	94°	7, 107, 108, 197
4-(3'-Dimethylamino-1'-methyl)-propylamino-2-(6'-methyl-2'-benzothiazolylamino)-	142–143°	108
1,2,3,4-Tetrahydro-3-phenyl-1-phenylcarbamoyl-2,4-bisphenylimino-	84–86°	13
2-2'-Hydroxyethylamino-4-morpholino-	179°	105
2-2'-Hydroxyethylamino-4-piperidino-	152°	105
4-2'-Hydroxyethylamino-2-piperidino-	130°	105
2-2'-Hydroxyethylamino-4-pyrrolidin-1'-yl-	167°	105
4-2'-Hydroxyethylamino-2-pyrrolidin-1'-yl-	155°	105
2,4-Bis-*o*-methoxycarbonyl-anilino-	2 HCl 261°	104
2-(6'-Methyl-2'-benzothiazolyl-amino)-4-2'-piperidinoethyl-amino-	204–206°; HCl 343–344°	109
2,4-Bismethylamino-	HCl 312°; picrate 232°	100
2,4-Dimorpholino-	177°	105
2-Morpholino-4-piperidino-	142°	105
4-Morpholino-2-piperidino-	127°	105

(Table continued)

TABLE VII.9 *(continued)*

Quinazoline	M.p. (°c)	References
2-Morpholino-4-pyrrolidin-1'-yl-	170°	105
4-Morpholino-2-pyrrolidin-1'-yl-	126°	105
2,4-Dipiperidino-	131°	105
2-Piperidino-4-pyrrolidin-1'-yl-	131°	105
4-Piperidino-2-pyrrolidin-1'-yl-	111°	105
2,4-Dipyrrolidin-1'-yl-	127°	105

TABLE VII.10. 4-Substituted-amino-2-*p*-chloroanilinoquinazolines.

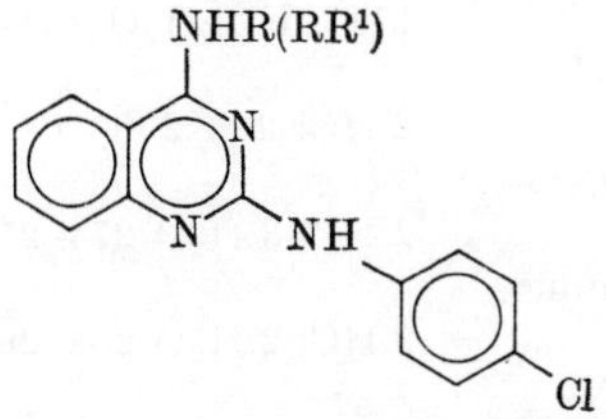

2-*p*-Chloroanilinoquinazoline	M.p. (°c)	References
4-2'-Acetamidoethylamino-	183–184°; HCl 278–280°	7, 8, 107
4-2'-Aminoethylamino-	142°; 2 HCl·1.5 H$_2$O 314–316°	7, 8, 107
4-6'-Aminohexylamino-	2 HCl·H$_2$O 261–263°	7, 8
4-5'-Aminopentylamino-	2 HCl·1.5 H$_2$O 278°	7
4-3'-Butylaminopropylamino-	2 HCl 254–256°	7, 8, 197
4-*p*-Chloroanilino-	185°; HCl 340–345°	7, 9
4-4'-Dibutylaminobutylamino-	2 HCl 181°	7, 8
4-3'-Dibutylaminopropylamino-	2 HCl·0.5 H$_2$O 193–194°	7, 8
4-(4'-Diethylamino-1'-methyl)-butylamino-	2 HCl·2 H$_2$O 122° (remelts at 250–252°)	7, 8
4-4'-Diethylaminobutylamino-	2 HCl 260–262°	7, 8
4-2'-Diethylaminoethyl-*N*-methylamino-	2 H$_2$O 76°	7, 107, 197
4-3'-(2-Diethylaminoethyl-*N*-methylamino)propylamino-	3 HI·2 H$_2$O 229°	7, 8
4-2'-Diethylaminoethylamino-	111–112°; 2 HCl·2 H$_2$O 254–255°; acetyl deriv. 2 HCl 248–249°	7, 8, 9, 107, 108, 197
4-3'-Diethylaminopropylamino-	127°; 2 HCl·2 H$_2$O 274°	7, 8, 107, 108, 197

(Table continued)

TABLE VII.10 (continued)

2-p-Chloroanilinoquinazoline	M.p. (°c)	References
4-4'-Dimethylaminobutylamino-	2 HCl· H$_2$O 261°	7, 8
4-2'-Dimethylaminoethylamino-	2 HCl·2.5 H$_2$O 267–268°	7, 8, 107, 197
4-6'-Dimethylaminohexylamino-	2 HCl·1.5 H$_2$O 156–158° (remelts at 236–238°)	7, 8
4-5'-Dimethylaminopentyl-amino-	2 HCl 278°	7, 8
4-3'-Dimethylaminopropyl-amino-	2 HCl·1.5 H$_2$O 256–258°	7, 8, 107, 197
4-2'-Hydroxyethylamino-	174°; HCl·H$_2$O 286–287°	7
4-3'-N-Isopropyl-N-methyl-aminopropylamino-	2 HCl 268–269°	8
4-(1'-Methyl-2'-piperidino)-ethylamino-	2 HCl·3 H$_2$O 274–275°	7
4-3'-N-Methyl-N-propylamino-propylamino-	2 HCl·2 H$_2$O 268–269°	7
4-3'-Methylaminopropyl-N-methylamino-	2 HCl 137–138° (remelts at 220–250°)	8
4-3'-Methylaminopropylamino-	2 HCl·2.5 H$_2$O 137–138°	7
4-3'-N-Piperazinopropylamino-	2 HCl 283–286°	8
4-2'-Piperidinoethyl-N-methylamino-	2 HCl 274–275°	8
4-2'-Piperidinoethylamino-	2 HCl·0.5 H$_2$O 276–278°	7, 8
4-2'-Piperidinopropylamino-	2 HCl 283–286°	7, 8
4-3'-Piperidinopropylamino-	2 HCl·0.5 H$_2$O 285–286°	7, 8, 107, 197
4-2'-(Pyrrolidin-1-yl)ethyl-amino-	2 HCl·2.5 H$_2$O 283–285°	7, 8

TABLE VII.11. 2,4-Diamino- (and Substituted-amino-) quinazolines with
Substituents in the Benzene Ring.

$$NH_2(R^2R^3)$$

$$R^4 \qquad NH_2(RR^1)$$

Quinazoline	M.p. (°c)	References
2-Amino-4-anilino-7,8-benzo-	230°	95
4-Amino-2-anilino-6-methyl-	190°; 2 HCl 250°	106
2,4-Dianilino-7,8-benzo-	183°; HCl 322°; picrate 282°; acetyl deriv. 248°	95
2-Anilino-7,8-benzo-4-p-chloroanilino-	310°	95
2,4-Dianilino-6-methyl-	125°; HCl 313°	106
4-Anilino-8-methyl-2-o-toluidino-	140–142°; HCl 310°	96
2,4-Bisbenzamido-6-bromomethyl-	213°	106
2,4-Bisbenzamido-6-p-ethoxycarbonylanilinomethyl-	120–123° (dec.)	106
2,4-Bisbenzamido-6-methyl-	198°	106
2,4-Bisbenzylamino-6-methyl-	147°	106
8-Methyl-2,4-di-o-toluidino-	138–140°; HCl 240–242°; picrate 268–270°	96
7-Methyl-2,4-di-m-toluidino-	HCl 256–257°; H$_3$PO$_4$ 252–254°; picrate 290–291°	97
7-Methyl-2,4-di-p-toluidino-	HCl 320–321°; picrate 289°; acetyl deriv. 262°	97

TABLE VII.12. Quinazolines with an Amino or Substituted-amino Group in the Benzene Ring.

$(RR^1)H_2N$ —

Quinazoline	M.p. (°c)	References
8-Acetamido-	H$_2$O 161–162°	55
6-Acetylsulphanilamido-	290–292° (dec.)	186
8-Acetylsulphanilamido-	215.5–216°	186
5-Amino-	192.5–193.5°	186
6-Amino-	213.5–214°	55
7-Amino-	190.5–191°	186
8-Amino-	150–150.5°	55
8-6′-Diethylaminohexylamino-	170–173°/0.1 mm; oxalate 90–92°	55

TABLE VII.13. 4-Alkylamino-2-*p*-chloroanilinoquinazolines with Substituents (including Amino Groups) in the Benzene Ring.

2-*p*-Chloroanilinoquinazolines	M.p. (°c)	References
6-Amino-4-2′-diethylamino-ethylamino-	3 HCl·5 H$_2$O 180° (remelts at 286°)	107, 181, 197
7-Amino-4-2′-diethylamino-ethylamino-	2 HCl·1.5 H$_2$O 295–296°	181
6,7-Benzo-4-2′-diethylamino-ethylamino-	2 HCl·3 H$_2$O 286–287°	107, 181, 197
6-Chloro-4-2′-diethylamino-ethylamino-	2 HCl 282°	197
4-2′-Diethylaminoethylamino-7-methyl-	2 HCl 264°	107, 197
4-2′-Diethylaminoethylamino-6-nitro-	200–201°; 2 HCl·1.5 H$_2$O 266°	107, 181, 197
4-2′-Diethylaminoethylamino-7-nitro-	159.5–160°; 2 HCl 264°	181, 197

TABLE VII.14. 4-Amino- (and Substituted-amino-) quinazolines with an Amino (and Substituted-amino) Group in the Benzene Ring.

$$NH_2(R^1R^2)$$

$(R^4R^3)H_2N-$ [quinazoline structure] $H(R)$

Quinazoline	M.p. (°C)	References
7-Acetamido-4-amino-	349–356°	179
7-Acetamido-4-butylamino-	303–304° (dec.)	179
6-m-Amidinophenylazoamino- 4-amino-2-methyl-	1-methyl chloride·HCl·3 H_2O 237–238°; 1-methyl sulphate· H_2O 205–208°	191
4,6-Diamino-	1-methyl chloride 344–346° (dec.)	82
4,7-Diamino-	253–254°	179
4,8-Diamino-	210–212°	179
4-Amino-6-(2′-amino-4′-methyl- pyrimidin-6′-ylamino)-2- methyl-	dimethyl chloride· 2 H_2O > 360° (dec.)	182
6-Amino-4-p-aminoanilino-	~260°	70
4-Amino-6-(2′-aminopyrimidin- 4′-ylamino)-	1-methiodide 278–280°; 1,1′-dimethyl chloride 348–350°	212
6-Amino-4-anilino-	1-methiodide 287–288°	78
7-Amino-4-anilino-	1-methiodide 266–268°	78
7-Amino-4-butylamino-	150–152°	179
4,8-Diamino-6-chloro-	258–259°	179
7-Amino-4-diethylamino-	89–91°	179
6-Amino-4-(4′-diethylamino-1′- methyl)butylamino-	89–90°; H_2SO_4 168–169°, 82; picrate 204–205°	215
7-Amino-4-ethylamino-	99–100°	179
4-Amino-6-m-guanidinophenyl- azoamino-	1-methyl chloride·HCl·2.75 H_2O 245°	82
4-Amino-6-m-guanidino- phenylazoamino-2-methyl-	1-methyl chloride·HCl·3 H_2O 241°	82

(*Table continued*)

13+Q.

TABLE VII.14 (*continued*)

Quinazoline	M.p. (°c)	References
4-Amino-6-*p*-guanidinophenyl-azoamino-2-methyl-	1-methyl chloride·HCl·0.5 H_2O 257–260°	80
7-Amino-4-isopropylamino-	2 HCl 239–240°	179
4,6-Diamino-2-methyl-	2 H_2O 244–246°; 1-methyl chloride·H_2O 319–320° (dec.)	82, 182
6-Amino-2-methyl-4-methyl-amino-	1-methyl chloride·1.25 H_2O 313–315°	82
7-Amino-4-methylamino-	221°	179
6-*m*-Guanidinophenylazoamino-2-methyl-4-methylamino-	1-methyl chloride·2.5 H_2O 243–244°	82

TABLE VII.15.   2-Amino (and Substituted-amino)-3,4-dihydro-4-oxo-quinazolines (including 3-Amino Derivatives).

3,4-Dihydro-4-oxoquinazoline	M.p. (°c)	References
2-*N*-Acetylisopropylamino-3-isopropyl-	140°	40
2-Amino-	> 280°, 306–308°, > 350°	12, 15, 36, 85, 115
2-Amino-6-bromo-3-ethyl-	228°	42
2-Amino-3-guanidino-	> 280°	229
2-Amino-3-methyl-	240°	42
2-Amino-6-methyl-	> 360°	106
2-Amino-3-phenyl-	237–238°	12, 38
2-Anilino-	256°, 261°	6, 12, 41, 227
2-Anilino-3-*p*-chlorophenyl-	320°; HCl 190–192°	41
2-Anilino-3-methyl-	206–207°	88
2-Anilino-3-phenyl-	163°, 283–285°; 1-methyl deriv. 174°; 1-phenyl-carbamoyl deriv. 127°; HCl 279–280°; picrate 276–278°	13, 41

(*Table continued*)

TABLE VII.15 (*continued*)

3,4-Dihydro-4-oxoquinazoline	M.p. (°c)	References
2-Anilino-3-o-tolyl-	159–161°; HCl 282–284°	41
2-Anilino-3-m-tolyl-	302–304°; HCl 280–282°	41
2-Anilino-3-p-tolyl-	241–243°; HCl 281–282°	41
2-p-Anisidino-	265–266°	7, 8
2-Benzamido-6-methyl-	205°	106
2-Butylamino-	184–186°	15
2-Carboxymethylamino-	220–240° (dec.)	16
7-Chloro-2-phenylsulphonamido-	284.5–286°	219
2-p-Chloroanilino-	280–282°; HCl 277°	7
2-Cyanamino-	306–307°	37
3-Cyclohexyl-2-cyclohexylamino-	122°	40
2-4′-Dibutylaminobutylamino-	103–104°	9
2-2′-Diethylaminoethylamino-	H$_2$O 96–98°	9
2-3′-Diethylaminopropylamino-	185–190°/0.001 mm; H$_2$O 96–97°	9
2-(4′-Diethylamino-1′-methyl)-butylamino-	177.5–181°	10
2-Ethoxycarbonylamino-	163°	39
2-Guanidino-	316–317°; H$_2$SO$_4$ 305°	37
2-o-Methoxycarbonylamino-	290–296°	220
3-Isopropyl-2-isopropylamino-	81°	40
2-Methylamino-3-t-butylamino-	132°	40
2-N-Methylanilino-3-phenyl-	123°; 1-methiodide 174°	13
2-Morpholino-	237°	15, 105
2-Morpholino-3-phenyl-	168°	11
3-Phenyl-2-piperidino-	154°	11
2-N′-Phenylguanidino-	242°	37
2-Piperidino-	270°	105
2-3′-Piperidinopropylamino-	0.5 H$_2$O 117–119°	9
2-Pyrrolidin-1′-yl-	224°	105
2-o-Toluidino-3-o-tolyl-	157–159°	38
2-p-Toluidino-3-p-tolyl-	149°	38

TABLE VII.16.   4-Amino (and Substituted-amino)-1,2-dihydro-2-
oxoquinazolines.

$$NH_2(R^1R^2)$$

$$(R^3)H$$

$$(R)$$

1,2-Dihydro-2-oxoquinazoline	M.p. (°c)	References
4-Amino-	> 350°	85
4-Anilino-	252–254°, 265–266°; HCl 256–	
	257°; picrate 262°	88, 93
4-Anilino-7,8-benzo-	309°	95
4-Anilino-7,8-benzo-1-methyl-	235°	95
4-Anilino-1-methyl-	252°	88
4-Anilino-8-methyl-	249–252°	96
7,8-Benzo-4-p-chloroanilino-	260°	95
3,4-Dihydro-4-imino-3-phenyl-	216–218° (dec.), 224°; HCl 250°	
	(dec.)	85, 86, 88
8-Methyl-4-o-toluidino-	243°	96
6-Methyl-4-p-toluidino-	302°	97
4-Morpholino-	233°	105
4-Piperidino-	74°	105
4-Pyrrolidin-1'-yl-	290°	105

TABLE VII.17. 4-Amino (and Substituted-amino)-1,2-dihydro-2-thioquinazolines.

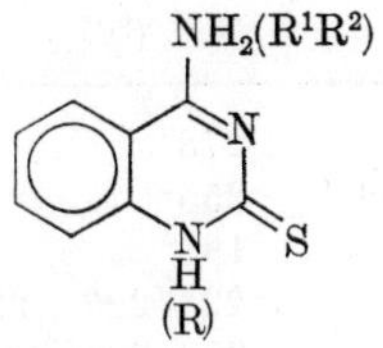

$$NH_2(R^1R^2)$$

(R)

1,2-Dihydro-2-thioquinazoline	M.p. (°c)	References
4-Amino-	300°	87
4-Anilino-	240–242°	88
4-Anilino-1-methyl-	184–186°	88
3,4-Dihydro-4-imino-3-phenyl-[a]	195–198°	88
3,4-Dihydro-4-imino-1-methyl-3-phenyl-	215–217°	88
4-(1'-Methylpyrrolidin-3'-ylmethylamino)-	223–225° (dec.)	5

[a] 3,4-Dihydro-4-methylimino-2-methylthio-3-phenylquinazoline has m.p. 135–136°.[88]

TABLE VII.18. 3,4-Dihydro-4-oxoquinazolines with Amino (and Substituted-amino) Groups in Positions 5 or 6.

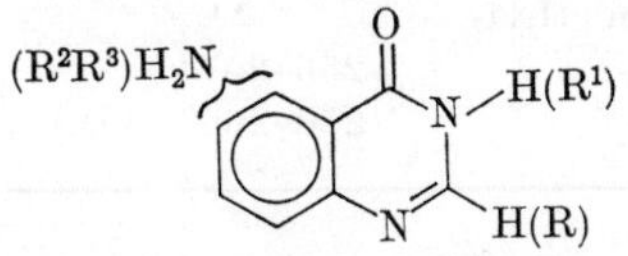

$$(R^2R^3)H_2N$$

3,4-Dihydro-4-oxoquinazoline	M.p. (°c)	References
5-Acetamido-	286–287°	171, 174
6-Acetamido-	324–326°, 335°	170, 175, 207
6-Acetamido-3-p-aminophenyl-	~280°	185
6-Acetamido-3-p-aminophenyl-2-methyl-	280°	183
6-Acetamido-3-ethyl-2-methyl-	229°	183
5-Acetamido-3-(3'-(3-hydroxy-2-piperidyl)-2'-oxo)propyl-	2 HCl·H₂O > 275° (dec.)	174
5-Acetamido-2-methyl-	> 300°	63
6-Acetamido-2-methyl-	351°	170
6-Acetamido-3-methyl-	269–271°	170, 207

(*Table continued*)

TABLE VII.18 *(continued)*

3,4-Dihydro-4-oxoquinazoline	M.p. (°c)	References
6-Acetamido-2,3-dimethyl-	278°	183
6-Acetamido-2-methyl-3-phenyl-	255°	183
6-Acetamido-2-methyl-3-propyl-	181°	183
5-Amino-	225–227°, 235–236°	171, 174
6-Amino-	302–304° (dec.); H$_2$O 318°	170, 172, 175, 180, 207
6-Amino-3-ethyl-2-methyl-	185°	170
6-Amino-3-(3′-(3-hydroxy-2-piperidyl)-2′-oxo)propyl-	2 HCl·4 H$_2$O 90°	175
5-Amino-3-(3′-(3-methoxy-2-piperidyl)-2′-oxo)propyl-	2 H$_2$O 115–120° (dec.)	174
6-Amino-3-(3′-(3-methoxy-2-piperidyl)-2′-oxo)propyl-	2 HCl·0.5 H$_2$O 118–120°	175
5-Amino-2-methyl-	295–310° (dec.)	171
6-Amino-2-methyl-	314–315°	183
6-Amino-3-methyl-	210°	170, 172, 207,
6-Amino-2,3-dimethyl-	244°	170
6-Amino-2-methyl-3-*o*-tolyl-	214–215°	173
6-*p*-Aminobenzamido-	309–311°	70
5-Benzamido-	263–264°	171
6-2′-Diethylaminoethylamino-3-methyl-	200–220°/0.1 mm; dipicrate 120°	172
6-Dimethylamino-3-*p*-dimethyl-aminophenyl-	256–257°	215
5-*N*′-Phenylureido-	250–260° (dec.)	171

TABLE VII.19. 3,4-Dihydro-4-oxoquinazolines with Amino (and Substituted-amino) Groups in Positions 7 or 8.

$$(R^2R^3)H_2N \quad \text{quinazoline with} \quad N-H(R^1) \quad R$$

3,4-Dihydro-4-oxoquinazoline	M.p. (°c)	References
7-Acetamido-	302–303°	175
7-Acetamido-3-(4'-(4-acetamido-3-ethoxyphenyl)-2'-ethoxy)phenyl-2-methyl-	239°	185
7-Acetamido-3-(4'-(4-acetamido-3-methoxyphenyl)-2'-methoxy)phenyl-2-methyl-	239°	185
7-Acetamido-3-(4'-(4-amino-3-ethoxyphenyl)-2'-ethoxy)phenyl-2-methyl-	105–110°	185
7-Acetamido-3-(4'-(4-amino-3-methoxyphenyl)-2'-methoxy)phenyl-2-methyl-	~144°	185
7-Acetamido-3-(4'-(4-amino-3-methylphenyl)-2'-methyl)phenyl-2-methyl-	120–125° (dec.)	185
7-Acetamido-3-m-aminophenyl-2-methyl-	>310°	185
7-Acetamido-3-p-aminophenyl-2-methyl-	>360°	185
7-Acetamido-3-p-(p-aminophenyl)phenyl-2-methyl-	296–297° (dec.)	185
7-Acetamido-6(?)bromo-2-methyl-	292°	183
7-Acetamido-3-(3',4'-dihydro-2'-methyl-4'-oxoquinazolin-7'-yl)-2-methyl-	332°	183
7-Acetamido-3-p-ethoxyphenyl-2-methyl-	259°	183
7-Acetamido-3-ethyl-2-methyl-	254°	183
7-Acetamido-2-(indan-1',3'-dion-2'-yl)-	>356°	217
7-Acetamido-3-isopentyl-2-methyl-	288°	183
7-Acetamido-3-p-methoxyphenyl-2-methyl-	273°	183
7-Acetamido-2-methyl-	344°	183
7-Acetamido-2,3-dimethyl-	284°	183
7-Acetamido-2,6-dimethyl-	~330°	184
7-Acetamido-2-methyl-3-1'-naphthyl-	256°	183
7-Acetamido-2-methyl-6,8-dinitro-	302° (dec.)	183
7-Acetamido-2-methyl-3-phenyl-	276°	183
7-Acetamido-2,6-dimethyl-3-phenyl-	271°	184
7-Acetamido-2-methyl-3-propyl-	206–207°	183
7-Acetamido-3-methyl-2-styryl-	272°	169

(*Table continued*)

TABLE VII.19 (*continued*)

3,4-Dihydro-4-oxoquinazoline	M.p. (°c)	References
7-Acetamido-2-phthalimido-	> 356°	217
7-Acetamido-2-styryl-	323–324°	169
7-Amino-	293–295°, 306° (dec.)	70, 175
8-Amino-	260–261°	55, 172
7-Amino-3-*m*-aminophenyl-2-methyl-	262°	185
7-Amino-3-*p*-aminophenyl-2-methyl-	287°	185
8-Amino-6-chloro-3-methyl-	170°	172
7-Amino-3-(3′,4′-dihydro-2′-methyl-4′-oxoquinazolin-7′-yl)-2-methyl-	335°	183
7-Amino-3-(3′-(3-hydroxy-2-piperidyl)-2′-oxo)propyl-	2 HCl · 1.5 H_2O 85°	175
7-Amino-3-(3′-(3-methoxy-2-piperidyl)-2′-oxo)propyl-	2 HCl · 0.5 H_2O 85°	175
7-Amino-2-methoxycarbonylmethyl-	100.5°	225
7-Amino-2-methyl-	311°	149
7-Amino-3-methyl-	220°	54, 172
8-Amino-3-methyl-	160°	54, 172
7-Amino-2,3-dimethyl-	H_2O 224°	183
7-Amino-2,6-dimethyl-	> 300°	184
7-Amino-3-methyl-2-styryl-	229.5–230°	169
6-Chloro-8-2′-diethylaminoethylamino-3-methyl-	220–240°/0.1 mm; picrate 184–187°	172
7-2′-Diethylaminoethylamino-3-methyl-	210–230°/0.1 mm; picrate 206°	172
8-2′-Diethylaminoethylamino-3-methyl-	200–210°/0.1 mm; picrate 94°	172
7-Formamido-2-methyl-	339–340°	183
2-Methyl-7-propionamido-	326–327°	183
8-Tosylamino-	268–269°	55

TABLE VII.20.   3-Amino-3,4-dihydro-4-oxoquinazoline and
2-Substituted Derivatives.

3-Amino-3,4-dihydro-4-oxo-quinazoline	M.p. (°c)	References
Unsubstituted	204–208°, 211°	140, 143, 158, 160, 196, 207
2-(3′-Amino-3′ 4′-dihydro-4′-oxoquinazolin-2′-ylmethyl)-	> 300°	155
2-o-Chlorophenyl-	153.5°	150
2-Ethyl-	123°	132
2-Fluoromethyl-	163–164°	230
2-1′-Hydroxyethyl-	108–110°	165
2-Hydroxymethyl-	216–220°	165
2-p-Methoxyphenyl-	185°	150
2-Methyl-	146–148°, 152°; methiodide 201° (dec.)	116, 132, 148, 150, 155, 159, 160, 202, 216
2-1′-Naphthyl-	211°	150
2-2′-Naphthyl-	220°	150
2-m-Nitrophenyl-	222°	132
2-Phenyl-	178–179°, 184–186°; acetyl deriv. 149°; benzoyl deriv. 295°; m-nitrobenzoyl deriv. 198°	132, 137, 150, 151, 156, 159
2-Styryl-	164°	169
2-p-Tolyl-	164.5°	150

TABLE VII.21.   3-Substituted-amino-3,4-dihydro-4-oxoquinazolines with a
Substituent in Position 2.

3,4-Dihydro-4-oxoquinazoline	M.p. (°c)	References
3-Acetamido-2-ethyl-	135°	132
3-Acetamido-2-methyl-	176.5°	132, 148, 160
3-Acetamido-2-phenyl-	H₂O 122°	132
3-Acetamido-2-*m*-nitrophenyl-	H₂O 183°	132
3-Acetamido-2-styryl-	259°	166
3-*N*-Acetylanilino-2-methyl-	147.5–148.5°	202
3-Acetylsulphanilamido-2-methyl-	243–244°	138
3-Anilino-2-2′-Carboxyethenyl-	217–217.4° (dec.)	233
3-Anilino-2-2′-carboxyethyl-	181.8–183.6°	233
3-Anilino-2-*p*-chlorophenyl-	190°	150
3-Anilino-2-*p*-chlorophenyl- hydrazinomethyl-	248°	154
3-Anilino-2-phenylhydrazono- methyl-	232°	154
3-Anilino-2-*p*-methoxyphenyl-	174°	150
3-Anilino-2-methyl-	208–209°, 212°	116, 146, 150, 152, 202
3-Anilino-2-phenyl-	151°, 162° (remelts at 182°)	150, 151
3-Anilino-2-styryl-	217°	166
3-Benzamido-2-*p*-chlorophenyl-	297°	136
3-Benzamido-2-methyl-	182°	132
3-Benzamido-2-*m*-nitrophenyl-	221°	132
3-Benzamido-2-phenyl-	202°	132
3-Benzamido-2-styryl-	165°	169
3-Benzylideneamino-2-methyl-	183–184°, 187°	148, 159, 160, 169, 231
3-Benzylideneamino-2-styryl-	155°	169
3-*m*-Chloroanilino-2-methyl-	200–201°	147
3-*p*-Chlorobenzamido-2-phenyl-	212°	136
3-*p*-Chlorobenzylamino-2-methyl-	150–152°	202
3-*p*-Chlorobenzylideneamino-2- methyl-	203.5–206°	202
2-*p*-Chlorophenyl-3-ureido-	340–345°	150
3-Cinnamylideneamino-2-methyl-	148–149°	169
3-Diacetylamino-2-phenyl-	153°	144
3-Dimethylamino-2-methyl-	95–97°; HCl 253–255°	141, 147, 202

(*Table continued*)

TABLE VII.21 (*continued*)

3,4-Dihydro-4-oxoquinazoline	M.p. (°c)	References
3-Ethoxycarbonylamino-2-methyl-	128°	135, 206
3-Ethylideneamino-2-methyl-	104–105°	168
3-Ethylideneamino-2-phenyl-	137°	167
3-Formamido-2-methyl-	185°	148
3-(4′-Hydroxy-3′-methoxy)-benzylideneamino-2-methyl-	206–209°, 215–216°	160, 169
3-o-Hydroxybenzylideneamino-2-methyl-	164–166°, 171°; HCl 250°	160, 169
3-o-Hydroxybenzylideneamino-2-styryl-	232–233°	169
3-2′-Hydroxyethoxycarbonyl-amino-2-methyl-	146°	142
3-p-Methoxybenzylideneamino-2-methyl-	174–176°	160
2-p-Methoxyphenyl-3-ureido-	311°	150
2-Methyl-3-N-methylanilino-	132–133°	147
2-Methyl-3-1′-methylbenzylidene-amino-	195°	132
2-Methyl-3-morpholino-	HCl 300–303°	141
2-Methyl-3-m-nitrobenzamido-	231°	132
2-Methyl-3-5′-nitrofurfurylidene-amino-	213–214° (dec.)	232
2-Methyl-3-phenylsulphonamido-	203–204°	138
2-Methyl-3-N′-phenylureido-	300°	148
2-Methyl-3-phthalimido-	205–207°	202
2-Methyl-3-N-propionylanilino-	139–141.5°	202
2-Methyl-3-pyrrolidin-2′-yl-methyleneamino-	214–216°	160
2-Methyl-3-sulphanilamido-	227–229°	138
2-Methyl-3-thioureido-	183–185°	160
2-Methyl-3-p-toluidino-	158–159°	147
2-Methyl-3-(2′,2′,2′-trichloro-1′-hydroxy)ethylamino-	151–152°	168
2-Methyl-3-m-trifluoromethyl-anilino-	208–210°	147
2-Methyl-3-3′,4′,5′-trimethoxy-benzamido-	220–222°; HCl 221–223°	153
2-Methyl-3-ureido-	231–232°	160
2-Phenyl-3-ureido-	300°	150

TABLE VII.22. 3-Amino (and Substituted-amino)-3,4-dihydro-4-oxo-quinazolines Substituted (and Unsubstituted) in the Benzene Ring.

$(R^2)H$ —— N—NH$_2$(RR^1)

3,4-Dihydro-4-oxoquinazoline	M.p. (°c)	References
3-Acetamido-	168–170°, 206°	160, 167
3-Amino-6-bromo-	227–228.2°	158
3-Amino-8-methoxy-	150–151°	126
3-Amino-8-methoxy-6,7-methylenedioxy-	219°	127
3-Amino-6,7-methylenedioxy-	280.5°	129
3-Amino-7,8-methylenedioxy-	252.5°	131
3-Amino-6-nitro-	170–171°	139
3-Anilino-	140°	140
3-Benzamido-	194°	167
3-Benzylideneamino-	129°	140, 160
6-Bromo-3-dimethylamino-	94–96°	141
6-Bromo-3-morpholino-	176–178°	141
3-o-Carboxyanilino-	295.2–298.2°	233
5-Chloro-3-ethoxycarbonylamino-	195–196°	206
6-Chloro-3-5′-nitrofurfurylideneamino-	225–226° (dec.)	232
6-Chloro-3-thioureido-	191–192°	160
3-2′-Chloropropionamido-	174–175°	196
3-Dibenzoylamino-	205°	167
3-2′-Dibenzylaminopropionamido-	170–185°	196
3-2′-Dibutylaminopropionamido-	HCl 220–223°	196
3-2′-Diethylaminopropionamido-	HCl 172–175°	196
3-Dimethylamino-	68.2–69.2°; HCl 205–207°	141, 233
3-Dimethylamino-6-nitro-	157–158°	141
3-2′-Dimethylaminopropionamido-	2 HCl 209–211°	196
3-(4′-Hydroxy-3′-methoxy)benzylidene-amino-	188–191°	160
3-o-Hydroxybenzylideneamino-	205–207°	140, 160
3-2′-Hydroxyethoxycarbonylamino-	146°	205
3-p-Methoxybenzylideneamino-	131–133°	160
3-Morpholino-	125–127°	141
3-Morpholino-6-nitro-	261°	141
3-2′-Morpholinopropionamido-	189–192°	196
3-(5′-Nitro-2′-pyrrolylmethyleneamino)-	200–202°	224
3-5′-Nitrofurfurylideneamino-	210–211° (dec.)	233
3-Propionamido-	104–107°, 170°	132, 160
3-2′-(1-Pyridyl)propionamido-	chloride 193–195°	196
3-2′-Pyrrolymethyleneamino-	206–208°	160
3-Ureido-	219–221°	160

TABLE VII.23.   3-Amino-3,4-dihydro-4-oxoquinazolines with Substituents
in Position 2 and in the Benzene Ring.

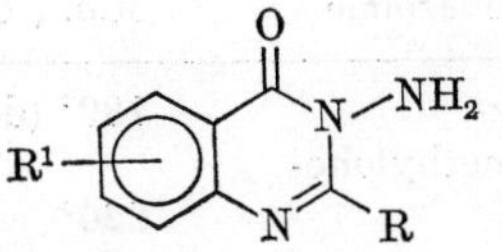

3-Amino-3,4-dihydro-4-oxoquinazoline	M.p. (°c)	References
2-(3′-(3-Amino-3,4-dihydro-6,7-methyl-enedioxy-4-oxoquinazolin-2-yl)-2′-methyl)propyl-6,7-methylenedioxy-	284–285°	129
2-3′-(3-Amino-3,4-dihydro-6,7-methyl-enedioxy-4-oxoquinazolin-2-yl)-propyl-6,7-methylenedioxy-	282.5°	129
2-(5′,6′-Benzo-2′-p-dioxino)-6,7-ethylene-dioxy-	193°	130
2-(5′,6′-Benzo-2′-p-dioxino)-6,7-methyl-enedioxy-	187–188°	129
2-Benzyl-8-hydroxy-	164–165°	126
2-Benzyl-8-methoxy-	152–153°	126
2-Benzyl-6,7,8-trimethoxy-	142°	128
5-Bromo-7,8-methylenedioxy-	204–206°	131
5-Bromo-7-nitro-2-phenyl-	240°	134
2-p-Bromophenyl-6,8-methylenedioxy-	242°	129
2-Butyl-6,7-methylenedioxy-	160.8°	129
5-Chloro-2-methyl-	156–157°	160
6-Chloro-2-methyl-	169–171°	160
7-Chloro-2-methyl-	186–188°	160
5-Chloro-7-nitro-2-phenyl-	252°	134
7-Chloro-2-phenyl-	—	156
2-p-Chlorobenzyl-8-methoxy-	179–180°	126
2-p-Chlorobenzyl-6,7-methylenedioxy-	246–248°	129
2-p-Chlorophenyl-8-methoxy-	225–226°	126
2-p-Chlorophenyl-6,7,8-trimethoxy-	191°	128
2-p-Chlorophenyl-8-methoxy-6,7-methyl-enedioxy-	256–257°	127
2-p-Chlorophenyl-6,7-methylenedioxy-	228.4°	129
2-Dec-9′-enyl-8-methoxy-6,7-methylene-dioxy-	105°	127
2-(2′,2′-Dimethyl-3′-(2-methylprop-1-enyl))cyclopropyl-8-methoxy-6,7-methylenedioxy-	163–164°	127
2-Ethyl-6,7-methylenedioxy-	176–178°	129
6,7-Ethylenedioxy-2-methyl-	258°	130
2-p-Fluorophenyl-6,7-methylenedioxy-	228.5°	129

(*Table continued*)

TABLE VII.23 (*continued*)

3-Amino-3,4-dihydro-4-oxoquinazoline	M.p. (°c)	References
2-2′-Furyl-6,7,8-trimethoxy-	189° (dec.)	128
2-2′-Furyl-8-methoxy-6,7-methylene-dioxy-	226°	127
2-2′-Furyl-6,7-methylenedioxy-	251.5° (dec.)	129
2-2′-Hydrazinocarbonylethyl-8-methoxy-	241–242°	126
2-2′-Hydrazinocarbonylethyl-6,7-methylenedioxy-	249.5°	129
8-Hydroxy-2-methyl-	257°	126
5-Hydroxy-2-methyl-6,7-methylenedioxy-	196.8°	213
8-Hydroxy-2-pentyl-	124–125°	126
8-Hydroxy-2-3′-phenylpropyl-	178–179°	126
5-Iodo-7-nitro-2-phenyl-	252°	134
2-*p*-Iodophenyl-6,7-methylenedioxy-	236.5°	129
2-Isobutyl-6,7-methylenedioxy-	141.6°	129
8-Methoxy-2-methyl-	192–193°	126
6,7,8-Trimethoxy-2-methyl-	155°	128
8-Methoxy-2-methyl-6,7-methylenedioxy-	243–246°	127
8-Methoxy-6,7-methylenedioxy-2-pentadecyl-	104–105°	127
8-Methoxy-6,7-methylenedioxy-2-pentyl-	179°	127
8-Methoxy-6,7-methylenedioxy-2-2′-pyrrolyl-	208–211° (dec.)	127
8-Methoxy-2-phenyl-	221–222°	126
6,7,8-Trimethoxy-2-phenyl-	170°	128
8-Methoxy-2-3′-phenylpropyl-	160–161°	126
6,7,8-Trimethoxy-2-3′-phenylpropyl-	92°	128
6,7,8-Trimethoxy-2-3′-pyridyl-	186° (dec.)	128
2,6,7-Trimethyl-	215°	133
2-Methyl-6,7-methylenedioxy-	284.5°	129
2-Methyl-5-nitro-	152–153°; HCl 253–254°	208
2-Methyl-6-nitro-	208–209°, 211–223°	160, 218
2-Methyl-7-nitro-	223–224°; acetyl deriv. 233°; diacetyl deriv. 132°	116, 149
6,7-Methylenedioxy-2-4′-pyridyl-	343.5°	129
6,7-Methylenedioxy-2-tridecyl-	119.2°	129
6,7-Methylenedioxy-2-3′,4′,5′-trimethoxyphenyl-	246.8°	129
7,8-Methylenedioxy-2-methyl-	230.5°	131
6,7-Methylenedioxy-2-1′-methylnonyl-	*dl* 97.6°	129
6,7-Methylenedioxy-2-nonyl-	111.5°	129

(*Table continued*)

TABLE VII.23 *(continued)*

3-Amino-3,4-dihydro-4-oxoquinazoline	M.p. (°c)	References
6,7-Methylenedioxy-2-pentadecyl-	105.8°	129
6,7-Methylenedioxy-2-phenyl-	190.2°	129
6,7-Methylenedioxy-2-3'-pyridyl-	244.5° (dec.)	129
7,8-Methylenedioxy-2-3'-pyridyl-	246.5° (dec.)	131
6,7-Methylenedioxy-2-3'-thienyl-	238.5°	129
6,7-Methylenedioxy-2-undecyl-	114.8°	129
7-Nitro-2-phenyl-	249°; acetyl deriv.	
	149°; benzoyl deriv.	
	295°	151

TABLE VII.24. 3-Substituted-amino-3,4-dihydro-4-oxoquinazolines with Substituents in Position 2 and in the Benzene Ring.

3,4-Dihydro-4-oxoquinazoline	M.p. (°c)	References
3-Acetylamino-5,6-ethylenedioxy-2-methyl-	158°	130
3-Acetamido-2-methyl-5-nitro-[a]	233°	208
3-Acetamido-2-methyl-7-nitro-[b]	233°	149
3-Acetamido-2-1'-methylbutyl-6,7-methylenedioxy-	142.6°	129
3-Acetylsulphanilamido-2-methyl-6-nitro-	248°	138
3-N'-Allylthioureido-8-hydroxy-2-methyl-	184–186°	126
3-N'-Allylthioureido-8-methoxy-2-methyl-	187–189°	126
3-Anilino-5-bromo-7-nitro-2-phenyl-	158°	134
3-Anilino-5-chloro-2-methyl-	188–189°	147
3-Anilino-7-chloro-2-methyl-	160–162°	147
3-Anilino-5-chloro-7-nitro-2-phenyl-	156°	134
3-Anilino-6-iodo-2-methyl-	217.5°	211
3-Anilino-5-iodo-7-nitro-2-phenyl-	159°	134
3-Anilino-2-methyl-7-nitro-	230°	149
3-Anilino-7-nitro-2-phenyl-	151°	151
3-Benzylideneamino-2-methyl-6-nitro-	173–175°	160
6-Chloro-3-m-chloroanilino-2-methyl-	215–217°	147
7-Chloro-3-m-chloroanilino-2-methyl-	149–150°	147

(Table continued)

TABLE VII.24 (*continued*)

3,4-Dihydro-4-oxoquinazoline	M.p. (°c)	References
5-Chloro-3-dimethylamino-2-methyl-	136–137°	147
6-Chloro-3-dimethylamino-2-methyl-	132–134°	147
7-Chloro-3-dimethylamino-2-methyl-	89–90°	147
5-Chloro-3-ethoxycarbonylamino-2-methyl-	151–153°	206
6-Chloro-3-ethoxycarbonylamino-2-methyl-	147–148°	206
7-Chloro-3-ethoxycarbonylamino-2-methyl-	134°	206
5-Chloro-3-o-hydroxybenzylideneamino-2-methyl-	207–209°	160
6-Chloro-3-o-hydroxybenzylideneamino-2-methyl-	184–186°	160
7-Chloro-3-o-hydroxybenzylideneamino-2-methyl-	221–222°	160
6-Chloro-3-2'-hydroxyethoxycarbonylamino-2-methyl-	177–178°	142, 205
6-Chloro-2-methyl-3-N-methylanilino-	147–148°	147
7-Chloro-2-methyl-3-N-methylanilino-	113–115°	147
5-Chloro-2-methyl-3-ureido-	215–220°	160
5-Chloro-2-methyl-3-thioureido-	182–184°	160
7-Chloro-2-methyl-3-thioureido-	174–176°	160
5-Chloro-2-methyl-3-p-toluidino-	137–139°	147
6-Chloro-2-methyl-3-p-toluidino-	188–190°	147
7-Chloro-2-methyl-3-p-toluidino-	162–163°	147
5-Chloro-2-methyl-3-m-trifluoromethylanilino-	168–170°	147
6-Chloro-2-methyl-3-m-trifluoromethylanilino-	218–220°	147
6-Chloro-2-methyl-3-ureido-	234–236°	160
7-Chloro-2-methyl-3-ureido-	268°	160
3-Decanoylamido-6,7-ethylenedioxy-2-methyl-	150°	130
3-Diacetylamino-8-methoxy-2-methyl-6,7-methylenedioxy-	175–176°	127
3-Diacetylamino-2-methyl-7-nitro-	132°	149
3-N,N'-Diacetylureido-2-methyl-7-nitro-	229–230°	208
3-2',4'-Dinitroanilino-6-iodo-2-methyl-	171–172°	211
3-Ethoxycarbonylamino-2-methyl-6-nitro-	174–175°	138, 206
6,7-Ethylenedioxy-3-5'-nitrofurfurylideneamino-2-methyl-	233°	130
3-N'-(3'-Ethylhex-4'-enoyl)thioureido-8-methoxy-2-methyl-	198–200°	126
3-N'-Hex-4'-enoylthioureido-8-methoxy-2-methyl-	205–206°	126
8-Hydroxy-2-methyl-3-N'-methylthioureido-	225–226°	126
3-o-Hydroxybenzylideneamino-2-methyl-6-nitro-	216–218°	160
3-2'-Hydroxyethoxycarbonylamino-2-methyl-6-nitro-	168–170°	142, 205

(*Table continued*)

TABLE VII.24 (*continued*)

3,4-Dihydro-4-oxoquinazoline	M.p. (°c)	References
8-Methoxy-2-methyl-3-4'-methyl-N'-hept-5-enoylthioureido-	202–204°	126
8-Methoxy-2-methyl-6,7-methylenedioxy-3-2'-(4-pyridyl)ethylamino-	157°	127
8-Methoxy-2-methyl-3-N'-methylthioureido-	224–225°	126
8-Methoxy-2-methyl-3-N'-non-7-enoyl-thioureido-	204–205°	126
8-Methoxy-2-methyl-3-N'-octanoylthioureido-	162–164°	126
6,7,8-Trimethoxy-2-methyl-3-2'-pyrrolyl-methyleneamino-	215°	128
2-Methyl-6-nitro-3-5'-nitrofurfurylidene-amino-	226–227° (dec.)	232
2-Methyl-7-nitro-3-5'-nitrofurfurylidene-amino-	220–221° (dec.)	232
2-Methyl-6-nitro-3-thioureido-	264–266°	160
2-Methyl-6-nitro-3-ureido-	273–274°	160
6,7-Methylenedioxy-2-methyl-3-4'-nitro-furfurylideneamino-	252.5° (dec.)	129
6,7-Methylenedioxy-2-methyl-3-4'-nitro-2-thenylideneamino-	284.5° (dec.)	129
2-Methyl-6-nitro-3-sulphanilamido-	252°	138
2-Methyl-5-nitro-3-ureido-	263–264°	208
2-Methyl-7-nitro-3-ureido-	266°	208

[a] 3-Acetamido-3,4-dihydro-2-methyl-5-nitro-4-phenylhydrazonoquinazoline has m.p. 124–125°.[208]

[b] 3-Acetamido-3,4-dihydro-2-methyl-7-nitro-4-phenylhydrazonoquinazoline has m.p. 315°.[149]

TABLE VII.25. 3-Amino (or Substituted-amino)-3,4-dihydro-4-oxoquin-azolines Substituted (and Unsubstituted) in Position 2, with Amino (and Substituted-amino) Groups in the Benzene Ring.

3,4-Dihydro-4-oxoquinazoline	M.p. (°c)	References
3-Acetamido-5-amino-8-methoxy-2-methyl-6,7-methylenedioxy-	117–228°	127
6-Acetamido-3-amino-2-methyl-	H_2O 262–263°	183
7-Acetamido-3-amino-2-methyl-	268°; H_2O 125–130°; 3 HCl 312° (dec.)	183
7-Acetamido-3-anilino-2-methyl-	214°	183
6-Acetamido-3-benzylideneamino-2-styryl-	238–239°	169
7-Acetamido-3-benzylideneamino-2-styryl-	261°	169
6-Acetamido-3-ethoxycarbonylamino-2-methyl-	191–192°	199
3,6-Bisacetamido-2-methyl-	254°	160
3,7-Bisacetamido-2-methyl-	304°	183
3,7-Bisacetamido-2-styryl-	283–284°	169
3-Amino-7-benzylideneamino-2-methyl-	324°	169
6-Amino-3-ethoxycarbonylamino-2-methyl-	189–190°	206
3,5-Diamino-6-methoxy-2-methyl-7,8-methylenedioxy-	180–195°	127
3,5-Diamino-8-methoxy-2-methyl-6,7-methylenedioxy-	224–225°	127
3,6-Diamino-2-methyl-	224–226°	160
3,7-Diamino-2-methyl-	238°	183
6-Amino-3-morpholino-	218–220°	141
3,7-Dibenzylideneamino-2-styryl-	238°	169
3,6-Bisethoxycarbonylamino-	172°	199
3,6-Bisethoxycarbonylamino-2-ethyl-	174–175°	199
6-Ethoxycarbonylamino-3-isopropoxycarbonylamino-2-methyl-	194–195°	199
3,6-Bisethoxycarbonylamino-2-methyl-	198–199°	138, 199
3,7-Bisethoxycarbonylamino-2-methyl-	202–203°	138, 199
3-Ethoxycarbonylamino-2-methyl-6-ureido-	202–204°	199

TABLE VII.26.   3-Amino (and Substituted-amino)-3,4-dihydro-4-thioquinazolines.

$$(R^3)H \underbrace{}_{} \overset{S}{\underset{N}{\bigcirc}} \overset{NH_2(R^1R^2)}{\underset{H(R)}{N}}$$

3,4-Dihydro-4-thioquinazoline	M.p. (°c)	References
3-Amino-2-benzyl-	129°	150
3-Amino-6-chloro-2-phenyl-	173°	150
3-Amino-2-p-chlorophenyl-	201°	150
3-Amino-2-ethyl-	121°	150
3-Amino-2-isopropyl-	121°	150
3-Amino-2-p-methoxyphenyl-	164.5°	150
3-Amino-2-1′-naphthyl-	210°	150
3-Amino-2-2′-naphthyl-	172°	150
3-Amino-2-o-nitrophenyl-	171°	150
3-Amino-2-phenyl-	177.5°	150
3-Amino-2-t-butyl-	132°	150
3-Amino-2-o-tolyl-	125.5°	150
3-Amino-2-p-tolyl-	175.5°	150
3-Anilino-2-o-chlorophenyl-	134°	150
3-Anilino-2-p-chlorophenyl-	176°	150
3-Anilino-2-p-methoxyphenyl-	143°	150
3-Anilino-2-1′-naphthyl-	199°	150
3-Anilino-2-2′-napthhyl-	198°	150
3-Anilino-2-phenyl-	137°	150
2-o-Chlorophenyl-3-ureido-	216°	150
2-Ethyl-3-ureido-	227°	150
2-p-Methoxyphenyl-3-ureido-	241°	150
2-Methyl-3-ureido-	210°	150
2-Phenyl-3-ureido-	224°	150
3-Ureido-	213°	150

TABLE VII.27.   3-Amino (and Substituted-amino)-1,2,3,4-tetrahydro-
2,4-dioxoquinazolines.

1,2,3,4-Tetrahydro-2,4-dioxoquinazoline	M.p. (°c)	References
3-Acetamido-	240°, 250°	135, 203
3-Acetamido-1-methyl-	140°	161
3-Amino-	296–297°	36, 135, 161, 162, 164
3-Amino-1-methyl-	165°	161
3-Diacetylamino-	212°	203
3-Benzylideneamino-	240°, 245–246°	164, 203
3-Benzylideneamino-1-methyl-	157°	161
3-Butylaminoacetamido-	HCl 220–225°	196
3-Chloroacetamido-	220–223°	196
3-2′-Chloropropionamido-	234–235°	196
3-Dibenzylaminoacetamido-	143–145°	196
3-Diethylaminoacetamido-	HCl 233–235°	196
3-2′-Diethylaminopropionamido-	HCl 192–194°	196
3-Dimethylaminoacetamido-	methiodide 132–134°	196
3-2′-Dimethylaminopropionamido-	HCl 196–200°	196
3-Ethoxycarbonylamino-	H₂O 227° (dec.)	135
3-o-Hydroxybenzylideneamino-1-methyl-	160°	161
3-Isopropylideneamino-	212°	145
3-Isopropylaminoacetamido-	HCl 229–230°	196
3-Methoxycarbonylamino-	240° (dec.)	135
1-Methyl-3-methylamino-	153°	161
3-Methylamino-	263°	161, 203
3-Morpholinoacetamido-	HCl 245–247°	196
3-α-Phenylbenzylideneamino-	240°	145
3-Phenylsulphonamido-	277°	162, 163
3-1′-Pyridylacetamido-	chloride 266–268°	196
3-2′-Pyridylcarbonylamino-	290°	162, 163
3-4′-Pyridylcarbonylamino-	309–310°	163

TABLE VII.28. 1,2,3,4-Tetrahydro-2,4-dioxoquinazolines with Amino (and Substituted-amino) Groups in the Benzene Ring.

1,2,3,4-Tetrahydro-2,4-dioxoquinazoline	M.p. (°c)	References
6-Acetamido-3-3'-(4-phenylpiperazin-1-yl)propyl-	256–258° (dec.); maleate 245–246° (dec.)	226
5-Amino-	295° (dec.)	177
6-Amino-	330° (dec.)	177
7-Amino-	320°, > 350°	70, 177
8-Amino-	279–281° (dec.)	177
6,8-Diamino-	335° (dec.)	176
6-Amino-3-3'-(4-phenylpiperazin-1-yl)propyl-	234–238°	226
6-Dimethylamino-3-phenyl-	281°	187

TABLE VII.29. Hydrazinoquinazolines with Hydrazino Groups in the Pyrimidine Ring.

Quinazoline	M.p. (°c)	References
4-p-Acetamidobenzylidenehydrazino-	265–266°	122, 123
4-Amino-2-hydrazino-	232° (dec.)	57
4-o-Aminobenzylidenehydrazino-	186–187°	122, 123
4-Anilino-7,8-benzo-2-hydrazino-	224°	95
4-N'-Benzoylhydrazino-	240°	121
4-Benzylidenehydrazino-	174–176°	84, 192, 122
2,4-Bisbenzylidenehydrazino-	286°	58
4-12'-Carboxydodecylidene-hydrazino-	182° (dec.)	122
4-1'-Carboxyethylidenehydrazino-	215–217° (dec.)	122, 123
4-Cinnamylidenehydrazino-	173–175°	122, 123
4-p-Dimethylaminobenzylidene-hydrazino-	244°	123
3,4-Dihydro-2-hydrazino-4-oxo-	360° (dec.)	57

(*Table continued*)

TABLE VII.29 (*continued*)

Quinazoline	M.p. (°c)	References
4-Furfurylidenehydrazino-	180–181°	122
2-Hydrazino-	132–133°	57
4-Hydrazino-	188–189°; HCl 193–194°	1, 57, 58, 91, 122
2,4-Dihydrazino-	215°, 226–227° (dec.); HCl 278°	57, 58, 103
4-Hydrazino-6-methyl-	162°	106
4-Hydrazino-2-morpholino-	226–227°	48
4-Hydrazino-6-nitro-2-trichloro-methyl-	188° (dec.)	74
2-Hydrazino-4-phenyl-	155–156°; N′-tosyl deriv. 203–205°	4
4-Hydrazino-2-phenyl-	216–217°	57, 58
4-Hydrazino-2-piperidino-	195–196°	48
4-Hydrazino-2-pyrrolidin-1′-yl-	222–223°	48
4-(4′-Hydroxy-3′-methoxy)-benzylidenehydrazino-	200–201°	122, 123
4-o-Hydroxybenzylidenehydrazino-	298–300°	122
4-Isopropylidenehydrazino-	177°	122, 123
6-Methoxy-7-nitro-[a]	202° (dec.); N′-tosyl deriv. 225° (dec.)	1
4-p-Methoxybenzylidenehydrazino-	205–206°	122, 123
4-o-Nitrobenzylidenehydrazino-	210–211°	122, 123
4-N′-Sulphomethylhydrazino-	Na salt 109° (dec.)	122

[a] See chapter V, section 2.D.

5. References

1. Dewar, *J. Chem. Soc.*, **1944**, 619.
2. Wolf, *U.S. Pat.*, 2,461,950 (1949); *Chem. Abstr.*, **43**, 4704 (1949).
3. Armarego and Smith, *J. Chem. Soc.* (C), **1966**, 234.
4. Schofield, *J. Chem. Soc.*, **1952**, 1927.
5. Scarborough, Lawes, Minielli, and Compton, *J. Org. Chem.*, **27**, 957 (1962).
6. Lange and Shiebley, *J. Am. Chem. Soc.*, **54**, 1994 (1932).
7. Curd, Landquist, and Rose, *J. Chem. Soc.*, **1947**, 775.
8. Curd, Landquist, Raison, and Rose, *Brit. Pat.*, 585,363 (1947); *Chem. Abstr.*, **41**, 4173 (1947).
9. Curd, Hoggarth, Landquist, and Rose, *J. Chem. Soc.*, **1948**, 1766.
10. Bunnett, *J. Am. Chem. Soc.*, **68**, 1327 (1946).
11. Pesson and Richer, *Compt. Rend.*, **260**, 603 (1965).
12. Wheeler, Johnson, and McFarland, *J. Am. Chem. Soc.*, **25**, 787 (1903).

13. McCoy, *Am. Chem. J.*, **21**, 111 (1899); *Ber. Deut. Chem. Ges.*, **30**, 1682 (1897).
14. Grout and Partridge, *J. Chem. Soc.*, **1960**, 3540.
15. Lempert and Breuer, *Magy. Kém. Folyóirat*, **68**, 452 (1962); *Chem. Abstr.*, **58**, 11355 (1963).
16. Lempert and Doleschall, *Chem. Ber.*, **96**, 1271 (1963).
17. Griess, *Ber. Deut. Chem. Ges.*, **2**, 415 (1869).
18. Griess, *Ber. Deut. Chem. Ges.*, **13**, 977 (1880).
19. Griess, *Ber. Deut. Chem. Ges.*, **18**, 2410 (1885).
20. Schofield, Osborn, and Short, *J. Chem. Soc.*, **1956**, 4191.
21. Rodda, *J. Chem. Soc.*, **1956**, 3509.
22. Tsuda, Ikuma, Kawamura, Tachikawa, Baba, and Miyadera, *Chem. Pharm. Bull. (Japan)*, **10**, 856 (1962).
23. Tsuda, Ikuma, Kawamura, Tachikawa, and Miyadera, *Chem. Pharm. Bull. (Japan)*, **10**, 865 (1962).
24. Theiling and McKee, *J. Am. Chem. Soc.*, **74**, 1834 (1952).
25. Bell, Gochman, and Childress, *J. Med. Pharm. Chem.*, **5**, 63 (1962).
26. Goto, Kishi, and Hirata, *Bull. Chem. Soc. Japan*, **35**, 1244 (1962).
27. Brown and Jackman, *J. Chem. Soc.*, **1964**, 3132.
28. Brown, *J. Chem. Soc.*, **1964**, 3012.
29. Brown, *Chem. Ind. (London)*, **1960**, 233.
30. Brown, *Brit. Pat.*, 908,187 (1962); *Chem. Abstr.*, **58**, 4583 (1963).
31. Brown, *Brit. Pat.*, 900,779 (1962); *Chem. Abstr.*, **58**, 533 (1963).
32. Rosowsky, Protopapa, Burke, and Modest, *J. Org. Chem.*, **29**, 2881 (1964).
33. Rosowsky, Protopapa, and Modest, *J. Org. Chem.*, **30**, 285 (1965).
34. Wessely, Zbiral, and Sturm, *Monatsh. Chem.*, **93**, 1211 (1962).
35. Zbiral, *Monatsh. Chem.*, **93**, 1203 (1962).
36. Kunckell, *Ber. Deut. Chem. Ges.*, **38**, 1212 (1905).
37. Skowrónska-Serafinowa and Urbanski, *Rocznicki Chem.*, **26**, 51 (1952); *Chem. Abstr.*, **47**, 7507 (1953).
38. Deck and Dains, *J. Am. Chem. Soc.*, **55**, 4986 (1933).
39. Murray and Dains, *J. Am. Chem. Soc.*, **56**, 144 (1934).
40. Hartke and Bartulin, *Angew. Chem.*, **74**, 214 (1962).
41. Dymek and Lucka-Sobstel., *Dissertationes Pharm.*, **17**, 195 (1965).
42. Nakao and Sunagawa, *Chem. Pharm. Bull. (Japan)*, **13**, 465 (1965).
43. Stefanović, Lorenc, and Mihailović, *Rec. Trav. Chim.*, **80**, 149 (1961).
44. Burnett, Jr., and Ainsworth, *J. Org. Chem.*, **23**, 1382 (1958).
45. Tsuda, Ikuma, Kawamura, Tachikawa, Miyadera, *Chem. Pharm. Bull. (Japan)*, **10**, 868 (1962).
46. Adachi, *J. Pharm. Soc. Japan*, **77**, 510 (1957).
47. Taylor and Jefford, *Chem. Ind. (London)*, **1963**, 1559.
48. Postovskii and Goncharova, *Zh. Obshch. Khim.*, **33**, 2334 (1963).
49. Dass, Vig, Gupta, and Narang, *J. Sci. Ind. Res. India*, **11B**, 461 (1952).
50. Chapman, Gibson, and Mann, *J. Chem. Soc.*, **1947**, 890.
51. Partridge, Vipond, and Waite, *J. Chem. Soc.*, **1962**, 2549.
52. Andrisano and Modena, *Gazz. Chim. Ital.*, **80**, 228 (1950).
53. Chapman and Taylor, *J. Chem. Soc.*, **1961**, 1908.
54. Tsuda, Ishii, Fukushima, and Yoshida, *J. Pharm. Soc. Japan*, **62**, 335 (1942).
55. Elderfield, Williamson, Gensler, and Kremer, *J. Org. Chem.*, **12**, 405 (1947).

56. Goodale and McKee, *J. Am. Chem. Soc.*, **71**, 1893 (1949).
57. Claesen and Vanderhaeghe, *Bull. Soc. Chim. Belges*, **68**, 220 (1959).
58. Libermann and Rouaix, *Bull. Soc. Chim. France*, **1959**, 1793.
59. Andrisano and Modena, *Boll. Sci. Fac. Chim. Ind. Bologna*, **8**, 1 (1950); *Chem. Abstr.*, **45**, 1601 (1951).
60. Price, Leonard, and Curtin, *J. Am. Chem. Soc.*, **68**, 1305 (1946).
61. Endicott, Wick, Mercury, and Sherrill, *J. Am. Chem. Soc.*, **68**, 1299 (1946).
62. Christensen, Graham, and Tomisek, *J. Am. Chem. Soc.*, **68**, 1306 (1946).
63. Tomisek and Christensen, *J. Am. Chem. Soc.*, **67**, 2112 (1945).
64. Smith, Elisberg, and Sherrill, *J. Am. Chem. Soc.*, **68**, 1301 (1946).
65. McKee, McKee, and Bost, *J. Am. Chem. Soc.*, **69**, 184 (1947).
66. McKee, McKee, and Bost, *J. Am. Chem. Soc.*, **69**, 940 (1947).
67. McKee, McKee, and Bost, *J. Am. Chem. Soc.*, **68**, 1902 (1946).
68. Parfitt, Partridge, and Vipond, *J. Chem. Soc.*, **1963**, 3062.
69. Goodale and McKee, *J. Am. Chem. Soc.*, **71**, 1871 (1949).
70. Ciba Ltd., *Belg. Pat.*, 611,898 (1962); *Chem. Abstr.*, **58**, 9267 (1963).
71. Sen and Singh, *J. Indian Chem. Soc.*, **36**, 787 (1959).
72. Partridge, Slorach, and Vipond, *J. Chem. Soc.*, **1964**, 3670.
73. Sen and Singh, *J. Indian Chem. Soc.*, **36**, 807 (1959).
74. Hepworth, *Brit. Pat.*, 857,362 (1960); *Chem. Abstr.*, **55**, 14487 (1961).
75. Meerwein, Laasch, Mersch, and Nentwig, *Chem. Ber.*, **89**, 224 (1956).
76. Leonard and Curtin, *J. Org. Chem.*, **11**, 341 (1946).
77. Morley and Simpson, *J. Chem. Soc.*, **1949**, 1354.
78. Morley and Simpson, *J. Chem. Soc.*, **1948**, 360.
79. Mead, Johnson, and Co., *Brit. Pat.*, 920,019 (1963); *Chem. Abstr.*, **59**, 3935 (1963).
80. Leonard and Curtin, *J. Org. Chem.*, **11**, 349 (1946).
81. Tomisek and Christensen, *J. Am. Chem. Soc.*, **70**, 2423 (1948).
82. Berg, *J. Chem. Soc.*, **1961**, 4041.
83. Falco, Russell, and Hitchings, *J. Am. Chem. Soc.*, **73**, 4466 (1951).
84. Higashino, *J. Pharm. Soc. Japan*, **80**, 1404 (1960).
85. Breukink and Verkade, *Rec. Trav. Chim.*, **79**, 443 (1960).
86. Sykes, *J. Chem. Soc.*, **1955**, 2390.
87. Ralhan and Sachdev, *J. Sci. Ind. Res. India*, **19B**, 215 (1960).
88. Taylor and Ravindranathan, *J. Org. Chem.*, **27**, 2622 (1962).
89. Taylor, Knopf, and Borror, *J. Am. Chem. Soc.*, **82**, 3152 (1960).
90. Taylor and Borror, *J. Org. Chem.*, **26**, 4967 (1961).
91. Higashino, *J. Pharm. Soc. Japan*, **80**, 245 (1960).
92. Higashino, *Chem. Pharm. Bull. (Japan)*, **9**, 635 (1961).
93. Dymek, Brzozowska, and Brzozowski, *Ann. Univ. Mariae Curie-Sklodowska, Lublin Polonia Sect. AA*, **9**, 35 (1954); *Chem. Abstr.*, **51**, 5095 (1957).
94. Dymek, *Ann. Univ. Mariae Curie-Sklodowska, Lublin Polonia Sect. AA*, **6**, 25 (1951); *Chem. Abstr.*, **49**, 1731 (1955).
95. Dymek and Sybistowicz, *Monatsh. Chem.*, **96**, 542 (1965).
96. Dymek, Malicki, and Waksmundzka, *Ann. Univ. Mariae Curie-Sklodowska, Lublin Polonia Sect. AA*, **8**, 65 (1953); *Chem. Abstr.*, **51**, 6646 (1957).
97. Dymek, *Ann. Univ. Mariae Curie-Sklodowska, Lublin Polonia Sect. AA*, **9**, 45 (1954); *Chem. Abstr.*, **51**, 5087 (1957).
98. Meerwein, *Ger. Pat.*, 1,074,047 (1960); *Chem. Abstr.*, **55**, 21152 (1961).

99. Kötz, *J. Prakt. Chem.*, **47** (2), 303 (1893).

100. Vopicka and Lange, *J. Am. Chem. Soc.*, **57**, 1068 (1935).

101. Wellcome Foundation Ltd., *Brit. Pat.*, 806,772 (1958); *Chem. Abstr.*, **53**, 12316 (1959).

102. Hitchings, Falco, and Ledig, *U.S. Pat.*, 2,945,859 (1960); *Chem. Abstr.*, **54**, 24820 (1960).

103. Liebermann, *Fr. Pat.*, 1,107,487 (1956); *Chem. Abstr.*, **53**, 11418 (1959).

104. Lange and Sheibley, *J. Am. Chem. Soc.*, **53**, 3867 (1931).

105. Postovskii and Goncharova, *Zh. Obshch. Khim.*, **32**, 3323 (1962).

106. Oakes, Rydon, and Undheim, *J. Chem. Soc.*, **1962**, 4678.

107. Curd, Landquist, Raison, and Rose, *U.S. Pat.*, 2,497,347 (1950); *Chem. Abstr.*, **44**, 4513 (1950).

108. Ciba Ltd., *Brit. Pat.*, 686,055 (1953); *Chem. Abstr.*, **48**, 3398 (1954).

109. Ciba Ltd., *Brit. Pat.*, 664,262 (1952); *Chem. Abstr.*, **47**, 617 (1953).

110. Goncharova and Postovskii, *Zh. Obshch. Khim.*, **33**, 2475 (1963).

111. Hitchings, Falco, and Ledig, *Ger. Pat.*, 1,125,939 (1962); *Chem. Abstr.*, **57**, 16633 (1962).

112. Zerweck and Kunze, *Ger. Pat.*, 737,931 (1943); *Chem. Abstr.*, **38**, 3993 (1944).

113. Keneford, Morley, Simpson, and Wright, *J. Chem. Soc.*, **1949**, 1356.

114. Hearn, Morton, and Simpson, *J. Chem. Soc.*, **1951**, 3318.

115. Grammaticakis, *Compt. Rend.*, **247**, 2013 (1958).

116. Grammaticakis, *Compt. Rend.*, **252**, 4011 (1961).

117. Keneford, Morley, Simpson, and Wright, *J. Chem. Soc.*, **1950**, 1104.

118. Wolf, *U.S. Pat.*, 2,473,931 (1949); *Chem. Abstr.*, **43**, 7042 (1949).

119. Sherrill, Ortelt, Duckworth, and Budenstein, *J. Org. Chem.*, **19**, 699 (1954).

120. Brown, England, and Harper, *J. Chem. Soc.* (*C*), **1966**, 1165, and earlier papers for reaction mechanisms.

121. Sidhu, Thyagarajan, and Rao, *Naturwiss.*, **50**, 732 (1963).

122. Asano and Asai, *J. Pharm. Soc. Japan*, **78**, 450 (1958).

123. Asano and Asai, *Japan. Pat.*, 3376 (1959); *Chem. Abstr.*, **54**, 14277 (1960).

124. Shirakawa and Tsujikawa, *Takeda Kenkyusho Nempo*, **22**, 27 (1963); *Chem. Abstr.*, **60**, 12009 (1964).

125. Schofield and Swain, *J. Chem. Soc.*, **1950**, 392.

125a. Vereshchagina, Postovskii, and Mertsalov, *Zh. Obshch. Khim.*, **34**, 1689 (1964).

126. Dallacker, Hollinger, and Lipp, *Monatsh. Chem.*, **91**, 1134 (1960).

127. Dallacker, Gohlke, and Lipp, *Monatsh. Chem.*, **91**, 1103 (1960).

128. Dallacker, Meunier, Limpens, and Lipp, *Monatsh. Chem.*, **91**, 1077 (1960).

129. Dallacker, *Monatsh. Chem.*, **90**, 846 (1959).

130. Lipp, Dallacker, and Schaffranek, *Chem. Ber.*, **91**, 2247 (1958).

131. Dallacker, *Ann. Chem.*, **633**, 14 (1960).

132. Heller, Göring, Kloss, and Köhler, *J. Prakt. Chem.*, **111** (2), 36 (1925).

133. Bogert and Bender, *J. Am. Chem. Soc.*, **36**, 568 (1914).

134. Gambhir and Joshi, *J. Indian Chem. Soc.*, **41**, 47 (1964).

135. Heller and Siller, *J. Prakt. Chem.*, **116** (2), 1 (1927).

136. Heller and Mecke, *J. Prakt. Chem.*, **126**, 76 (1930).

137. Hirwe and Kulkarni, *Proc. Indian Acad. Sci.*, **16A**, 294 (1942); *Chem. Abstr.*, **37**, 4061 (1943).

138. Petersen, *Belg. Pat.*, 612,441 (1962); *Chem. Abstr.*, **57**, 15018 (1962).

139. Kratz, *J. Prakt. Chem.*, **53** (2), 210 (1896).
140. Thode, *J. Prakt. Chem.*, **69** (2), 92 (1904).
141. Herlinger, Petersen, Tietze, Hoffmeister, and Wirth, *Belg. Pat.*, 614,243 (1962); *Chem. Abstr.*, **58**, 4585 (1963).
142. Petersen, Tietze, Hoffmeister, and Wirth, *Belg. Pat.*, 612,389 (1962); *Chem. Abstr.*, **57**, 16638 (1962).
143. Vincent, Maillard, and Benard, *Bull. Soc. Chim. France*, **1962**, 1580.
144. Heller, Köhler, Gottfried, Arnold, and Herrmann, *J. Prakt. Chem.*, **120** (2), 49 (1928).
145. Wilson and Crawford, *J. Chem. Soc.*, **1925**, 103.
146. Grimmel, Guenther, and Morgan, *J. Am. Chem. Soc.*, **68**, 542 (1946); Guenther and Morgan, *U.S. Pat.*, 2,439,386 (1948); *Chem. Abstr.*, **42**, 5055 (1948).
147. Somasekhara, Dighe, Mankad, and Mukherjee, *Indian J. Chem.*, **2**, 369 (1964).
148. Bogert and Gortner, *J. Am. Chem. Soc.*, **31**, 943 (1909).
149. Bogert and Klaber, *J. Am. Chem. Soc.*, **30**, 807 (1908).
150. Legrand and Lozach, *Bull. Soc. Chim. France*, **1961**, 1400.
151. Joshi and Gambhir, *J. Org. Chem.*, **26**, 3714 (1961).
152. Anschütz, Schmidt, and Greiffenberg, *Ber. Deut. Chem. Ges.*, **35**, 3480 (1902).
153. Schlager, *Arch. Pharm.*, **296**, 217 (1963).
154. Gärtner, *Ann. Chem.*, **336**, 229 (1904)
155. Heller, *Ber. Deut. Chem. Ges.*, 48, 1183 (1915).
156. Heller and Hessel, *J. Prakt. Chem.*, **120** (2), 64 (1928).
157. Paal and Busch, *Ber. Deut. Chem. Ges.*, **22**, 2683 (1889).
158. Cairncross and Bogert, *Collection Czech. Chem. Commun.*, **7**, 548 (1935).
159. Leonard and Ruyle, *J. Org. Chem.*, **13**, 903 (1948).
160. Dighe, Somasekhara, Bagavant, and Mukherjee, *Current Sci. (India)*, **33**, 78 (1964); *Chem. Abstr.*, **60**, 10681 (1964).
161. Kunckell, *Ber. Deut. Chem. Ges.*, **43**, 1234 (1910).
162. Kühle and Wegler, *Ann. Chem.*, **616**, 183 (1958).
163. Kühle and Wegler, *Ger. Pat.*, 1,068,263 (1959); *Chem. Abstr.*, **55**, 12435 (1961).
164. Darapsky and Gaudian, *J. Prakt. Chem.*, **147**, 43 (1936).
165. Uskoković, Iacobelli, Toome, and Wenner, *J. Org. Chem.*, **29**, 582 (1964).
166. Bogert and Beal, *J. Am. Chem. Soc.*, **34**, 516 (1912).
167. Heller and Mecke, *J. Prakt. Chem.*, **131**, 82 (1931).
168. Kulkarni, *J. Indian Chem. Soc.*, **19**, 180 (1942).
169. Bogert, Beal, and Amend, *J. Am. Chem. Soc.*, **32**, 1654 (1910).
170. Bogert and Geiger, *J. Am. Chem. Soc.*, **34**, 524 (1912).
171. Bogert and Chambers, *J. Am. Chem. Soc.*, **28**, 207 (1906).
172. Tsuda, Fukushima, Ichikawa, Yoshida, and Ishii, *J. Pharm. Soc. Japan*, **62**, 69 (1942).
173. Wallace and Tiernan Inc., *Brit. Pat.*, 916,139 (1963); *Chem. Abstr.*, **59**, 1663 (1963).
174. Baker, Schaub, Joseph, McEvoy, and Williams, *J. Org. Chem.*, **17**, 164 (1952).
175. Baker, Schaub, Joseph, McEvoy, and Williams, *J. Org. Chem.*, **17**, 141 (1952).
176. Bogert and Scatchard, *J. Am. Chem. Soc.*, **41**, 2052 (1919).

177. Huntress and Gladding, *J. Am. Chem. Soc.*, **64**, 2644 (1942).
178. Niementowski, *J. Prakt. Chem.*, **51** (2), 510 (1895).
179. Spinks and Young, *Brit. Pat.*, 750,175 (1956); *Chem. Abstr.*, **51**, 1303 (1957).
180. Magidson and Golovchinskaya, *Zh. Obshch. Khim.*, **8**, 1787 (1938); *Chem. Abstr.*, **33**, 4993 (1939).
181. Curd, Landquist, and Rose, *J. Chem. Soc.*, **1948**, 1759.
182. Berg and Parnell, *J. Chem. Soc.*, **1961**, 5275.
183. Bogert, Amend, and Chambers, *J. Am. Chem. Soc.*, **32**, 1297 (1910).
184. Bogert and Kropff, *J. Am. Chem. Soc.*, **31**, 1071 (1909).
185. Bogert, Gortner, and Amend, *J. Am. Chem. Soc.*, **33**, 949 (1911).
186. Naff and Christensen, *J. Am. Chem. Soc.*, **73**, 1372 (1951).
187. Murahashi and Horiie, *J. Am. Chem. Soc.*, **78**, 4816 (1956); *U.S. Pat.*, 2,944,056 (1960); *Chem. Abstr.*, **55**, 1667 (1961).
188. Armarego, *J. Chem. Soc.*, **1962**, 561.
189. Schofield and Swain, *J. Chem. Soc.*, **1949**, 1367; Schofield and Swain, *Nature*, **161**, 690 (1948).
190. Wu and Hamilton, *J. Am. Chem. Soc.*, **74**, 1863 (1952).
191. Berg and Lucas, *Nature*, **189**, 64 (1961).
192. Iyer, Anand, and Dhar, *J. Sci. Ind. Res. India*, **13B**, 451 (1954).
193. Iyer, Anand, and Dhar, *J. Sci. Ind. Res. India*, **15C**, 1 (1956).
194. Simpson and Morley, *J. Chem. Soc.*, **1949**, 1014.
195. Chapman, Clarke, and Wilson, *J. Chem. Soc.*, **1963**, 2256.
196. Sandberg, *Svensk. Farm. Tidskr.*, **61**, 417 (1957); *Chem. Abstr.*, **52**, 1180 (1958).
197. Curd, Landquist, Raison, and Rose, *Brit. Pat.*, 587,936 (1947); *Chem. Abstr.*, **42**, 4615 (1948).
198. Tsuda, Ikuma, Kawamura, Tachikawa, Baba, and Miyadera, *Chem. Pharm. Bull. (Japan)*, **10**, 247 (1962).
199. Petersen, Kroneberg, and Stoepel, *Ger. Pat.*, 1,133,390 (1962); *Chem. Abstr.*, **58**, 1477 (1963).
200. Biniecki and Muszynski, *Acta Polon. Pharm.*, **17**, 99 (1960); *Chem. Abstr.*, **54**, 21119 (1960).
201. Biniecki, Gora, Moll, Rylski, Gogolimska, Kurowska, and Pindor, *Acta Polon. Pharm.*, **18**, 261 (1961); *Chem. Abstr.*, **57**, 16613 (1962).
202. Boltze, Dell, Lehwald, Lorenz, and Rüberg-Shweer, *Arzneimittelforsch.*, **13**, 688 (1963).
203. Kunckell, *Ber. Deut. Chem. Ges.*, **43**, 1021 (1910).
204. Dehoff, *J. Prakt. Chem.*, **42** (2), 346 (1890).
205. Petersen, Tietze, Hoffmeister, and Wirth, *Brit. Pat.*, 932,680 (1963); *Chem. Abstr.*, **60**, 4162 (1964).
206. Tietze, Petersen, and Hoffmeister, *U.S. Pat.*, 3,075,982 (1963); *Chem. Abstr.*, **59**, 2837 (1963).
207. Maillard, Morin, Vincent, and Bernard, *U.S. Pat.*, 3,047,462 (1962); *Chem. Abstr.*, **58**, 1474 (1963).
208. Bogert and Seil, *J. Am. Chem. Soc.*, **28**, 884 (1906).
209. Macbeth and Rodda, *Nature*, **156**, 207 (1945).
210. Geigy, A.-G., *Brit. Pat.*, 822,069 (1959); *Chem. Abstr.*, **55**, 2005 (1961).
211. Kishor, Arora, and Parmar, *J. Med. Chem.*, **8**, 550 (1965).
212. Curd and Young, *U.S. Pat.*, 2,643,253 (1953); *Chem. Abstr.*, **49**, 384 (1955).

213. Dallacker, *Ann. Chem.*, **633**, 23 (1960).
214. Andrisano and Modena, *Gazz. Chim. Ital.*, **80**, 321 (1950).
215. Denney and Rosen, *U.S. Dept. Comm. Office Tech. Services*, A.D., 260,401, p. 11 (1960); *Chem. Abstr.*, **59**, 4839 (1963).
216. Bogert and Geiger, *J. Am. Chem. Soc.*, **34**, 683 (1912).
217. Bogert and Heidelberger, *J. Am. Chem. Soc.*, **34**, 183 (1912).
218. Bogert and Cook, *J. Am. Chem. Soc.*, **28**, 1449 (1906).
219. Price and Reitsema, *J. Org. Chem.*, **12**, 269 (1947).
220. Butler and Partridge, *J. Chem. Soc.*, **1959**, 1512.
221. Stephen and Stephen, *J. Chem. Soc.*, **1956**, 4173.
222. Hayashi and Higashino, *Chem. Pharm. Bull. (Japan)*, **12**, 43 (1964).
223. Ciba Ltd., *Swiss Pat.*, 282,950 (1952); *Chem. Abstr.*, **48**, 7645 (1954).
224. Weuffen, Starke, and Hermann, *Pharmazie*, **18**, 490 (1963); *Chem. Abstr.*, **60**, 7381 (1964).
225. deCat, Sevens, and van Dormael, *U.S. Pat.*, 2,668,112 (1954); *Chem. Abstr.*, **48**, 5699 (1954).
226. Hayo, Havera, Strycker, Leipzig, Kulp, and Hartzler, *J. Med. Chem.*, **8**, 807 (1965).
227. Dymek and Berezowski, *Dissertationes Pharm.*, **15**, 23 (1963); *Chem. Abstr.*, **59**, 11491 (1963).
228. Tsuda, Ikuma, Kawamura, Tachikawa, Sakai, Tamura, and Amakasu, *Chem. Pharm. Bull. (Japan)*, **12**, 1357 (1964).
229. Cohn, *J. Prakt. Chem.*, **84** (2), 394 (1911).
230. Abezgauz, Sokolov, and Udilov, *Zh. Obshch. Khim.*, **34**, 2965 (1964).
231. Grammaticakis, *Compt. Rend.*, **254**, 501 (1962).
232. Casagrande, Canova, and Ferrari, *Farmaco Pavia (Ed. Sci.)*, **20**, 544 (1965).
233. Kirchner and Zalay, *U.S. Pat.*, 3,217,005 (1965); *Chem. Abstr.*, **64**, 3570 (1966).

CHAPTER VIII

The Reduced Quinazolines

The term 'hydro' which is adopted in the current nomenclature of oxo and thio heterocyclic compounds, for example in 1,2-dihydro-1-methyl-2-oxoquinazoline (1), is a little confusing (Ch. IV). These are not reduced compounds although they are derivatives of a parent hydro compound. We will now be concerned with reduced quinazolines, some of which may have 'real' as well as 'imaginary' hydrogens. 1,2,3,4-Tetrahydro-4-oxo-3-methylquinazoline (2), for example, has two 'real' and two 'imaginary' hydrogen atoms. The sections of this chapter are selected according to the positions of reduction in the quinazoline nucleus (i.e. positions where the 'real' hydrogen atoms are present). The compound 2 is therefore classified as a 1,2-dihydroquinazoline, and 1,2,3,4,5,6,7,8-octahydro-2,4-dioxoquinazoline (3) as a 5,6,7,8-tetrahydroquinazoline. Reduced thioquinazolines (Ch. VI, Sect. 1.B.) and quinazoline-3-oxides (Ch. IX, Sect. 3.) are discussed in the chapters cited.

(1)   (2)   (3)

1. Preparation of 1,2-Dihydroquinazolines

A. By the Reaction of o-Aminobenzaldehyde with Amines and Formaldehyde

1,2-Dihydroquinazoline is not known. 3-Allyl- and 3-methyl-1,2-dihydroquinazolinium salts (4) have been prepared from o-amino-benzaldehyde, formaldehyde, and allylamine or methylamine under

$$(1)$$

(4)

physiological conditions, and were isolated as their picrates (Eq. 1). Similarly, by using γ-aminobutyraldehyde diethylacetal, 1,2-dihydro-2,3-trimethylenequinazolinium picrate was prepared.[1] This work was done in connection with the biosynthesis of peganine (Ch. XI, Sect. 1.B.). The formation of 1,2-dihydroquinazolines from the reaction of o-aminobenzaldehyde, methylamine, and several aliphatic aldehydes was used in an analytical study. Although the 2-substituted 1,2-dihydro-3-methylquinazolinium salts formed were not isolated, their ultraviolet spectra were used for the estimation of formaldehyde, acetaldehyde, propionaldehyde, butyraldehyde, and chloral hydrate.[2]

B. From Anthranilamides and Aldehydes, Ketones or Related Compounds

Anthranilamides condense with aromatic aldehydes to form anils which rearrange under the influence of heat, dilute acid, or dilute alkali, to 1,2,3,4-tetrahydro-4-oxoquinazolines (Reaction 2).[3] When aliphatic aldehydes or ketones are used, the intermediates are not readily isolable and the dihydroquinazolines are obtained directly. This is a general method and was used to prepare several substituted 1,2,3,4-tetrahydro-4-oxoquinazolines (Eq. 3).[4-11] 1,2,3,4-Tetrahydro-4-oxoquinazoline was isolated from the reaction of anthranilamide and formalin,[12] but with excess of formalin, 1,3-dihydroxymethyl-

$$(2)$$

1,2,3,4-tetrahydro-4-oxoquinazoline (5),[11] or a polymeric material,[12] was formed. N-o-Aminobenzoyl-N'-benzoylhydrazine and acetaldehyde yielded 3-benzoylamino-1,2,3,4-tetrahydro-2-methyl-4-oxoquinazoline.[13] o-Aminothiobenzamide and o-aminobenzamidine condensed with

$$(3)$$

(5)

acetone to form 1,2,3,4-tetrahydro-2,2-dimethyl-4-thio- and 4-amino-1,2-dihydro-2,2-dimethylquinazoline respectively.[14] N,N'-Disubstituted formamidines were also used instead of formaldehyde for the preparation of 1,2,3,4-tetrahydro-4-oxoquinazolines.[11]

C. By Reduction of 3,4-Dihydro-4-oxoquinazolines and Related Compounds

Reduction of 6,7-benzo- and 3-methyl- 3,4-dihydro-4-oxoquinazolines with lithium aluminium hydride afforded 6,7-benzo-[15] and 3-methyl-[16] 1,2,3,4-tetrahydro-4-oxoquinazolines, although care was taken to avoid further reduction of the oxo group.[16] The use of sodium

$$(4)$$

borohydride in the presence of anhydrous aluminum chloride was found to be a more satisfactory reagent for these reductions (Reaction 4)[8,17] and (Reaction 5).[6] Reduction of 4-methoxy- and 4-phenoxyquinazoline

$$(5)$$

with lithium aluminium hydride gave 4-methoxy- and 4-phenoxy-1,2-dihydroquinazoline, respectively, which were characterized by conversion to their 1-phenylcarbamoyl derivatives with phenyl isocyanate. 4-Phenylthioquinazoline, on the other hand, was extensively reduced to o-aminobenzylamine.[18]

Raney nickel desulphurized 1,2,3,4-tetrahydro-1-methyl-4-oxo-3-phenyl-2-thioquinazoline to 1,2,3,4-tetrahydro-1-methyl-4-oxo-3-phenylquinazoline.[19] 2-o-Aminophenyl-1,2,3,4-tetrahydro-4-oxoquinazoline was the only 1,2-dihydroquinazoline prepared by catalytic hydrogenation of a 3,4-dihydro-4-oxoquinazoline.[20]

2. Preparation of 1,4-Dihydroquinazolines

In 1893 Bischler[21] claimed to have prepared 1,4-dihydro-2-methylquinazoline by the dehydration of o-acetamidobenzylamine (6) because his product appeared to be different from 3,4-dihydro-2-methylquinazoline obtained by Gabriel and Jansen[22] by dehydration of o-acetamidomethylaniline (7). In 1961 it was shown,[23] however, that these two

(6)   (7)

dihydroquinazolines were identical with 3,4-dihydro-2-methylquinazoline and the earlier confusion arose because the latter formed a dimorphic picrate. Details of the preparation of 1,4-dihydroquinazolines were first described in 1961.[23,24] 1-Methyl- and 1-benzyl-1,4-dihydroquinazoline were obtained by boiling o-methylamino- and o-benzylaminobenzylamine with anhydrous formic acid (Reaction 6). Attempts

(6)

to debenzylate 1-benzyl-1,4-dihydroquinazoline with sodium and liquid ammonia, however, gave 70% yield of 3,4-dihydroquinazoline and not the expected 1,4-dihydroquinazoline.[23] 2-Methyl-, 2-phenyl-, and 2-o-nitrophenyl- 1,4-dihydro-1-methylquinazolines were prepared by the

$$\text{(7)}$$

reaction of o-methylaminobenzyl chloride with methyl, phenyl, and o-nitrophenyl nitriles in the presence of stannic chloride (Reaction 7) (see Sect. 4.E.).[24-26]

3. Preparation of 2,3-Dihydroquinazolines

2,3-Dihydroquinazolines require o-quinonoid structures in both rings and are therefore expected to be rather unstable unless they are substituted with large groups. 6-Chloro-3-p-chlorophenyl-, 6-methyl-3-p-tolyl-, and 7,8-benzo-3-1'-naphthyl- 2,3-dihydro-2-hydroxy-2,4-diphenylquinazolines were obtained by heating the isomeric 3,4-dihydro-4-hydroxy-2,4-diphenylquinazolines (see Sect. 4.F.) at 250° (Eq. 8.)[27-29] Their structures, however, are questionable.

$$\text{(8)}$$

4. Preparation of 3,4-Dihydroquinazolines

A. From o-Aminobenzylamines or o-Aminobenzyl Alcohols

3,4-Dihydroquinazolines that are unsubstituted in position 2 are conveniently prepared by heating o-aminobenzylamines with anhydrous formic acid (sometimes in the presence of sodium formate),[30-39] with ethyl orthoformate[35,36,39] or with formamidines (Reaction 9).[39] o-Amidobenzylamines can be cyclized to 3,4-dihydroquinazolines by heating directly,[22,23,38-42] or in the presence of acid.[43-45] An alternative

$$\text{(9)}$$

14+Q.

synthesis is the reductive cyclization of *o*-amidomethylnitrobenzenes with zinc and hydrochloric or acetic acids (Reaction 10).[41,42,46-57] Catalytic reduction of *o*-amidobenzonitriles followed by cyclization of the resulting benzylamines with dilute alkali affords another modification of this method.[58]

$$R^2 \underset{NO_2}{\overset{\overset{R}{\underset{|}{N}}-COR^1}{\bigcirc}} \xrightarrow{Zn/H^+} R^2 \underset{N}{\overset{N-R}{\bigcirc}} R^1 \tag{10}$$

Several 3,4-dihydro-2-guanidinoquinazolines were prepared by heating *o*-aminobenzylamines with dicyandiamide in water.[59]

1,2,3,4-Tetrahydro-2-oxoquinazolines were prepared by fusion of *o*-aminobenzyl alcohols with urea at temperatures above 160°.[60-63] Reaction of phosgene with *o*-aminobenzylamines gave similar products.[36,37] These were also obtained from *o*-aminobenzyl alcohols by reaction with potassium cyanate in acid solution, followed by cyclization of the resulting *o*-ureidobenzyl alcohol with concentrated hydrochloric acid (Reaction 11).[64,65] In a variant of this method 1,2,3,4-tetrahydro-1,6-dimethyl-2-oxoquinazoline was obtained by heating *N*-methyl 2-cyanamino-5-methylbenzyl alcohol with alcoholic sulphuric acid.[66]

$$R \underset{NH_2}{\overset{\overset{R^1}{\underset{|}{C}}-OH}{\bigcirc}} \xrightarrow{HNCO} R \underset{NHCONH_2}{\overset{\overset{R^1}{\underset{|}{C}}-OH}{\bigcirc}} \xrightarrow{H^+} R \underset{\underset{H}{N}}{\overset{NH}{\bigcirc}} O \tag{11}$$

B. From Anilines and Formaldehyde

The reaction of *p*-toluidine with formaldehyde in the presence of mineral acid was first studied by Tröger in 1887 who isolated a base with the molecular formula $C_{17}H_{18}N_2$.[67] This compound was later called 'Tröger's base' (Sect. 7.). Maffei repeated this reaction and isolated two other bases, in addition to Tröger's base, and showed that they were 3,4-dihydro-6-methyl-3-*p*-tolyl- and 1,2,3,4-tetrahydro-6-methyl-3-*p*-tolylquinazoline.[68,69] Phenetidine behaved similarly and the reaction (12) was postulated.[34,69] It was assumed that the formic acid required to give the dihydro compound was formed by oxidation of formaldehyde. This reaction scheme was supported by Wagner and his collaborators,[70-75] and the reaction proceeded equally well when formic acid was added to the mixture.[71,76] The reaction takes place at

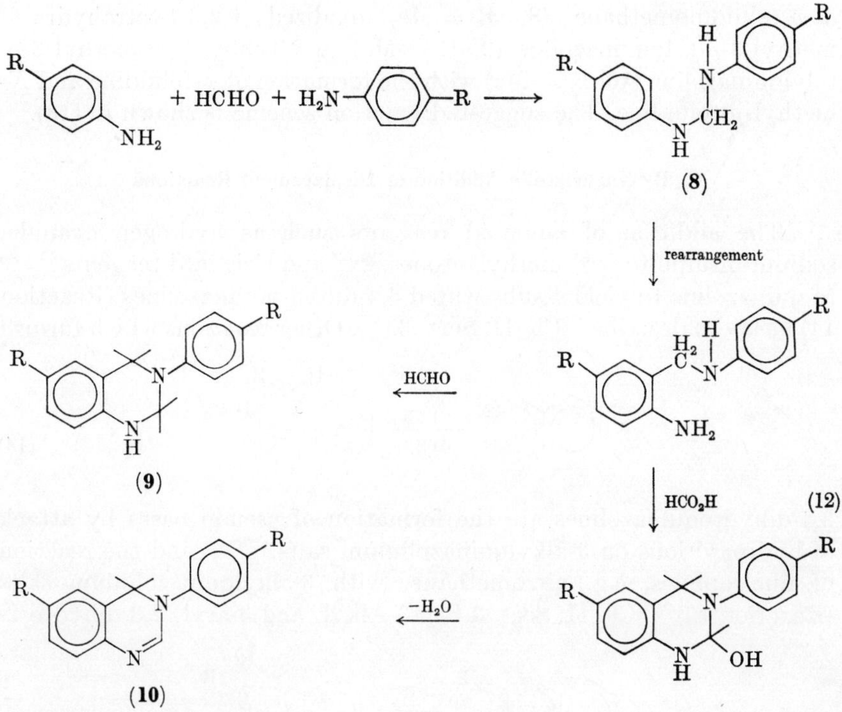

(8)

rearrangement

(9)

HCHO

(12)

(10)

$-H_2O$

HCO$_2$H

R = Me, MeO, EtO, Cl, Br, F.

room temperature during several hours, or at 100° for 0.5 hours if formic acid is added. With p-bromoaniline the product was 6-bromo-3-p-bromophenyl-3,4-dihydro-4-oxoquinazoline,[77] and it was stated that the dihydro compound was formed first but was oxidized during the lengthy work-up.[78] Formic acid is not necessarily the agent for the formation of the dihydroquinazoline because Simons showed that the

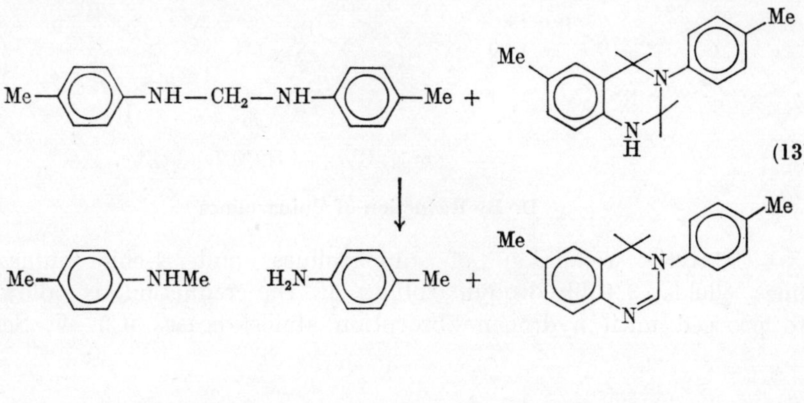

(13)

di-p-toluidinomethane (**8**, R = Me) oxidized 1,2,3,4-tetrahydro-6-methyl-3-p-tolyquinazoline (**9**, R = Me) to 3,4-dihydro-6-methyl-3-p-tolylquinazoline (**10**, R = Me) with the formation of p-toluidine and N-methyl-p-toluidine. The suggested reaction scheme is shown in (13).[79]

C. By Nucleophilic Addition or Displacement Reactions

The addition of anionoid reagents such as hydrogen cyanide, sodium bisulphite,[80,81] methylketones,[82,83] and Grignard reagents[84–86] to quinazoline to yield 4-substituted 3,4-dihydroquinazolines (Reaction 14) has been described (Ch. II, Sect. 3.C.). Other reactions which furnish

$$\text{(14)}$$

3,4-dihydroquinazolines are the formation of pseudo bases by attack of hydroxyl ions on 3-alkylquinazolinium salts,[1,30,85] and the reaction of nucleophiles, e.g. nitromethane, with 3-alkylquinazolinium salts (Reaction 15)[87] (Ch. II, Sect. 3.B.). 3-Alkyl- and 3-aryl- 2,3-dihydro-2-

$$\text{(15)}$$

$$R^1 = OH^- \text{ or } CH_2NO_2^-$$

oxo(or thio)quinazolines react with ethanol to form 4-ethoxy-1,2,3,4-tetrahydro-2-oxo(or thio)quinazolines and the ethoxy group can be displaced by other nucleophiles, e.g. ethyl acetoacetate (Reaction 16) (see Ch. VI, Sect. 1.B.).[88,89,90,90a]

$$\text{(16)}$$

$$X = O \text{ or } S; \ R^1 = -CH(COMe)CO_2Et$$

D. By Reduction of Quinazolines

Catalytic reduction of quinazolines and 4-chloroquinazolines yields 3,4-dihydroquinazolines if the reduction is allowed to proceed until hydrogen absorption almost ceases (Ch. V, Sect.

1.E.b.(iv)).[15,23,80,91,92] Catalytic reduction of 2-chloro-4-phenylquina-
zoline yields 3,4-dihydro-4-phenylquinazoline.[93] Similarly 4-methyl-,
4-ethyl-, and 4-isopropylquinazoline in neutral media yield 4-methyl-,
4-ethyl-, and 4-isopropyl-3,4-dihydroquinazoline but the rates of
reduction are considerably slower than those for quinazoline or 2-
methylquinazoline[86] (Reaction 17). The reductions are faster in acid
media, e.g. acetic acid.[93a] No reduction of the 1,2-double bond occurs
during these slow reductions (see Ch. III, Sect. 2.B.b.). Catalytic
reduction of quinazoline-3-oxides also gives 3,4-dihydroquinazolines[94,95]
(Ch. IX, Sect. 2.A.).

$$(17)$$

Reduction of 2-chloro-4-phenyl-, 2-chloro-6-methyl-4-phenyl-, and
2,4-dichloro-8-methyl- quinazoline with hydriodic acid and red phosphorus furnished 4-phenyl-,[61] 6-methyl-4-phenyl-,[63] and 8-methyl-
3,4-dihydroquinazolines[96] respectively. Sodium borohydride reduces
quinazoline to 3,4-dihydroquinazoline, and lithium aluminium hydride
reduces 2-chloro-4-phenyl- and 4-chloro-2-phenylquinazoline to 4-
phenyl- and 2-phenyl-3,4-dihydroquinazoline respectively. This reagent
also reduced 4- and 2-chloroquinazoline, but cleavage of the products
occurred and o-aminobenzylamine was isolated.[18]

E. From o-Aminobenzyl Chloride and Nitriles

o-Aminobenzyl chloride hydrochloride and aliphatic or aromatic
nitriles react in the presence of anhydrous stannic chloride to yield

$$(18)$$

2-substituted 3,4-dihydroquinazolines in high yields (Reaction 18). 2-Methyl-, 2-ethyl-, 2-propyl-, 2-methoxymethyl-, 2-phenyl-, 2-*p*-methoxyphenyl-, 2-*o*-nitrophenyl-, 2-*m*-nitrophenyl-, 2-benzyl-, 2-*o*-chlorobenzyl-, 2-*p*-chlorobenzyl-, 2-1′-naphthyl-3,4-dihydroquinazoline were prepared in this manner[24,25,97] (see Sect. 2.). Similarly *o*-aminobenzyl chloride hydrochloride and 5-benzyloxyvaleronitrile gave 3,4-dihydro-2,3-trimethylenequinazoline.[97a]

F. Miscellaneous

The condensation between aromatic amines and benzoyl chloride takes place in the presence of anhydrous zinc chloride at 180° to yield 3-aryl-3,4-dihydro-4-hydroxy-2,4-diphenylquinazolines. This reaction appears to be of general applicability because *p*-chloroaniline, *p*-toluidine, 2,4-xylidine, and 1-naphthylamine reacted with benzoyl chloride to form 6-chloro-3-*p*-chlorophenyl-, 6-methyl-3-*p*-tolyl-, 6,8-dimethyl-3-2′,4′-xylyl-[27] and 7,8-benzo-3-1′-naphthyl-[28] 3,4-dihydro-4-hydroxy-2,4-diphenylquinazolines (Reaction 19). Similar treatment of *p*-nitroaniline and benzoyl chloride apparently stops at an intermediate stage to give 2-benzamido-5-nitrobenzophenone. The latter yields 6-nitro-2,4-diphenylquinazoline by a Bischler synthesis.[97b]

$$\tag{19}$$

The authenticity of the 4-substituted 3-aryl-3,4-dihydro-4-hydroxyquinazolines prepared by the reaction of Grignard reagents on 3-aryl-3,4-dihydro-4-oxoquinazolines[98,99] has been questioned, and their structures require further investigation (see Ch. IV, Sect. 2.C.b.(vi)). The desulphurization of 3,4-dihydro-4-thioquinazolines to 3,4-dihydroquinazolines has been achieved with Raney nickel.[100]

5. Preparation of 1,2,3,4 Tetrahydroquinazolines

A. From Anilines and Formaldehyde

The formation of 1,2,3,4-tetrahydroquinazolines as by-products in the reaction of *p*-substituted anilines and formaldehyde in the presence of acid has been described (Sect. 4.B.). When p-nitroaniline was used, the product was 1,2,3,4-tetrahydro-2-hydroxy-6-nitro-3-p-nitrophenyl-quinazoline which probably resulted after oxidation of some of the formaldehyde.[45,101] Acetic anhydride dehydrates this compound to 3,4-dihydro-6-nitro-3-p-nitrophenylquinazoline, although acetylation to the 2-acetoxy derivative was also achieved.[69,101] Further reaction of 6-chloro-3-p-chlorophenyl- and 6-bromo-3-p-bromophenyl-1,2,3,4-tetrahydroquinazoline with formaldehyde can occur with the formation of 6-chloro-3-p-chlorophenyl- and 6-bromo-3-p-bromophenyl-1,2,3,4-tetrahydro-1-hydroxymethylquinazoline respectively (11).[73]

CH$_2$OH

(11) R = Cl or Br

B. From o-Aminobenzylamines and Aldehydes

o-Aminobenzylamines and aliphatic or aromatic aldehydes yield 1,2,3,4-tetrahydroquinazolines (Reaction 20).[16,56,101-103] Formaldehyde

$$R^2 \overset{NHR^1}{\underset{NH}{\bigcirc}} \quad \xrightarrow{R^3CHO} \quad R^2 \overset{N-R^1}{\underset{R}{\bigcirc}} R^3 \quad + H_2O \qquad (20)$$

can be replaced by diaminomethanes, e.g. di-p-toluidinomethane, dipiperidinomethane, as in the preparation of 1,2,3,4-tetrahydro-6-methyl-3-p-tolyquinazoline.[11,79]

C. By Reduction of 3,4-Dihydroquinazolines (including their 4-Oxo Derivatives)

a. *Chemical Reductions*

1,2,3,4-Tetrahydroquinazolines are most conveniently prepared by the reduction of 3,4-dihydroquinazolines with 1.5–4% sodium amalgam in aqueous alkali,[22,31,41,57,104,105] or with sodium and ethyl or amyl alcohol (Reaction 21).[32,34,36,38,42,46-49,51,55,71,106,107] The latter reagent reduced 3-p-chlorophenyl-[49] and 3-p-bromophenyl-3,4-dihydroquinazolines[108] to 1,2,3,4-tetrahydro-3-phenylquinazoline. Desulphurization of 1,2,3,4-tetrahydro-2-thioquinazolines to 1,2,3,4-tetrahydroquinazolines was also accomplished with sodium and alcohol.[36,37,61,109] Zinc and sulphuric acid reduced 3,4-dihydro-6-methyl-2-methylthio-3-p-tolylquinazoline to 1,2,3,4-tetrahydro-6-methyl-3-p-tolylquinazoline,[36] and tin and hydrochloric acid converted 3,4-dihydro-4-oxo-3-phenylquinazoline to 3,4-dihydro-3-phenylquinazoline.[110] 3,4-Dihydro-3-methyl-4-oxo-[16,111] and 1,4-dihydro-1-methyl-4-oxoquinazoline[111] were reduced with lithium aluminium hydride to 3-methyl- and 1-methyl-1,2,3,4-tetrahydroquinazoline respectively.

$$\text{(21)}$$

b. *Catalytic and Electrolytic Reductions*

Although the catalytic reduction of quinazoline with palladium on charcoal appears to stop after the formation of 3,4-dihydroquinazoline,[23] it can apparently be made to proceed further to yield 1,2,3,4-tetrahydroquinazoline.[112]

Electrolytic reduction of 3,4-dihydro-4-oxo-3-phenylquinazoline in aqueous alcoholic sodium carbonate at 25°, using a lead cathode, gave 1,2,3,4-tetrahydro-4-hydroxy-3-phenylquinazoline. On the other hand, 1,2,3,4-tetrahydro-3-phenylquinazoline was obtained when a cathode of copper coated with platinum black was used and the electrolyses performed at 50–60°.[113]

6. Physical and Chemical Properties of 1,2-, 1,4-, and 3,4-Dihydro-, and 1,2,3,4-Tetrahydroquinazolines

All the 1,2-dihydroquinazolines that have been prepared possess an oxo, amino, or thio substituent in position 4 which reacts in the normal manner. Thus 1,2,3,4-tetrahydro-2,2-dimethyl-4-thioquinazoline gave 1,2-dihydro-2,2-dimethyl-4-methylthioquinazoline on treatment with methyl iodide, and this in turn gave 4-amino-1,2-dihydro-2,2-dimethylquinazoline when heated with alcoholic ammonia. Also, when the latter compound was boiled with hydrochloric acid, 1,2,3,4-

tetrahydro-2,2-dimethyl-4-oxoquinazoline was formed.[14] The ultraviolet spectra of a few 1,2,3,4-tetrahydro-4-oxoquinazolines were
similar to those of anthranilamides.[7]

1,4-Dihydroquinazoline is not known, and there is no evidence as
yet that it exists in tautomeric equilibrium with 3,4-dihydroquinazo-
line.[23] 1-Substituted 1,4-dihydroquinazolines and 3-substituted 3,4-
dihydroquinazolines have similar physical properties. They can be
distilled without decomposition, but are slowly oxidized in air to the
corresponding 4-oxo compounds. They are stronger bases than 1,2,3,4-
tetrahydroquinazoline (see Table VIII.1). This is most probably
attributed to the stabilization of their cations by amidinium resonance
(Eq. 22). It is present in both the 1,4- and the 3,4-dihydroquinazolines
which have very similar basic strengths. They readily form stable salts
and picrates (see Tables VIII, 4–7). The ultraviolet spectra of the
neutral species and cations of a few 1,4- and 3,4-dihydroquinazolines
have been recorded.[81,85,86]

$$
\tag{22}
$$

3,4-Dihydro-3-methylquinazoline was the sole product isolated
from the methylation of 3,4-dihydroquinazoline,[23] and 3,4-dihydro-2-
methylquinazoline gave 3,4-dihydro-2,3-dimethylquinazoline.[40] Methylation of 3-substituted 3,4-dihydroquinazolines with methyl iodide gave
the 1-methiodides.[46,114] 3,4-Dihydro-1,6-dimethyl-3-p-tolylquinazoli-
nium iodide is a particularly useful reagent for the synthesis of aldehydes. It reacts with Grignard reagents to give 2-substituted 1,2,3,4-
tetrahydro-1,6-dimethyl-3-p-tolylquinazolines which yield the alde-

$$
\tag{23}
$$

14*

hydes (containing one carbon atom more than in the Grignard reagent) on hydrolysis (Reaction 23).[114-116] 3,4-Dihydroquinazolines without a substituent on $N_{(3)}$ can be acetylated[92] and nitrosated[61] on $N_{(3)}$, and are smoothly oxidized to quinazolines (**12**), by alkaline potassium ferricyanide (Reaction 24)[41,57,80,84,86,92] (Ch. III, Sect. 1.B.). 3,4-Dihydro-4-

$$ R^2 \underset{N}{\overset{R^1}{\bigcirc}} \underset{R}{\overset{NH}{}} \xrightarrow[\text{OH}^-]{\text{K}_3\text{Fe(CN)}_6} R^2 \underset{N}{\overset{R^1}{\bigcirc}} \underset{R}{\overset{N}{}} \tag{24} $$

(**12**)

t-butylquinazoline is the only known example which is oxidized to quinazoline, with the loss of the 4-t-butyl group, by this reagent.[23] 3-Substituted 3,4-dihydroquinazolines, on the other hand, are oxidized to the corresponding 4-oxo derivatives (Reaction 25). Potassium permanganate was used to effect this oxidation (see Ch. IV, Sect.

$$ \overset{}{\bigcirc} \underset{N}{\overset{N-R}{}} \xrightarrow{\text{[O]}} \overset{O}{\bigcirc} \underset{N}{\overset{N-R}{}} \tag{25} $$

TABLE VIII.1.   Ionization Constants of Reduced Quinazolines in Water.

Quinazoline	pK_a	References
3,4-Dihydro-	9.19	81
	8.62	92
Acetyl-3,4-dihydro-	2.81[a]	92
8-Amino-3,4-dihydro-	8.08[a]	92
Diacetyl-8-amino-3,4-dihydro-	2.43[a]	92
3,4-Dihydro-4-hydroxy-3-methyl-	7.64	85
1,4-Dihydro-1-methyl-	9.43	81
3,4-Dihydro-2-methyl-	10.16	81
3,4-Dihydro-3-methyl-	9.23	81
3,4-Dihydro-4-methyl-	9.19	85
3,4-Dihydro-4-ethyl-	9.21	86
3,4-Dihydro-4-isopropyl-	9.21	86
3,4-Dihydro-4-t-butyl-	9.36	86
3,4-Dihydro-4-sulpho-	~7.1	85
1,2,3,4-Tetrahydro-	7.65	81
1,2,3,4-Tetrahydro-1,3-dimethylene-	7.3	125
1,2,3,4-Tetrahydro-1,3-trimethylene-	7.3	125
1,2,3,4-Tetrahydro-2-methyl-1,3-trimethylene-	7.5	125

[a] Values of pH at half neutralization in 50% aqueous ethanol.

2.A.k.).[34,46,55,78,110] 3-Substituted 3,4-dihydroquinazolines are normally stable in air but they deteriorate on long standing, with the formation of the respective 4-oxo derivatives. 3,4-Dihydro-3-methylquinazoline was readily converted to 3,4-dihydro-3-methyl-4-oxoquinazoline on repeated recrystallization from light petroleum,[111] and 6-fluoro-3-p-fluorophenyl-3,4-dihydroquinazoline was oxidized to 6-fluoro-3-p-fluorophenyl-3,4-dihydro-4-oxoquinazoline at its melting point (137–138°).[78] 6-Chloro-3-p-chlorophenyl-3,4-dihydroquinazoline behaved similarly but the oxidation was slower than in the case of the fluoro compound.[78] Oxidation of 3,4-dihydro-3-methylquinazoline with one equivalent of iodine in boiling ethanol gave 3,4-dihydro-4-hydroxy-3-methylquinazoline.[111] 3,4-Dihydro-2-methyl-6-nitro-3-p-nitrophenylquinazoline gave 1,2,3,4-tetrahydro-2-hydroxy-2-methyl-6-nitro-3-p-nitrophenylquinazoline on boiling with dilute hydrochloric acid, and the hydroxy group was readily acetylated, or displaced by chlorine when heated with ethanolic hydrochloric acid.[45]

Substituents in the 2-position of 3,4-dihydroquinazolines react in the normal way. Thus 3,4-dihydro-4-phenyl-2-thioquinazoline reacted with bromine in glacial acetic acid to yield 2-bromo-3,4-dihydro-4-phenylquinazoline, and with methyl iodide it gave the 2-methylthio derivative.[60,61,63] In 2-2'-carboxyethyl- and 2-o-carboxyphenyl-3,4-dihydroquinazoline, cyclization of the carboxylic function on to $N_{(3)}$ takes place readily.[57]

1,2,3,4-Tetrahydroquinazolines form salts and picrates (see Tables VIII. 9 and 10) but are hydrolyzed by hot acid or alkali to o-aminobenzylamines and aldehydes. The ultraviolet spectrum of the neutral species and cation of 1,2,3,4-tetrahydroquinazoline was recorded, and the pK_a value (7.65) indicated that protonation occurred on $N_{(3)}$[81] (compare N-methylaniline, 4.8; and N-methylbenzylamine, 9.2).[117] 1,2,3,4-Tetrahydroquinazolines can be alkylated,[16,36,114] acetylated,[107] and benzoylated.[106] By careful oxidation with manganese dioxide,[114] iodine, or lead tetraacetate[111] they form the corresponding 3,4-dihydroquinazolines (Reaction 26). 6-Ethoxy-3-p-ethoxyphenyl-, 6-methoxy-3-p-methoxyphenyl-,[71] and 6-methyl-3-p-tolyl-1,2,3,4-tetrahydroquinazolines[39] are converted to the respective 3,4-dihydro derivatives by boiling with formic acid (Reaction 26).

$$\text{(26)}$$

7. Tröger's Base and Related Compounds

Tröger's base is given a separate entry because of its unique importance in the chemistry of reduced quinazolines. It was prepared by Tröger in 1887, from p-toluidine and formaldehyde in the presence of hydrochloric acid[67,118] (Sect. 4.B.), who considered it to be an anil (13). The alternative formula 14 was suggested by Eisner and Wagner in 1934,[70] but the correct structure 15 was deduced by Spielman in 1935.[119] According to *The Ring Index* it was called 2,8-dimethyl-5,11-6H,12H-methanodibenzo(b,f)(1,5)diazocine[120,121] (Ring Index No. 2651), but it was also named as a phenhomiazine derivative, viz 5,6,11,12-tetrahydro-2,8-dimethyl-5,11-*endo*methylenephenhomiazine.[121]

(13)   (14)

Tröger's base does not react with phenyl isocyanate, but gives a diacetyl derivative (16, R = Ac) with acetic anhydride with the loss of one carbon atom which was identified as formaldehyde.[119] It also gives a dinitroso derivative (16, R = NO) when treated with nitrous acid,

(15)   (16) R = Ac, NO or PhCO

with loss of carbon monoxide. The latter was probably formed by the oxidation of the formaldehyde liberated.[119] It resists reduction with sodium and ethanol, or metal and acid, but reduction with hydriodic acid at 200°, or reduction of its dinitroso derivative (16, R = NO) with tin and hydrochloric acid, furnished more than one equivalent of 2,4-xylidine.[119] The synthesis of Tröger's base was accomplished from 1,2,3,4-tetrahydro-6-methyl-3-p-tolylquinazoline (17) and formaldehyde in acid medium,[118] and from 5,6,11,12-tetrahydro-2,8-dimethylphenhomiazine (18) and formaldehyde in over 90% yield (Reaction

27).[121] These two syntheses are good evidence for the structure of Tröger's base. Moreover 2,3,5-trimethyl-4-methoxyaniline and formaldehyde in the presence of acid, and derivatives of 1,2,3,4-tetrahydro-1-hydroxymethyl-3-phenylquinazoline, e.g. **19**, on heating,[73] yield compounds with the same ring system as Tröger's base. Alkylation takes place on $N_{(5)}$ or $N_{(11)}$.[121a] The anhydro tetramer of o-aminobenzaldehyde was also shown to have this ring system (Ch. II, Sect. 3.A.).[122]

The ultraviolet spectrum of Tröger's base was measured,[121,123] and its pK_a value in 50% ethanol was ~3.2[123] (compare N-methylaniline, 4.8 in water).[117]

$$\text{(17)} \xrightarrow{\text{HCHO}} \text{Tröger's base} \xleftarrow{\text{HCHO}} \text{(18)}$$

(15)

(27)

heat

(19)

Tröger's base has added to our knowledge of the stereochemistry of trivalent nitrogen. It was resolved by Prelog and Wieland[124] in 1944 by passage through an activated d-lactose hydrate column. The optical rotations of the enantiomorphs were $[\alpha]_D^{17} + 287 \pm 7°$ ($c = 0.281$, in hexane) and $[\alpha]_D^{16.5} - 272° \pm 8°$ ($c = 0.275$, in hexane); the specific rotations showed considerable variation with concentration. The stereochemistry is depicted in **20**. This is the first demonstration of optical activity due to an asymmetric nitrogen atom. It racemizes in acid solution at 20° in a short time, probably due to the instability of the NCH_2N— group, but it does not lose its optical activity when it is sublimed at high vacuum.[124]

Tetrahydroquinazolines related to Tröger's base were prepared by the condensation of 1,2,3,4,5,6-hexahydrobenzo(b)(1,5)diazocine (**21**)

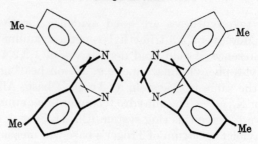

Tröger's base

(20)

with formaldehyde, acetyldehyde, and benzaldehyde, and for simplicity, the products will be called 1,3-trimethylene- **(22**, R = H), 2-methyl-1,3-trimethylene- **(22**, R = Me), and 2-phenyl-1,3-trimethylene-1,2,3,4-

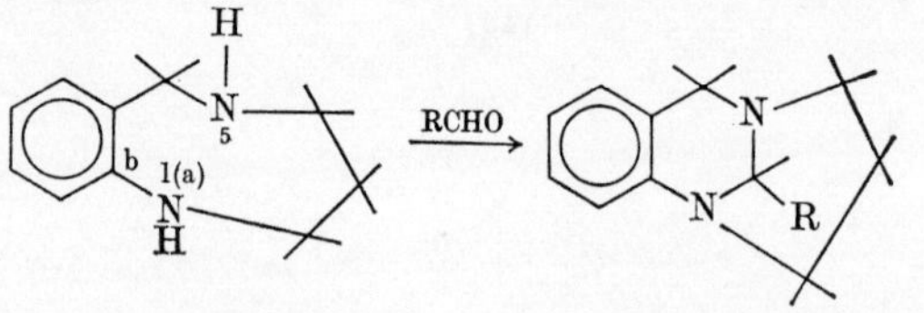

$$
\text{(21)} \xrightarrow{\text{RCHO}} \text{(22)} \tag{28}
$$

(21)   **(22)** R = H, Me or Ph

tetrahydroquinazoline **(22**, R = Ph) respectively (Reaction 28). Similarly 2,3,4,5-tetrahydro-1-*H*-benzo(e)(1,4)diazepine **(23)** yields 1,3-dimethylene- **(24**, R = H) and 1,3-dimethylene-2-phenyl-(**24**, R = Ph)

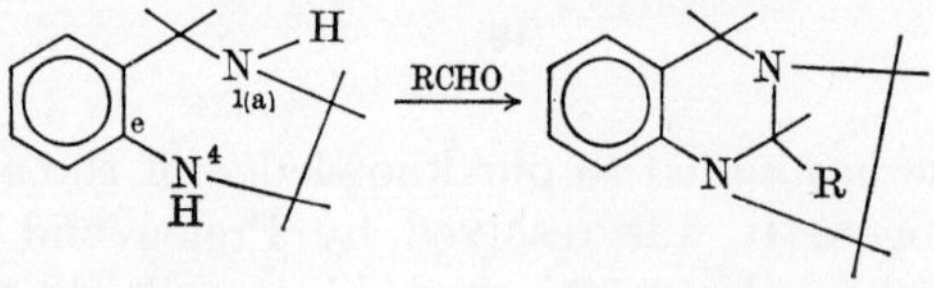

$$
\text{(23)} \xrightarrow{\text{RCHO}} \text{(24)} \tag{29}
$$

(23)   **(24)** R = H or Ph

1,2,3,4-tetrahydroquinazoline by reaction with formaldehyde and benzaldehyde respectively (Reaction 29).[125] These are tetrahydro-

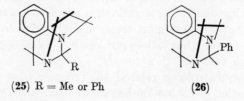

(25) R = Me or Ph   **(26)**

quinazolines because their pK_a values are comparable with those of known 1,2,3,4-tetrahydroquinazoline (see Table VIII.1). The nuclear magnetic resonance spectra of **22** (R = Me, Ph), and **24** (R = Ph) suggest the conformations shown in **25** (R = Me, Ph) and **26** respectively.[125]

8. 5,6,7,8-Tetrahydroquinazolines

5,6,7,8-Tetrahydroquinazolines are 4,5-tetramethylenepyrimidines, but are included in this work because they have the quinazoline nucleus, and because they have been called tetrahydroquinazolines on many occasions in the literature.

A. Preparation of 5,6,7,8-Tetrahydroquinazolines

Most of the syntheses of these compounds involve condensations of derivatives of cyclohexane. The methods of preparation are therefore classified according to the cyclohexane derivative used.

a. *From Cyclohexanones*

Cyclohexanone reacts with *N,N'*-diphenyl-, *N,N'*-di-*p*-methoxyphenyl-, *N,N'*-di-*p*-tolyl-,[126] and *N,N'*-di-*m*-tolylthiourea[127] (at temperatures above 150° for several hours) to yield 1,3-diphenyl-, 1,3-di-

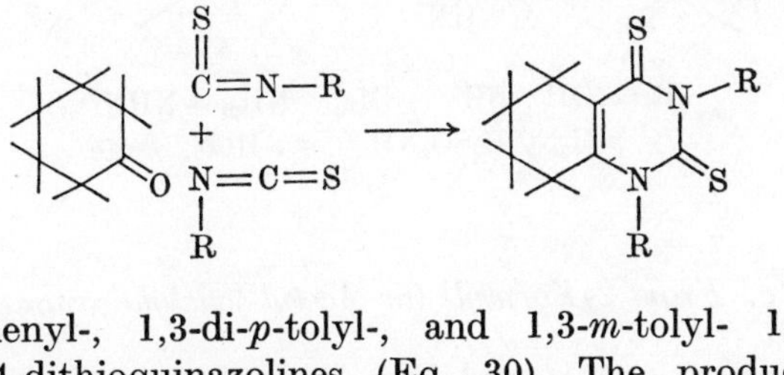

(30)

p-methoxyphenyl-, 1,3-di-*p*-tolyl-, and 1,3-*m*-tolyl- 1,2,3,4,5,6,7,8-octahydro-2,4-dithioquinazolines (Eq. 30). The product from the reaction of cyclohexanone and dicyandiamide[128] was shown to be

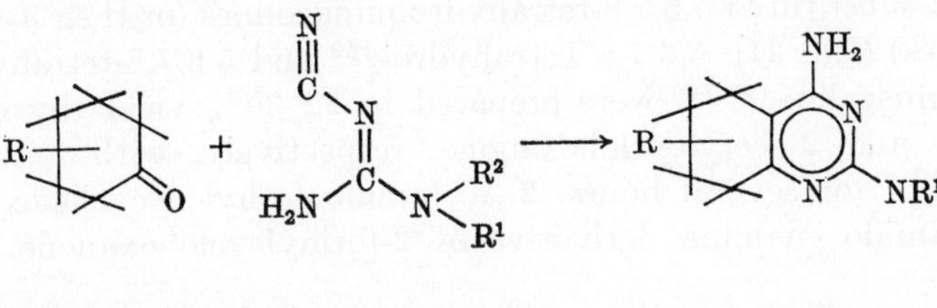

(31)

2,4-diamino-5,6,7,8-tetrahydroquinazoline.[129] This reaction is of general applicability because several tetrahydroquinazolines were prepared from various cyclohexanones and dicyandiamide or its N-substituted derivatives (Eq. 31).[129,130] The parent substance, 5,6,7,8-tetrahydroquinazoline, was obtained in 36% yield by heating cyclohexanone with trisformamidomethane in formamide in the presence of toluene-p-sulphonic acid (Eq. 32).[131]

$$\tag{32}$$

b. *From 2-Ethoxycarbonylcyclohexanones*

2-Ethoxycarbonylcyclohexanones react with urea,[132,133] thiourea,[133-135] S-methylthiourea,[136] guanidines,[137-139] N-nitroguanidines,[140,141] sulphoguanidine,[142] dicyandiamide,[143] and acetamidine[144] to give 3,4,5,6,7,8-hexahydro-4-oxoquinazolines substituted in the 2-position with oxo, thio, methylthio, amino, nitroamino, sulphanilamido, cyanamino, and methyl groups respectively (Eq. 33).

$$\tag{33}$$

$$R_v = \text{'OH', 'SH',} \ \text{—SMe,} \ \text{—NH}_2, \ \text{—NHNO}_2,$$
$$p\text{-H}_2\text{NC}_6\text{H}_4\text{SO}_2\text{NH—, —NHCN, or Me}$$

c. *From 2-Formyl- (or Acetyl-)cyclohexanones*

2-Formyl-(or acetyl-)cyclohexanones condense with amidines[145,146] and guanidines[145-147] in the presence of piperidine or sodium ethoxide to yield 2-substituted 5,6,7,8-tetrahydroquinazolines (or their 4-methyl derivatives) (Eq. 34). 5,6,7,8-Tetrahydro-[148] and 5,6,7,8-tetrahydro-4-methylquinazoline[148,149] were prepared in 22–30% yields by heating 2-formyl- and 2-acetylcyclohexanone, respectively, with formamide at 180–190° for several hours. 2-Acetamidomethylenecyclohexanone, the acetamido enamine derivative of 2-formylcyclohexanone, reacts with guanidine and acetamidine at 200° to furnish 2-amino- and 2-methyl- 5,6,7,8-tetrahydroquinazolines.[150] 2-Ethoxalylcyclohexanone reacts in a similar manner and the 4-ethoxycarbonyl-5,6,7,8-tetrahydro derivatives that result can be hydrolyzed and decarboxylated to give products similar to those obtained from condensations with 2-formyl-cyclohexanone.[151-153]

$$R = Me, CO_2Et; R^1 = alkyl, aryl, NH_2$$

d. *From Cyclohexenes*

3-o-Chlorophenyl-, 3-p-methoxyphenyl-, 3-phenyl-, and 3-p-tolyl-1,2,3,4,5,6,7,8-octahydro-4-oxo-2-thioquinazolines were formed when ethyl 3,4,5,6-tetrahydroanthranilate (**27**) was heated with the respective aryl isothiocyanate (Eq. 35).[126,154] 1-Morpholino-2-thiocarbamoyl-

cyclohex-1-ene reacts similarly with aryl isocyanates to yield 1,3-substituted 1,2,3,4,5,6,7,8-octahydro-2-oxo-4-thioquinazolines.[155] 5,6,7,8-Tetrahydroquinazoline was obtained from 1-chloro-2-formylcyclohex-1-ene and formamide at 180°.[156,157] 1-Cyano-2-isobutoxycyclohex-1-ene and guanidine condense in the presence of sodium ethoxide to give 2,4-diamino-5,6,7,8-tetrahydroquinazoline.[158,159] Benzoyl isothiocyanates react with 1-morpholinocyclohex-1-ene to yield 5,6-tetramethylene-2-phenyl-4-thio(1,3)oxazines (**28**).[160] The oxazines are valuable intermediates because the oxygen atom in the ring can be displaced by nitrogen with ammonia, or a variety of amines, to furnish thioquinazolines (Reaction 36).[160,161] These are converted to the corresponding oxo compounds with mercuric acetate. Attempted synthesis of compounds related to **28** with substituents in the 2-phenyl group by using substituted aroyl isothiocyanates led to tars. Phenylbenzimidoyl isothiocyanate (prepared from phenylbenzimidoyl chloride and lead

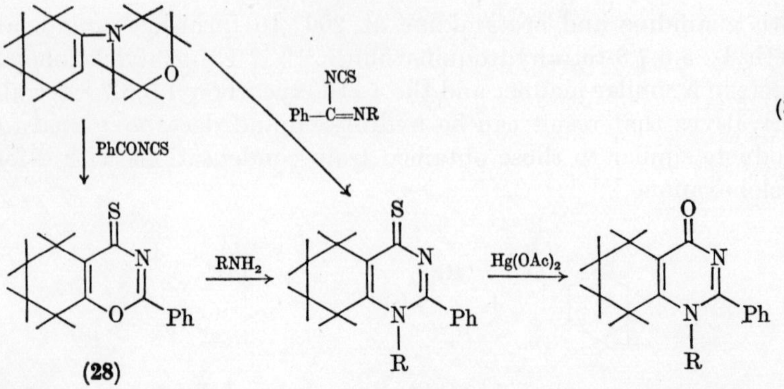

(36)

(28)

thiocyanate), reacts with 1-morpholinocyclohex-1-ene to yield 1,4,5,6,
7,8-hexahydro-1,2-diphenyl-4-thioquinazoline directly (Reaction 36).
This reaction was found to be a general one regardless of the nature of
the substituents in the benzene ring.[161a]

B. Properties of 5,6,7,8-Tetrahydroquinazolines

The pyrimidine ring of 5,6,7,8-tetrahydroquinazolines is only
slightly affected by the cyclohexene ring and their properties are typical
of 4,5-dimethylpyrimidines. Substituents in positions 5, 6, 7, or 8 of
5,6,7,8-tetrahydroquinazolines react as in cyclohexenes,[133,138,139,159]
and substituents in the 2- and 4-positions react as in pyrimidines, for
example oxo groups are converted to chloro in the usual way,[132,133,160]
which in turn can be displaced by amines.[160,162] 2- and 4-Thio derivatives
are desulphurized with a sponge nickel catalyst,[163] they can be methylated to methylthio derivatives[136,160] and these in turn are readily
converted to aminoquinazolines.[132,136,160,164,165] 2-Amino-, 2-methyl-,
and 2-phenyl-5,6,7,8-tetrahydroquinazoline are dehydrogenated by
heating in boiling decalin in the presence of palladium charcoal catalyst
(Reaction 37)[166,167] (see Ch. III, Sect. 1.J.).

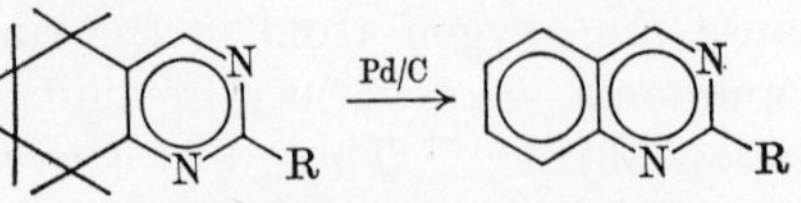

(37)

R = Me, Ph, or NH$_2$

Ultraviolet[160] and infrared[168,169] spectra and polarographic[170]
studies of 5,6,7,8-tetrahydroquinazolines have been made.

9. Miscellaneous Reduced Quinazolines

Few 5,6-dihydroquinazolines are known. Some were prepared by condensation of 2-acylcyclohex-5-enone with guanidine as outlined in section 8 (Eq. 38).[171,172] 1-Chloro-2-formyl-3,4-dihydronaphthalene condenses with formamide to yield 7,8-benzo-5,6-dihydroquinazoline.[156]

$$ (38) $$

Two 3,4,5,6,7,8-hexahydroquinazolines are described in the literature. The first is 4-o-chlorophenyl-1,2,3,4,5,6,7,8-octahydro-2-oxoquinazoline which is prepared by a Biginelli synthesis from cyclohexa-1,3-dione, o-chlorobenzaldehyde, and urea, but this does not appear to be a general reaction.[173] The second is 3-benzyl-1,2,3,4,5,6,7,8-octahydro-2-oxoquinazoline (29), and is obtained by reacting 2-benzyl-aminomethylcyclohexanone hydrobromide and potassium cyanate. It disproportionates by boiling in 2% hydrochloric acid to 3-benzyl-2,3,5,6,7,8-hexahydro- (30) and 3-benzyldecahydro-2-oxoquinazoline (31) (Reaction 39).[174] The last named compound is an octahydroquinazoline. A second octahydroquinazoline, supposedly 4-carboxy-decahydro-2-oxoquinazoline, was obtained by reduction of 4-carboxy-1,2,5,6,7,8,9,10-octahydro-2-oxoquinazoline.[175] The third octahydro-

$$ (39) $$

quinazoline known is the naturally occurring neurotoxin called tetrodotoxin (a perhydro 2-iminoquinazoline derivative) and its chemistry is described in chapter XI, section 1.E.

Four other perhydroquinazolines have been described but as the above they are not true decahydroquinazolines. Perhydro-11-hydroxy-2,4-dioxoquinazoline was obtained from 2-amino-1-carboxy-1-hydroxy-cyclohexanone and sodium cyanate (Reaction 40).[176] trans-3-Benzoyl-

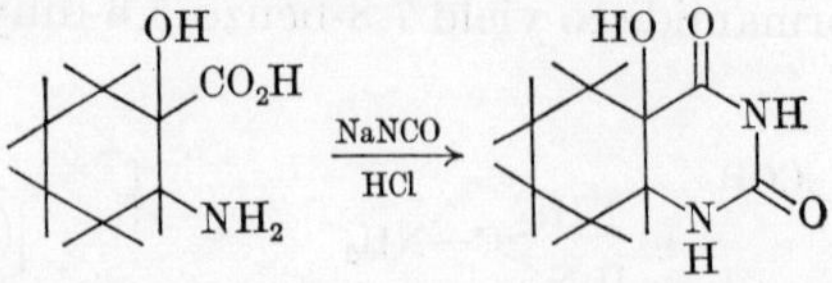

(40)

oxyperhydro-2,4-dioxoquinazoline (32) was prepared by treating trans-O,O-dibenzoylhexahydrophthalohydroxamate with one mole of sodium hydroxide (Reaction 41),[177] and was hydrolyzed by benzylamine to

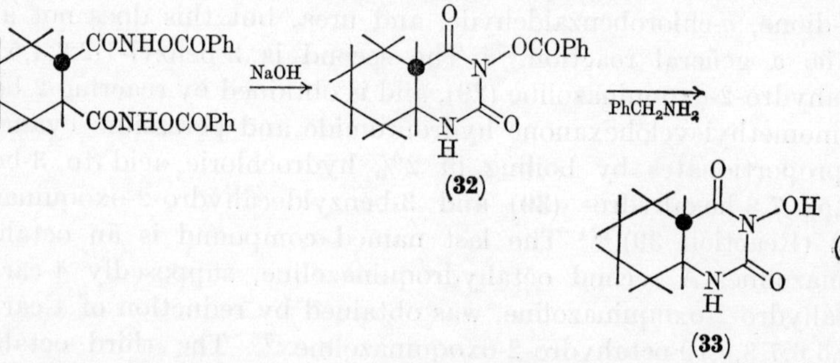

(41)

trans-perhydro-3-hydroxy-2,4-dioxoquinazoline (33). trans-Perhydro-2,4-dioxo-3-phenylsulphonyloxyquinazoline was also prepared.[177]

No true decahydroquinazolines are known.

10. Tables

TABLE VIII.2.   1,2-Dihydroquinazolines.

1,2-Dihydroquinazoline	M.p. (°c)	References
Unsubstituted	3-allyl picrate 139–140°; 3-methyl picrate 185–186°	1
4-Amino-7-chloro-2,2-dimethyl-	198–200°	14
4-Amino-2,2-dimethyl-	HCl 255–256°	14
4-Methoxy-	168–169°	18
2,2-Dimethyl-4-methylthio-[a]	62–64°	14
4-Phenoxy-	130–132°	18
4-Phenoxy-1-phenylcarbamoyl-	183–184°	18
2,3-Trimethylene-	picrate 171°	1

[a] 1,2,3,4-Tetrahydro-2,2-dimethyl-4-thioquinazoline has m.p. 151–152°,[14] 163°.[4]

TABLE VIII.3.   1,2,3,4-Tetrahydro-4-oxoquinazolines.

1,2,3,4-Tetrahydro-4-oxoquinazoline	M.p. (°c)	References
Unsubstituted	154–155°, 260–261°	12, 189
2-Acetoxy-2-methyl-	159–161°	4
1-Acetyl-2,2-dimethyl-	204°	4
2-o-Aminophenyl-	173–174°; picrate 174–175° (dec.); diacetyl deriv. 210–211°	20
3-Anilino-2,2-dimethyl-	235°	4
3-Anilino-2-phenyl-	198–200°	4

(*Table continued*)

TABLE VIII.3 (*continued*)

1,2,3,4-Tetrahydro-4-oxoquinazoline	M.p. (°c)	References
3-Benzamido-2-methyl-	193°	13
6,7-Benzo-	269–272°	15
2-Benzyl-1-methyl-	199–200°	201
3-*p*-Bromophenyl-	199–200°	11
1-Butyl-2-phenyl-	111–112.5°	5
2-(2′-Carboxy-3′,4′-dimethoxy)-phenyl-	196°	3
7-Chloro-1-2′-dimethylaminoethyl-2-*p*-chlorophenyl-	154°	6
7-Chloro-1-2′-dimethylaminoethyl-2-phenyl-	161°	6
7-Chloro-1-2′-dimethylaminoethyl-2-2′-pyridyl-	oxalate 166°	6
7-Chloro-2-ethyl-	130–132°; acetyl deriv. 200–217°	9
7-Chloro-2-methyl-	143–147°	9
2-*p*-Chlorophenyl-1-2′-diethylaminoethyl-	oxalate 137°	6
2-*p*-Chlorophenyl-1-2′-dimethylaminoethyl-	132.5°	6
2-*p*-Chlorophenyl-1-2′-dimethylaminoethyl-3-methyl-	oxalate 168°	6
2-2′,4′-Diethoxyphenyl-	149°	3
1-2′-Diethylaminoethyl-2-phenyl-	oxalate 149°	6
1-2′-Diethylaminoethyl-2-2′-pyridyl-	oxalate 151°	6
2-2′,4′-Dimethoxyphenyl-	187°	3
2-3′,4′-Dimethoxyphenyl-	226°	3
1-2′-Dimethylaminoethyl-2-*p*-methoxyphenyl-	103°	6
1-2′-Dimethylaminoethyl-2-phenyl-	157°	6
1-2′-Dimethylaminoethyl-2-2′-pyridyl-	119°	6
1-2′-Dimethylaminoethyl-2-3′-pyridyl-	148°	6
1-2′-Dimethylaminoethyl-2-4′-pyridyl-	168°	6
1-2′-Dimethylaminoethyl-2-*p*-tolyl-	106°	6
1-3′-Dimethylaminopropyl-2-phenyl-	186°	6
1-3′-Dimethylaminopropyl-2-2′-pyridyl-	90°	6
2-(4′-Ethoxy-2′-hydroxy)phenyl-	305°	3
2-(3′-Ethoxy-4′-hydroxy)phenyl-	218°	3
2-(3′-Ethoxy-4′-methoxy)phenyl-	89°	3

(*Table continued*)

TABLE VIII.3 *(continued)*

1,2,3,4-Tetrahydro-4-oxoquinazoline	M.p. (°c)	References
1-Ethyl-	110–111°	12
2-Ethyl-2-methyl-	183°	4
1-Ethyl-2-phenyl-	141–143.5°	5
2-2'-Furyl-1-methyl-	184.2–185.6°	5
2-2'-Furyl-1-propyl-	150.5–152°	5
2-(2'-Hydroxy-3'-methoxy)phenyl-	279°	3
2-(3'-Hydroxy-4'-methoxy)phenyl-	191°	3
2-(4'-Hydroxy-3'-methoxy)phenyl-	224°	3
3-Hydroxy-2,2-dimethyl-	145°	4
2-Hydroxyimino-3-phenyl-	138°	90
1,3-Bishydroxymethyl-	141°	11
1-Hydroxymethyl-3-phenyl-	109–110°	11
2-o-Hydroxyphenyl-	300°	3
2-m-Hydroxyphenyl-	209°	3
2-p-Hydroxyphenyl-	332°	3
2-3'-Indolyl-1-methyl-	217–220°	5
1-Isopropyl-2-phenyl-	122–125°	5
3-Isopropylideneamino-2,2-dimethyl-	244°	181
2-o-Methoxyphenyl-	181°	3
2-p-Methoxyphenyl-	195°	3
3-p-Methoxyphenyl-	185–185.5°	11
1-Methyl-	113.5–114.5°	12
2-Methyl-	138°	4
3-Methyl-	115°	16
2,2-Dimethyl-	182°, 262°	4, 14
1,2,2-Trimethyl-	158°	4
1,3-Dimethyl-2-hydroxy-	picrate 189°	192
2,2-Dimethyl-1-nitroso-	165°	4
1-Methyl-2,2-pentamethylene-	186°	4
1-Methyl-2-phenyl-	203°, 206–207.5°	4, 5
1-Methyl-3-phenyl-	115°; picrate 142°	19
3-Methyl-2-phenyl-	165°	4
1-Methyl-2-2'-thienyl-	178.8–181.2°	5
1-Methyl-2,2-trimethylene-	139°	4
2-3',4'-Methylenedioxyphenyl-	202°	3
2-o-Nitrophenyl-	192°	3
2,2-Pentamethylene-	225°	4
1-Pentyl-2-phenyl-	123.5–126°	5
2-Phenyl-	223–224°, 228°	3, 4
3-Phenyl-	180°	11
2-Phenyl-1-propyl-	120–121°	5
1-Propyl-2-2'-thienyl-	146–148°	5

(Table continued)

TABLE VIII.3 (*continued*)

1,2,3,4-Tetrahydro-4-oxoquinazoline	M.p. (°c)	References
2-Styryl-	294°	3
2,2-Tetramethylene-	254°	4
2-*p*-Tolyl-	230°	3
2-Trichloromethyl-	202°; acetyl deriv. 194–195°	10
1,2-Trimethylene-	168°	7

TABLE VIII.4.   1,4- and 2,3-Dihydroquinazolines.

Quinazoline	M.p. (°c)	References
7,8-Benzo-2,3-dihydro-2-hydroxy-2,4-diphenyl-	265°	28
1-Benzyl-1,4-dihydro-	101–102°; picrate 199–200°	23
6-Chloro-3-*p*-chlorophenyl-2,3-dihydro-2-hydroxy-4-phenyl-	199–201°	27
1,4-Dihydro-4-1'ethoxycarbonyl-2'-(3-ethyl-4-oxo-2-thiothiazolidin-5-ylidene)ethylidene-1-methyl-	240–245°	196
2,3-Dihydro-2-hydroxy-6-methyl-2,4-diphenyl-3-*p*-tolyl-	194–195°	27
1,4-Dihydro-1-methyl-	90–91°/2.5 mm; picrate 176–177°	23
1,4-Dihydro-1,2-dimethyl-	80–81°/0.2 mm; HBr 273–274°; HClO₄ 196–197°; picrate 196–197°	24, 25
1,4-Dihydro-1-methyl-2-*o*-nitrophenyl-	131–132°; picrate 174–175°	24, 25
1,4-Dihydro-1-methyl-2-phenyl-	113–114°; HClO₄ 207–208.5°; picrate 163–164°	24, 25

TABLE VIII.5.   3,4-Dihydroquinazolines Unsubstituted in Positions 3 and 4.

3,4-Dihydroquinazoline	M.p. (°c)	References
Unsubstituted	127°, 303–304°/769 mm; HCl 231–234°; picrate 188–190°, 215°, 219–220°; zinc chloride double salt 184–185°	18, 40, 41, 80, 91, 103
8-Amino-	98.5–99°	92
6,7-Benzo-	196°	15
2-Benzyl-	123–125°, 130–131°; HCl 208–211°; picrate 168–169°	24, 25, 100
2-2'-Carboxyethyl-	221–223° (dec.)	57
2-o-Carboxyphenyl-	182–183°	57
5-Chloro-2-guanidino-	HCl 278–279°	59
6-Chloro-2-guanidino-	HCl 268°	59
7-Chloro-2-guanidino-	HCl 274°	59
2-o-Chlorophenyl-	108–109.5°; picrate 200–202°	24, 25
2-p-Chlorophenyl-	125–126°; picrate 208–209.5°	24, 25, 97
6-Ethoxy-	125–127°	34
2-Ethyl-	103–104°, 290–300°/760 mm; picrate 176°	24, 42, 95, 97
2-Guanidino-	202–204°; HCl 245–247°	59
2-1'-Hydroxyethyl-	178–179°; HCl 217–218°	58
2-1'-Hydroxypropyl-	139–140°; HCl 216–217°	58
2-α-Methoxybenzyl-	HCl 101–106°	100
2-o-Methoxybenzyl-	HCl 209–211°	100
2-Methoxymethyl-	131–132°/0.1 mm; HClO$_4$ 195–196°; picrate 187–188°	24
2-p-Methoxyphenyl-	178–179°; picrate 222–223°	24, 97
2-Methyl-	126–127°/0.9 mm, 140–144°/8 mm; HCl 286–290°, 312°; picrate 189–190° and 286–290° (dimorphic)	21, 23–26, 95, 97
5-Methyl-	112°	96
6,7-Methylenedioxy-	153° (dec.); HCl 267–268°; chloroplatinate 235°; picrate 234°	31
2-N'-Methylguanidino-	233–236°	59
2-1'-Naphthyl-	152–153°; picrate 239–240° (dec.)	24, 25
2-o-Nitrophenyl-	94–95°; picrate 234–235° (dec.)	24, 25
2-m-Nitrophenyl-	124–125°; picrate 186–187° (dec.)	24, 25, 97
2-3'-Phenoxypropyl-	111.5–112.5°	44

(*Table continued*)

TABLE VIII.5 (*continued*)

3,4-Dihydroquinazoline	M.p. (°c)	References
2-Phenyl-	142–143°; HCl 256°; HBr 242–243°; chloroplatinate 211° (dec.); picrate 161–162°, 182–183°	18, 24, 25, 42, 95, 97
2-Propyl-	122–123°/0.3 mm; picrate 178–179°	24, 25

TABLE VIII.6.   3-Substituted, 3,4-Dihydroquinazolines.

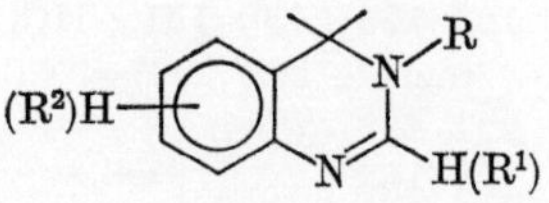

3,4-Dihydroquinazoline	M.p. (°c)	References
8-Acetamido-3-acetyl-	167–168°	92
3-Acetyl-	H₂O 131–132°	92
3-Allyl-	oil 280–290° (dec.); HCl 165°; HBr 168°; HI 189°; oxalate 173–174°; chloroplatinate 191–192°; picrate 172–173°, 180–181°	32, 55
3-o-Aminophenyl-	165°; picrate 184°	50
3-m-Aminophenyl-	147°; HCl 230–232°; oxalate 157–159°; zinc chloride double salt 157–159°; chloroplatinate 240° (dec.); picrate 189°	51
3-p-Aminophenyl-	175°; HCl > 230° (dec.); oxalate 237°; picrate 199°	52
3-m-Benzamidophenyl-	82°	51
3-Benzyl-8-hydroxy-	197°	35
3-Benzyl-8-methoxy-	118°	35
2-Benzyl-3-methyl-	HCl 243–245°	100
6-Bromo-3-p-bromophenyl-	200°, 205.8°	39, 72
3-p-Bromophenyl-	142°; picrate 202°	108
3-p-Bromophenyl-2-methyl-	89°	43
3-Butyl-8-hydroxy-	109°	35

(*Table continued*)

TABLE VIII.6 (*continued*)

3,4-Dihydroquinazoline	M.p. (°c)	References
3-Butyl-8-methoxy-	113°	35
6-Chloro-3-*p*-chlorophenyl-	186–187°, 192°	39, 72
3-*p*-Chlorophenyl-	143°; HCl 240°; HNO$_3$ 156°; H$_2$SO$_4$ 185°; oxalate 168°; ZnCl$_2$ 240°; chloroplatinate 317°; picrate 192°	49
3-*p*-(*p*-3,4-Dihydroquinazolin-3-ylphenyl)phenyl-	> 300° (dec.)	53
4-Ethoxy-3-*p*-ethoxyphenyl-	140°; picrate 185.7°	34, 68, 71, 76
3-*p*-Ethoxyphenyl-	109°; HCl 207°; oxalate 162°; chloroplatinate 206°; picrate 194°	48
3-Ethyl-	oil; chloroplatinate 199–202° (dec.); picrate 170–172°	42
6-Ethyl-3-*p*-ethylphenyl-	110–111°	76
3-Ethyl-8-hydroxy-	163°	75
3-Ethyl-8-methoxy-	H$_2$O 70°	35
6-Fluoro-3-*p*-fluorophenyl-	137–138°	78
8-Hydroxy-3-isobutyl-	126°	35
8-Hydroxy-3-isopropyl-	126°	35
8-Hydroxy-3-pentyl-	173°	35
8-Hydroxy-3-phenethyl-	161°	35
8-Hydroxy-3-propyl-	127°	35
3-*p*-Hydroxyphenyl-	235°	47
3-Isobutyl-8-methoxy-	146°	35
3-Isopropyl-8-methoxy-	141°	35
6-Methoxy-3-(4'-methoxy-2',3',5'-trimethyl)phenyl-5,7,8-trimethyl-	138–139°	120
6-Methoxy-3-*p*-methoxy-phenyl-	136–138°; picrate 214°	71
6,7-Dimethoxy-2,3-3'-oxo-trimethylene-	226–227°	56
8-Methoxy-3-pentyl-	97°	35
8-Methoxy-3-phenethyl-	141°	35
8-Methoxy-3-propyl-	114°	35
3-*o*-Methoxyphenyl-	oil; HCl 128°; picrate 197°	38
3-*p*-Methoxyphenyl-	115°; HCl 237°; picrate 181°	47
3-Methyl-	91–92°, 309°/766 mm; picrate 197–199°	23, 30, 111
2,3-Dimethyl-	75–77°, 300–305°/706 mm; picrate 215–217°	40, 95

(Table continued)

TABLE VIII.6 (*continued*)

3,4-Dihydroquinazoline	M.p. (°c)	References
6-Methyl-2-methylthio-3-*p*-tolyl-	87°; HCl 258°; HI 260° (dec.); H₂SO₄ 208°; chloroplatinate 222°; picrate 168°	36
2-Methyl-6-nitro-3-*p*-nitro-phenyl-	188–191°; HCl > 300°; HNO₃ 179° (dec.); H₂SO₄ 265–267° (dec.)	45
2-Methyl-3-phenyl-	80–82°, 345–346°/760 mm; HCl 263°; ZnCl₂ 122–123°; chloroplatinate 223° (dec.)	43, 54, 107
2-Methyl-3-*p*-tolyl-	104–106°; ZnCl₂ 139–140°	43
6-Methyl-3-*p*-tolyl-	158°, 160°; HCl 212°; HNO₃ 95° (dec.); H₂SO₄ 132°; chloroplatinate 202° and 235° (dimorphic); picrate 201°; 1-methiodide 272–274°	36, 39, 68, 69, 70, 75, 114
2,6-Dimethyl-3-*p*-tolyl-	89–93°; HCl 261°; chloroplatinate 207° and 235° (dimorphic)	36
3-*m*-Methylaminophenyl-	185°	51
6-Nitro-3-*p*-nitrophenyl-	243–246°	69
2,3-3′-Oxotrimethylene-	183–184°	57
3-Phenyl-	95°, 119°, 121–122°; HCl 221°; H₂SO₄ 140–143°; H₂SO₄·2H₂O 79°; stannic chloride 130–134°; chloroplatinate 208°; 1-methiodide 170°; 1-methiodide periodide 157°	46, 72, 108, 110
2,3-Tetramethylene-	85–87°; H₂SO₄ 283–285°; reineckate 209–210°; picrate 216–217°	97a, 202
3-*o*-Tolyl-	oil; chloroplatinate 210°	46
3-*p*-Tolyl-	120°; HCl 251°; HCl·2 H₂O 85°; stannic chloride 165°; chloroplatinate 216°; 1-methiodide 186°	46
2,3-Trimethylene-	96.5–97.5°; picrate 202–203°	44, 97a

TABLE VIII.7.   4-Substituted 3,4-Dihydroquinazolines.

3,4-Dihydroquinazoline	M.p. (°c)	References
4-Acetonyl-	167–168°	83
4-Acetonyl-3-methyl-6,7-methyl- enedioxy-	picrate 187°	87
3-Allyl-4-hydroxy-	136–137°	1, 87
3-Allyl-4-nitromethyl-	picrate 152–153°	87
7,8-Benzo-4-ethoxy-3-1′-naphthyl- 2,4-diphenyl-	224°; HCl 292°	28
7,8-Benzo-4-hydroxy-3-1′- naphthyl-2,4-diphenyl-	184°; HCl 209°; picrate 260–261°	28
7,8-Benzo-4-methoxy-3-1′- naphthyl-2,4-diphenyl-	193°	28
3-Benzoyl-6-methyl-4-phenyl-	185–186°	63
2-Bromo-6-methyl-4-phenyl-	155°	63
2-Bromo-4-phenyl-	165°; HBr 273–274° (dec.)	61, 63
2-Bromo-4-2′,4′-xylyl-	170–171°; HBr 232–233° (dec.)	60
4-Butan-2′-onyl-	165°	82
4-Butyl-4-hydroxy-2-methyl- 3-1′-naphthyl-[a]	162°; acetyl deriv. 95°	98
3-Butyl-4-hydroxy-2-methyl-4- phenyl-[a]	165°; acetyl deriv. 105°	98
4-Butyl-4-hydroxy-2-methyl-3- phenyl-[a]	272°	98
3-Butyl-4-hydroxy-2-methyl-4- propyl-[a]	170°	98
3-Butyl-4-hydroxy-2-methyl-4-p- tolyl-[a]	162°	98
6-Chloro-3-p-chlorophenyl-4- ethoxy-2,4-diphenyl-	225–226°	27
6-Chloro-3-p-chlorophenyl-4- hydroxy-2,4-diphenyl-	159°; HCl 353°; picrate 178°	27
6-Chloro-4-phenyl-	173–174°; HCl 173–175°	33
4-Cyano-	128–129° (dec.)	80, 197
3-Cyclohexanon-2′-yl-	235° (dec.)	83
2-Dimethylaminomethyl-6,7- dimethyl-4-phenyl-	125–126°; 2 HCl 235–236° (dec.)	94

(*Table continued*)

TABLE VIII.7 (*continued*)

3,4-Dihydroquinazoline	M.p. (°c)	References
4-Ethoxy-6-methyl-2,4-diphenyl-3-*p*-tolyl-	161°	27
4-Ethyl-	138°/0.5 mm; picrate 192–194°	86
4-Hydroxy-3-methyl-6,7-methyl-enedioxy-	158–159°	87
4-Hydroxy-2-methyl-3-1'-naphthyl-4-phenyl-ᵃ	210°; acetyl deriv. 145°	98
4-Hydroxy-2-methyl-3-1'-naphthyl-4-propyl-ᵃ	190°; acetyl deriv. 145°	98
4-Hydroxy-2-methyl-3-1'-naphthyl-4-*p*-tolyl-ᵃ	172°; acetyl deriv. 150°	98
4-(4'-Hydroxy-1'-methyl-2'-oxo)pentyl-	167–168°; semicarbazone 131° (dec.)	83
4-Hydroxy-2-methyl-3,4-diphenyl-ᵃ	258–260°	98
4-Hydroxy-2-methyl-3-phenyl-4-propyl-ᵃ	262–265°	98
4-Hydroxy-6-methyl-2,4-diphenyl-3-*p*-tolyl-	148–149°; HCl 320°; picrate 143°	27
4-Hydroxy-2-nitroso-3-phenyl-ᵇ	156°	90
4-Hydroxy-2-nitroso-3-*p*-tolyl-ᵇ	115°	90
4-Isopropyl-	152–154°/0.6 mm; picrate 139–140°	86
7-Methoxy-4-methyl-	oxalate 188–190° (efferv.) remelts at 248–250° (efferv.); picrate 0.5 H₂O 196–198°	93a
4-Methyl-	124°/2.5 mm; picrate 234–236° (dec.)	80, 86
2,4-Dimethyl-	280°/722 mm; chloroplatinate 205–206°; picrate 173°	21
3-Methyl-6,7-methylenedioxy-4-nitromethyl-	159–160°	87
3-Methyl-4-nitromethyl-	137°	87
2-Methyl-4-phenyl-	168°	95
6-Methyl-4-phenyl-	186–188°; HCl 240°; HNO₃ 186° (dec.); picrate 173–175°; benzoyl deriv. 185–186°	63
3-Nitroso-4-phenyl-	131° (dec.)	61
4-Phenacyl-	151–152°	82

(*Table continued*)

TABLE VIII.7 (*continued*)

3,4-Dihydroquinazoline	M.p. (°c)	References
4-Phenyl-	165–166°; HCl 242–243°; aurichloride 181–182°; chloroplatinate 234° (dec.); picrate 213–214°	18, 61, 80, 93
4-*t*-Butyl-	141–143°/0.2 mm; picrate 190–191°	86

[a] See section 4.F. and chapter IV, section 2.C.b.(vi).
[b] These are 4-hydroxy-2-hydroxyimino-1,2,3,4-tetrahydroquinazoline derivatives.

TABLE VIII.8.   1,2,3,4-Tetrahydro-2-oxo-(and thio-)quinazolines.

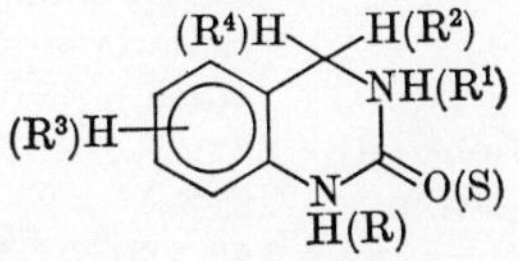

1,2,3,4-Tetrahydroquinazoline	M.p. (°c)	References
4-Acetoxy-2-oxo-3-phenyl-	HBr 253°	198
3-*o*-Aminophenyl-2-thio-	212°	102
1-Benzyl-3-phenyl-2-thio-	93°; HCl 240°; HNO₃ 126° (dec.)	178
6-Chloro-4-hydroxy-3-methyl-2-oxo-4-phenyl-	307–309°	90a
6-Chloro-4-hydroxy-3-methyl-4-phenyl-2-thio-	200–202° (dec.)	90a
6-Chloro-4-methoxy-3-methyl-2-oxo-4-phenyl-	194–197°	90a
6-Chloro-4-methoxy-3-methyl-4-phenyl-2-thio-	167–170°	90a
6-Chloro-3-methyl-2-oxo-4-phenyl-	224–226°	90a
6-Chloro-3-methyl-4-phenyl-2-thio-	245–247°	90a
4-α,α-Diethoxycarbonylmethyl-2-oxo-3-phenyl-	172°	90
4-Ethoxy-3-methyl-2-oxo-	146–148°	88
4-Ethoxy-2-oxo-3-phenyl-	185–186°	89

(*Table continued*)

TABLE VIII.8 (*continued*)

1,2,3,4-Tetrahydroquinazoline	M.p. (°c)	References
4-α-Ethoxycarbonylacetonyl-2-oxo-3-phenyl-	165°; HgCl₂ 215°	90
3-Ethyl-2-oxo-	142°	37
3-Ethyl-2-thio-	185°	37
4-Hydroxy-2-oxo-3-phenyl-	182–184°	89
4-Hydroxyamino-2-oxo-3-phenyl-	195–196°	199
1,6-Dimethyl-2-oxo-	59–60°, 166–168°/8 mm; chloroplatinate 214°	66
6-Methyl-2-oxo-4-phenyl-	206–207°; picrate 157–158°	63
6-Methyl-2-oxo-3-*p*-tolyl-	238–240°	36
6-Methyl-4-phenyl-2-thio-	265–270°	63
3-Methyl-2-thio-	181°	37
6-Methyl-2-thio-3-*p*-tolyl-	258–260°; HCl 220–225°; H₂SO₄ > 275°; acetate 257°; oxalate 247–252°; chloroplatinate 250° (dec.); picrate 240°	36
4-*p*-Methylphenacyl-2-oxo-3-phenyl-	222°	90
3-*o*-(2′-Naphthylazo)phenyl-2-thio-	225°	102
2-Oxo-	159–160.5°; chloroplatinate 204–205°; aurichloride 179°	37, 64, 95
2-Oxo-4-phenyl-	197°; acetate 132–133°	61, 65
2-Oxo-3-phenyl-4-phenacyl-	238–240°; HgCl₂ 198°	90
2-Oxo-3-phenyl-4-α-phenylphenacyl-	222°; HgCl₂ 246°	90
2-Oxo-3-phenyl-4-phthalimido-	285–290°	90
2-Oxo-4-*p*-tolyl-	208–209°	62
2-Oxo-4-2′,4′-xylyl-	200°; acetate 118–119°; picrate 160°	60
2-Thio-	210–212°	37
2-Thio-4-*p*-tolyl-	224°	62
2-Thio-4-2′,4′-xylyl-	222–223°	60

TABLE VIII.9.   1,2,3,4-Tetrahydroquinazolines (Unsubstituted in Position 2).

1,2,3,4-Tetrahydroquinazoline	M.p. (°c)	References
Unsubstituted	81°; H_2O 49–51°; HCl 193–195°; chloroplatinate > 270°; picrate 195–197°, 205–206° (dec.)	18, 37, 41, 103 112
3-Allyl-	105–110°/3 mm, 270–272°/760 mm; oxalate 164°, 176–179°	32, 55
3-o-Aminobenzyl-	88–89°; HCl > 300° (dec.)	102
3-m-Aminophenyl-	156°; HCl 210° (dec.)	51
3-p-Aminophenyl-	138°	52
6-Bromo-3-p-bromophenyl-	135–136°, 173°	72, 73
6-Bromo-3-p-bromophenyl-1-hydroxymethyl-	139–140.5°; HCl 276–278° (dec.); picrate 203.5–204.5°; O-phenylurethane 159.5–160.5°	73
6-Chloro-3-p-chlorophenyl-	158°	72
6-Chloro-3-p-chlorophenyl-1-hydroxymethyl-	135–136°; HCl 273–274° (dec.); picrate 184–185°; O-phenylurethane 141–142°	73
1,3-Dimethylene-	84–93°/0.36 mm; picrate 182–183.5° (dec.)	125
6-Ethoxy-3-p-ethoxyphenyl-	144°	34, 69
3-p-Ethoxyphenyl-	124°, 129°	48, 180
4-Hydroxy-3-phenyl-	170–171°	113
6-Methoxy-3-(4′-methoxy-2′,3′,5′-trimethyl)phenyl-5,7,8-trimethyl-	136–137°; HCl 163–164°; 1-acetyl deriv. 136–137°	120
6-Methoxy-3-methoxyphenyl-	135°	71
3-o-Methoxyphenyl-	96°, 141–142°	38, 103
3-p-Methoxyphenyl-	134°	47
1-Methyl-	picrate 161° (dec.)	111
3-Methyl-	83–83.5°; picrate 134°; methiodide 200°	16, 18, 111

(*Table continued*)

15 + Q.

TABLE VIII.9 (*continued*)

1,2,3,4-Tetrahydroquinazoline	M.p. (°c)	References
6-Methyl-3-*p*-tolyl-	138°, 141°; chloroplatinate 203–205°; picrate 200°	36, 79
1,6-Dimethyl-3-*p*-tolyl-	155°	36
6,7-Methylenedioxy-	101°; picrate 172–173° (dec.)	31
3-2′-Naphthyl-	155–158°	179
3-Phenyl-	118–119°; HCl 220–221°	46, 110, 113, 200
4-Phenyl-	HCl > 200° (dec.)	61
3-*o*-Tolyl-	140°	103
3-*p*-Tolyl-	127°	43, 46
1,3-Trimethylene-	107–108°/0.6 mm; picrate 171–172° (dec.)	125

TABLE VIII.10.   2-Substituted 1,2,3,4-Tetrahydroquinazolines.

1,2,3,4-Tetrahydroquinazoline	M.p. (°c)	References
2-Acetoxy-6-nitro-3-*p*-nitro-phenyl-	223–225° (dec.)	69
1-Acetyl-2-methyl-	120–125°	107
3-*o*-Aminobenzyl-2-*o*-hydroxy-phenyl-	166°	102
3-*o*-Aminobenzyl-2-*p*-hydroxy-phenyl-	90°	102
3-*o*-Aminobenzyl-2-phenyl-	140°	102
1-Benzoyl-2-benzoyloxy-3-phenyl-	168–169°	183
1,3-Dibenzoyl-2-methyl-4-phenyl-	188–189°	106
1-Benzyl-2-*o*-hydroxyphenyl-2,3-diphenyl-	172°	178
1-Benzyl-2,3-diphenyl-	120°	178
2-*o*-Carboxyphenyl-	205–206°; H$_2$O 137–140°	57

(*Table continued*)

TABLE VIII.10 (*continued*)

1,2,3,4-Tetrahydroquinazoline	M.p. (°c)	References
2-Chloro-2-methyl-6-nitro-3-*p*-nitrophenyl-	> 300° (dec.)	45
1,3-Dimethylene-2-phenyl-	155–160°/0.33 mm; picrate 181–183°	125
2-Ethyl-	86–88°	42
4-Hydroxy-6-methyl-2,4-diphenyl-3-*p*-tolyl-	194–195°	27
4-Hydroxy-6,8-dimethyl-2,4-diphenyl-3-2′,4′-xylyl-	163–164°; picrate 204°	27
2-Hydroxy-2-methyl-6-nitro-3-*p*-nitrophenyl-	243–246°	45
2-Hydroxy-1-*p*-toluidinomethyl-3-*p*-tolyl-	139–140°	70
2-Hydroxy-6-nitro-3-*p*-nitrophenyl-	207–208°; *O*-acetyl deriv. 223–225°	69, 101
2-*p*-Hydroxyphenyl-	167–168°	103
6,7-Dimethoxy-2-*p*-nitrophenyl-	119–120°	56
2-Methyl-	picrate 175–178°	41
2-Methyl-3-phenyl-	94–95°	107
2-Methyl-4-phenyl-	oil; picrate 197°	106
6-Methyl-2-phenyl-3-*p*-tolyl-	105°	114
2-Methyl-1,3-trimethylene-	100–105°/0.32 mm; picrate 163–164° (dec.)	125
6,7-Methylenedioxy-2-3′,4′-methylenedioxybenzyl-	212–213°; HCl 238° (dec.)	105
2-*m*-Nitrophenyl-	84–85°	103
2-Phenyl-	101–102°	37, 42
2-Phenyl-1,3-trimethylene-	85.5–87°, 150–154°/0.09 mm	125
2,3-Tetramethylene-	H_2O 100–101°; HBr 239–240°; HI 224–225°; picrate 161–162°	97a, 202

TABLE VIII.11.   5,11-Methano-6H,12H-dibenzo(b,f)(1,5)diazocines.

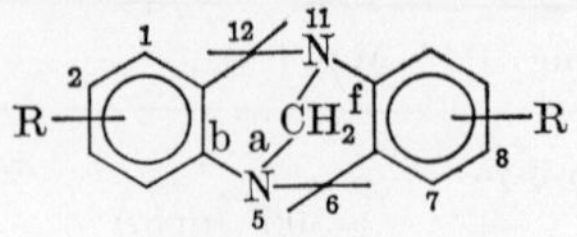

R—⟨ ⟩—R

5,11-Methano-6H,12H-dibenzo-(b,f)(1,5)diazocine	M.p. (°c)	References
Unsubstituted	138–139°; HCl > 360°; picrate 190–191°	121
2,8-Diethoxy-	131.5–132°; HCl 230–232° (dec.); picrate 196.5–197.5°	73
2,8-Dihydroxy-1,3,4,7,9,10-hexamethyl-	279–280° (dec.)	120
2,8-Dimethoxy-1,3,4,7,9,10-hexamethyl-	191–192°; HCl 224–226°	120
2,8-Dimethoxy-	169–169.5°	73
2,8-Dimethyl-(Tröger's base)	138–139°; HCl 213°; picrate 190–191°; 5-phenylphenacyl bromide 249.5–250°; 5-cyclohexyl chloride 240° (dec.)	118, 119, 121, 121a

TABLE VIII.12.   5,6,7,8-Tetrahydroquinazolines.

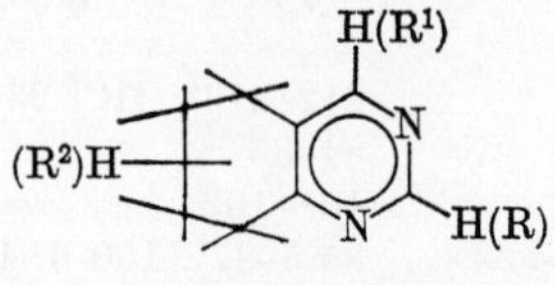

(R²)H—⟨ ⟩—H(R)

5,6,7,8-Tetrahydroquinazoline	M.p. (°c)	References
Unsubstituted	106–108°/12 mm, 121–123°/23 mm; picrate 108–109°	131, 148, 149, 156, 157
2,4-Bisacetamido-6-butoxy-carbonyl-	163–165°	133
2,4-Bisacetamido-6-4′-carboxy-anilinomethyl-	265.5–267°	159
2,4-Bisacetamido-6-dimethoxy-methyl-	~ 140°	159

(*Table continued*)

TABLE VIII.12 (*continued*)

5,6,7,8-Tetrahydroquinazoline	M.p. (°c)	References
2,4-Bisacetamido-6-hydroxy-methyl-	260–270°	133
2,4-Bisacetamido-6-methoxy-	161–164° and 185–186.5° (dimorphic)	159
2,4-Bisacetamido-6-N-trifluoro-acetylcarboxyanilinomethyl-	240–242°	159
2-Acetylsulphanilamido-	258–260°	147, 190
2-Acetylsulphanilamido-8-iso-propyl-5-methyl-	227.5–228.5°	147
2-Acetylsulphanilamido-8-methyl-5,8-1′methylethylidene-	261.5–262°	147
4-Amidinothio-2-(3′,5′-dimethyl-1′-pyrazolyl)-	205° (dec.)	185
2-Amino-	210°; picrate 240° (dec.)	150, 151, 172
2,4-Diamino-	243–245°; p-toluene sulphonate 203–206°	129, 130, 132, 133, 158
2,4-Diamino-6-carbamoyl-	> 300°	133
2,4-Diamino-6-carboxy-	> 300°	133
2-Amino-4-chloro-	213–213.5°, 132–133°/11 mm	137, 162, 165
2,4-Diamino-6-p-chlorophenyl-carbamoyl-	285–286°	133
2,4-Diamino-6-cyano-	> 290°	133
4-(5′-Amino-4′-cyano-1′-pyrazolyl)-2-(3′,5′-dimethyl-1′-pyrazolyl)-	225°	187
4-Amino-2-decylamino-	98–100°	129
2,4-Diamino-6-p-(1,3-dicarboxy-propylcarbamoyl)anilinomethyl-	240–260° (dec.)	159
2-Amino-4-2′-diethylaminoethyl-amino-	117–118°	137
2-Amino-4-3′-diethylamino-propylamino-	87–90°	137
2,4-Diamino-6-diethylcarbamoyl-	70–75° (cryst. transformation); 115–118° and 231–234° (double m.p.)	133
2,4-Diamino-6-dimethoxymethyl-	202.5–204°	159
4-Amino-2-dimethylamino-	135–136°	129
4-(5′-Amino-4′-ethoxycarbonyl-1′-pyrazolyl)-2-(3′,5′-dimethyl-1′-pyrazolyl)-	197–198°	187
2-Amino-4-hydrazino-	190–191°	162, 165

(*Table continued*)

TABLE VIII.12 (*continued*)

5,6,7,8-Tetrahydroquinazoline	M.p. (°c)	References
2-Amino-8-isopropyl-5-methyl-	139–141°; acetyl deriv.	
	125–127°	172
2-Amino-4-methyl-	177–178°	145
2-Amino-4,8-dimethyl-	103–104°	145
2,4-Diamino-5 (or 7)-methyl-	199–203°	129, 130
2,4-Diamino-6-methyl-	232–234°	129, 130
4-Amino-4-(1′-methyl-4′-diethyl-amino)butylamino-	112.5–113°	137
2,4-Diamino-8-methyl-5,8-1′-methylethylidene-	241–242°	158
4-Amino-2-methylamino-	204–205°	129
2,4-Bisbenzylamino-6-bromo-methyl-	140–143°	133
2,4-Bisbenzylamino-6-carboxy-	188–195°	133
2,4-Bisbenzylamino-6-chloro-methyl-	141–142°	133
2,4-Bisbenzylamino-6-cyano-	212–214°	133
2,4-Bisbenzylamino-6-diethyl-carbamoyl-	82–85°	133
2,4-Bisbenzylamino-6-hydroxy-methyl-	130–131°	133
2,4-Bisbenzylamino-6-phenyl-carbamoyl-	169–170°	133
6-Carbamoyl-2,4-dichloro-	220–225°	133
4-Carbamoyl-2-methylthio-	195–196°	152
2,4-Dichloro-	78°	132
2,4-Dichloro-6-carboxy-	159–160°	133
4-Chloro-2-*p*-chloroanilino-	137–138°	136
2,4-Dichloro-6-*p*-chloroanilino-carbamoyl-	88–96° and 164–166° (double m.p.)	133
4-Chloro-2-*N*′-*p*-chlorophenyl-guanidino-	173–175°	143
2,4-Dichloro-6-cyano-	108–109°	133
2,4-Dichloro-6-diethylcarbamoyl-	109–110°	133
4-Chloro-2-(3′,5′-dimethyl-1′-pyrazolyl)-	130–132°	185, 187
4-Chloro-2-phenyl-	105–108°	160
2-*p*-Chloroanilino-4-2′-diethyl-aminoethylamino-	132–134°; 2 HCl·2 H₂O	
	224–226°	136
2-*p*-Chloroanilino-4-3′-diethyl-aminopropylamino-	138–140°; 2 HCl·1.5 H₂O	
	202–204°	136

(*Table continued*)

TABLE VIII.12 (*continued*)

5,6,7,8-Tetrahydroquinazoline	M.p. (°c)	References
2-*p*-Chloroanilino-4-3'-dimethyl-aminopropylamino-	125–127°; 2 HCl 290° (dec.)	136
4-2'-Diethylaminoethylamino-2-phenyl-	1-2'-diethylaminoethyl iodide 116–118°	160
2-(3',5'-Dimethyl-1'-pyrazolyl)-4-(4'-ethoxycarbonyl-5'-methyl-1'-pyrazolyl)-	130–133°	187
1-2'-Dimethylaminoethylamino-2-phenyl-	87–90°	160
4-Hydrazino-	173–174°	162
2,4-Dihydrazino-	210–211°	193
4-Hydrazino-2-methyl-	172–173°, 178–180°	162, 194
4-Hydrazino-2-(3',5'-dimethyl-1-'pyrazolyl)-	128–132°	187
4-Hydrazino-2-phenyl-	203–205°	160
4-Hydrazinocarbonyl-2-methylthio-	159–160°	152
4-2'-Hydroxyethylamino-2-phenyl-	159–161°	160
8-Isopropyl-5-methyl-2-sulphanilamido-	185–187°	147
4-Methoxycarbonyl-2-methylthio-	81–82°	152
2-Methyl-	110–115°/15 mm; picrate 100°	150
4-Methyl-	62–66°, 125–135°/12–15 mm; picrate 152–153°	149
8-Methyl-5,8-1'-methylethylidene-2-sulphanilamido-	276–277°	147
4-Methyl-2-phenyl-	103°; picrate 144–145°	145
4,7-Dimethyl-2-phenyl-	111–112°	145
4,8-Dimethyl-2-phenyl-	84–85°	145
2,4-Bis-(3',5'-dimethyl-1'-pyrazolyl)-	103°	187
2-(3',5'-Dimethyl-1'-pyrazolyl)-4-thiocyanato-	169–171°	195
4-Methyl-2-*p*-tolyl-	129–130°	145
4,7-Dimethyl-2-*p*-tolyl-	135°	145
4,8-Dimethyl-2-*p*-tolyl-	95°	145
4-Methylthio-2-phenyl-	118–119°	161
1-2'-Morpholinoethylamino-2-phenyl-	109–110°	160
2-Phenyl-	52–53°	145

(*Table continued*)

TABLE VIII.12 (*continued*)

5,6,7,8-Tetrahydroquinazoline	M.p. (°c)	References
2-Phenyl-4-propylamino-	1-2′-diethylaminoethyl iodide 170–172°	160
2-Sulphanilamido-	255–256°	147, 190
2-p-[p-(5,6,7,8-Tetrahydroquinazolin-2-ylamino)phenylsulphinyl]-anilino-	298–299°	146
2-p-[p-(5,6,7,8-Tetrahydroquinazolin-2-yl)phenylsulphinyl]phenyl-	234.5–237°	146
2-p-[p-(5,6,7,8-Tetrahydroquinazolin-2-ylamino)phenylsulphonyl]-anilino-	334.5–335.5°	146
2-p-[p-(5,6,7,8-Tetrahydroquinazolin-2-yl)phenylsulphonyl]phenyl-	258–260°	146
2-p-[p-(5,6,7,8-Tetrahydroquinazolin-2-ylamino)phenylthio]anilino-	244–245.5°	146
2-p-[p-(5,6,7,8-Tetrahydroquinazolin-2-yl)phenylthio]phenyl-	195–197°	146

TABLE VIII.13.   3,4,5,6,7,8-Hexahydro-4-oxoquinazolines.

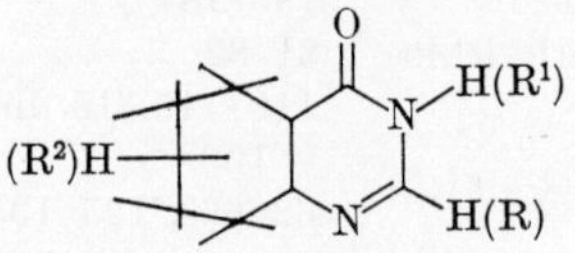

3,4,5,6,7,8-Hexahydro-4-oxoquinazoline[a]	M.p. (°c)	References
Unsubstituted-	162–164°	134
2-Acetamido-6-acetoxymethyl-	207.5–210°	139
2-Acetamido-6-p-carboxyanilino-methyl-	276–277°	138
2-Acetamido-6-p-carboxyphenyl-iminomethyl-	200–240° (dec.)	138
2-Acetamido-6-dimethoxymethyl-	188–189.5°	138
2-Acetamido-6-formyl-	208.5–211°	138
2-Amino-	> 300°	137, 145
2,6-Diamino-	2 HCl 272–273°; dipicrate 285° (dec.)	139
2-Amino-6-carbamoyl-	> 300°	139

(*Table continued*)

TABLE VIII.13 (*continued*)

3,4,5,6,7,8-Hexahydro-4-oxoquinazoline[a]	M.p. (°c)	References
2-(5'-Amino-4'-carboxy-1'-pyrazolyl)-	250° (dec.)	185, 187
2-Amino-6-p-carboxyanilinomethyl-	>300°	138
2-Amino-6-p-chloroanilinomethyl-	229–231°	139
2-Amino-6-chloromethyl-	287–288.5°	139
2-Amino-6-p-chlorophenylcarbamoyl-	>300°	139
2-(5'-Amino-4'-cyano-1'-pyrazolyl)-	261.5–263.5°	184, 185, 186
2-Amino-6-p-(1,3-dicarboxypropylcarbamoyl)anilinocarbonyl-	221–223°	139
2-Amino-6-p-(1,3-dicarboxypropylcarbamoyl)anilinomethyl-	199–202°; H_2O > 260° (dec.)	138, 139
2-Amino-6-3',4'-dichlorobenzamido-	>300°	139
2-Amino-6-p-(1,3-dimethoxycarbonylpropylcarbamoyl)-anilinocarbonyl-	285–285.5°	139
2-Amino-6-dimethoxymethyl-	>300°	138
2-(5'-Amino-4'-ethoxycarbonyl-1'-pyrazolyl)-	169–171°	184, 186
2-Amino-6-ethylthiocarbonyl-	>295°	139
2-Amino-6-p-fluorobenzamido-	265° (dec.)	139
2-Amino-6-formyl-	>300°	138
2-Amino-6-hydrazinocarbonyl-	>300°	139
2-Amino-6-hydroxymethyl-	>300°; picrate 209–211°	139
2-Amino-7-methyl-	310° (dec.)	145
2-Amino-8-methyl-	>300°	145
2-Amino-6-phenylthiocarbonyl-	>300°	139
2-Amino-6-tosyloxy-	212–213.5°	129
3-Benzyl-2-hydrazino-	136–137°; HCl 222–223°	141
3-Benzyl-2-nitroamino-	180° (dec.)	141
2-p-Chloroanilino-	284–287°	136
2-N'-p-Chlorophenylguanidino-	260–261°	143
2-Cyanoamino-	278° (dec.)	143
2-(4'-Ethoxycarbonyl-5'-methyl-1'-pyrazolyl)-	164–165°	184, 185, 186

(*Table continued*)

TABLE VIII.13 *(continued)*

3,4,5,6,7,8-Hexahydro-4-oxoquinazoline[a]	M.p. (°c)	References
2-(4'-Ethoxycarbonyl-5'-phenyl-1'-pyrazolyl)-	150–152°, 176–178°	185, 186
2-Hydrazino-	258° (dec.), 324° (dec.)	140, 164
2-Hydrazino-3-phenyl-	209–210°	154
6-Methoxy-2-methyl-	129–137°; HCl 221–222° (dec.)	144
6-Methoxycarbonyl-2-methylthio-	277–280°	133
2-Methyl-	209–210°; picrate 207–208°	144, 165
2,3-Dimethyl-	108–109°; 1-methiodide 156°	188
7-Methyl-2-phenyl-	214–216°, 227°	145, 182
8-Methyl-2-phenyl-	200°	145
2-(3'-Methyl-5'-phenyl-1'-pyrazolyl)-	197–199°	185, 186
2-(3',4'-Dimethyl-1'-pyrazolyl)-	195–196°	184
2-(3',5'-Dimethyl-1'-pyrazolyl)-	163–165°	185, 187
7-Methyl-2-p-tolyl-	254–256°	145
8-Methyl-2-p-tolyl-	231–232°	145
2-Methylthio-	220–222°	136, 164
2-Methylthio-3-phenyl-	204–205°	154
2-Nitroamino-	217°	140
3-Phenacyl-	171–173°	134
2-Phenyl-	238–239°	145, 161
2-Phenylhydrazino-	275° (dec.)	140
2-Sulphanilamido-	257–257.5°	142
2-(4',5'-Tetramethylene-1'-pyrazolyl)-	171–172°	185
2-p-Tolyl-	255–257°	145

[a] 3,4,5,6,7,8-Hexahydro-2-(3',5'-dimethyl-1'-pyrazolyl)-4-thioquinazoline has m.p. 199–200°,[185] and 3,4,5,6,7,8-hexahydro-2-phenyl-4-thioquinazoline has m.p. 199–201°.[160]

TABLE VIII.14.   1,2-Disubstituted 1,4,5,6,7,8-Hexahydro-4-oxo- (and thio-)quinazolines.

1,4,5,6,7,8-Hexahydroquinazoline	M.p. (°c)	References
1-Benzyl-2-phenyl-4-thio-	215–216°	160
1-Cyclohexyl-2-phenyl-4-thio-	241–242°	160
1-Decyl-2-phenyl-4-thio-	155–156°	160
1-3′,4′-Dichlorophenyl-2-phenyl-4-thio-	330–332°	160
1-2′-Diethylaminoethyl-2-phenyl-4-thio-	166–167°	160
1-3′-Diethylaminopropyl-2-phenyl-4-thio-	174–175°	160
1-3′,4′-Dimethoxyphenethyl-2-phenyl-4-thio-	218–220°	160
1-2′-Dimethylaminoethyl-2-phenyl-4-thio-	166–167°	160
1-p-Fluorophenyl-4-oxo-2-phenyl-	211–213°	160
1-p-Fluorophenyl-2-phenyl-4-thio-	307–310°	160
1-2′-Hydroxyethyl-2-phenyl-4-thio-	244–246°	160
1-p-Methoxyphenyl-2-phenyl-4-thio-	243–245°	160
1-3′-Methoxypropyl-2-phenyl-4-thio-	169–170°	160
1-2′-Morpholinoethyl-2-phenyl-4-thio-	195–197°	160
4-Oxo-1,2-diphenyl-	207–209°	160
4-Oxo-2-phenyl-1-p-trifluoromethylphenyl-	207–208°	160
2-Phenyl-1-pyrrolidin-2′-yl-4-thio-	158–159°	160
1,2-Diphenyl-4-thio-	268–270°	160
2-Phenyl-4-thio-1-p-trifluoromethylphenyl-	294–295°	160

TABLE VIII.15.   1,2,3,4,5,6,7,8-Octahydro-2,4-dioxoquinazolines.

1,2,3,4,5,6,7,8-Octahydro-2,4-dioxoquinazoline	M.p. (°c)	References
Unsubstituted	298–299°, 305°	132, 135
1-Benzyl-3-phenyl-	190–192°	168
6-Butoxycarbonyl-	273–274°	133
6-Carbamoyl-	> 300°	133
6-Carboxy-	> 300°	133
2-o-Chlorophenyl-	254–255°	154
6-Diethylcarbamoyl-	> 300°	133
3-p-Methoxyphenyl-	249–250°	126
1,3-Di-p-methoxyphenyl-	197.5–198.5°	126
1-Methyl-3-phenyl-	162–163°	168
3-Phenyl-	265–266°	126
1,3-Diphenyl-	191–193°	126, 155
3-s-butyl-	103–104°	191
3-p-Tolyl-	304–305°	126
1,3-Di-m-tolyl-	128–139°	127
1,3-Di-p-tolyl-	211–212.5°	126

TABLE VIII.16. 1,2,3,4,5,6,7,8-Octahydro-2,4-dithio- (and oxothio-) quinazolines.

1,2,3,4,5,6,7,8-Octahydroquinazoline	M.p. (°c)	References
6-Carboxy-4-oxo-2-thio-	> 300°	133
6-Diethylcarbamoyl-4-oxo-2-thio-	272–276°	133
6-Methoxycarbonyl-4-oxo-2-thio-	269–271°	133
3-*p*-Methoxyphenyl-4-oxo-2-thio-	276–278°	126
1,3-Di-*p*-methoxyphenyl-2,4-dithio-	288–289°	126
8-Methyl-5,8-1′-methylethylidene-4-oxo-2-thio-	71°	135
4-Oxo-3-phenyl-2-thio-	310–313°	126, 154
2-Oxo-1,3-diphenyl-4-thio-	239°	155
2 (or 4)-Oxo-1,3-diphenyl-4 (or 2)-thio-	269–271°	126
4-Oxo-2-thio-	315–317° (dec.)	134, 135, 136
4-Oxo-2-thio-3-*p*-tolyl-	316–318°	126
2 (or 4)-Oxo-4 (or 2)-thio-1,3-di-*m*-tolyl-	231–232°	127
2 (or 4)-Oxo-4 (or 2)-thio-1,3-di-*p*-tolyl-	210–211°	126
2,4-Dithio-1,3-di-*m*-tolyl-	275–276°	127
2,4-Dithio-1,3-di-*p*-tolyl-	254–255°	126

TABLE VIII.17.   Miscellaneous Reduced Quinazolines.

Quinazoline	M.p. (°c)	References
2-Amino-6-ethyl-5,6-dihydro-1,7-dimethyl-	158–160°	171
2-Amino-5,6-dihydro-5-isoprop-1'-enyl-8-methyl-	165–167°	172
2-Amino-5,6-dihydro-1,7-dimethyl-	160–161°	171
3-Benzyl-1,2,3,4,5,6,7,8-octahydro-2-oxo-	153° (dec.); HCl 212° (dec.)	174
3-Benzyl-1,2,3,4,5,6,7,8-octahydro-2-oxo-	191°	174
3-Benzyl-decahydro-2-oxo-	175°	174
3-Benzyl-decahydro-2,4-dioxo-	210–211°	177
4-Carboxy-1,2,5,6,7,8-hexahydro-2-oxo-	189–190°	175
4-Carboxy-decahydro-2-oxo-	320°; ethyl ester 212–214°	175
Decahydro-3-hydroxy-2,4-dioxo-	trans form 201–203°	177
Decahydro-10-hydroxy-2,4-dioxo-	220°	176
1,2,5,6,7,8,9,10-Octahydro-2-oxo-	168°	174
Decahydro-2,4-dioxo-3-phenylsulphonyloxy-	trans form 208–209°	177

11. References

1. Schöpf and Oechler, *Ann. Chem.*, **523**, 1 (1936).
2. Albrecht, Scher, Jr., and Vogel, *Anal. Chem.*, **34**, 398 (1962).
3. Smith and Stephen, *Tetrahedron*, **1**, 38 (1957).
4. Böhme and Böing, *Arch. Pharm.*, **293**, 1011 (1960).
5. Gurien and Brown, *J. Pharm. Sci.*, **52**, 1102 (1963).
6. Hauptmann, *Arzneimittelforsch.*, **15**, 610 (1965).
7. Böhme and Böing, *Arch. Pharm.*, **294**, 556 (1961).
8. Cohen, Klarberg, and Vaughan, Jr., *J. Am. Chem. Soc.*, **82**, 2731 (1960).
9. Song and Cohen, *U.S. Pat.*, 3,092,631 (1963); *Chem. Abstr.*, **59**, 12821 (1963).
10. Hirwe and Kulkarni, *Proc. Indian Acad. Sci.*, **13A**, 49 (1941); *Chem. Abstr.*, **35**, 5502 (1941).
11. Feldman and Wagner, *J. Org. Chem.*, **7**, 31 (1942).
12. Pala and Mantegani, *Gazz. Chim. Ital.*, **94**, 595 (1964).
13. Heller and Mecke, *J. Prakt. Chem.*, **131**, 82 (1931).
14. Carrington, *J. Chem. Soc.*, **1955**, 2527.
15. Etienne and Legrand, *Compt. Rend.*, **229**, 1372 (1949).
16. Mirza, *Sci. Cult. (Calcutta)*, **17**, 530 (1952).
17. Cohen, Klarberg, and Vaughan, Jr., *J. Am. Chem. Soc.*, **81**, 5508 (1959).
18. Smith, Briggs, Kent, Albright, and Walsh, *J. Heterocyclic Chem.*, **2**, 157 (1965).
19. Párkányi and Vystrčil, *Chem. Listy*, **50**, 666 (1956); *Chem. Abstr.*, **50**, 8657 (1956).

20. Butler, Partridge, and Waite, *J. Chem. Soc.*, **1960**, 4970.
21. Bischler, *Ber. Deut. Chem. Ges.*, **26**, 1891 (1893).
22. Gabriel and Jansen, *Ber. Deut. Chem. Ges.*, **23**, 2807 (1890).
23. Armarego, *J. Chem. Soc.*, **1961**, 2697.
24. Lora-Tamayo, Madroñero, and Muñoz, *Chem. Ber.*, **94**, 208 (1961).
25. Muñoz, Lora-Tamayo, Madroñero, and Marzal, *Anales Real Soc. Espan.*, *Fis. Quim. (Madrid)*, **57**, 277 (1961); *Chem. Abstr.*, **56**, 7273 (1962).
26. Lora-Tamayo, Madroñero, and Muñoz, *Chem. Ind. (London)*, **1959**, 657.
27. Dziewónski and Sternbach, *Bull. Intern. Acad. Polonaise, Classe Sci. Mat. Nat.*, **1953A**, 333; *Chem. Abstr.*, **30**, 2971 (1936).
28. Dziewónski and Sternbach, *Bull. Intern. Acad. Polonaise, Classe Sci. Mat. Nat.*, **1933A**, 416; *Chem. Abstr.*, **28**, 2717 (1934).
29. Dziewónski and Sternbach, *Bull. Intern. Acad. Polonaise, Classe Sci. Mat. Nat.*, **1935A**, 327; *Chem. Abstr.*, **30**, 2971 (1936).
30. Gabriel and Colman, *Ber. Deut. Chem. Ges.*, **37**, 3643 (1904).
31. Wilkendorf, *Ber. Deut. Chem. Ges.*, **52**, 606 (1919).
32. Hanford, Liang, and Adams, *J. Am. Chem. Soc.*, **56**, 2780 (1934).
33. Bell and Childress, *J. Org. Chem.*, **27**, 1691 (1962).
34. Maffei, *Gazz. Chim. Ital.*, **59**, 3 (1929).
35. Iyer, Anand, and Dhar, *J. Sci. Ind. Res. India*, **16C**, 157 (1957).
36. Walther and Bamberg, *J. Prakt. Chem.*, **73** (2), 209 (1906).
37. Busch, *J. Prakt. Chem.*, **51** (2), 113 (1895).
38. Paal and Schilling, *J. Prakt. Chem.*, **54** (2), 277 (1896).
39. Wagner, *J. Org. Chem.*, **5**, 133 (1940).
40. Gabriel and Jansen, *Ber. Deut. Chem. Ges.*, **24**, 3091 (1891).
41. Gabriel, *Ber. Deut. Chem. Ges.*, **36**, 800 (1903).
42. Wolff, *Ber. Deut. Chem. Ges.*, **25**, 3030 (1892).
43. Widman, *J. Prakt. Chem.*, **47** (2), 343 (1893).
44. Hanford and Adams, *J. Am. Chem. Soc.*, **57**, 921 (1935).
45. Stillich, *Ber. Deut. Chem. Ges.*, **36**, 3115 (1903); **38**, 1241 (1905).
46. Paal and Busch, *Ber. Deut. Chem. Ges.*, **22**, 2683 (1889).
47. Paal and Schilling, *J. Prakt. Chem.*, **54** (2), 283 (1896).
48. Paal and Küttner, *J. Prakt. Chem.*, **48** (2), 555 (1893).
49. Paal and Krückeberg, *J. Prakt. Chem.*, **48** (2), 542 (1893).
50. Paal and Kromschröder, *J. Prakt. Chem.*, **54** (2), 265 (1896).
51. Paal and Neuburger, *J. Prakt. Chem.*, **48** (2), 561 (1893).
52. Paal and Poller, *J. Prakt. Chem.*, **54** (2), 271 (1896).
53. Francis, *Ber. Deut. Chem. Ges.*, **29**, 1450 (1896).
54. Paal and Krecke, *Ber. Deut. Chem. Ges.*, **23**, 2634 (1890).
55. Paal and Stollberg, *J. Prakt. Chem.*, **48** (2), 569 (1893).
56. Downes and Lions, *J. Am. Chem. Soc.*, **72**, 3053 (1950).
57. Gabriel, *Ber. Deut. Chem. Ges.*, **45**, 713 (1912).
58. Robinson, *U.S. Pat.*, 2,758,996 (1956); *Chem. Abstr.*, **51**, 2061 (1957).
59. Doub, Richardson, and Campbell, *Ger. Pat.*, 1,139,124 (1962); *Chem. Abstr.*, **58**, 9100 (1963).
60. Drawert, *Ber. Deut. Chem. Ges.*, **32**, 1259 (1899).
61. Gabriel and Stelzner, *Ber. Deut. Chem. Ges.*, **29**, 1300 (1896).
62. Kippenberg, *Ber. Deut. Chem. Ges.*, **30**, 1130 (1897).
63. Hanschke, *Ber. Deut. Chem. Ges.*, **32**, 2021 (1899).

64. Söderbaum and Widman, *Ber. Deut. Chem. Ges.*, **22**, 1665 (1889).
65. Puckowski and Ross, *J. Chem. Soc.*, **1959**, 3555.
66. Braun, Kruber, and Aust, *Ber. Deut. Chem. Ges.*, **46**, 3056 (1913).
67. Tröger, *J. Prakt. Chem.*, **36**, (2), 225 (1887).
68. Lepetit, Maffei, and Maimeri, *Gazz. Chim. Ital.*, **57**, 862 (1927).
69. Maffei, *Gazz. Chim. Ital.*, **58**, 261 (1928).
70. Eisner and Wagner, *J. Am. Chem. Soc.*, **56**, 1938 (1934).
71. Wagner, *J. Org. Chem.*, **2**, 157 (1937).
72. Wagner and Eisner, *J. Am. Chem. Soc.*, **59**, 879 (1937).
73. Miller and Wagner, *J. Am. Chem. Soc.*, **63**, 832 (1941).
74. Wagner, *J. Org. Chem.*, **19**, 1862 (1954).
75. Borkowski and Wagner, *J. Org. Chem.*, **17**, 1128 (1952).
76. Denney and Rosen, *U.S. Dept. Comm., Office Tech. Service, A.D.*, 260,401 (1960); *Chem. Abstr.*, **59**, 4839 (1963).
77. Cairncross and Bogert, *Collection Czech. Chem. Commun.*, **7**, 548 (1935).
78. Farrar, *J. Chem. Soc.*, **1954**, 3253.
79. Simons, *J. Am. Chem. Soc.*, **59**, 518 (1937).
80. Higashino, *J. Pharm. Soc. Japan*, **80**, 245 (1960).
81. Albert, Armarego, and Spinner, *J. Chem. Soc.*, **1961**, 2689.
82. Hayashi and Higashino, *Chem. Pharm. Bull. (Japan)*, **12**, 1111 (1964).
83. Hayashi and Higashino, *Chem. Pharm. Bull. (Japan)*, **13**, 291 (1965).
84. Higashino, *Chem. Pharm. Bull. (Japan)*, **10**, 1043 (1962).
85. Albert, Armarego, and Spinner, *J. Chem. Soc.*, **1961**, 5267.
86. Armarego and Smith, *J. Chem. Soc.*, **1965**, 5360.
87. Reynolds and Robinson, *J. Chem. Soc.*, **1936**, 196.
88. Albert and Barlin, *J. Chem. Soc.*, **1962**, 3129.
89. Reissert and Schaaf, *Ber. Deut. Chem. Ges.*, **59**, 2494 (1926).
90. Crivetz, *Ann. Sci. Univ. Jassy*, **29**, 140 (1943); *Chem. Abstr.*, **42**, 1595 (1948).
90a. Metlesics, Silverman, Toome, and Sternbach, *J. Org. Chem.*, **31**, 1007 (1966).
91. Marr and Bogert, *J. Am. Chem. Soc.*, **57**, 729 (1935).
92. Elderfield, Williamson, Gensler, and Kremer, *J. Org. Chem.*, **12**, 405 (1947).
93. Schofield, *J. Chem. Soc.*, **1952**, 1927.
93a. Jones, *J. Chem. Soc.*, **1964**, 5911.
94. Sternbach, Kaiser, and Reeder, *J. Am. Chem. Soc.*, **82**, 475 (1960).
95. Ried and Stahlhofen, *Chem. Ber.*, **87**, 1814 (1954).
96. Jürgens, *Ber. Deut. Chem. Ges.*, **40**, 4409 (1907).
97. Juan de la Cieva, *Span. Pat.*, 260,050 (1963); *Chem. Abstr.*, **60**, 9290 (1964).
97a. Muñoz and Madroñero, *Chem. Ber.*, **95**, 2182 (1962).
97b. Nelson, *Chem. Ind. (London)*, **1965**, 653.
98. Sen and Upadhyaya, *J. Indian Chem. Soc.*, **27**, 40 (1950).
99. Sen and Sidhu, *J. Indian Chem. Soc.*, **25**, 437 (1948).
100. Lawes and Scarborough, *U.S. Pat.*, 3,127,401 (1964); *Chem. Abstr.*, **60**, 14526 (1964).
101. Meyer and Stillich, *Ber. Deut. Chem. Ges.*, **35**, 739 (1902).
102. Busch, Birk, and Lehrmann, *J. Prakt. Chem.*, **55** (2), 356 (1897).
103. Busch and Dietz, *J. Prakt. Chem.*, **53** (2), 414 (1896).
104. Fetscher and Bogert, *J. Org. Chem.*, **4**, 71 (1939).

105. Shamshurin, *Zh. Obshch. Khim.*, **13**, 573 (1943); *Chem. Abstr.*, **39**, 704 (1945).
106. Bischler and Barad, *Ber. Deut. Chem. Ges.*, **25**, 3080 (1892).
107. Paal and Krecke, *Ber. Deut. Chem. Ges.*, **24**, 3049 (1891).
108. Paal and Koch, *J. Prakt. Chem.*, **48** (2), 549 (1893).
109. Busch and Brunner, *J. Prakt. Chem.*, **52** (2), 373 (1895).
110. Kulisch, *Chem. Zentr.*, **I**, 847 (1899).
111. Osborn and Schofield, *J. Chem. Soc.*, **1956**, 3977.
112. Adachi, *J. Pharm. Soc. Japan*, **77**, 507 (1957).
113. Itoml, *Mem. Coll. Sci. Univ. Kyoto*, **13A**, 311 (1930); *Chem. Abstr.*, **25**, 2057 (1931).
114. Fales, *J. Am. Chem. Soc.*, **77**, 5118 (1955).
115. Crombie and Krasinski, *J. Soc. Chem. Ind.*, **1962**, 983.
116. Crombie, Krasinski, and Manzoor-i-Khuda, *J. Chem. Soc.*, **1963**, 4970.
117. Perrin, *Dissociation Constants of Organic Bases in Aqueous Solutions*, Butterworths, 1965.
118. Goecke, *Z. Elektrochem.*, **9**, 470 (1903).
119. Spielman, *J. Am. Chem. Soc.*, **57**, 583 (1935); Patterson and Capell, *The Ring Index*, Reinhold Publ. Corp., **1940**, p. 358.
120. Smith and Schubert, *J. Am. Chem. Soc.*, **70**, 2656 (1948).
121. Cooper and Partridge, *J. Chem. Soc.*, **1955**, 991.
121a. Rutter, Jr., *J. Am. Chem. Soc.*, **74**, 3454 (1952).
122. Albert and Yamamoto, *J. Chem. Soc. (B)*, **1966**, 956.
123. Wepster, *Rec. Trav. Chim.*, **72**, 661 (1953).
124. Prelog and Wieland, *Helv. Chim. Acta*, **27**, 1127 (1944) cf. Mason, Vane, Schofield, Wells and Whitehurst, *J. Chem. Soc. (B)* **1967**, 553.
125. Shiotani and Mitsuhashi, *J. Pharm. Soc. Japan*, **84**, 656 (1964).
126. Schoen, *Roczniki Chem.*, **29**, 549 (1955); *Chem. Abstr.*, **50**, 8660 (1956).
127. Schoen and Bogdanowicz, *Roczniki Chem.*, **36**, 1493 (1962); *Chem. Abstr.*, **59**, 6396 (1963).
128. Appelquest, *U.S. Pat.*, 2,517,824 (1950); *Chem. Abstr.*, **44**, 10375 (1950).
129. Modest, Chatterjee, and Protopapa, *J. Org. Chem.*, **30**, 1837 (1965).
130. Modest, Chatterjee, and Kangur, *J. Org. Chem.*, **27**, 2708 (1962).
131. Bredereck, Gompper, and Geiger, *Chem. Ber.*, **93**, 1402 (1960).
132. Kano, *Japan. Pat.*, 12,079 (1960); *Chem. Abstr.*, **55**, 11445 (1961).
133. DeGraw, Goodman, Koehler, and Baker, *J. Org. Chem.*, **24**, 1632 (1959).
134. Baker, Schaub, Joseph, McEvoy, and Williams, *J. Org. Chem.*, **18**, 133 (1953).
135. Polonovski and Libermann, *Bull. Soc. Chim. France*, **1947**, 1073.
136. Curd, Richardson, and Rose, *J. Chem. Soc.*, **1946**, 378.
137. Hull, Lovell, Openshaw, Payman, and Todd, *J. Chem. Soc.*, **1946**, 357.
138. Degraw, Goodman, and Baker, *J. Org. Chem.*, **26**, 1156 (1961).
139. Koehler, Goodman, DeGraw, and Baker, *J. Am. Chem. Soc.*, **80**, 5779 (1958).
140. Shirakawa, *J. Pharm. Soc. Japan*, **79**, 1477 (1959).
141. Shirakawa, *J. Pharm. Soc. Japan*, **79**, 1487 (1959).
142. Hunter and Nathan, *U.S. Pat.*, 2,425,326 (1947); *Chem. Abstr.*, **41**, 6673 (1947).
143. Cliffe, Curd, Rose, and Scott, *J. Chem. Soc.*, **1948**, 574.
144. McCasland and Bryce, *J. Am. Chem. Soc.*, **74**, 842 (1952).

145. Miller and Bhattacharya, *J. Indian Chem. Soc.*, **4**, 149 (1927).
146. Sugasawa and Iwao, *J. Pharm. Soc. Japan*, **65** (5), 5 (1945).
147. Caldwell, Kornfeld, and Donnell, *J. Am. Chem. Soc.*, **63**, 2188 (1941).
148. Bredereck, Gompper, and Morlock, *Angew. Chem.*, **68**, 151 (1956).
149. Bredereck, Gompper, and Morlock, *Chem. Ber.*, **90**, 942 (1957).
150. Bredereck, Effenberger, and Treiber, *Chem. Ber.*, **96**, 1505 (1963).
151. Cook, Gentles, and Tucker, *Rec. Trav. Chim.*, **69**, 1201 (1950).
152. Buděšínský and Roubínek, *Collection Czech. Chem. Commun.*, **26**, 2871 (1961).
153. Buděšínský and Roubínek, *Collection Czech. Chem. Commun.*, **29**, 2341 (1964).
154. DeStevens, Halamandaris, Wenk, Mull, and Schlittler, *Arch. Biochem. Biophys.*, **83**, 141 (1959).
155. Bianchetti, Pocar, and Rossi, *Gazz. Chim. Ital.*, **93**, 255 (1963).
156. Ziegenbein and Franke, *Angew. Chem.*, **71**, 628 (1959).
157. Ziegenbein, *Ger. Pat.*, 1,114,497 (1959); *Chem. Abstr.*, **56**, 5981 (1962).
158. Chase and Walker, *J. Chem. Soc.*, **1953**, 3518.
159. DeGraw, Goodman, Weinstein, and Baker, *J. Org. Chem.*, **27**, 576 (1962).
160. Carney, Wojtkunski, and DeStevens, *J. Org. Chem.*, **29**, 2887 (1964).
161. Hünig and Hübner, *Chem. Ber.*, **95**, 937 (1962).
161a. DeStevens, Blatter, and Carney, *Angew. Chem. (English Translation)*, **5**, 35 (1966).
162. Kano and Makisumi, *Japan. Pat.*, 6,725 (1959); *Chem. Abstr.*, **54**, 16472 (1960).
163. Schlein, Israel, Chatterjee, and Modest, *Chem. Ind. (London)*, **1964**, 418.
164. Brady and Herbst, *J. Org. Chem.*, **24**, 922 (1959).
165. Miller and Rose, *J. Chem. Soc.*, **1963**, 5642.
166. Burnett, Jr., and Ainsworth, *J. Org. Chem.*, **23**, 1382 (1958).
167. Baumgarten, Creger, and Villars, *J. Am. Chem. Soc.*, **80**, 6609 (1958).
168. Schoen, *Roczniki Chem.*, **35**, 967 (1961); *Chem. Abstr.*, **56**, 3041 (1962).
169. Baumgarten, Murdock, and Dirks, *J. Org. Chem.*, **26**, 803 (1961).
170. Párkányi, *Chem. Listy*, **51**, 709 (1957); *Chem. Abstr.*, **51**, 11889 (1957).
171. Lacey, *J. Chem. Soc.*, **1960**, 1625.
172. Benary, *Ber. Deut. Chem. Ges.*, **63**, 2601 (1930).
173. Chi and Wu, *Hua Hsüeh Hsüeh Pao*, **22**, 188 (1956); *Chem. Abstr.*, **52**, 6360 (1958).
174. Mannich and Hieronimus, *Ber. Deut. Chem. Ges.*, **75**, 49 (1942).
175. Sprague and Schultz, *U.S. Pat.*, 2,650,921 (1953); *Chem. Abstr.*, **48**, 10784 (1954).
176. Fourneau and Maréchal, *Bull. Soc. Chim. France*, **12**, 990 (1945).
177. Bauer and Nambury, *J. Org. Chem.*, **26**, 1106 (1961).
178. Busch and Roegglen, *Ber. Deut. Chem. Ges.*, **27**, 3239 (1894).
179. Busch and Brand, *J. Prakt. Chem.*, **52** (2), 410 (1895).
180. Busch and Hartmann, *J. Prakt. Chem.*, **52** (2), 396 (1895).
181. Thode, *J. Prakt. Chem.*, **69** (2), 92 (1904).
182. Kötz and Merkel, *J. Prakt. Chem.*, **79** (2), 102 (1909).
183. Heller, *Ber. Deut. Chem. Ges.*, **37**, 3112 (1904).
184. Shirakawa, *Japan. Pat.*, 3032 (1960); *Chem. Abstr.*, **55**, 1669 (1961).
185. Shirakawa, *U.S. Pat.*, 3,040,047 (1962); *Chem. Abstr.*, **58**, 533 (1963).
186. Shirakawa and Tsujikawa, *Takeda Kenkyusho Nempo*, **22**, 19 (1963); *Chem. Abstr.*, **60**, 12009 (1964).

187. Shirakawa and Tsujikawa, *Takeda Kenkyusho Nempo*, **22**, 27 (1963); *Chem. Abstr.*, **60**, 12009 (1964).
188. Berlin and Heimke, *U.S. Pat.*, 2,861,989 (1958); *Chem. Abstr.*, **53**, 9866 (1959).
189. Jacini, *Gazz. Chim. Ital.*, **74**, 3 (1944).
190. Raiziss and Freifelder, *J. Am. Chem. Soc.*, **64**, 2340 (1942).
191. Loux, Luckenbaugh, and Soboczénski, *Belg. Pat.*, 625,897 (1963); *Chem. Abstr.*, **60**, 14519 (1964).
192. Simpson and Morley, *J. Chem. Soc.*, **1949**, 1354.
193. Libermann, *Fr. Pat.*, 1,170,121 (1959); *Chem. Abstr.*, **55**, 9439 (1961).
194. Miller and Rose, *Brit. Pat.*, 864,731 (1961); *Chem. Abstr.*, **55**, 24798 (1961).
195. Kinugawa, Ochiai, and Yamamoto, *J. Pharm. Soc. Japan*, **83**, 1086 (1963).
196. Fry and Lea, *Brit. Pat.*, 846,298 (1960); *Chem. Abstr.*, **55**, 7117 (1961).
197. Teshigawara, Hayashi, and Tono, *Japan. Pat.*, 8,133 (1963); *Chem. Abstr.*, **59**, 11527 (1963).
198. Gheorghiu and Manolescu, *Bull. Soc. Chim. France*, **3** (5), 1830 (1936).
199. Gheorghiu, *Bull. Soc. Chim. France*, **49** (4), 1205 (1931).
200. Busch, *Ber. Deut. Chem. Ges.*, **27**, 2897 (1894).
201. Chakravarti, Chakravarti, and Chakravarti, *J. Chem. Soc.*, **1953**, 3337.
202. Fitzgerald, Johns, Lamberton, and Redcliffe, *Australian J. Chem.*, **19**, 151 (1966).

CHAPTER IX

Quinazoline *N*-oxides (including 1- and 3-Hydroxyquinazolines)

The chemistry of quinazoline *N*-oxides was virtually unknown a decade ago. The 1-acylindazoles prepared by Auwers and Meyenburg[1] in 1891 were shown to be quinazoline-3-oxides by Sternbach, Kaiser, and Reeder[2] in 1960. The discovery, by these workers, of the rearrangement of 2-chloromethylquinazoline-3-oxides to the biologically active benzodiazepine-*N*-oxides has prompted research in this field. Also, Adachi, Higashino, and Yamanaka in Japan contributed much to our knowledge of the reactions of quinazoline *N*-oxides.

1- and 3-Hydroxy- 3,4-dihydro-4-oxo-, and 1,2,3,4-tetrahydro-2,4-dioxoquinazolines are tautomeric with 4-hydroxy- and 2,4-dihydroxyquinazoline 1- and 3-oxides. These are described in detail in this chapter because of their obvious relationship with the *N*-oxides.

1. Quinazoline-1-oxides

Quinazoline-1-oxide is not known, but a few 4-substituted derivatives have been prepared. Oxidation of 4-alkoxyquinazolines with hydrogen peroxide in acetic acid[3] yields 3,4-dihydro-4-oxoquinazoline, probably as a result of hydrolysis. Perphthalic acid in ether, on the other hand, oxidized 4-methoxy-, 4-ethoxy-, 4-propoxy-, 4-phenoxy-, and 4-benzyloxyquinazoline to the respective quinazoline-1-oxides (**1**). The yields varied between 10 and 54% and the 1-oxides were formed together with about 20% of the respective 4-alkoxy-1,2-dihydro-1-hydroxy-2-oxoquinazolines (**2**), which were readily separated by the preferential solubility of the latter in alkali (Reaction 1).[3] A similar oxidation of 4-isopropylquinazoline gave 4-isopropylquinazo-

$$(1)$$

$$(1) \qquad (2)$$

R = Me, Et, Pr, PhCH$_2$-, or Ph

line-1-oxide together with 1,2-dihydro-4-isopropyl-2-oxoquinazoline and a small amount of 3,4-dihydro-4-oxoquinazoline.[4] Oxidation to give the 1-oxide with hydrogen peroxide in acetic acid was possible when less sensitive groups were present in the molecule. 2-Chloromethyl- and 2-methyl- 6-chloro-4-phenylquinazoline-1-oxides,[2] and 3-phenyl-, 3-*p*-bromophenyl-, and 3-*o*-tolyl- 3,4-dihydro-2-methyl-4-oxoquinazoline-1-oxides[5] were obtained in this manner. The last three compounds, however, were accompanied by *N*-phenyl-, *N*-*p*-bromophenyl-, and *N*-*o*-tolyl-*o*-nitrobenzamide respectively (Reaction 2).

$$(3)$$

$$(4) \qquad (5)$$

$$(2)$$

R = H, *p*-Br, or *o*-Me

The structure of the 4-alkoxyquinazoline-1-oxides was deduced by deoxygenation with phosphorus trichloride, or by catalytic reduction with Raney nickel, to the respective 4-alkoxyquinazolines. They were hydrolyzed by boiling water (3–4 hours) to the same 3,4-dihydro-4-oxoquinazoline-1-oxide. The position of the *N*-oxide linkage was shown by methylation of the latter, followed by catalytic reduction of the methyl derivative to the known 3,4-dihydro-3-methyl-4-oxoquinazoline (Reaction 3).[3] Whereas hydrogenation with palladium on charcoal catalyst reduces 4-benzyloxyquinazoline-1-oxide first to 3,4-dihydro-4-oxoquinazoline-1-oxide then to 3,4-dihydro-4-oxoquinazoline, Raney nickel catalyst gives first 4-benzyloxyquinazoline which is reduced further to 3,4-dihydro-4-oxoquinazoline.[6]

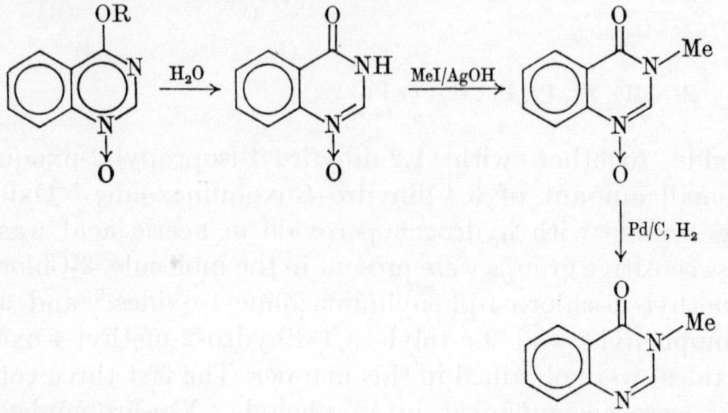

(3)

4-Alkoxyquinazoline-1-oxides undergo the Reissert reaction with benzoyl chloride in the presence of cyanide to yield 4-alkoxy-2-cyano-quinazolines,[4,7] and with acetic anhydride, or toluene-p-sulphonyl chloride, followed by alkali, they furnish 4-alkoxy-1,2-dihydro-2-oxoquinazolines[7] (see Ch. IV, Sect. 1.A.). Sulphuryl chloride, or phosphoryl chloride, converts 4-methoxy- and 4-isopropylquinazoline-1-oxide to 4-methoxy- and 4-isopropyl-2-chloroquinazoline respectively.[4] Phenyl magnesium bromide, or phenyl lithium, reacts with 4-methoxy-

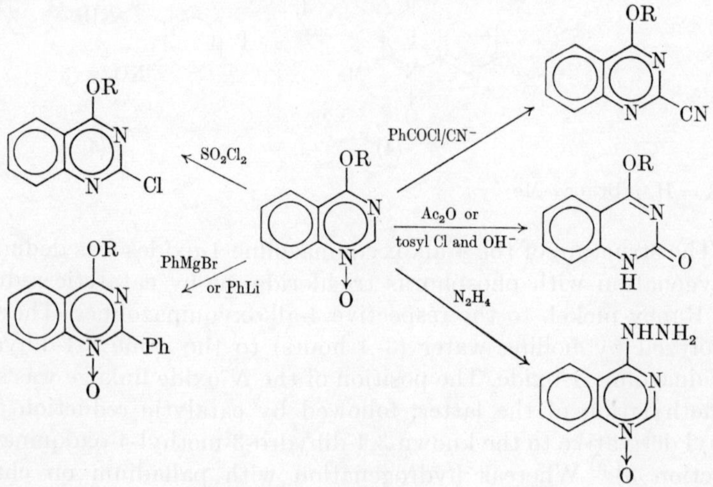

(4)

and 4-isopropylquinazoline-1-oxide, without causing loss of the *N*-oxide function, to give 4-methoxy- and 4-isopropyl- 2-phenyl-quinazoline-1-oxides respectively. 4-Hydrazinoquinazoline-1-oxide is obtained by reacting 4-methoxyquinazoline-1-oxide with hydrazine.[4] These reactions are summarized in (4).

A Reissert reaction with 4-isopropylquinazoline-1-oxide yields, in addition to the normal product, i.e. 2-cyano-4-isopropylquinazoline, 4-(1′-carbamoyl-1′-methyl)ethylquinazoline. Similarly the reaction with benzoyl chloride and alkali gave 1,2-dihydro-4-isopropyl-2-oxoquinazo-line together with 4-(1′-benzoyloxy-1′-methyl)ethylquinazoline. The latter was oxidized to 4-(1′-benzoyloxy-1′-methyl)ethylquinazoline-1-oxide with perphthalic acid (Reaction 5).[4]

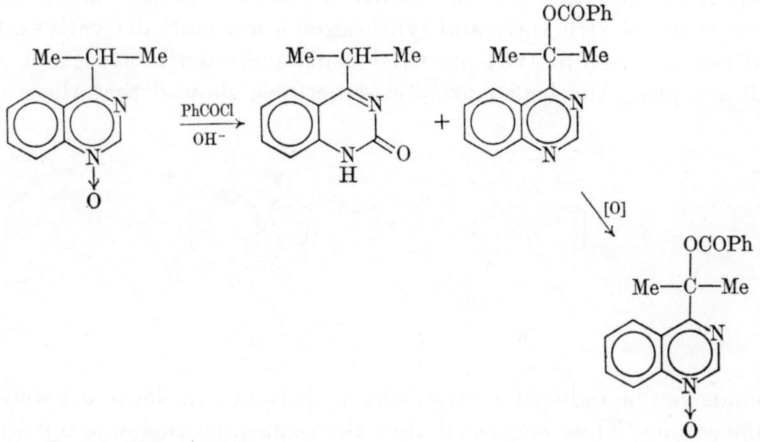

(5)

Acetic anhydride deoxygenated 3-phenyl-, 3-*p*-bromophenyl-, and 3-*o*-tolyl- 3,4-dihydro-4-oxoquinazoline-1-oxides (**4**) to **3**, and further oxidation of **4** gave the respective *o*-nitrobenzamides (**5**).[5] 6-Chloro-2-chloromethyl-4-phenylquinazoline-1-oxide reacted with methylamine to yield 6-chloro-2-methyliminomethyl-4-phenylquinazoline (Reaction 6),[8] and is unlike the corresponding 3-oxide which undergoes ring enlargement (Sect. 3.C.).

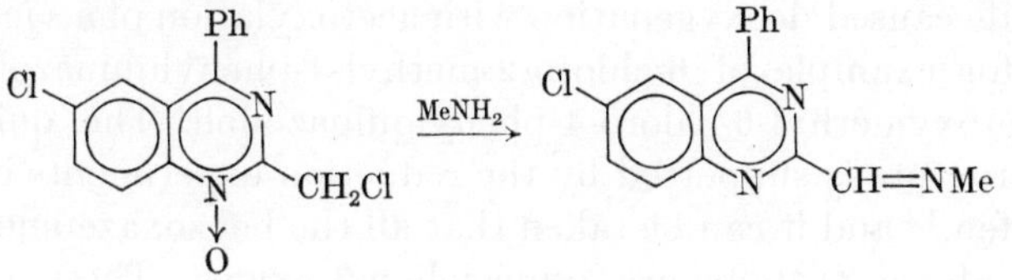

(6)

2. Quinazoline-3-oxides

A. Preparation and Structure of Quinazoline-3-oxides

Auwers and Meyenburg[1] dehydrated *o*-acetamidoacetophenone oxime and *o*-acetamidobenzophenone oxime with Beckmann's mixture and assigned the indazole structures **6** to their products. Bischler[9] in 1893 refuted these structures on the evidence that hydrolysis caused degradation, instead of deacetylation to yield indazoles. He then postulated the benzoxazepine formula **7** which explained the hydrolysis reactions. Also Meisenheimer and Diedrich[10] synthesized 1-acetyl- and 1-benzoylindazole from 1-cyanoindazole and methyl and phenyl magnesium bromides respectively, and showed that they were different from those described by the earlier workers. Auwers[11] accepted the benzoxazepine structures and synthesized a few more derivatives. Ried and Stahlhofen[12] in 1954 prepared many more derivatives, and while still accepting the benzoxazepine structures, showed that these com-

(6)   (7)

pounds can be reduced catalytically with Raney nickel to 3,4-dihydroquinazolines. They suggested that the oxazepine ring was opened by reduction and that the products then cyclized by dehydration to 3,4-dihydroquinazolines. Oxidation of these with potassium ferricyanide gave the authentic quinazoline derivatives. Sternbach, Kaiser, and Reeder[2] in 1960 showed that cyclization of *o*-amidobenzophenone oximes gave quinazoline-3-oxides on the evidence that the infrared spectra of the products had bands characteristic of the *N*-oxide group (Sect. 2.B.) and that they gave typical reactions of *N*-oxides. Thus, phosphorus trichloride reduced them to quinazolines, and acetic anhydride caused deoxygenation with acetoxylation of a vicinal methyl group, for example of 6-chloro-2-methyl-4-phenylquinazoline-3-oxide to 2-acetoxymethyl-6-chloro-4-phenylquinazoline. The quinazoline-3-oxide structure is supported by the reduction experiments of Ried and Stahlhofen,[12] and it can be taken that all the benzoxazepines described by the above authors are quinazoline-3-oxides. These compounds, formerly described as benzoxazepines, are listed as quinazoline-3-oxides in table IX.3.

Quinazoline-3-oxide was first prepared by Adachi[13] in 1957 by heating the product obtained from the reaction of quinazoline and hydroxylamine at room temperature with acetone. He also prepared it, more conveniently, from *o*-aminobenzaldehyde oxime and ethyl orthoformate (Reaction 7). It was the 3-oxide because its ethiodide,

$$\tag{7}$$

obtained by alkylation, was hydrolyzed by alkali to the known *o*-ethyl-aminobenzaldehyde oxime. Similarly 4-methylquinazoline-3-oxide was formed from 4-methylquinazoline and hydroxylamine, or from *o*-amino-acetophenone oxime and ethyl orthoformate.[14] When the reaction of quinazoline and hydroxylamine was performed at 125° a second molecule of hydroxylamine reacted, and the product was 2-amino-quinazoline-3-oxide (Reaction 8). 4-Methoxy- and 4-phenoxyquinazo-

$$\tag{8}$$

line reacted with this reagent to yield the same 4-aminoquinazoline-3-oxide. The structure of this product was deduced by reduction to 4-aminoquinazoline and by ethylation followed by hydrolysis to the known *o*-ethylaminobenzoic acid (Reaction 9).[15]

$$\tag{9}$$

7-Chloro-, 7-methyl-, 4,7-dimethyl-, 5-, 6-, 7-, 8-methoxy-, 7-methoxy-4-methyl-, and 8-methoxy-4-methyl- quinazoline-3-oxides were prepared from *o*-aminobenzaldehyde oximes or *o*-aminoacetophenone oximes and ethyl orthoformate.[16] Several 4-methylquinazoline-3-oxides were obtained by heating *o*-amidoacetophenone oximes with 85% sulphuric acid at ~55°, 10% hydrochloric acid (boiling), or polyphosphoric acid at 85° for a short period.[17] Many 4-aryl-2-chloromethyl-quinazoline-3-oxides were made from *o*-aminobenzophenone oximes and chloroacetyl chloride in acetic acid containing hydrogen chloride, in connection with the preparation of the biologically active benzodiazepine *N*-oxides (Reaction 10).[2,18-30] 6-Chloro-2-chloromethyl-4-phenyl-

$$\text{(10)}$$

quinazoline-3-oxide-2-^{14}C was prepared by using chloroacetyl chloride 1-^{14}C, and converted to the labelled 7-chloro-5-phenyl-1,3-dihydro-2*H*-1,4-benzodiazepin-2-one-4-oxide for tracer studies.[31]

B. Physical Properties of Quinazoline-3-oxides

Quinazoline-3-oxides are readily crystallizable solids which melt about 70–100° higher, and are more soluble in water, than the corresponding deoxygenated quinazolines. This is most probably because of their more polar nature. Their infrared spectra show the characteristic *N*-oxide bands between 1250 and 1300 cm^{-1}, but as these are not always of high intensity it is necessary to have a direct comparison with the corresponding quinazolines before making assignments.[16] The ultraviolet spectra of the neutral species are similar to those of the corresponding quinazolines but the whole of the spectra are shifted to longer wavelengths.[16,32] The ultraviolet spectra of the neutral species also showed increasing 'blue' shifts with increasing polarity of the solvent. The fluorescence spectra, however, did not show this effect.[32]

The cation of quinazoline-3-oxide, like the cation of quinazoline, is hydrated (covalent) across the 3,4-double bond. As a consequence of this, the ultraviolet spectrum of the cation is shifted by 66 mμ to shorter wavelengths when compared with that of the neutral species, this spectrum becomes similar to that of the neutral species when the acidity of the solution is increased (i.e. decrease in the activity of water), and mild oxidation yields 3,4-dihydro-3-hydroxy-4-oxoquinazoline. Moreover it is a stronger base than 4-methylquinazoline-3-oxide (see Table IX.1.) which is characteristic of covalent hydration in these compounds[16] (compare Ch. II, Sect. 2.C.a.). By analogy with the quinazoline cation the resonance-stabilized hydrated cation of quinazoline-3-oxide (8) was postulated. The proton magnetic spectrum of the neutral species of quinazoline-3-oxide in deuterium oxide is similar to that of quinazoline, except that the 2 and 4 protons split each other ($J_{2,4}$ 1.8 c/s) (see Fig. 1). The chemical shifts of the 2 and 4 protons at τ 0.86 and

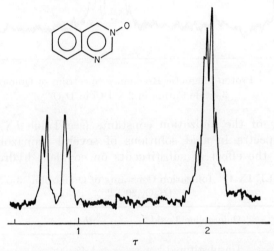

FIG. 1.   Proton Magnetic Resonance Spectrum of Quinazoline-
3-oxide in D_2O.

τ 0.89, respectively, were assigned by inspection.[33] These assignments are contrary to those in quinazoline in which the 4 proton was shown conclusively to be the one further downfield and more work is necessary along these lines (see Ch. II, Sect. 2.B.d.). The proton magnetic resonance spectrum of quinazoline-3-oxide cation in deuterium oxide

(8)

(see Fig. 2) is consistent with the hydrated structure **8** and has the same features as the quinazoline cation spectrum where the 4 proton moves upfield (to τ 3.38).[34]

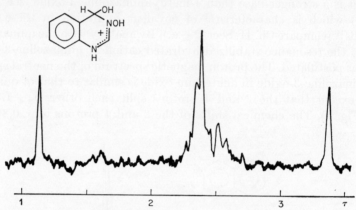

FIG. 2.   Proton Magnetic Resonance Spectrum of Quinazoline-3-oxide Cation in 2 N DCl in D_2O.

A study of the ionization constants (see Table IX.1.) and the ultraviolet spectra in acid solutions of several quinazoline-3-oxides showed that the effect of substituents on covalent hydration in the

TABLE IX.1.   Ionization Constants of Quinazoline-3-oxides (H_2O, 20°).[16]

Quinazoline-3-oxide	pK_a
Unsubstituted	1.47
7-Chloro-	1.49
5-Methoxy-	1.20
6-Methoxy-	0.58
7-Methoxy-	0.66
8-Methoxy-	1.21
7-Methoxy-4-methyl-	0.73
8-Methoxy-4-methyl-	0.02
4-Methyl-	0.06
7-Methyl-	1.00

cations followed a patter similar to the one found in the quinazoline cations. A 4-methyl group and a 7-methoxy group decreased the amount of hydration in the quinazoline-3-oxide cations (see Ch. II, Sects. 2.C.b. and c.).[16]

C. Reactions of Quinazoline-3-oxides

Quinazoline-3-oxide is degraded to o-aminobenzaldehyde oxime on treatment with strong alkali,[13,35] and because it forms a hydrated cation it is readily oxidized to 3,4-dihydro-3-hydroxy-4-oxoquinazoline (Sect. 2.B.). Reduction with phosphorus tribromide, phosphorus trichloride,[35] iron and ferrous sulphate,[15] or catalytically with Raney nickel,[13,15] yields quinazoline as is typical of N-oxides.[2]

Quinazoline-3-oxide behaves as quinazoline towards anionoid reagents which react by addition. In the N-oxide, however, the products eliminate water to furnish a 4-substituted quinazoline. Hydrogen cyanide, sodium bisulphite, and hydrazine yield 4-cyano-, 4-sulpho- and 4-hydrazinoquinazoline as shown in reaction (11) (compare Ch. II,

$$ \text{(11)} $$

R = —CN, —SO$_3$Na, or —NHNH$_2$

Sect. 3.C.). Benzoyl chloride and potassium cyanide (Reissert reagent), and acetic anhydride, cause ring fission between the nitrogen atoms, and the products are O,N-dibenzoyl o-aminobenzaldehyde oxime and o-isocyanobenzonitrile respectively (Reaction 12).[35]

$$ \text{(12)} $$

6-Chloro-2-chloromethyl-4-phenylquinazoline-3-oxide reacts with secondary aliphatic amines, e.g. diethylamine, to yield the normal substitution products, i.e. 6-chloro-2-dimethylaminomethyl-4-phenyl-quinazoline-3-oxide.[19] With primary amines, e.g. methylamine, a rearrangement occurs with ring enlargement, for example to 7-chloro-2-methylamino-5-phenyl-3H-1,4-benzodiazepin-4-oxide (Reaction 13).[18,19] Several examples of this reaction are known.[18-27,31,36] Ring enlargement occurs concurrently with the normal substitution reaction with a few primary amines, e.g. ethanolamine, also when the benzene ring of the quinazoline-3-oxide has electron-releasing groups, e.g. methyl, in position 6. When electron-releasing groups are present in the 6- and 8-positions then the reaction with primary amines yields only the normal substitution products; as in the formation of 2-methylamino-methyl-6,8-dimethyl-4-phenylquinazoline-3-oxide.[18] 2-Chloromethyl-4-phenylquinazoline-3-oxides undergo a similar reaction with sodium hydroxide, but the products are the corresponding 1,2-dihydro-2-oxo-5-phenyl-3H-1,4-benzodiazepin-4-oxides (Reaction 13).[21,24-26,31]

$$(13)$$

3. 1,2-Dihydroquinazoline-3-oxides

A detailed study of 1,2-dihydroquinazoline-3-oxides was made by Kövendi and Kircz[17] in 1965, although this class of compounds was first mentioned in the literature by Busch[37] in 1938. They were prepared by the reaction of o-aminoacetophenone oximes with aldehydes (Reaction 14).[17,37] Acetone also reacts with o-aminoacetophenone

$$(14)$$

oxime to yield 1,2-dihydro-2,2,4-trimethylquinazoline-3-oxide (9).[38] o-Aminoacetophenone and methazonic acid gave a constant melting mixture of o-aminoacetophenone (25%) and 1,2-dihydro-4-methyl-2-nitromethylquinazoline-3-oxide (75%) (10). The latter was separated from the mixture by thin-layer chromatography and its structure deduced from its elemental analysis, facile hydrolysis to 4-methylquinazoline-3-oxide (Reaction 15), and its proton magnetic resonance spectrum.[38]

(9)

(10)   + CH$_3$NO$_2$

(15)

1,2-Dihydroquinazoline-3-oxides with one substituent in position 2 are readily oxidized with 2% potassium permanganate[17] to quinazoline-3-oxides, and yield a 1-nitroso derivative with nitrous acid.[37] Benzoyl chloride degraded 1,2-dihydro-4-methyl-2-phenylquinazoline-3-oxide to the O,N-dibenzoyl derivative of o-aminobenzaldehyde oxime.[37] The *gem*-dimethyl groups in 1,2-dihydro-2,2,4-trimethyl-quinazoline-3-oxide (9) are magnetically equivalent and give rise to a sharp singlet in the proton magnetic resonance spectrum.[38] If the compound had the isopropylidene structure these groups would most probably be non-equivalent, as are similar groups in such compounds as acetone 2,4-dinitrophenylhydrazone.[39] The ultraviolet spectra of 9 and 10 are very similar.[38]

4. 1- and 3-Hydroxyoxoquinazolines

4-Alkoxy-1,2-dihydro-1-hydroxy-2-oxoquinazolines were obtained as by-products in the oxidation of 4-alkoxyquinazolines with perphthalic acid (Sect. 1.). They are also obtained by oxidation of 4-alkoxyquinazoline-1-oxide (Reaction 16), but not by the oxidation of 4-alkoxy-1,2-dihydro-2-oxoquinazoline. They are hydrolyzed by dilute acetic acid to 1,2,3,4-tetrahydro-1-hydroxy-2,4-dioxoquinazoline (11) which was also obtained by oxidation of 3,4-dihydro-4-oxoquinazoline-1-oxide.[3] 4-Alkoxy-1,2-dihydro-1-hydroxy-2-oxoquinazolines resist catalytic reduction using palladium–charcoal catalyst, but are smoothly reduced with Raney nickel to 4-alkoxy-1,2-dihydro-2-oxoquinazoline. They form deep red colours with ferric chloride, and are not deoxygenated with phosphorus trichloride.[3,40] These are characteristic properties of hydroxamic acids. 4-Alkoxyquinazoline-1-oxides are readily hydrolyzed to 3,4-dihydro-4-oxoquinazoline-1-oxide which can

(16)

(11)

exist in the three tautomeric forms **12**, **13**, and **14**. The presence of the tautomeric structure **13** was shown by methylation to 3,4-dihydro-3-methyl-4-oxoquinazoline-1-oxide.[3]

(12)   (13)   (14)

Catalytic hydrogenation of 3-o-nitrobenzoyl-1,3-benoxazolin-2-one with palladium–charcoal in the presence of acid gave 1,2,3,4-tetrahydro-1-hydroxy-2-o-hydroxyphenyl-2,4-dioxoquinazoline.[41] o-Nitrobenzoyl cyanamide afforded 2-amino-3,4-dihydro-4-oxoquinazoline-1-oxide (or the tautomeric 2-amino-1,4-dihydro-1-hydroxy-4-oxoquinazoline) on hydrogenation in the presence of platinum oxide. Further reduction of this, with Raney nickel catalyst, yields 2-amino-3,4-dihydro-4-oxo-quinazoline.[42]

3,4-Dihydro-3-hydroxy-2-methyl-4-oxoquinazoline was prepared by Anschütz, Schmidt, and Greiffenberg[43] in 1902 from 2-methyl-3,1,4-benzoxazone (acetanthranil) and hydroxylamine, and its hydroxamic acid structure was confirmed by the formation of a red colour with ferric chloride. Several derivatives have since been prepared by this reaction by using substituted 3,1,4-benzoxazones with hydroxyl-amine,[44–46] or O-alkyl or O-aryl hydroxylamines.[47,48] 3,1,4-Benzoxaza-thiones or 3,1,4-benzothiazathiones and hydroxylamine yield 3,4-di-hydro-3-hydroxy-4-thioquinazolines (Reaction 17)[45] (compare Ch. IV, Sect. 2.A.e.). 3,4-Dihydro-3-hydroxy-4-oxoquinazolines have also been prepared by heating o-amidophenylhydroxamates at 130–140° for a few hours, and by reacting isatoic anhydride with hydroxylamines followed

$$X = O \text{ or } S \qquad \xrightarrow{H_2NOR^2} \qquad (17)$$

by heating with formic acid, acetic anhydride, or ethyl orthoformate[47,49] (compare Ch. IV, Sects. 2.A.b. and f.).

3,4-Dihydro-3-hydroxy-4-oxoquinazoline can exist in the three possible tautomeric structures **15**, **16**, and **17**. It has a strong carbonyl band at 1690 cm^{-1} which favours **15** and **16**; and of these two, **15** is most probably the predominant form.[16] Iodine and red phosphorus reduce these 3-hydroxy compounds to 3,4-dihydro-4-oxoquinazolines.[45]

(15)   **(16)**   **(17)**

1,2-Dihydro-4-methyl-2-oxoquinazoline-3-oxide, obtained from *o*-aminoacetophenone oxime and phosgene,[37] is not likely to exist in the tautomeric form: 2,3-dihydro-3-hydroxy-4-methyl-2-oxoquinazoline.

1,2,3,4-Tetrahydro-3-hydroxy-2,4-dioxoquinazoline was prepared from 2,3-dihydroxyindole by reaction with amyl nitrite,[50] and from *N*-methylsulphonyloxyphthalimide and hydroxylamine.[51] This 3-hydroxy compound and its *O*-benzyl derivative were obtained from ethyl *o*-ethoxycarbonylaminobenzoate and hydroxylamine and *O*-benzylhydroxylamine respectively.[48] The dihydroxamate of phthalic acid reacted with phenyl and toluene-*p*-sulphonyl chlorides to form the 3-phenylsulphonyloxy and 3-toluene-*p*-sulphonyloxy derivatives of 1,2,3,4-tetrahydro-2,4-dioxoquinazoline respectively,[52] and its dibenzoyl derivative gave 3-benzyloxy-1,2,3,4-tetrahydro-2,4-dioxoquinazoline.[53]

Oxidation of 3,4-dihydro-4-oxoquinazoline with hydrogen peroxide for 14–28 hours gave 3,4-dihydro-3-hydroxy-4-oxoquinazoline-1-oxide (**18**) (1,4-dihydro-1-hydroxy-4-oxoquinazoline-3-oxide and 4-hydroxyquinazoline-1,3-dioxide are other possible tautomeric forms) together with 1,2,3,4-tetrahydro-6-hydroxy-2,4-dioxoquinazoline (**19**) and *o*-formamidobenzamide (Reaction 18). The di-*N*-oxide nature of **18** was revealed by reduction with sodium dithionite to 3,4-dihydro-4-oxoquinazoline. With acetic acid, **18** rearranged to **19**, which gave

16+Q.

2,4,6-trichloroquinazoline on treatment with phosphorus pentachloride and phosphoryl chloride. Acetic anhydride converted **18** to 6-acetoxy-1,2,3,4-tetrahydro-2,4-dioxoquinazoline.[54] On boiling with concentrated

(18)   **(19)**

hydrochloric acid, the N-oxide (**18**) gave 75–81% of the 6-hydroxy compound **19** together with 11–17% of 6-chloro-3,4-dihydro-3-hydroxy-4-oxoquinazoline (**20**) and 2–3% of 3,5-dichloroanthranilic acid (Reaction 19). The structure of **20** was established by oxidative

(20)

cleavage with peracetic acid to 5-chloro-2-nitrobenzamide, by hydrolysis with 2 N sodium hydroxide to 5-chloroanthranilic acid, by reduction with iron and hydrochloric acid to the known 6-chloro-3,4-dihydro-4-oxoquinazoline, and by the formation of an insoluble copper salt. It did not rearrange further with hydrochloric acid, but gave a chloro derivative with phosphorus pentachloride in phosphoryl chloride which was hydrolyzed by acid to 6-chloro-1,2,3,4-tetrahydro-2,4-dioxoquinazoline.[55] 3,4-Dihydro-3-hydroxy-6-methyl-4-oxoquinazoline-1-oxide was prepared by the oxidation of 3,4-dihydro-6-methyl-4-oxoquinazoline with peracetic acid. This 'N-oxide', in 50% acetic acid, liberated iodine from potassium iodide.[55]

The compound described as 3-benzyloxy-3,4-dihydro-6-nitro-4-oxoquinazoline-1-oxide, obtained from the oxidation of 3-benzyloxy-3,4-dihydro-6-nitro-4-oxoquinazoline with 30% hydrogen peroxide, is probably 3-benzyloxy-1,2,3,4-tetrahydro-6-nitro-2,4-dioxoquinazoline.[47]

5. Tables

TABLE IX.2.   Quinazoline-1-oxides.

Quinazoline-1-oxide	M.p. (°c)	References
4-Benzyloxy-	126–127°	3
4-(1′-Benzyloxy-1′-methyl)ethyl-	178°	4
6-Chloro-2-chloromethyl-4-phenyl-	168–169°	2
6-Chloro-2-methyl-4-phenyl-	156°	2
4-Ethoxy-	75–76°	3
4-Hydrazino-	167–168° (dec.)	35
4-Isopropyl-	97–98°	4
4-Isopropyl-2-phenyl-	115–116°	4
4-Methoxy-	80–81°	3
4-Methoxy-2-phenyl-	134°	4
4-Phenoxy-	152–153°	3
4-Propoxy-	95–96°	3

TABLE IX.3. Quinazoline-3-oxides.

Quinazoline-3-oxide	M.p. (°c)	References
Unsubstituted	153°	13
2-Allyl-	132°; HgCl$_2$ 157° (dec.)	12
2-Allylaminomethyl-6-chloro-4-phenyl-	135–136°; HCl 168–169°	19
2-Amino-	272° (dec.)	15
4-Amino-	227° (dec.); 1-ethiodide·H$_2$O 160–164° (dec.)	15
2-Anilinomethyl-6-chloro-4-phenyl-	HCl 171–173°	20
6-Bromo-2-chloromethyl-4-p-chlorophenyl-	180–181°	21
6-Bromo-2-chloromethyl-4-phenyl-	189–190°	18
6-Bromo-2-chloromethyl-4-2′-pyridyl-	206°	29
6-Bromo-2-chloromethyl-4-p-tolyl-	162–164°	18
6-Bromo-2-p-methoxyphenyl-4-methyl-	165–166°	17
6-Bromo-2,4-dimethyl-	187–188°	17
6-Bromo-4-methyl-2-phenyl-	140–141°	17
6,8-Dibromo-4-methyl-2-phenyl-	154–155°	17
2-1′-Bromobutyl-4-phenyl-	173–174°	19
2-1′-Bromoethyl-6-chloro-4-phenyl-	183–184°	19
7-Chloro-	216–218° (dec.)	16
6-Chloro-2-2′-benzylthioethylaminomethyl-4-phenyl-	HCl 159–160°	20
6-Chloro-2-carbamoylmethylaminomethyl-4-phenyl-	HCl 212°	20
6-Chloro-2-chloromethyl-4-o-chlorophenyl-	140–143°	18
6-Chloro-2-chloromethyl-4-p-chlorophenyl-	163–164°	18
6-Chloro-2-chloromethyl-4-p-methoxyphenyl-	151–153°	36
6-Chloro-2-chloromethyl-4-phenyl-	133–134°; HCl 128–150° (dec.)	2
6,7-Dichloro-2-chloromethyl-4-phenyl-	159–160°	18
6,8-Dichloro-2-chloromethyl-4-phenyl-	185–186°	18

(*Table continued*)

TABLE IX.3 (*continued*)

Quinazoline-3-oxide	M.p. (°c)	References
6-Chloro-2-chloromethyl-4-2'-thienyl-	159–160°	20, 30
6-Chloro-2-diethylaminomethyl-4-phenyl-	183.5–184°	22
6-Chloro-2-dimethylaminomethyl-4-phenyl-	133–133.5°; HCl 172–173°	19, 22
6-Chloro-2-2'-hydroxyethylamino-methyl-4-phenyl-	149–150°	19
6-Chloro-2-2'-methoxyethylamino-methyl-4-phenyl-	127–130°	19
6-Chloro-2-methyl-4-phenyl-	157–158°	2
6-Chloro-2-1'-methylaminobutyl-4-phenyl-	106–107°; HCl 187–189°	19
6-Chloro-2-*N*-methylhydrazino-methyl-4-phenyl-	232–233°; *N*-methyl chloride 174–175°	20
6-Chloro-2-methylsulphonyloxy-methyl-4-phenyl-	172.5°	58
6-Chloro-2-piperazin-1'-ylmethyl-4-phenyl-	175–176°; 2 HCl 178–180°	19
6-Chloro-2-piperidinomethyl-4-phenyl-	140.5–142.5°	22
6-Chloro-2-3'-pyridylmethylamino-methyl-4-phenyl-	2 HCl·EtOH 178–179°	20
2-Chloromethyl-4-*p*-chlorophenyl-6,7-dimethyl-	192–193°	18
2-Chloromethyl-4-3',4'-dimethoxy-phenyl-	138–139°	18
2-Chloromethyl-6-methoxycarbonyl-4-phenyl-	191–192°	23
2-Chloromethyl-4-*p*-methoxyphenyl-	179–180°	18
2-Chloromethyl-4-methyl-	169–170°	21
2-Chloromethyl-6-methyl-4-phenyl-	152–153°	18
2-Chloromethyl-6,7-dimethyl-4-phenyl-	169–170°	2
2-Chloromethyl-6,8-dimethyl-4-phenyl-	179–185°	18
2-Chloromethyl-6-methylthio-4-phenyl-	155–156°	27
2-Chloromethyl-6-nitro-4-phenyl-	205–207°	26, 27, 28
2-Chloromethyl-4-phenyl-	160–161°	18
2-Chloromethyl-4-phenyl-6-trifluoromethyl-	148–150°	24, 27

(*Table continued*)

TABLE IX.3 (*continued*)

Quinazoline-3-oxide	M.p. (°c)	References
2-*p*-Chlorophenyl-4-methyl-	176°	17
4-*p*-Chlorophenyl-6,7-dimethyl-2-methylaminomethyl-	139–140°; HCl 215–216°	18
2-Dimethylaminomethyl-6,7-dimethyl-4-phenyl-	129–130°; HCl 180–184°	2
2-2′-Furyl-4-methyl-	206°	17
2-Isobutyl-	85–86°	11
2-Isopropyl-	108–108.5°	11
5-Methoxy-	183–184°	16
6-Methoxy-	186–187°	16
7-Methoxy-	200–201°	16
8-Methoxy-	195–196°	16
7-Methoxy-4-methyl-	145–146°	16
8-Methoxy-4-methyl-	198–199°	16
2-Methyl-	170.5°; HgCl$_2$ 182° (dec.)	12
4-Methyl-	170–172°; 0.25 H$_2$O 106°	14
7-Methyl-	153–154°	16
2,4-Dimethyl-	103–105°	1, 9, 17
4,7-Dimethyl-	175–176°	16
6-Methyl-2-methylamino-4-phenyl-	113–114°	18
6,7-Dimethyl-2-methylamino-methyl-	135–137°	18
6,8-Dimethyl-2-methylamino-methyl-4-phenyl-	163–165°; HCl 158–159°	18
2-Methyl-6,7-methylenedioxy-	250° (dec.)	12
6-Methyl-2-4′-methylpiperazin-1′-ylmethyl-4-phenyl-	178–179° (dec.)	20
4-Methyl-2-1′-methylstyryl-	141–141.5°	17
2-Methyl-6-nitro-	178.5° (dec.)	12
4-Methyl-2-*p*-nitrophenyl-	241–242°	17
2-Methyl-4-phenyl-	185–186°	1, 12
4-Methyl-2-phenyl-	139–140°	17
6-Methyl-4-phenyl-2-piperidino-methyl-	149–151°	20
4-Methyl-2-styryl-	175–176°	17
6-Nitro-2-phenyl-	196°	12
2-Phenyl-	146°, 163–164°; HgCl$_2$ 140°	11, 12
4-Phenyl-	168°	11, 12
2,4-Diphenyl-	168–169°	12
2-Styryl-	188°	12

TABLE IX.4.   1,2-Dihydro-4-methylquinazoline-3-oxides.

1,2-Dihydro-4-methylquinazoline-3-oxide	M.p. (°c)	References
2-*p*-Acetamidophenyl-	228–230°	17
6-Bromo-2-3′,4′-dimethoxyphenyl-	110–112°	17
6-Bromo-2-2′-furyl-	159–161°	17
6-Bromo-2-*p*-methoxyphenyl-	191–192°	17
6-Bromo-2-*o*-nitrophenyl-	176–177°	17
6-Bromo-2-phenyl-	190–191°	17
6,8-Dibromo-2-phenyl-	172°	17
6-Bromo-2-styryl-	171–172°	17
2-3′,4′-Dimethoxyphenyl-	192–193°	17
2-*p*-Dimethylaminophenyl-	162°	17
2-2′-Furyl-	165–166°	17
2-*o*-Hydroxyphenyl-	203°	17
2-*p*-Methoxyphenyl-	166°	17
2,2-Dimethyl-	149–150°	38
2-Nitromethyl-	109.5–110°	38
2-*o*-Nitrophenyl-	208–209°	17
2-*m*-Nitrophenyl-	172–173°	17
2-*p*-Nitrophenyl-	175°, 177–178°	17, 37
1-Nitroso-2-phenyl-	109° (dec.)	37
2-Phenyl-	166°	17, 37
2-Propyl-	118–119°	17
2-Styryl-	159–160°	17

TABLE IX.5.   1-Hydroxy- and 3-Oxo- 1,2-Dihydro-2-oxoquinazolines.

1,2-Dihydro-2-oxoquinazoline	M.p. (°c)	References
4-Benzyloxy-1-hydroxy-	206–207°	3
4-Ethoxy-1-hydroxy-	208–210°	3, 40
1-Hydroxy-4-methoxy-	229–231°	3, 40
1-Hydroxy-4-phenoxy-	246–247°	3
1-Hydroxy-4-propoxy-	152–154°	3
1,4-Dimethoxy-[a]	110°	3
4-Methyl-3-oxo-	215° (dec.), 227° (dec.)	12, 37
3-Oxo-	244° (dec.)	12

[a] This is the 1-O-methyl derivative of 1,2-dihydro-1-hydroxy-4-methoxy-2-oxoquinazoline.

TABLE IX.6.   3,4-Dihydro-4-oxoquinazoline-1-oxides.

3,4-Dihydro-4-oxoquinazoline-1-oxide	M.p. (°c)	References
Unsubstituted	225–230°	3, 6
2-Amino-	331° (dec.)	42
3-Benzyloxy-6-nitro-[a]	272–274°	47
3-p-Bromophenyl-2-methyl-	207–209° (dec.)	5
3-Hydroxy-	150–151°	54, 55
6-Methyl-3-hydroxy-	146–147° (dec.)	55
2-Methyl-3-phenyl-	193–195° (dec.)	5
2-Methyl-3-p-tolyl-	188–190° (dec.)	5

[a] See section 4.

TABLE IX.7.   3,4-Dihydro-3-hydroxy-4-oxoquinazolines.

3,4-Dihydro-3-hydroxy-4-oxo-quinazoline	M.p. (°c)	References
Unsubstituted	245°	45, 49
6-Amino-2-methyl-	HCl 286–290°; *O,N*-diacetyl deriv. 214°	47
5-Bromo-7-nitro-2-phenyl-	214°	44
2-*m*-Bromophenyl-	208°	45
2-*p*-Bromophenyl-	235°	45
6-Chloro-	> 360°	55
6-Chloro-2-*p*-chlorophenyl-	272°	45
7-Chloro-2-ethyl-	169–170°	57
5-Chloro-7-nitro-2-phenyl-	234°	44
6-Chloro-2-phenyl-	203°	45
2-*o*-Chlorophenyl-	226°	45
2-*p*-Chlorophenyl-	226°	45
2-Ethyl-	144–145°	57
5-Iodo-7-nitro-2-phenyl-	231°	44
2-*p*-Methoxyphenyl-	211°	43
2-Methyl-	214–215°; *O*-acetyl deriv. 115–116°	43, 45, 47, 49, 56
2-Methyl-7-nitro-	232–234°, 237	48, 57
2-Methyl-6,8-dinitro-	238–240°; *O*-acetyl deriv. 194–196°	47
2-1′-Naphthyl-	265.5°	45
2-2′-Naphthyl-	200°	45
7-Nitro-2-phenyl-	246°; *O*-acetyl deriv. 157°; *O*-benzoyl deriv. 273°	46
2-Phenyl-	176–177°, 179.5°	45, 46, 49
2-*o*-Tolyl-	177°	45
2-*p*-Tolyl-	158.5°	45

16*

TABLE IX.8.   3,4-Dihydro-3-hydroxy-4-thioquinazolines.

3,4-Dihydro-3-hydroxy-4-thioquinazoline	M.p. (°c)	References
Unsubstituted	152°	45
2-Benzyl-	115°	45
2-o-Bromophenyl-	150°	45
2-m-Bromophenyl-	180°	45
2-p-Bromophenyl-	206°	45
6-Chloro-2-phenyl-	196.5°	45
2-o-Chlorophenyl-	121°	45
2-p-Chlorophenyl-	209°	45
2-Ethyl-	82°	45
2-Isopropyl-	76–77°	45
2-p-Methoxyphenyl-	173°	45
2-Methyl-	138°	45
2-1'-Naphthyl-	183°	45
2-2'-Naphthyl-	154°	45
2-Phenyl-	148°	45
2-t-Butyl-	80°	45
2-o-Tolyl-	139.5°	45
2-p-Tolyl-	164°	45

TABLE IX.9.   3-Alkoxy- and 3-Aryloxy- 3,4-Dihydro-4-oxoquinazolines.

$(R^2)H$—quinazoline structure with =O at 4-position, N—OR^1 at 3-position, H(R) at 2-position

3,4-Dihydro-4-oxoquinazoline	M.p. (°c)	References
6-Amino-3-benzyloxy-	182–184°	47
6-Amino-3-benzyloxy-2-methyl-	161–163°	47
6,8-Diamino-3-benzyloxy-2-methyl-	172–173°; diacetyl deriv.	
	283–285°	47
6-Amino-3-decyloxy-2-methyl-	92°	47
6,8-Diamino-3-dodecyloxy-2-methyl-	115–120°	47
3-Benzyloxy-	116–118°	47
3-Benzyloxy-7-chloro-2-ethyl-	114–116°	57
3-Benzyloxy-6,8-dichloro-2-methyl-	165–166°	47
3-Benzyloxy-2-chloromethyl-	114–115°	47
3-Benzyloxy-2-3′,5′-dinitrophenyl-	191–192°	47
3-Benzyloxy-2-ethyl-	103–104°	57
3-Benzyloxy-2-methyl-	109–110°, 114°	47, 48, 57
3-Benzyloxy-2-methyl-6-nitro-	186–188°	47
3-Benzyloxy-2-methyl-7-nitro-	186–188°, 194°	48, 57
3-Benzyloxy-2-methyl-6,8-dinitro-	224°, 226°	47
3-Benzyloxy-6-nitro-	190–192°	47
3-Benzyloxy-7-nitro-2-phenyl-	246°	46
5-Chloro-3-3′,4′-dichlorophenoxy-2-methyl-	214–216°	47
6,8-Dichloro-3-3′,4′-dichlorophenoxy-2-methyl-	223–225°	47
7-Chloro-2-ethyl-3-3′-dimethylaminopropoxy-	2 HCl 164–166°	57
3-3′,4′-Dichlorophenoxy-2-methyl-	163–165°	47
3-Decyloxy-	29–30°	47
3-Decyloxy-2-methyl-	39–40°	47
3-Decyloxy-2-methyl-6-nitro-	106–108°	47
3-Decyloxy-2-methyl-6-sulphanilamido-	158–160°; acetyl deriv.	
	199–201°	47
3-3′-Dimethylaminopropoxy-2-methyl-	2 HCl 195–196°	57
3-Dodecyloxy-2-methyl-6,8-dinitro-	78–80°	47
3-Ethoxy-2-methyl-	62–63°	57
2-Ethyl-3-3′-dimethylaminopropoxy-	2 HCl 95–102°	57

(*Table continued*)

TABLE IX.9 (*continued*)

3,4-Dihydro-4-oxoquinazoline	M.p. (°c)	References
2-Ethyl-3-methoxy-	85–86°	57
3-Heptyloxy-	33–34°	47
3-Heptyloxy-2-*p*-nitrophenyl-	107–108°	47
3-Hexyloxy-	33–35°	47
3-Hexyloxy-2-methyl-	39–40°	47
3-Methoxy-2-methyl-	91–92°	57
2-Methyl-3-1′-naphthylmethoxy-	170–172°	47
2-Methyl-6-nitro-3-*p*-nitrophenoxy-	231–232°	47
2-Methyl-6,8-dinitro-3-*p*-nitro-phenoxy-	236°	47
3-1′-Naphthylmethoxy-	129–131°	47
6-Nitro-3-*p*-nitrobenzyloxy-	241–243°	47

TABLE IX.10.   *N*-Hydroxy-1,2,3,4-tetrahydro-2,4-dioxoquinazolines and Derivatives.

1,2,3,4-Tetrahydro-2,4-dioxoquinazoline	M.p. (°c)	References
3-Benzoyloxy-	264–266°	53
3-Benzyloxy-	218°	48
1-Hydroxy-	287–288° (dec.)	3, 40
3-Hydroxy-	319°, 322–326°	50, 51
1-Hydroxy-3-*o*-hydroxyphenyl-	284–285° (dec.)	41
3-Phenylsulphonyloxy-	235–236°	52
3-Tosyloxy-	280–281°	52

6. References

1. Auwers and Meyenburg, *Ber. Deut. Chem. Ges.*, **24**, 2370 (1891).
2. Sternbach, Kaiser, and Reeder, *J. Am. Chem. Soc.*, **82**, 475 (1960).
3. Yamanaka, *Chem. Pharm. Bull. (Japan)*, **7**, 152 (1959).
4. Hayashi and Higashino, *Chem. Pharm. Bull. (Japan)*, **12**, 43 (1964).
5. Toyoshima, Hamano, and Shimada, *J. Pharm. Soc. Japan*, **85**, 507 (1965).
6. Higashino, *J. Pharm. Soc. Japan*, **79**, 831 (1959).
7. Higashino, *J. Pharm. Soc. Japan*, **79**, 699 (1959).
8. Sternbach, Reeder, Stempel, and Rachlin, *J. Org. Chem.*, **29**, 332 (1964).
9. Bischler, *Ber. Deut. Chem. Ges.*, **26**, 1891 (1893).
10. Meisenheimer and Diedrich, *Ber. Deut. Chem. Ges.*, **57**, 1715 (1924).
11. Auwers, *Ber. Deut. Chem. Ges.*, **57**, 1723 (1924).
12. Ried and Stahlhofen, *Chem. Ber.*, **87**, 1814 (1954).
13. Adachi, *J. Pharm. Soc. Japan*, **77**, 507 (1957).
14. Adachi, *J. Pharm. Soc. Japan*, **77**, 514 (1957).
15. Adachi, *J. Pharm. Soc. Japan*, **77**, 510 (1957).
16. Armarego, *J. Chem. Soc.*, **1962**, 5030.
17. Kövendi and Kircz, *Chem. Ber.*, **98**, 1049 (1965).
18. Sternbach, Reeder, Keller, and Metlesics, *J. Org. Chem.*, **26**, 4488 (1961).
19. Sternbach and Reeder, *J. Org. Chem.*, **26**, 1111 (1961).
20. Bell, Gochman, and Childress, *J. Med. Pharm. Chem.*, **5**, 63 (1962).
21. Bell, Sulkowski, Gochman, and Childress, *J. Org. Chem.*, **27**, 562 (1962).
22. Farber, Wuest, and Meltzer, *J. Med. Chem.*, **7**, 235 (1964).
23. Sternbach, Saucy, Smith, Müller, and Lee, *Helv. Chim. Acta*, **46**, 1720 (1963).
24. Saucy and Sternbach, *Helv. Chim. Acta*, **45**, 2226 (1962).
25. Sternbach and Reeder, *J. Org. Chem.*, **26**, 4936 (1961).
26. Sternbach, Fryer, Keller, Metlesics, Sach, and Steiger, *J. Med. Chem.*, **6**, 261 (1963).
27. Reeder, Sternbach, Keller, Steiger, and Saucy, *Ger. Pat.*, 1,145,625 (1963); *Chem. Abstr.*, **59**, 10056 (1963).
28. Keller, Steiger, and Sternbach, *Belg. Pat.*, 616,024 (1962); *Chem. Abstr.*, **58**, 10222 (1963).
29. Fryer, Schmidt, and Sternbach, *U.S. Pat.*, 3,100,770 (1963); *Chem. Abstr.*, **60**, 1780 (1964).
30. Berger, Stempel, Sternbach, Wenis, Fryer, and Schmidt, *Belg. Pat.*, 619,101 (1962); *Chem. Abstr.*, **59**, 10092 (1963).
31. Walkenstein, Wiser, Gudmundsen, Kimmel, and Corradino, *J. Pharm. Sci.*, **53**, 1181 (1964).
32. Kubota and Miyazaki, *Chem. Pharm. Bull. (Japan)*, **9**, 948 (1961).
33. Tori, Ogata, and Kano, *Chem. Pharm. Bull. (Japan)*, **11**, 681 (1963).
34. Armarego, unpublished results (1966).
35. Higashino, *Chem. Pharm. Bull. (Japan)*, **9**, 635 (1961).
36. Walker, *J. Org. Chem.*, **27**, 1929 (1962).
37. Busch, Strätz, Uuger, Reichold, and Eckardt, *J. Prakt. Chem.*, **150**, 1 (1938).
38. Armarego, Batterham, Schofield, and Theobald, *J. Chem. Soc.* (C), **1966**, 1433.
39. *N.M.R. Spectra Catalog*, Varian Associates, Palo Alto, California, 1962, Vol. I, p. 233.

40. Hayashi, Yamanaka, and Higashino, *Chem. Pharm. Bull. (Japan)*, **7**, 149 (1959).
41. Sam and Richmond, *J. Heterocyclic Chem.*, **1**, 245 (1964).
42. Taylor and Jefford, *Chem. Ind. (London)*, **1963**, 1559.
43. Anschütz, Schmidt, and Greiffenberg, *Ber. Deut. Chem. Ges.*, **35**, 3480 (1902).
44. Gambhir and Joshi, *J. Indian Chem. Soc.*, **41**, 47 (1964).
45. Legrand and Lozach, *Bull. Soc. Chim. France*, **1961**, 618.
46. Joshi and Gambhir, *J. Org. Chem.*, **26**, 3714 (1961).
47. Mamalis, Rix, and Sarsfield, *J. Chem. Soc.*, **1965**, 6278.
48. Taniyama, Yasui, Uchida, and Okuda, *J. Pharm. Soc. Japan*, **81**, 431 (1961).
49. Harrison and Smith, *J. Chem. Soc.*, **1960**, 2157.
50. Jacini, *Gazz. Chim. Ital.*, **74**, 3 (1944).
51. Kühle and Wegler, *Ann. Chem.*, **616**, 183 (1958); Kühle and Wegler, *Ger. Pat.*, 1,068,263 (1959); *Chem. Abstr.*, **55**, 12435 (1961).
52. Buess and Bauer, *J. Org. Chem.*, **20**, 33 (1955).
53. Hurd, Buess, and Bauer, *J. Org. Chem.*, **19**, 1140 (1954).
54. Chiang and Li, *Hua Hsüeh Hsüeh Pao*, **23**, 391 (1957); *Chem. Abstr.*, **52**, 15539 (1958).
55. Chiang and Li, *Hua Hsüeh Hsüeh Pao*, **29**, 44 (1963); *Chem. Abstr.*, **59**, 2812 (1963).
56. Grammaticakis, *Compt. Rend.*, **252**, 4011 (1961).
57. Somasekhara, Dighe, Arur, and Mukherjee, *Current Sci. (India)*, **33**, 746 (1964).
58. Wuest, *U.S. Pat.*, 3,215,695 (1965); *Chem. Abstr.*, **64**, 3569 (1966).

CHAPTER X

Quinazoline Carboxylic and Sulphonic Acids, and Related Compounds

This chapter includes the cyano and the formyl quinazolines as well as the carboxylic acids, esters, and amides. Sulphonic acids, acid chlorides, and sulphonamides have been described in chapter IV, section 2.C.b.(iv), and only a brief mention will be made. Quinazolines with these functional groups directly attached only to the nucleus are discussed here.

1. Cyano- and Carbamoylquinazolines

The first cyanoquinazoline, 2-cyano-3,4-dihydro-4-oxoquinazoline, was prepared by Griess[1] in 1869 from anthranilic acid and cyanogen (see Ch. IV, Sect. 3.A.a.). Only a few cyanoquinazolines were obtained by direct nucleophilic substitution of halogenoquinazolines. 2-Cyano-3,4-dihydro-4-oxo-2-phenylquinazoline[2] was formed from the 2-chloro compound and potassium cyanide in dimethyl sulphoxide, and 4-bromo-2-phenylquinazoline gave 4-cyano-2-phenylquinazoline[3] when it was heated with cuprous cyanide in nitrobenzene. 4-Chloroquinazoline in aqueous or alcoholic sodium cyanide preferred to react with the solvent (see Ch. V, Sect. 1.E.b.(ii)), and when it was fused with cuprous cyanide it gave a 2% yield of 4-cyanoquinazoline.[4] 4-Cyanoquinazoline is most conveniently prepared by the reaction of quinazoline with methanolic hydrogen cyanide at ~10° (which yields 4-cyano-3,4-dihydroquinazoline) followed by oxidation with alkaline potassium ferricyanide.[5,6] 4-Carbamoylquinazoline was formed when the reaction with cyanide was performed at 70°.[5] Quinazoline-3-oxide also reacts with methanolic hydrogen cyanide by addition, but oxidation of the adduct is not

473

necessary because it loses water spontaneously to give 4-cyanoquinazoline (see Ch. IX, Sect. 2.C.).[7,8] Quinazoline-1-oxides are a useful source of 2-cyanoquinazolines because they react with potassium cyanide in the presence of benzoyl chloride (Reissert reagent) (see Ch. IX, Sect. 1.) to form 2-cyanoquinazolines. Thus 4-methoxy-, 4-ethoxy-, 4-propoxy-4-phenoxy-, 4-benzyloxy-,[9] and 4-isopropyl-2-cyanoquinazoline[10] were obtained from the corresponding 1-oxides. The last named was formed together with 4-(1'-carbamoyl-1'-methyl)ethylquinazoline.[10] Quinazolines with amino groups in the benzene ring are a source of cyanoquinazolines because the amino group can be diazotized in the usual manner and the diazonium salt reacts with cuprous cyanide as in the preparation of 5-cyano-[11] and 7-cyano-[12] 3,4-dihydro-2-methyl-4-oxoquinazolines (Ch. VII, Sect. 3.B.).

2-Carbamoylquinazoline was formed in high yield when o-ethoxalyl-amidobenzaldehyde was heated with saturated ethanolic ammonia at 100°[13] (Reaction 1), although earlier workers claimed that the product

$$\text{(1)}$$

was 2-quinazolin-2'-ylcarbonylcarbamoylquinazoline (**1**, R = H).[14] Similarly 2-carbamoyl-4-methylquinazoline was obtained from o-ethoxalylamidoacetophenone.[15] Oxidation of cyanoquinazolines with alkaline hydrogen peroxide in acetone yields carbamoylquinazolines.[9,10,16,17]

(**1**) R = H or OMe

The cyano group in 2- and 4-cyanoquinazoline behaves like a halogen towards nucleophiles, but the 4-cyano group is not hydrolyzed quite as readily as the 4-chloro group.[4] Because of this, 4-cyanoquinazoline reacts with methylketones, cyclohexanone and cyclopentanone,[18,19] and nitromethane or nitroethane[20] in aqueous alkaline solution to give the normal substitution products (Eq. 2) (see Ch. III, Sect. 1.H.). 4-Chloroquinazoline yields 3,4-dihydro-4-oxoquinazoline under similar conditions.[18] 4-Methoxy-, 4-phenoxy-, 4-hydrazino-, 4-butylamino-, 4-anilino-, 4-piperidino-,[21] 4-α,α-diethoxycarbonylmethyl-, 4-α-ethoxycarbonylacetonyl-, and 4-α-cyanoethoxycarbonylmethylquinazoline[20] are formed from 4-cyanoquinazoline and the respective nucleophile. 4-Cyanoquinazoline reacts with methyl, ethyl, isopropyl, benzyl, and phenyl magnesium halides by displacement to furnish 4-methyl-, 4-ethyl-, 4-isopropyl-, 4-benzyl- and 4-phenylquinazoline[22] (see Ch.

$$\text{(structure: CN-quinazoline)} + RCOCH_3 \xrightarrow{OH^-} \text{(structure: CH}_2\text{COR-quinazoline)} + CN^- \qquad (2)$$

III, Sect. 1.G.). The cyano group in 2-cyanoquinazolines is displaced by nucleophiles, e.g. OMe⁻, OEt⁻,[10,11] but also undergoes the more usual nitrile reactions. Thus with amines, amidines[10,23] are formed, and with phenyl magnesium bromide, 2-benzoyl derivatives are produced (Reaction 3).[10] Hydrolysis of 2- and 4-cyanoquinazolines with hydrogen

$$\text{(structure: R-quinazoline-COPh)} \xleftarrow{PhMgBr} \text{(structure: R-quinazoline-CN)} \xrightarrow{R^1NH_2} \text{(structure: R-quinazoline-C(NHR}^1\text{)=NH)} \qquad (3)$$

chloride in ethanol followed by acid treatment gave the respective carbamoyl derivatives, but when this reaction was followed by alkali treatment, a mixture of the carbamoyl and the respective ethoxycarbonyl derivatives was formed.[9,16,17] 3,4-Dihydro-4-oxo-2-thiocarbamoylquinazoline was obtained from the corresponding 2-cyano compound and ammonium sulphide.[23] 2-Carbamoylquinazoline was dehydrated with phosphoryl chloride to 2-cyanoquinazoline.[13] For the ionization of 4-carbamoylquinazolines see section 2.B.

2. Carboxyquinazolines

A. 2-Carboxyquinazolines

In 1895 Bischler and Lang[24] prepared 2-carboxyquinazoline from o-hydroxyoxalylamidobenzaldehyde and alcoholic ammonia, and used it as an intermediate in the first synthesis of quinazoline (Ch. II, Sect. 1.). Hydrolysis of Griess's 2-cyano-3,4-dihydro-4-oxoquinazoline (Sect. 1.) with aqueous barium hydroxide furnished 2-carboxy-3,4-dihydro-4-oxoquinazoline[23] which was identical with the product from the reaction of o-hydroxyoxalylamidobenzonitrile with hydrochloric acid.[25]

2-Ethoxycarbonyl-3,1,4-benzoxazone (2) reacted with methylamine, aniline, and phenylhydrazine to form 3-methyl-2-N-methylcarbamoyl-, 2-ethoxycarbonyl-3-phenyl-, and 2-ethoxycarbonyl-3-anilino- 3,4-di-hydro-4-oxoquinazolines respectively (compare Ch. IV, Sect. 2.A.e.). With hydrazine, two products were formed, namely 3-amino-2-hydrazinocarbonyl (3) and 3-amino-2-N'-3'-amino-3',4'-dihydro-4'-oxoquinazolin - 2'-ylcarbonylhydrazinocarbonyl-3,4-dihydro-4-oxoquin-azoline (4), depending on the amount of hydrazine used (Reaction 4).[26]

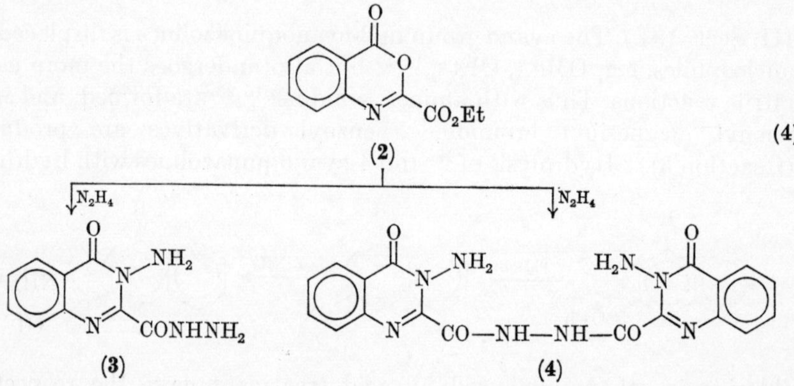

(2)

(4)

(3)   (4)

It was claimed that when ammonia reacted with 2, the ammonium salt of 2-carboxy-3,4-dihydro-4-oxoquinazoline (5) was formed,[26] but, in a recent investigation,[27] it was shown that the 'ammonium salt' was o-aminooxalylamidobenzamide. The carboxylic acid 5 was best obtained by fusing o-aminobenzamide with ethyl oxalate at 180° followed by alkaline hydrolysis of the resulting 2-ethoxycarbonyl-3,4-dihydro-4-oxoquinazoline (Reaction 5).[27]

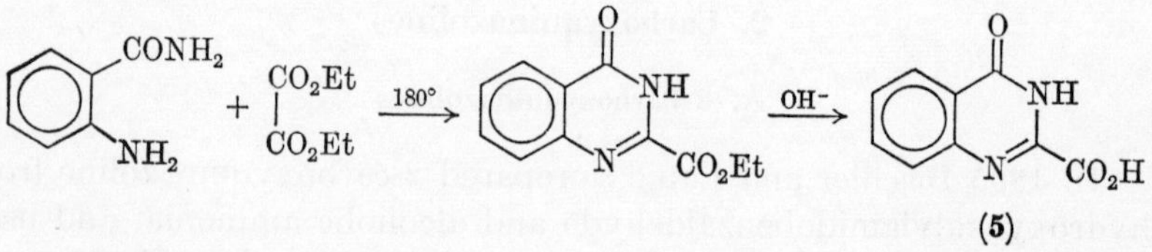

(5)

(5)

2 - Acetamido - 7 - chloro - 5 - phenyl - 3H - 1,4 - benzodiazepin - 3 - one (6) undergoes ring contraction to 2-acetylcarbamoyl-, 2-ethoxycarbonyl-, and 2-carboxy- 6-chloro-4-phenylquinazolines when heated with acetic acid, ethanolic hydrogen chloride, and sodium hydroxide respectively

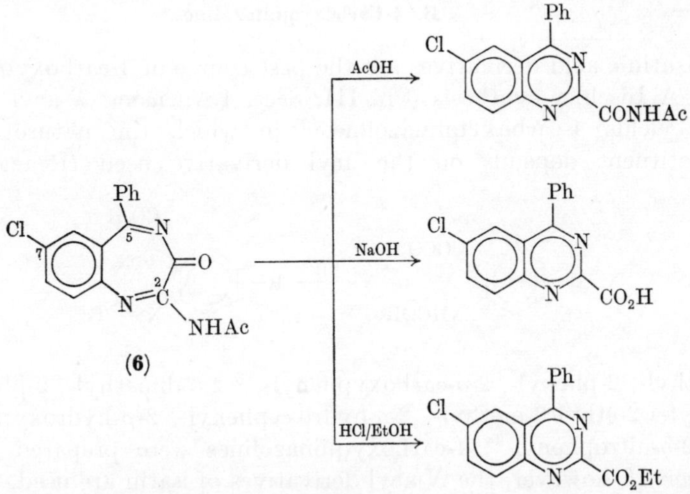

(6)

(Reaction 6).[28] Similarly 7-chloro-1,3-dihydro-3-hydroxy-5-phenyl-2H-1,4-benzodiazepin-2-one (7) yields 2-carboxy-6-chloro-3,4-dihydro-4-phenylquinazoline with alkali.[29] The latter compound was also prepared from 2-amino-5-chlorobenzyl-α-phenylamine and oxalic acid,[29] and was oxidized with permanganate to 2-carboxy-6-chloro-4-phenylquinazoline.[30] 2-Carboxy-4-phenylquinazoline was obtained by oxidation of 2-methyl-4-phenylquinazoline with chromic oxide in sulphuric acid.[31] The formation of 3,4-dihydro-2-methoxycarbonyl-4-oxoquinazoline from 2-methoxycarbonylisatogen and tetracyano-ethylene in boiling xylene requires further investigation (Reaction 7).[32]

Decarboxylation of 2-carboxyquinazolines takes place readily on heating alone, in dilute acid,[24,26] or in alcohol.[27]

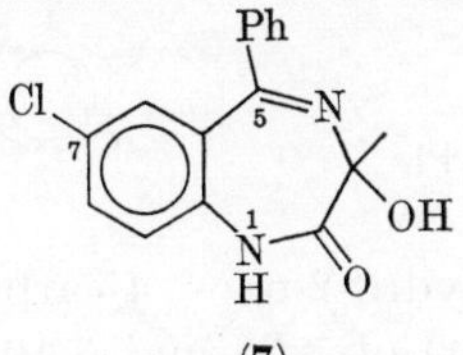

(7)

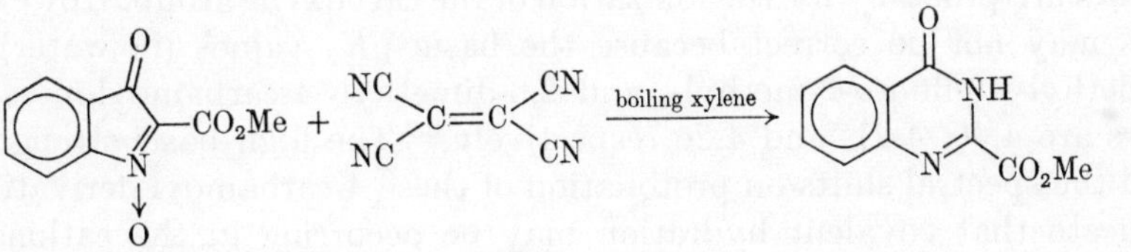

(7)

B. 4-Carboxyquinazolines

Isatinic acid derivatives are the best source of 4-carboxyquinazolines. A Bischler synthesis (Ch. III, Sect. 1.A.) using N-acyl isatinic acids yields 4-carboxyquinazolines[33] in which the nature of the 2-substituent depends on the acyl derivative used (Reaction 8).

$$\tag{8}$$

2-Methyl-, 2-phenyl-, 2-o-carboxyphenyl-,[15] 2,6-dimethyl-, 2-phenyl-6-methyl-, 2-ethyl-6-methyl-, 2-o-hydroxyphenyl-, 2-p-hydroxyphenyl-, and 2-o-nitrophenyl-[34] 4-carboxyquinazolines were prepared in this manner. If, however, the N-acyl derivatives of isatin are used, instead of the isatinic acids, the 4-carbamoyl derivatives are obtained, as in the preparation of 2-methyl-, 6-fluoro-2-methyl-,[35] and 2,6-dimethyl-[33,35] 4-carbamoylquinazolines. 2-Amino- and 1,2-dihydro-2-oxo- 4-carboxyquinazolines are formed when isatinic acid is fused with guanidine and urea respectively.[36]

Isatinic acids react with aryl isocyanates or isothiocyantes to yield 3-aryl-4-carboxy-1,2,3,4-tetrahydro-4-hydroxy-2-oxo- (or thio-) quinazolines[37,38] (see Ch. VI, Sects. 1.B. and 6.).

N-Phenylbenzimidoyl chloride and ethyl cyanoformate, in o-dichlorobenzene containing stannic chloride, give 4-carboxy-2-phenylquinazoline in 52% yield (Reaction 9).[3]

$$\tag{9}$$

2-Methoxy- and 1,2-dihydro-2-oxo- 4-carboxyquinazolines have pK_a values (in ethanol–water) of 3.05 and 3.10 respectively.[36] These values are probably for the ionization of the carboxylic group. However, this may not be correct because the basic pK_a values (in water) of 2-methyl-, 6-fluoro-2-methyl-, and 2,6-dimethyl- 4-carbamoylquinazolines are 4.40, 4.21, and 4.20 respectively.[35] The high basic strengths, and the spectral shifts on protonation of these 4-carbamoyl derivatives indicate that covalent hydration may be occurring in the cations.[35]

Decarboxylation of 4-carboxyquinazolines takes place on melting or on distillation.[3,33,36] These acids are best esterified by heating their silver salts with alkyl iodides,[33,36] or by diazomethane in ether.[36] The esters yield the respective carbamoyl derivatives by treatment with ammonia.[33]

C. Quinazolines with Carboxy Groups in the Benzene Ring

Quinazolines with carboxy groups in the benzene ring are usually prepared by standard syntheses. Aminophthalic acids with the amino group *ortho* to at least one carboxy group are convenient starting materials. These react with amides (Niementowski's synthesis) (see Ch. IV, Sect. 2.A.a.) to yield carboxy-3,4-dihydro-4-oxoquinazolines,[39-41] and they can be converted to carboxy-3,1,4-benzoxazones which furnish carboxy-3,4-dihydro-4-oxoquinazolines on treatment with ammonia or amines (compare Ch. IV, Sect. 2.A.e.).[39,42-45] 3-Acetamidophthalimide and its N-phenyl derivative are isomerized to 5-carboxy-3,4-dihydro-2-methyl-4-oxoquinazoline[42] and its 3-phenyl[46] derivative with 5% aqueous potassium hydroxide. 3-Ureidophthalic acids, obtained from 5-carboxy isatoic anhydride, cyclize to 5-carboxy-1,2,3,4-tetrahydro-2,4-dioxoquinazolines under the influence of acid (see Ch. IV, Sect. 3.A.c.).[47,48] 2-Cyanaminoisophthalic acid is converted to 8-carboxy-1,2,3,4-tetrahydro-2,4-dioxoquinazoline[49] by alkali, and 5-carboxy-3,4-dihydro-2-methyl-4-oxoquinazoline is formed by hydrolysis of 5-cyano-3,4-dihydro-2-methyl-4-oxoquinazoline with acid.[11] Oxidation of 1,2,3,4-tetrahydro-7-methyl-2,4-dioxoquinazoline with alkaline permanganate furnishes 7-carboxy-1,2,3,4-tetrahydro-2,4-dioxoquinazoline.[50] p-Aminobenzoic acid (or its ethyl ester) reacts with formaldehyde in the presence of hydrochloric acid, as do other anilines (see Ch. VIII, Sect. 4.B.), to give 6-carboxy-(or ethoxycarbonyl)-3-p-carboxy-(or ethoxycarbonyl) phenyl-3,4-dihydro-4-oxoquinazoline.[40]

Carboxy groups in the benzene ring of quinazoline are not decarboxylated as readily as those in the pyrimidine ring (see Sects. 2.A. and B.) and can be esterified by the usual procedures, e.g. alcoholic hydrogen chloride,[51-53] or dimethyl sulphate.[41,42,48] Thionyl chloride converts them to the acid chlorides without affecting the oxo groups, as in the preparation of 8-chlorocarbonyl-3,4-dihydro-4-oxo-[54] and 5-chlorocarbonyl-1,2,3,4-tetrahydro-2,4-dioxoquinazoline.[52] Phosphorus pentachloride in phosphoryl chloride, on the other hand, chlorinates the oxo groups as well (see Ch. IV, Sect. 3.B.b.).

3. Formyl- and Acetylquinazolines

A very small number of these quinazolines are known. 2-Formyl-3,4-dihydro-4-oxoquinazoline is formed when 3,4-dihydro-2-methyl-4-oxoquinazoline is oxidized with selenium dioxide.[55,56] This formyl derivative reacts with nitromethane to yield 3,4-dihydro-2-(1'-hydroxy-2'-nitro)ethyl-4-oxoquinazoline.[55] A similar oxidation of 3-benzyl-3,4-dihydro-2-methyl-4-oxoquinazoline provided 3-benzyl-2-formyl-3,4-dihydro-4-oxoquinazoline.[57] 7-Chloro-1,3-dihydro-3-hydroxy-5-phenyl-2H-1,4-benzodiazepin-2-one (7) undergoes ring contraction to 6-chloro-2-formyl-4-phenylquinazoline on boiling with acid[58] (compare the reaction with alkali in Sect. 2.A.). This formyl derivative is also obtained by a similar reaction of 7-chloro-3-hydroxy-2-methylamino-5-phenyl-3H-1,4-benzodiazepine (a reduced derivative of 6) with aqueous hydrochloric acid.[30] These formyl derivatives form hydrazones[58] and acetals,[30] and are oxidized to the corresponding 2-carboxylic acids with sodium hypochlorite[30] or potassium permanganate.[58]

A Bischler synthesis (Ch. III, Sect. 1.A.) using 2,4-, 2,5-, and 2,6-diacetylacetanilide gave 6-,[59] 7-,[60,61] and 8-acetyl-2,4-dimethylquinazoline[54] respectively. In a different synthesis 8-chlorocarbonyl-3,4-dihydro-4-oxoquinazoline reacted with diazomethane then with hydrobromic acid to yield 8-bromoacetyl-3,4-dihydro-3-methyl-4-oxoquinazoline.[54] The acetyl groups are oxidized to carboxy groups with sodium hypobromite[61] and undergo Mannich reactions with alkylamines and formaldehyde (see Ch. III, Sect. 2.B.a.).[60]

4. Sulphoquinazolines and Related Compounds

The sulphonation and chlorosulphonation of 3,4-dihydro-4-oxoquinazolines is discussed in chapter IV, section 2.C.b.iv. The sodium salt of 4-sulphoquinazoline is the only derivative known with a sulphonic acid group in the pyrimidine ring and was prepared from quinazoline-3-oxide and sodium bisulphite (see Ch. IX, Sect. 2.C.).[7] 3,4-Dihydro-4-oxoquinazolines with sulpho or sulphamoyl groups in the benzene ring were prepared by standard methods, for example by Niementowski's synthesis using sulphoanthranilic acids and formamide[62–64] or its derivatives,[65] and from sulpho-3,1,4-benzoxazones and ammonia.[66] 1,2,3,4-Tetrahydro-2,4-dioxosulphoquinazolines were obtained from sulphoanthranilic acids and ureas[65] or potassium cyanate in acid medium.[66] Sulphoanthranilamides reacted with aldehydes or their acetals to yield 2-substituted 1,2,3,4-tetrahydro-4-oxo-sulphoquinazolines.[67-70] The latter were also obtained by reduction of the corresponding 3,4-dihydro-4-oxoquinazolines with sodium borohydride in the presence of aluminium chloride (see Ch. VIII, Sect. 1.C.).[65,70]

Several anthraquinone vat dyes were prepared from 6- and 8-sulphamoyl derivatives of 2,4-dichloroquinazolines and aminoanthraquinones.[71]

5. Tables

TABLE X.1.   Cyanoquinazolines.

Quinazoline	M.p. (°c)	References
4-Benzyloxy-2-cyano-	83–86°	9
4-Butylamino-2-cyano-	109–110°	10
2-Cyano-	173–175°	13
4-Cyano-	118–119°	4–8
2-Cyano-4-ethoxy-	143–145°	9
4-Cyano-3,4-dihydro-	128–129°	5, 6
5-Cyano-3,4-dihydro-2-methyl-4-oxo-	> 300°	11
7-Cyano-3,4-dihydro-2-methyl-4-oxo-	303–304°	12
2-Cyano-3,4-dihydro-4-oxo-3-phenyl-	198°	2
2-Cyano-4-isopropyl-	84°	10
2-Cyano-4-methoxy-	131–133°	9
2-Cyano-4-phenoxy-	89–93°	9
4-Cyano-2-phenyl-	166–167°	3
2-Cyano-4-propoxy-	80–81°	9

TABLE X.2.   Carbamoyl- and Hydrazinocarbonylquinazolines.

Quinazoline	M.p. (°c)	References
3-Amino-2-N'-(3-amino-3,4-dihydro-4-oxoquinazolin-2-ylcarbonyl)-hydrazinocarbonyl-3,4-dihydro-4-oxo-	157–158°	26
3-Amino-2-hydrazinocarbonyl-3,4-dihydro-4-oxo-	202.5°; HCl 190–191°; diacetyl deriv. 125°	26
4-Benzyloxy-2-carbamoyl-	156–157°	17
4-Butoxy-2-carbamoyl-	148–150°	17
2-Carbamoyl-	162–163°	13
4-Carbamoyl-	171–172°	5, 16
2-Carbamoyl-6-chloro-4-phenyl-	264–266°	28

(*Table continued*)

TABLE X.2 (*continued*)

Quinazoline	M.p. (°c)	References
2-Carbamoyl-4-ethoxy-	183–184°	17
4-Carbamoyl-2-ethyl-6-methyl-	168°	33
4-Carbamoyl-6-fluoro-2-methyl-	194°	35
2-Carbamoyl-3,4-dihydro-4-oxo-	130°	27
5-Carbamoyl-1,2,3,4-tetrahydro-2,4-dioxo-	359°	52
2-Carbamoyl-4-isopropyl-	171°	10
2-Carbamoyl-4-methoxy-	204–206°	17
2-Carbamoyl-4-methyl-	235.5°	15
4-Carbamoyl-2-methyl-	171°	35
4-Carbamoyl-2,6-dimethyl-	212°	33, 35
4-Carbamoyl-6-methyl-2-phenyl-	256°	33
4-Hydrazinocarbonyl-	181–182°	16
3,4-Dihydro-3-methyl-2-methyl-carbamoyl-4-oxo-	160°	26
2-(8-Methoxyquinazolin-2-ylcarbonyl)-carbamoyl-8-methoxy-	230°	14
2-(Quinazolin-2-ylcarbonyl)carbamoyl-	198°	14

TABLE X.3.   Quinazolines with Carboxy (and Ester) Groups in Positions
2 and 4.

Quinazoline	M.p. (°c)	References
2-Amino-4-carboxy-	210°	36
2-Amino-4-methoxycarbonyl-	144–145°	36
4-Butoxy-2-ethoxycarbonyl-	48–50°	17
4-Carboxy-2-*o*-carboxyphenyl-	188–189°	15
2-Carboxy-6-chloro-3,4-dihydro-4-phenyl-	168–169°	29
2-Carboxy-6-chloro-4-phenyl-	215–216°	28, 30, 58
4-Carboxy-2-ethyl-6-methyl-	154° (dec.); NH$_4$ salt 146°	33
4-Carboxy-2-*o*-hydroxyphenyl-	171°	34
4-Carboxy-2-*p*-hydroxyphenyl-	251°	34
4-Carboxy-2-methoxy-	156°	36
4-Carboxy-2-methyl-	175.5–176.5°	15
4-Carboxy-2,6-dimethyl-	160–161° (dec.); H$_2$O 110–115° (dec.)	33
4-Carboxy-6-methyl-2-phenyl-	155° (dec.); NH$_4$ salt 161°	33
4-Carboxy-2-*o*-nitrophenyl-	235°	34
4-Carboxy-2-phenyl-	151° (dec.)	3, 15

(*Table continued*)

TABLE X.3 *(continued)*

Quinazoline	M.p. (°c)	References
4-Ethoxy-2-ethoxycarbonyl-	70–71°	17
2-Ethoxycarbonyl-3,4-dihydro-3-2'-naphthyl-4-2'-naphthylimino-	253–254°	26
2-Ethoxycarbonyl-3,4-dihydro-3-phenyl-4-phenylimino-	291° (dec.)	26
4-Ethoxycarbonyl-2-o-hydroxyphenyl-	115°	34
4-Ethoxycarbonyl-2-p-hydroxyphenyl-	159°	34
4-Ethoxycarbonyl-2,6-dimethyl-	71°	33
4-Ethoxycarbonyl-6-methyl-2-phenyl-	121°	33
2-Ethyl-4-methoxycarbonyl-6-methyl-	30°	33
2-Methoxy-4-methoxycarbonyl-	99–100°	36
4-Methoxycarbonyl-2,6-dimethyl-	96°	33

TABLE X.4.   3,4-Dihydro-4-oxo- and 1,2-Dihydro-2-oxoquinazolines with a Carboxy (or Ester) Group in the Pyrimidine Ring.

Quinazoline	M.p. (°c)	References
3-Anilino-2-ethoxycarbonyl-3,4-dihydro-4-oxo-	142°	26
4-Carboxy-1,2,3,4,-tetrahydro-4-hydroxy-2-oxo-3-phenyl-	174° (dec.)	37
2-Carboxy-3,4-dihydro-4-oxo-	215–216° (dec.); 0.5 H_2O 201–202°	25, 27
4-Carboxy-1,2-dihydro-2-oxo-	264–266° (dec.)	36
2-Ethoxycarbonyl-3,4-dihydro-4-oxo-	178–180°	27
2-Ethoxycarbonyl-3,4-dihydro-4-oxo-3-phenyl-	291° (dec.)	26
1,2-Dihydro-4-methoxycarbonyl-2-oxo-	200–201°; MeOH 216°	36
3,4-Dihydro-2-methoxycarbonyl-4-oxo-	203–204°	32
3,4-Dihydro-2-methoxycarbonyl-4-oxo-3-phenyl-	203.5°	26

TABLE X.5. 3,4-Dihydro-4-oxoquinazolines with a Carboxy (or Ester) Group in the Benzene Ring.[a]

$(R^2O_2C)HO_2C$ —

3,4-Dihydro-4-oxoquinazoline	M.p. (°c)	References
3-Acetamido-6-carboxy-2,7-dimethyl-	220°	44
3-Amino-6-carboxy-2,7-dimethyl-	306° (dec.)	44
3-Benzylideneamino-6-carboxy-2,7-dimethyl-	278°	44
6-Carboxy-	> 300° (dec.)	39
7-Carboxy-	> 300 °(dec.)	39, 51
8-Carboxy-	310–315° (dec.)	54
6-Carboxy-3-2′,4′-dicarboxyphenyl-2-methyl-	416°	41
6-Carboxy-3-ethyl-2,7-dimethyl-	250.8°	44
6-Carboxy-3-(3′-(3-methoxypiperidin-2-yl)-2′-oxo)propyl-	2 HCl·H₂O 180°	51
7-Carboxy-3-(3′-(3-methoxypiperidin-2-yl)-2′-oxo)propyl-	2 HCl 224°	51
5-Carboxy-2-methyl-	342° (dec.)	42
6-Carboxy-2-methyl-	300°, 310° (dec.)	39, 61
7-Carboxy-2-methyl-	> 300° (dec.)	39
6-Carboxy-2,7-dimethyl-	340° (dec.)	44
7-Carboxy-2,3-dimethyl-	298° (dec.)	39
6-Carboxy-2,3,7-trimethyl-	299.5°	44
6-Carboxy-2-methyl-7-nitro-	> 300°	43
6-Carboxy-2-methyl-7-nitro-3-phenyl-	315°	43
5-Carboxy-2-methyl-3-phenyl-	270°	46
6-Carboxy-2-methyl-3-phenyl-	270°	46
7-Carboxy-2-methyl-3-phenyl-	> 300° (dec.)	39
6-Carboxy-2,7-dimethyl-3-phenyl-	300–301°	44
3-2′,4′-Diethoxycarbonylphenyl-6-ethoxycarbonyl-2-methyl-	332°	41
3-2′,4′-Dimethoxycarbonylphenyl-6-methoxycarbonyl-2-methyl-	205.5°	41, 53
6-Ethoxycarbonyl-3-p-ethoxycarbonylphenyl-	138.5–139.5°	40
3-(3′-(1-Ethoxycarbonyl-3-methoxypiperidin-2-yl)-2′-oxo)propyl-6-methoxycarbonyl-	128–129°	51

(*Table continued*)

TABLE X.5 *(continued)*

3,4-Dihydro-4-oxoquinazoline	M.p. (°c)	References
3-(3′-(3-Hydroxypiperidin-2-yl)-2′-oxo)-propyl-7-methoxycarbonyl-	2 HCl·1.5 H$_2$O 178–179°	51
6-Methoxycarbonyl-	219°	51
7-Methoxycarbonyl-	252–254°	51
5-Methoxycarbonyl-2-methyl-	235° (subl.), 273–274°	11, 42

[a] The following 3,4-dihydroquinazolines have the melting points given in brackets: 6-carboxy-3-p-carboxyphenyl- (186–187°), 6-2′-chloroethoxycarbonyl-3-p-2′-chloroethoxycarbonylphenyl- (173–174°), 6-2′-diethylaminoethoxy-3-p-2′-diethylaminoethoxycarbonylphenyl- (114–115°), and 6-methoxy-carbonyl-3-p-methoxycarbonylphenyl- (241–242°) 3,4-dihydroquinazolines.[40]

TABLE X.6. 1,2,3,4-Tetrahydro-2,4-dioxoquinazolines with a Carboxy (or Related) Group in the Benzene Ring.

1,2,3,4-Tetrahydro-2,4-dioxoquinazoline	M.p. (°c)	References
5-Benzyloxycarbonyl-	257–261°	52
5-Carboxy-	332–333°, 346°	47, 48, 52
7-Carboxy-	405° (dec.)	50
8-Carboxy-	—	49
5-Carboxy-1-methyl-	320°	47
5-Carboxy-3-methyl-	332°	47
6-Carboxy-2,3-dimethyl-	>300°	39
5-Carboxy-1,3-dimethyl-	307–311°, 318°	48, 52, 76
5-Chlorocarbonyl-	331–332° (dec.)	52
5-Chlorocarbonyl-1,3-dimethyl-	178–180° (dec.)	76
5-Ethoxycarbonyl-	297–299°	52
5-Ethoxycarbonyl-1,3-dimethyl-	142–143°	76
5-Methoxycarbonyl-	307–309°, 318°	48, 52
5-Methoxycarbonyl-3-methyl-	190–193°	47
5-Methoxycarbonyl-1,3-dimethyl-[a]	144.5–145.5°	48, 52, 76

[a] The isomeric 2,4-dimethoxy-5-methoxycarbonylquinazoline has m.p. 134.5–135.5°.[52]

TABLE X.7.   Quinazolines with Formyl or Acyl Substituents.

Quinazoline	M.p. (°c)	References
6-Acetyl-2,4-dimethyl-	92°	59, 61
7-Acetyl-2,4-dimethyl-	100°	60
8-Acetyl-2,4-dimethyl-	97–98°	54
7,8-Benzo-6-benzoyl-2,4-diphenyl-	190°	80
2-Benzoyl-4-isopropyl-	107–109°	10
2-Benzyl-4-methoxy-	124°	10
3-Benzyl-2-formyl-3,4-dihydro-4-oxo-	143–144°; 2,4-dinitrophenylhydrazone 275–277°	57
8-Bromoacetyl-3,4-dihydro-3-methyl-4-oxo-	165–168.5°	54
6-Chloro-2-formyl-4-phenyl-	177–178°; ethylacetal 101–103°; hydrazone, 166–167°; methyl imino deriv. 155–156°; 2,4-dinitrophenylhydrazone 275–276°	30, 58
7-2′-Dimethylaminopropionyl-2,4-dimethyl-	HCl 145–147°; picrate 162°	60
2-Ethoxalyl-3,4-dihydro-3-methyl-4-oxo-	173°; phenylhydrazone 168–169°	72
2-Formyl-3,4-dihydro-4-oxo-	nitromethane adduct 216–218°	54

TABLE X.8.   3,4-Dihydro-4-oxoquinazolines with a Sulpho (or Related) Group in the Benzene Ring.[a]

3,4-Dihydro-4-oxoquinazoline	M.p. (°c)	References
2-Benzyl-7-chloro-1,2-dihydro-6-sulphamoyl-	178–181°	69
2-Butyl-7-chloro-1,2-dihydro-6-sulphamoyl-	219°	65
7-Chloro-2-chloromethyl-1,2-dihydro-6-sulphamoyl-	225°	68
7-Chloro-6-chlorosulphonyl-2-ethyl-1,2-dihydro-	179° (dec.)	67
7-Chloro-2-ethyl-1,2-dihydro-6-sulphamoyl-	232–235°, 250–252°	65, 67
7-Chloro-1,2-dihydro-2-isopropyl-6-sulphamoyl-	~230°	65

(Table continued)

TABLE X.8 (*continued*)

3,4-Dihydro-4-oxoquinazoline	M.p. (°c)	References
7-Chloro-1,2-dihydro-2-methyl-6-sulphamoyl-	275°	65, 74
7-Chloro-1,2-dihydro-3-methyl-6-sulphamoyl-	257–259°	65
7-Chloro-1,2-dihydro-1,2-dimethyl-6-sulphamoyl-	233–235°	65
7-Chloro-1,2-dihydro-2-oxo-6-sulphamoyl-	275°	65
7-Chloro-1,2-dihydro-6-sulphamoyl-	256–258°	74
7-Chloro-2-isopropyl-6-sulphamoyl-	290°	65
7-Chloro-2-methyl-6-sulphamoyl-	345° (dec.)	65, 66
7-Chloro-3-methyl-6-sulphamoyl-	238–240°	65
7-Chloro-2,3-dimethyl-6-sulphamoyl-	245°	65
7-Chloro-6-sulphamoyl-	318°	63, 64, 65, 73
1,2-Dihydro-2-oxo-7-sulphamoyl-	400° (dec.)	66
2-2′-Indan-1′,3′-dionyl-6-sulpho-	355–360°	75
2-Methyl-6-sulphamoyl-	>320°	73
2-Methyl-7-sulphamoyl-	315°	66
6-Sulphamoyl-	293–294°; H_2O 217–220°	64, 73
8-Sulpho-	decomp. at high temps.	62

[a] 3,4-Dihydro-4-sulphoquinazoline has m.p. 210–212° (zwitterion), 181–182°,[4] 195–199° (dec.) (Na salt),[5] and 4-sulphoquinazoline has m.p. >360°.[7]

TABLE X.9. Unsubstituted Nitroquinazolines and 3,4-Dihydro-4-oxo-quinazolines with an Arsono Group in the Benzene Ring.

Quinazoline	M.p. (°c)	References
5-Nitro-	107–108°	77
6-Nitro-	174.5–175°	78
7-Nitro-	156–157°	77
8-Nitro-	153–156°	77
5-Arsono-3,4-dihydro-4-oxo-	>320°	79
6-Arsono-3,4-dihydro-4-oxo-	>320°	79
7-Arsono-3,4-dihydro-4-oxo-	>320°	79
7-Arsono-1,2,3,4-tetrahydro-2,4-dioxo-	—	81

6. References

1. Griess, *Ber. Deut. Chem. Ges.*, **2**, 415 (1869); see also **11**, 1985 (1878).
2. Pesson and Richer, *Compt. Rend.*, **260**, 603 (1965).
3. Meerwein, Laasch, Mersch, and Nentwig, *Chem. Ber.*, **89**, 224 (1956).
4. Albert, Armarego, and Spinner, *J. Chem. Soc.*, **1961**, 2689.
5. Higashino, *J. Pharm. Soc. Japan*, **80**, 245 (1960).
6. Teshigawara, Hayashi, and Tono, *Japan. Pat.*, 8,133 (1963); *Chem. Abstr.*, **59**, 11527 (1963).
7. Higashino, *Chem. Pharm. Bull. (Japan)*, **9**, 635 (1961).
8. Hayashi and Higashino, *Japan. Pat.*, 9,592 (1962); *Chem. Abstr.*, **59**, 3940 (1963).
9. Higashino, *J. Pharm. Soc. Japan*, **79**, 699 (1959).
10. Hayashi and Higashino, *Chem. Pharm. Bull. (Japan)*, **12**, 43 (1964).
11. Tomisek and Christensen, *J. Am. Chem. Soc.*, **67**, 2112 (1945).
12. Bogert, Amend, and Chambers, *J. Am. Chem. Soc.*, **32**, 1297 (1910).
13. Biffin, personal communication (1966).
14. Tröger and Bohnekamp, *J. Prakt. Chem.*, **117**, 161 (1927).
15. Bogert and Nabenhauer, *J. Am. Chem. Soc.*, **46**, 1702 (1924).
16. Higashino, *J. Pharm. Soc. Japan*, **80**, 842 (1960).
17. Higashino, *J. Pharm. Soc. Japan*, **79**, 702 (1959).
18. Higashino, *Chem. Pharm. Bull. (Japan)*, **10**, 1048 (1962).
19. Hayashi and Higashino, *Chem. Pharm. Bull. (Japan)*, **12**, 1111 (1964).
20. Higashino, *Chem. Pharm. Bull. (Japan)*, **10**, 1052 (1962).
21. Higashino, *J. Pharm. Soc. Japan*, **80**, 1404 (1960).
22. Higashino, *Chem. Pharm. Bull. (Japan)*, **10**, 1043 (1962).
23. Griess, *Ber. Deut. Chem. Ges.*, **18**, 2408, 2410 (1885).
24. Bischler and Lang, *Ber. Deut. Chem. Ges.*, **28**, 279 (1895).
25. Reissert and Grube, *Ber. Deut. Chem. Ges.*, **42**, 3710 (1909).
26. Bogert and Gortner, *J. Am. Chem. Soc.*, **32**, 119 (1910).
27. Baker and Almaula, *J. Org. Chem.*, **27**, 4672 (1962).
28. Bell, Gochman, and Childress, *J. Org. Chem.*, **28**, 3010 (1963).
29. Bell and Childress, *J. Org. Chem.*, **27**, 1691 (1962).
30. Sternbach, Reeder, Stempel, and Rachlin, *J. Org. Chem.*, **29**, 332 (1964).
31. Bischler and Barad, *Ber. Deut. Chem. Ges.*, **25**, 3080 (1892).
32. Noland and Jones, *J. Org. Chem.*, **27**, 341 (1962).
33. Bischler and Muntendam, *Ber. Deut. Chem. Ges.*, **28**, 723 (1895).
34. Bogert and McColm, *J. Am. Chem. Soc.*, **49**, 2650 (1927).
35. Armarego and Smith, unpublished results (1966).
36. Stefanović, Lorenc, and Mihailović, *Rec. Trav. Chim.*, **80**, 149 (1961).
37. Reissert and Schaaf, *Ber. Deut. Chem. Ges.*, **59**, 2494 (1926).
38. Gheorghiu, *Bull. Soc. Chim. France*, **2**, 223 (1935).
39. Bogert, Wiggin, and Sinclair, *J. Am. Chem. Soc.*, **29**, 82 (1907).
40. Cairncross and Bogert, *Collection Czech. Chem. Commun.*, **8**, 57 (1936).
41. Wegscheider, Malle, Ehrlich, and Skutezky, *Monatsh. Chem.*, **39**, 375 (1918).
42. Bogert and Jouard, *J. Am. Chem. Soc.*, **31**, 483 (1909).
43. Bogert and Kropff, *J. Am. Chem. Soc.*, **31**, 1071 (1909).
44. Bogert and Bender, *J. Am. Chem. Soc.*, **36**, 568 (1914).

45. Bogert and Nelson, *J. Am. Chem. Soc.*, **29**, 729 (1907); Bogert and Kropff, *J. Am. Chem. Soc.*, **31**, 841 (1909).
46. Arcoria, *Ann. Chim. (Italy)*, **52**, 149 (1962).
47. Wang, Feng, and Christensen, *J. Am. Chem. Soc.*, **72**, 4887 (1950).
48. Scott and Cohen, *J. Chem. Soc.*, **1921**, 664.
49. Schuhmacher and Ehrhardt, *Ger. Pat.*, 1,117,130 (1961); *Chem. Abstr.*, **56**, 11602 (1962).
50. Niementowski, *Ber. Deut. Chem. Ges.*, **29**, 1356 (1896).
51. Baker, Schaub, Joseph, McEvoy, and Williams, *J. Org. Chem.*, **17**, 141 (1952).
52. Lange, Chisholm, and Szabo, *J. Am. Chem. Soc.*, **61**, 2170 (1939).
53. Taub, *Monatsh. Chem.*, **41**, 141 (1920).
54. Isensee and Christensen, *J. Am. Chem. Soc.*, **70**, 4061 (1948).
55. Monti, *Atti Accad. Naz. Lincei, Rend. Classe Sci. Fis. Mat. Nat.*, **28**, 96 (1938); *Chem. Abstr.*, **33**, 2897 (1939).
56. Vène, *Bull. Soc. Chim. France*, **12**, 506 (1945).
57. Anet and Somasekhara, *Can. J. Chem.*, **38**, 746 (1960).
58. Bell and Childress, *J. Org. Chem.*, **29**, 506 (1964).
59. Siegle and Christensen, *J. Am. Chem. Soc.*, **72**, 4186 (1950).
60. Christensen, Graham, and Griffith, *J. Am. Chem. Soc.*, **67**, 2001 (1945).
61. Siegle and Christensen, *J. Am. Chem. Soc.*, **73**, 5777 (1951).
62. Sucharda, *Chem. Zentr.*, **I**, 3005 (1927).
63. Novello, *U.S. Pat.*, 2,910,488 (1959); *Chem. Abstr.*, **54**, 2271 (1960).
64. Horii, *Japan. Pat.*, 3,580 (1962); *Chem. Abstr.*, **58**, 9097 (1963).
65. Cohen, Klarberg, and Vaughan, Jr., *J. Am. Chem. Soc.*, **82**, 2731 (1960).
66. Jackman, Petrow, Stephenson, and Wild, *J. Pharm. Pharmacol.*, **15**, 202 (1963).
67. Song and Cohen, *U.S. Pat.*, 3,092,631 (1963); *Chem. Abstr.*, **59**, 12821 (1963).
68. Cohen and Klarberg, *U.S. Pat.*, 3,065,235 (1962); *Chem. Abstr.*, **58**, 6843 (1963).
69. Ciba Ltd., *Brit. Pat.*, 907,847 (1962); *Chem. Abstr.*, **58**, 5700 (1963).
70. Cohen and Vaughan, Jr., *U.S. Pat.*, 2,976,289 (1961); *Chem. Abstr.*, **55**, 17663 (1961).
71. Ebel, Randebrock, and Rupp, *U.S. Pat.*, 2,792,397 (1957); *Chem. Abstr.*, **51**, 18632 (1957); *Brit. Pat.*, 771,347 (1957); *Chem. Abstr.*, **51**, 14280 (1957).
72. Cook and Naylor, *J. Chem. Soc.*, **1943**, 397.
73. Somasekhara and Mukherjee, *Current Sci. (India)*, **32**, 547 (1963); *Chem. Abstr.*, **60**, 8031 (1964).
74. Cohen, Klarberg, and Vaughan, Jr., *J. Am. Chem. Soc.*, **81**, 5508 (1959).
75. Bogert and Heidelberger, *J. Am. Chem. Soc.*, **34**, 183 (1912).
76. Wang and Christensen, *J. Am. Chem. Soc.*, **71**, 1440 (1949).
77. Armarego, *J. Chem. Soc.*, **1962**, 561.
78. Elderfield, Williamson, Gensler, and Kremer, *J. Org. Chem.*, **12**, 405 (1947).
79. Wu and Hamilton, *J. Am. Chem. Soc.*, **74**, 1863 (1952).
80. Dziewónski and Sternbach, *Bull. Intern. Acad. Polonaise, Classe Sci. Mat. Nat.*, **1935A**, 327; *Chem. Abstr.*, **30**, 2971 (1936).
81. Stickings, *J. Chem. Soc.*, **1928**, 3131.

CHAPTER XI

Naturally Occurring and Biologically Active Quinazolines

1. Naturally Occurring Quinazolines

The quinazoline alkaloids form a small but important group of naturally occurring bases which were isolated from a number of different families in the plant kingdom. Thus quinazolines were found in the botanical families: Rutaceae (evodiamine, rutaecarpine, arborine, glycosmicine, glycorine, glycosminine), Acanthaceae (vasicine), Zygophyllaceae (vasicine), Saxifragaceae (febrifugine, isofebrifugine), Palmaceae (vasicine), and Araliaceae (2,3-tetramethylenequinazolines). The only other naturally occurring quinazoline is not an alkaloid and is the potent neurotoxin, tetrodotoxin, which was isolated from the Japanese puffer fish and from the California newt.

A. Arborine, Glycosmicine, Glycorine, and Glycosminine

Arborine was isolated at almost the same time by two Indian groups [1,2,3] from *Glycosmis arborea*. Chatterjee and Majumdar [3] gave the name 'glycosine' to the substance they isolated from *Glycosmis pentaphylla*, but this plant was later identified as *Glycosmis arborea* correa.[4] Glycosine was shown to be identical with arborine and the former name was abandoned.[4] Arborine is a relatively simple quinazoline (1) and its structure was derived on the basis of its hydrolysis with 20% aqueous potassium hydroxide to *N*-methylanthranilic acid, phenylacetic acid, and ammonia. Acid hydrolysis of the dihydro derivative (2), obtained by catalytic reduction, gave *N*-methylanthranilic acid and its amide, and phenylacetaldehyde. The structure 1 was

Arborine
(1)

(2)

(3)

Glycosmicine
(4)

Glycorine
(5)

Glycosminine
(6)

confirmed by synthesis from N-methylanthranilamide via its phenyl-acetamido derivative followed by cyclization at 170–190°.[5] However, Chatterjee and Majumdar[6] argued in favour of a 2-benzylidene structure 3 on the evidence that oxidations with periodic acid and ozone yielded benzaldehyde, and neutral permanganate gave 1,2,3,4-tetra-hydro-2,4-dioxoquinazoline. These authors also synthesized the alkaloid by refluxing N-methylanthranilamide with phenylacetic acid in xylene in the presence of an excess of phosphorus pentoxide.[7] The benzylidene structure 3 was later discarded because the nuclear magnetic resonance spectrum of arborine revealed two equivalent protons arising from the benzyl CH_2 group.[4] In view of the enhanced activity of 2-alkyl groups in oxoquinazolines (see Ch. IV, Sect. 2.C.b.(ii)) it is probable that in the above oxidations hydroxylation of the 2-CH_2 group occurred prior to C—C cleavage, hence the formation of benzalde-hyde and 1,2,3,4-tetrahydro-2,4-dioxoquinazoline. The biogenesis of arborine from an anthranilic acid unit and a phenylethylamine unit has been suggested.[4,8]

Three other alkaloids, glycosmicine (4), glycorine (5), and glycos-minine (6), were also isolated from the leaves of *Glycosmis arborea* in minor quantities. Glycosmicine was shown to be 1,2,3,4-tetrahydro-1-methyl-2,4-dioxoquinazoline from its infrared and nuclear magnetic resonance spectra, and by direct comparison with a synthetic sample (see Ch. IV, Sect. 3.B.b.). Similarly glycorine was shown to be 1,4-dihydro-1-methyl-4-oxoquinazoline, and the early difficulties in its

17+Q.

identification were due to its hygroscopic nature (Ch. IV, Sect. 2.B.).[9]
An impure form of glycosminine was recorded earlier in the literature,[6]
and because it was identical with 'glycosmine' the latter name was
abandoned.[9] Glycosminine was found to be 2-benzyl-3,4-dihydro-4-
oxoquinazoline (6) from studies similar to the above. The mass spectra
of these four alkaloids were measured and the cracking patterns were
consistent with the derived structures.[9]

B. Vasicine and Related Alkaloids

Vasicine was discovered in *Adhatoda vasica* Nees (named vasicine)[10]
and in *Peganum harmala* residues (named peganine).[11] The chemistry
of the constitution of this alkaloid has been discussed in detail in three
reviews,[8,12,13] and only the important features together with more
recent investigations are described here.

Vasicine was regarded successively as a propyl- or isopropyl-3,4-
dihydro-4-oxoquinazoline,[10] and an allyldihydrohydroxyquinazoline
(7)[11] before the structure was finally elucidated as 3,4-dihydro-2,3-2'-
hydroxytrimethylenequinazoline (8). Early work rapidly established
the quinazoline nature of the simple degradation products; 3,4-
dihydro-4-oxoquinazoline being isolated in one instance[14] and 3-
carboxymethyl-3,4-dihydro-4-oxoquinazoline in the other.[11] The alkyl
structures for the alkaloid were disproved by synthesis. The main
difficulty appears to have been the ready oxidizability of the 4-position
of the dihydroquinazoline, and the presence of an hydroxyl group
in the pyrrolidine ring. Thus oxidative procedures which ruptured the

Vasicine

(7)   (8)

aliphatic ring system and eliminated the hydroxyl group simultaneously
oxidized the quinazoline system with the introduction of a new oxygen atom, resulting in confusion between the two oxygen atoms.
Progress in the structure elucidation came with the synthesis and
identification of desoxyvasicine (9). This substance was prepared by
Ghose[14] by chlorination of vasicine and subsequent reduction of the
chloro derivative with zinc and hydrochloric acid (Reaction 1). Desoxy-

vasicine reacted with benzaldehyde to give a well-defined benzal derivative,[15] a reaction which is characteristic of 2-alkylquinazolines (Ch. III, Sect. 2.B.a.). This favoured formula **9** over the possible isomeric arrangements of the pyrrolidine type. Desoxyvasicine was synthesized almost simultaneously by Hanford and Adams[15] and Späth, Kuffner, and Platzer.[16] The latter condensed methyl 4-aminobutyrate with o-nitrobenzyl chloride to give the pyrrolidone (**10**). The nitro group was reduced and the resulting aniline cyclized by boiling with phosphoryl choride (Reaction 1). Hanford and Adams proceeded via the cyclization of 2-3'-bromopropyl-3,4-dihydroquinazoline.[15] The

(9) **(10)** (1)

hydroxyl group was shown to be in the pyrrolidine ring by oxidation of vasicine with hydrogen peroxide to the dioxo derivative (**11**). Chlorination of this derivative followed by reduction gave 3,4-dihydro-4-oxo-2,3-trimethylenequinazoline (**12**), which was also obtained by oxidation of desoxyvasicine (**9**)[17] with hydrogen peroxide as above, or with lead tetraacetate (Reaction 2). The position of the hydroxyl group in the pyrrolidine ring was demonstrated shortly

Vasicinone
(11) **(12)** (2)

afterwards by the synthesis of vasicine in Späth's laboratory in 1935. Condensation of methyl 4-amino-2-hydroxybutyrate with o-nitrobenzyl chloride gave 1-o-nitrobenzyl-3-hydroxypyrrolid-2-one, which, after reduction, cyclized readily to dl-vasicine[18] (compare **10 → 9**). A somewhat simpler synthesis was published the following year in which the racemic alkaloid was obtained in 25% yield directly from o-amino-benzylamine and α-hydroxybutyrolactone.[19]

The sulphate of Hooper's original vasicine was slightly *dextro*-rotatory[20] but later preparations of the alkaloid from plant material were optically inactive. However, by mild isolation procedures it was possible to obtain the optically active *l*-vasicine.[21] Späth and collaborators resolved *dl*-vasicine by fraction crystallization of the *d*- and the *l*-tartrate salts and showed that, like the naturally occurring *l*-vasicine, both the synthetic enantiomorphs racemized on repeated sublimation *in vacuo*, or when heated with dilute hydrochloric acid at 100°.[22] This accounted for the optical inactivity of some of the earlier preparations of the alkaloid.

A possible route for the biosynthesis of vasicine was suggested by Schöpf and Oechler who succeeded in preparing desoxyvasicine by condensation of o-aminobenzaldehyde with α-aminobutyraldehyde in citrate buffer at 30° followed by shaking with palladium black and hydrogen.[23] More recently Leonard and Martell, Jr., in a parallel synthesis and using the long-sought γ-amino-α-hydroxybutyraldehyde diethyl acetal, prepared *dl*-vasicine in 39% overall yield (Reaction 3).[24] In 1965 Gröger, Johne, and Mothes[25] demonstrated that anthranilic

$$(3)$$

$$(8)$$

acid was a precursor in the biosynthesis of vasicine, by administering anthranilic acid ($^{14}CO_2H$) to rooted leaves of *Adhatoda vasica* Nees. They degraded the labelled vasicine that was isolated and, by following previous methods,[11] showed that the specific radioactivity in the alkaloid was the same as in the anthranilic acid obtained from the degradation.

Späth and Kesztler-Gandini[26] isolated *l*-vasicine contaminated with another alkaloid which they purified. Its analytical figures suggested that it was a hydroxyvasicine. It was *dextro*rotatory in 5% aqueous acetic acid. The racemate of this substance was identical with 3,4-dihydro-6-hydroxy-2,3-2'-hydroxytrimethylenequinazoline (**13**), which was synthesized[27] by a route developed earlier for *dl*-vasicine.[28] The synthesis is depicted in reaction (4).

$$(4)$$

l-Vasicine isolated from *Adhatoda vasica* Nees had bronchodilator activity. Because this activity was typical of 3,4-dihydro-4-oxoquinazoline,[29] and because aerial oxidation of *l*-vasicine gave vasicinone (**11**), it was argued that the latter was the active principle in the alkaloid.[29] Mehta and collaborators isolated *l*-vasicinone from this plant and showed that it was not an artefact because it had bronchodilator activity whereas *l*-vasicine was a bronchoconstrictor.[30] It was claimed that photochemical oxidation of *l*-vasicine gave *l*-vasicinone,[31] but later workers failed to repeat this work and prepared vasicinone by acetylating vasicine, oxidizing the acetate with chromic oxide, and hydrolyzing the resulting 2,3-2'-acetoxytrimethylene-3,4-dihydro-4-oxoquinazoline.[32] Vasicinone was also isolated from *Peganum harmala*[33] and from *Galega officinalis*.[34] The bronchodilator activity of vasicine, vasicinone, and 3,4-dihydro-4-oxoquinazoline was studied in detail but was in no way comparable with known bronchodilator drugs.[32]

Two alkaloids were isolated in 1965 from the leaves of *Mackinlaya subulata* Philipson and *Mackinlaya macrosciadia* (F. Muell) F. Muell,

and were the first alkaloids to be obtained from plants of the family
Araliaceae. Lamberton and Johns identified them as 3,4-dihydro-2,3-
tetramethylene- (14) and 3,4-dihydro-4-oxo-2,3-tetramethylenequina-
zoline (15).[35] These two quinazolines had not been previously isolated
as natural products but they had been synthesized by earlier
workers.[36,37,38] The nuclear magnetic resonance spectra of these two
alkaloids and of their reduction products, 1,2,3,4-tetrahydro-2,3-
tetramethylene- and 1,2,3,4-tetrahydro-4-oxo-2,3-tetramethylenequina-
zoline, are consistent with their structures.[39] Biogenetically they are
closely related to the vasicine alkaloids which are considered to be

(14)   (15)

derived from anthranilic acid and ornithine.[8,40] The Australian authors
suggested that these two alkaloids may also be derived from anthranilic
acid, but in this instance condensation would be with lysine rather than
with ornithine.[35,39]

C. Febrifugine and Isofebrifugine

The antimalarial properties of preparations of *Dichroa febrifuga*
Lour (Ch'ang Shan) were known to the Chinese for many years. During
the World War II antimalarial programme in the United States, the
activity of Ch'ang Shan was confirmed,[41] and a number of laboratories
isolated the active principle.[42-44] These workers[42-46] agreed that two
active alkaloids could be isolated which differed by about 10° in melting
point and could be differentiated by optical rotation. The alkaloids
were interconvertible,[43,45] and a further dimorphic modification of
one was reported.[45] Koepfli and collaborators[42,45,46] used the names
febrifugine (dimorphic) and isofebrifugine, whereas the Chinese
workers[43] named their substances α-, β-, and γ-dichroines. The corre-
spondence of the dichroines and the febrifugines was not exact, but
Koepfli's compounds were in agreement with those of Folkers and
collaborators.[44] Analysis of the alkaloids and derivatives established
the empirical formula $C_{16}H_{19}N_3O_3$ for both compounds and the structures were partially deduced by degradative studies.[46] Isofebrifugine
differed from febrifugine by not giving a semicarbazone or an oxime.[45]
The presence of a 3-substituted 3,4-dihydro-4-oxoquinazoline moiety

was postulated from the ultraviolet absorption spectra.[46] Both bases gave 3,4-dihydro-4-oxoquinazoline on oxidation with alkaline permanganate, and with 2.5 N sodium hydroxide they furnished anthranilic acid. The presence of two basic centres was established by titration and solvent distribution measurements ($pK_{b_1} = 5.7$ and $pK_{b_2} = 12$ for isofebrifugine, and $pK_{b_1} = 6.3$ for febrifugine). One of the basic centres was shown to be a secondary amine and the probable presence of an hydroxyl group was indicated. A key derivative was obtained by oxidation of the alkaloids with periodate which gave an optically inactive compound, and this, on treatment with semicarbazide, gave 3,4-dihydro-4-oxo-3-3'-pyrazolylmethylquinazoline. Koepfli and collaborators suggested that febrifugine and isofebrifugine were probably diastereoisomers of the hemiketal 16 rather than the ketone 17.[46]

Isofebrifugine

(16)

Febrifugine

(17)

The structure of febrifugine was confirmed by independent studies of the *Hydrangea* alkaloids, and by synthesis, by the Lederle group. A survey of natural sources for antimalarial activity had indicated significant activity in extracts of *Hydrangea* species which included the common garden varieties. As the chemical studies of these species progressed, it became apparent that the material isolated was similar to the alkaloids from *Dichroa*, and the identity of the substances from the two sources was established.[47,48] Extensive degradative studies which included, at each step, direct comparison with synthetic models led to the structure 17 except for the allocation of the hydroxyl group in the piperidine ring.[48] The synthesis of *dl*-febrifugine was then accomplished by the route[49] shown in reaction (5). The antimalarial activity of the synthetic *dl*-febrifugine was one half that of the naturally occurring compound.[49]

$$(5)$$

In a second synthesis, 2-amino-2-2'-furylpropionic acid (18) (prepared from furfural, malonic acid, and ammonium acetate) was reduced and converted to the piperidine intermediate (20) (Reaction 6). Completion of the synthesis along the lines shown in reaction (5) led to two stereoisomeric racemates with the structure 17, viz, *dl*-febrifugine and the hitherto unknown *dl*-pseudo febrifugine.[50] Attempted inversion of the configuration of the pseudo alkaloid was unsuccessful. It was therefore necessary to return to the isomer-determining step, i.e. the reduction, to attempt the preparation of the normal series. Hydrogenation of the benzoyl derivative of 18 gave the alternate

$$(6)$$

stereoisomer of 19. When this isomer was treated with hydrogen bromide it gave the lactone (21), which was cyclized by triethylamine to the lactone (22). The ease of lactone formation in this series (compared with the stability of **20**) established the *cis* configuration of **22**. The lactone (**22**) was converted to the methoxy derivative (**23**), and the synthesis completed as in reaction (5) to give *dl*-febrifugine. By starting with the *laevo* form of the benzoyl derivative (**19a**), the synthesis of *d*-febrifugine (Reaction 7) was achieved, and the product was identical in every respect with natural alkaloid.[51] From the mother liquors of this synthesis an isomeric base was isolated in smaller yield and proved to be identical with isofebrifugine.

As noted above, febrifugine formed ketone derivatives unlike isofebrifugine. Another important difference was in the distribution coefficient between chloroform and water—for isofebrifugine it was 14 times higher. Baker and collaborators[51] suggested that febrifugine might be the ketone (**17**) and isofebrifugine the hemiketal (**16**). The infrared spectra, earlier reported to be identical,[44] were reexamined over a wider range of wavelengths and important differences were observed. Febrifugine was found to have a ketone band at 5.79 μ which was missing from isofebrifugine, and the latter had bands at 9.05 and 9.48 μ which were absent in febrifugine, and which were plausibly attributed to the cyclic ketal ring. Stabilization of the hemiketal ring by hydrogen bonding to the carbonyl of the quinazoline ring (as shown in **24**) would reduce the ketonic reactivity, but probably not enough to prevent the formation of ketone derivatives under all the conditions tried. Furthermore, two diastereoisomeric forms of **24** should exist but only one was found under a variety of circumstances. There remain some doubts, therefore, regarding fine details of structure in these interesting alkaloids.

17*

Isofebrifugine
(24)

The antimalarial activity of the alkaloid had a quinine equivalent of approximately 100 against *Plasmodium lophurae* in ducks.[52] However, the toxicity was also high, and the therapeutic index low. The synthesis of a number of febrifugine analogues[53-56] (see Table IV.34.) appeared to show that the ketonic side-chain and the hydroxypiperidine nucleus were highly specific for activity. On the other hand, substitution of the benzene nucleus gave active antimalarials, some of which possessed more favourable therapeutic indices than the parent compound.[52]

For further reading see Price[8] and Openshaw.[12,57]

D. Evodiamine, Rutaecarpine, Hortiamine, and Rhetsinine

The two alkaloids, evodiamine and rutaecarpine, were isolated from the dried fruits of *Evodia rutaecarpa*. They are harmane derivatives, and the structure of evodiamine (25) was partly revealed by alkaline hydrolysis to N-methylanthranilic acid and 3,4-dihydro-β-carboline (26) (Reaction 8).[58-60] When boiled with alcoholic hydro-

(8)

(25)   (26)

chloric acid it gives optically inactive isoevodiamine (27) (evodiamine hydrate) (Reaction 9),[61] and this can be cyclized with acetic anhydride or oxalic acid to optically inactive evodiamine.[60] Boiling alcoholic potassium hydroxide degraded evodiamine and isoevodiamine to N-methylanthranilic acid, carbon dioxide, and a base $C_{10}H_{12}N_2$. A similar degradation of rutaecarpine gave anthranilic acid instead of the N-methyl derivative.[61] The 2-2'-aminoethylindole structure proposed

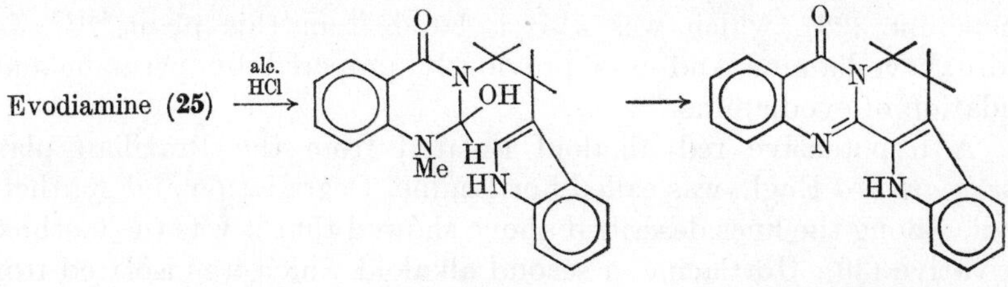

Evodiamine (25) $\xrightarrow{\text{alc. HCl}}$

Isoevodiamine
(27)

Rutaecarpine
(28)

(9)

for the base $C_{10}H_{12}N_2$ [62] was questioned [63] because it led to the proposal that these alkaloids could not be derived from tryptophan. This base was later shown to be 3-2'-aminoethylindole (tryptamine). [58] The relationship between evodiamine and rutaecarpine was demonstrated by fusion of isoevodiamine hydrochloride; chloromethane was liberated and rutaecarpine (28) was formed (Reaction 9). [60] Several syntheses of rutaecarpine have been effected. [64] The most direct synthesis was by condensation of 1,2,3,4-tetrahydro-1-oxo-β-carboline with methyl anthranilate. [65] Evodiamine was synthesized from tryptamine and N-methylisatoic anhydride which gave the intermediate o-methyl-aminobenzoyltryptamine that was cyclized to evodiamine by boiling with ethyl orthoformate (Reaction 10). [66] As in the case of vasicine (see

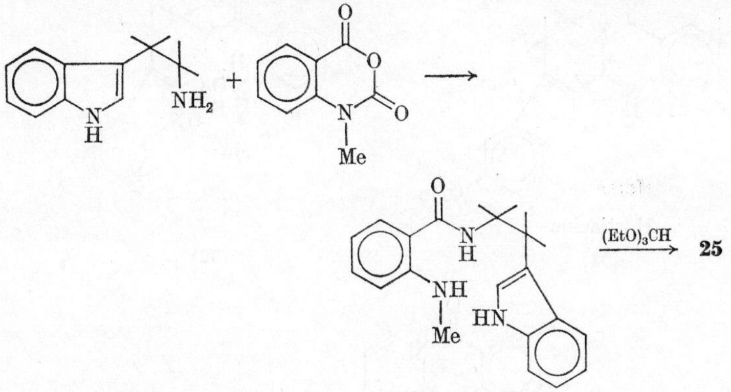

$\xrightarrow{\text{(EtO)}_3\text{CH}}$ **25** (10)

Sect. B.), Schöpf and Steuer [67] prepared rutaecarpine in over 70% yield by condensing o-aminobenzaldehyde with 3,4-dihydro-β-carboline under 'physiological conditions' at pH 5 to the intermediate carbinol-amine which was then oxidized with potassium ferricyanide at pH 7.

Evodiamine was also isolated from *Xanthoxylum rhetsa* DC, and was apparently named rhetsine. [68] It was shown to be *dl*-evodiamine. [69]

Rhetsinine (**29**), which was also isolated from this plant,[68,70] was hydroxyevodiamine and was previously prepared by permanganate oxidation of evodiamine.[60]

A hypotensive red alkaloid isolated from the Brazilian plant *Hortia arborea* Engl., was called hortiamine. Degradation and synthetic studies along the lines described above showed that it was the methoxy derivative (**30**). Hortiacine, a second alkaloid which was isolated from *Hortia arborea*, was the methoxyrutaecarpine (**31**), and could be obtained by pyrolysis of hortiamine hydrochloride.[71] Hortiamine was also isolated from *Hortia braziliana* Vel. and its chemistry was studied in detail. It was synthesized from the accessible amide (**32**) in quanti-

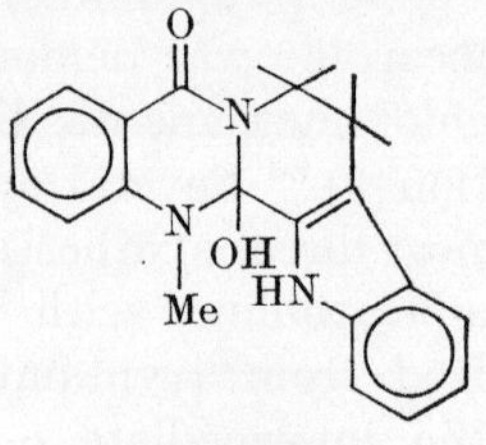

Rhetsinine
(**29**)

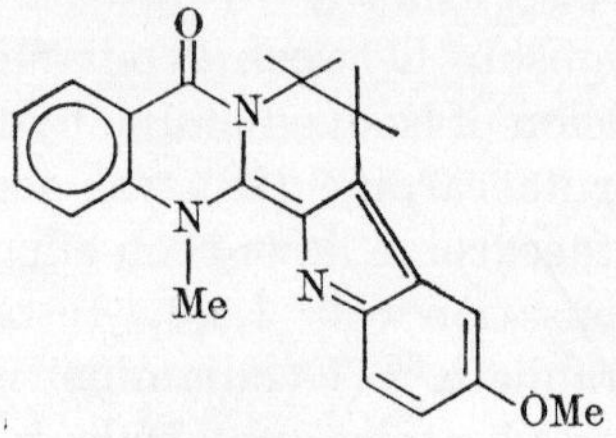

Hortiamine
(**30**)

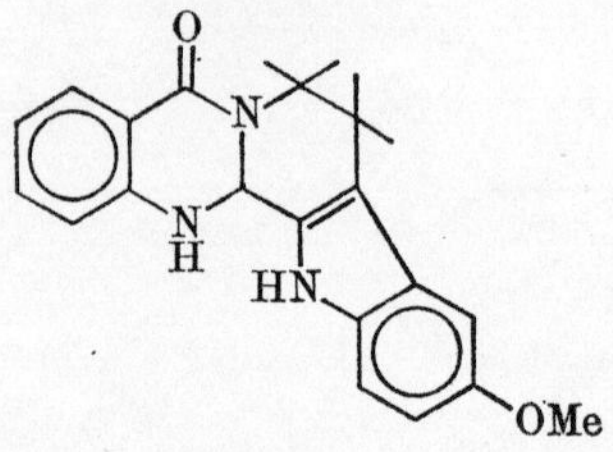

Hortiacine
(**31**)

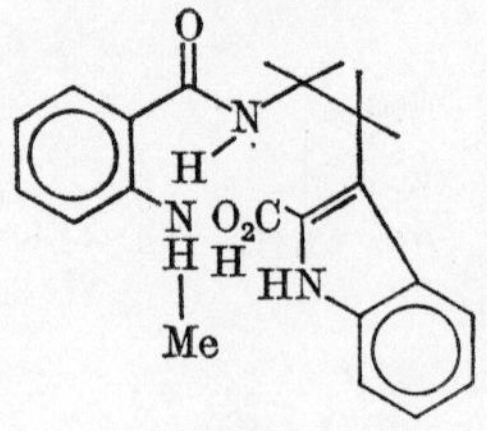

(**32**)

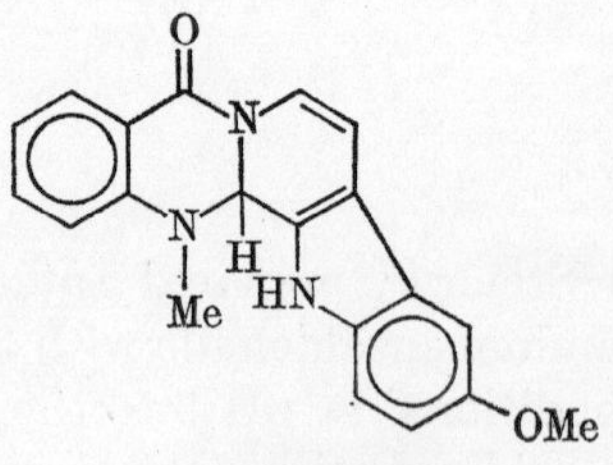

Isohortiamine
(**33**)

tative yield by the action of polyphosphoric acid. Hortiamine was transformed to the isomeric isohortiamine (**33**), and there was evidence that the isohortiamine system also occurred naturally.[72]

E. Tetrodotoxin

One of the most potent non-protein neurotoxins, 'tetrodotoxin', was isolated from certain varieties of the Japanese puffer fish, particularly the tiger puffer (tora fugu, *Sphoeroides rubripes*) and the closely related common puffer (ma fugu, *Sphoeroides phyreus*). The puffer fish is a delicacy in Japan, and poses quite a problem as several deaths are caused annually through eating it. The toxin is present, in very low concentrations, in the liver and the ovaries. It is of interest that the poison is also found in the embryos of the California Newt (salamander, *Taricha torosa*), whose taxonomic relation to the puffer fish is remote. The toxin from the newt was called *tarichatoxin*, and the identity of the two toxins was demonstrated by direct comparison of their acetate derivatives. Apart from the bacterial toxins, tetrodotoxin is one of the most potent toxins known. At concentrations larger than 1–5 µg/kg, it causes respiratory failure and complete neuromuscular block in cats, dogs, and rats, in a few seconds.[73]

Tetrodotoxin has been known, through its effects, since antiquity, and was first isolated in a crystalline form by Yokoo[74] in 1950 who called it *spheroidin*. The study of its constitution was made difficult by its chemical lability, and because it was present in very small concentrations. Thus 100 kg of chopped ovaries afforded 1–2 g of crude toxin.[75] The structure of the toxin was elucidated by three different schools; two in Japan led by Hirata and Goto (Nagoya)[75] and Tsuda (Tokyo),[76] and the third in America by Woodward (Harvard).[77] The structure of tetrodotoxin is shown in **34**. It is a zwitterionic polyhydroxy perhydro 2-iminoquinazoline (Ch. VIII, Sect. 9.) which has a hitherto unknown hemilactal structure. It only dissolves in acidic solvents and has a pK_a value of 8.76. Anhydroepitetrodotoxin (**35**) is an impurity in the precipitated toxin. Because the pK_a value of **35** was 7.95, the shape of the pH–alkali titration curve was the best test for the purity of the toxin. The toxin was purified by recrystallization of its picrate (darkens above 200°; hydrobromide has no definite melting point).[75] Molecular weight, nuclear magnetic resonance and mass spectrometric measurements, and analytical values of derivatives lead to the molecular formula $C_{11}H_{17}O_8N_3 \cdot xH_2O$.

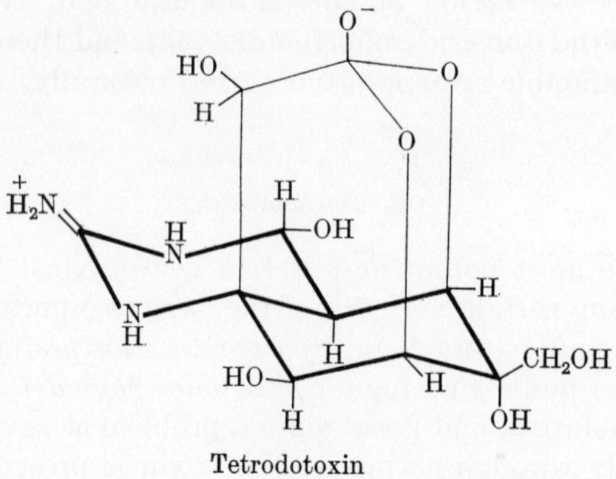

Tetrodotoxin
(34)

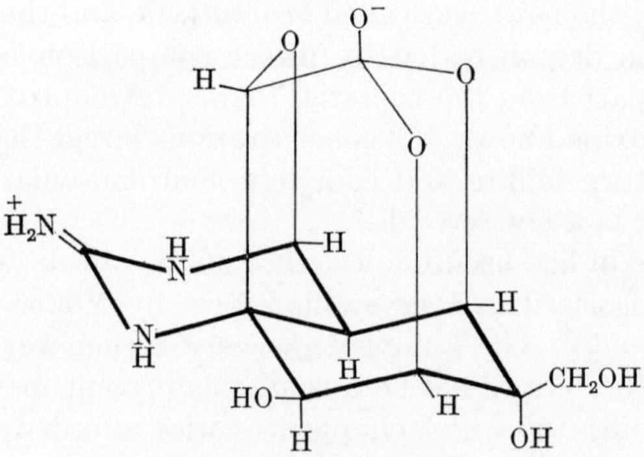

Anhydroepitetrodotoxin
(35)

The three nitrogen atoms are part of a guanidine system since oxidation of tetrodotoxin by concentrated aqueous sodium permanganate at 75° gave guanidine which was characterized as its picrate. The presence of a quinazoline skeleton was indicated by transformation of the toxin to the many quinazoline derivatives shown in scheme (1). The structures of these derivatives, i.e. 2-amino-8-hydroxy-6-hydroxymethyl- (36), 2-amino-6-methyl- (37), 2-acetamido-8-acetoxy-6-methyl- (38), 2-acetamido-8-acetoxy-6-acetoxymethyl- (39), 2-amino-6-hydroxy- (40), 8-acetoxy-6-acetoxymethyl-2-N-deuteroacetamido- (41), 8-acetoxy-6-acetoxymethyl-5-deutero-2-N-deuteroacetamido- (42), 8-acetoxy-6-acetoxymethyl-7-deutero-2-N-deuteroacetamido- (43), and 8-acetoxy-6-acetoxymethyl-2-N-deuteroacetamido-5,7-dideutero- (44) quinazolines, were deduced by nuclear magnetic resonance spectroscopy and by direct comparison with synthetic materials.[75-79] The formation of these quinazolines, however, does not exclude the possibility that the toxin

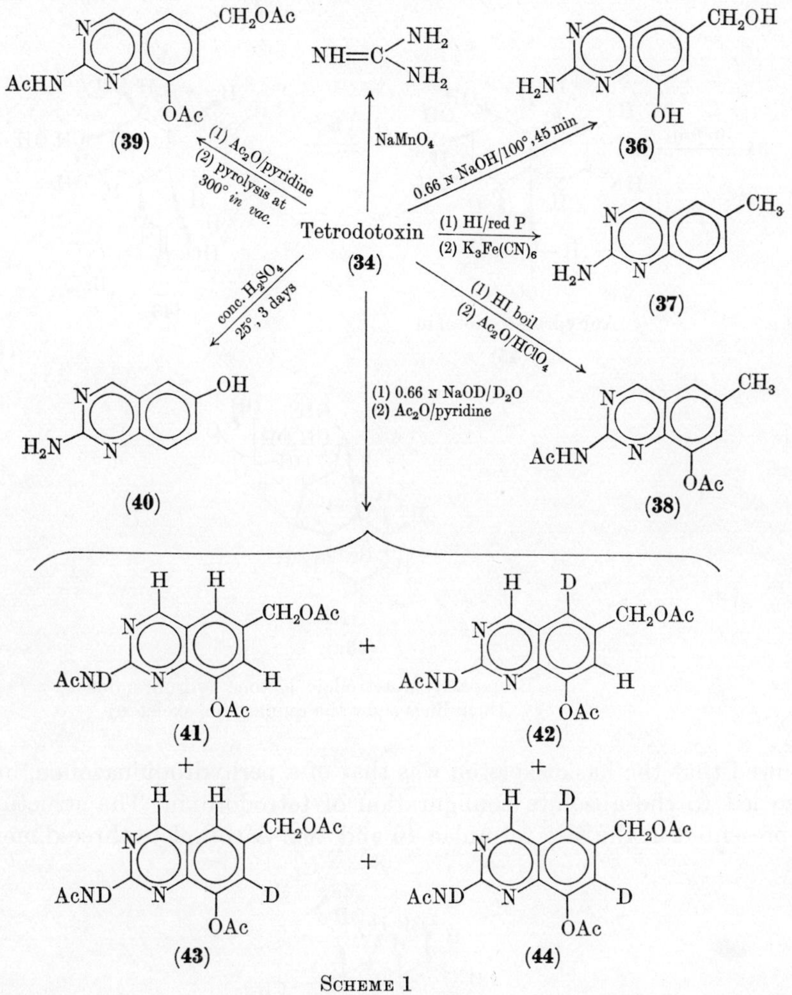

SCHEME 1

may have an open-chain structure. Acetylation gives di-, tetra-, penta-, hexa-, hepta-, and octa- acetylanhydroepitetrodotoxins,[75,77] which are derivatives of structure **35**. Treatment of tetrodotoxin with 5% barium hydroxide solution at 20° in a nitrogen atmosphere, followed by neutralization with carbon dioxide, afforded anhydrotetrodotoxin

(45). This consumed 1 mole of bromine to give bromoanhydrotetrodoic lactone hydrobromide (46) (Reaction 11). The detailed X-ray analysis of this bromolactone by Nitta and collaborators,[80] using a three-dimensional Fourier synthesis and the least squares method, not only

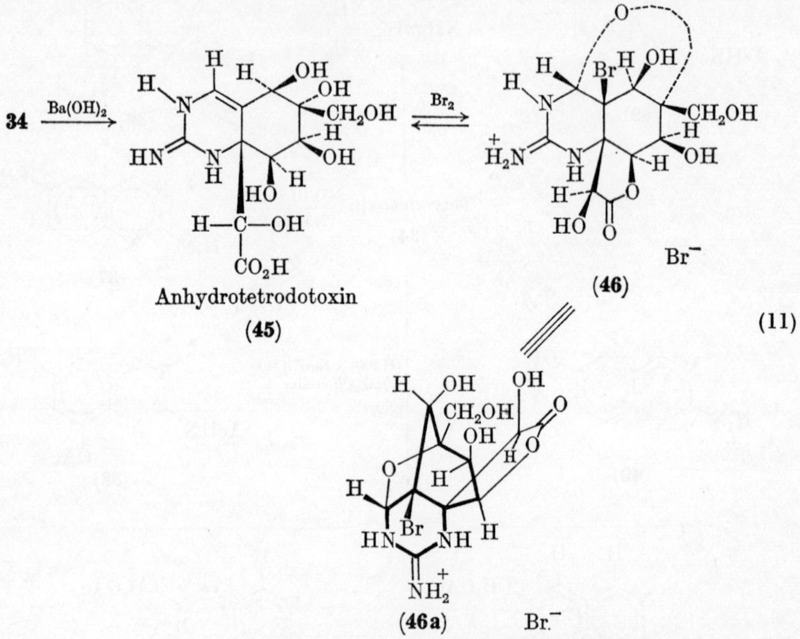

$$34 \xrightarrow{Ba(OH)_2} \text{(45)} \underset{}{\overset{Br_2}{\rightleftharpoons}} \text{(46)} \qquad (11)$$

Anhydrotetrodotoxin
(45)

(46)

(46a)   Br⁻

Bromoanhydrotetrodoic lactone hydrobromide
(thick lines show the quinazoline skeleton)

showed that the basic skeleton was that of a perhydroquinazoline, but also led to the absolute configuration of tetrodotoxin. The structure is presented in the two formulae 46 and 46a. A complete three-dimen-

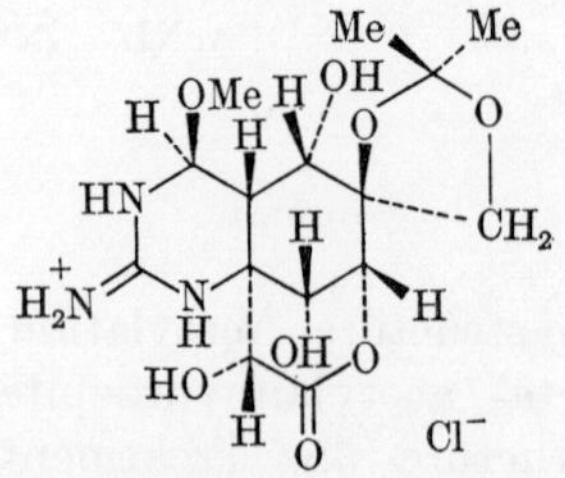

Goutougas hydrochloride
(47)

sional X-ray crystallographic analysis of the Goutougas hydrochloride, O-methyl-O',O''-isopropylidenetetrodotoxin hydrochloride hydrate (47), which was prepared by the action of hydrogen chloride on tetrodotoxin in the presence of acetone and methanol, was also of considerable value.[77] The X-ray analyses of tetrodoic acid hydrobromide (see below) and other derivatives were also made.[76]

When the toxin was heated with water in a sealed tube at 100°, it gave a crystalline compound called tetrodoic acid (48) (previously named tetrodonic acid), which consumed one mole of periodic acid and gave formaldehyde (released from the 6-hydroxymethyl group) and nortetrodoic acid (49). This used up a further mole of periodic acid and yielded seconortetrodioic acid (50). Nortetrodoic acid (49) afforded

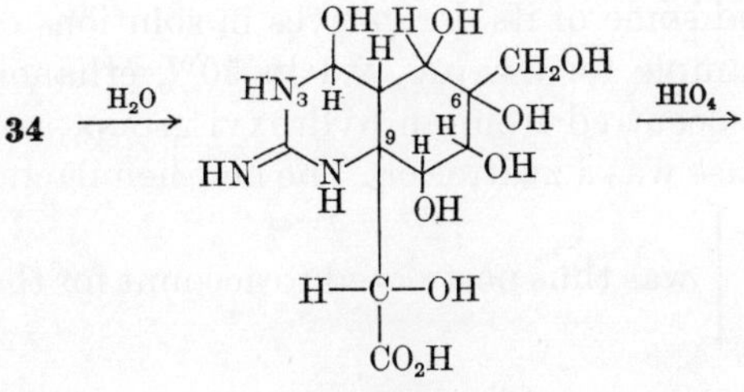

Tetrodoic acid
(48)

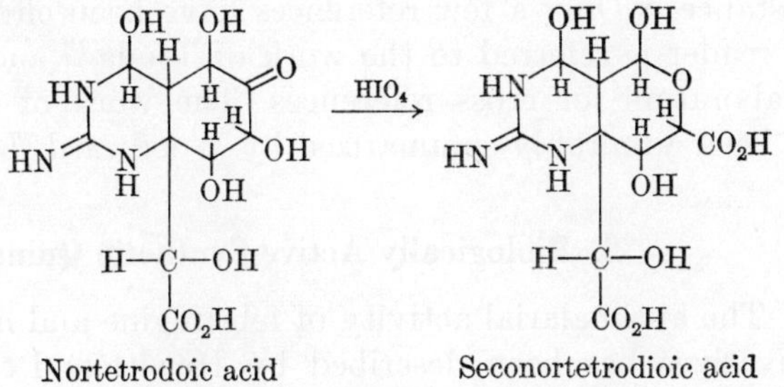

(12)

Nortetrodoic acid
(49)

Seconortetrodioic acid
(50)

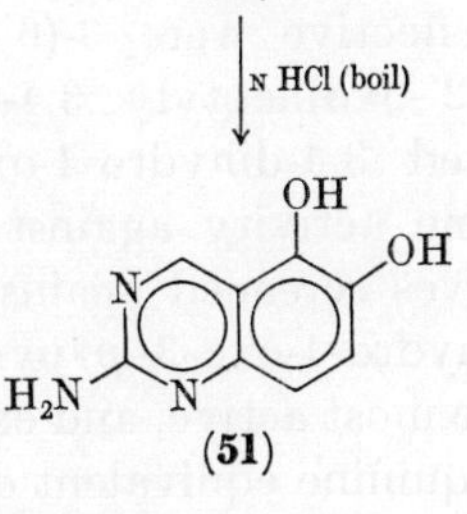

(51)

2-amino-5,6-dihydroxyquinazoline (**51**) when refluxed with N hydrochloric acid (Reaction 12).[75,81] The presence of the glyoxylic acid
group on the bridgehead carbon atom $C_{(9)}$ was indicated by the liberation
of oxalic acid and 2-amino-8-hydroxy-6-hydroxymethylquinazoline (**36**)
from the degradation of tetrodotoxin or tetrodoic acid with alkali.[76]

Tetrodotoxin is not a lactone because, unlike its hydrochloride,
and the Goutougas hydrochloride (**47**), the lactone bands in the infrared
spectrum are absent. Also, the basicity (pK_a 8.76) is too low for a
guanidinium system, even if allowance were made for the many electron-withdrawing groups in the molecule. An amide structure involving
the *exocyclic* carboxy group (attached, indirectly, to the bridgehead
carbon $C_{(9)}$) and $N_{(3)}$, for example in tetrodoic acid (**48**), was postulated,[82]
but was later discarded on spectroscopic and ionization evidence. The
increase in pK_a of the toxin and some of its derivatives in solutions of
low dielectric constant, for example for **34**, pK_a 9.4 in 50% ethanol,
indicated that the dissociation occurred from an hydroxyl group, and
it was concluded that the free base was a zwitterion. The new hemilactal

system (in **34**) $\left[-C(OH) \begin{matrix} O- \\ \diagup \\ \diagdown \\ O- \end{matrix} \right]$ was thus postulated to account for the

properties of tetrodotoxin.

It is of interest to note that the toxicities of the derivatives of
tetrodotoxin examined were considerably lower than that of the parent
substance.[76] Only a few references have been cited in this report and
the reader is referred to the work of Tsuda[76] and Hirata[75] and their
collaborators for cross references. The work of the Harvard School
has been admirably summarized by Woodward.[77]

2. Biologically Active Synthetic Quinazolines

The antimalarial activity of febrifugine and many of its synthetic
derivatives has been described by Hewitt and collaborators[52] (Sect.
1.C.). Several closely related bases were also synthesized by Russian
workers,[83,84] and the most effective were 3-(6'-morpholino-2'-oxo)-
hexyl- and 3-(7'-piperidino-2'-oxo)heptyl- 3,4-dihydro-4-oxoquina-
zolines. Many 2,3-disubstituted 3,4-dihydro-4-oxoquinazolines were
tested and found to have some activity against avian malaria.[85-87]
Out of seventy-seven derivatives screened against *P. Gallinaceum* in
chicks, 6-chloro-2-ethyl-3,4-dihydro-4-oxo-3-*p*-pyrimidin-2'-ylsulpha-
moylphenylquinazoline was the most active, and exhibited antimalarial
activity at a dose 4 times the quinine equivalent dose.[86] Other deriva-

tives were inactive antimalarials but were toxic at higher dosage.[85] Quinazolines with amino groups in positions 4 and/or 2 were similarly tested[88–90] and the highest activity was found in derivatives that possessed a 4-(4'-diethylamino-1'-methyl)butylamino group, and the presence also of a chlorine atom in position 7 led to enhanced activity.[88]

Methaqualone
(52)

B.D.H. 1880
(53)

Following the discovery of the hypnotic activity of 2-alkyl-3-aryl-3,4-dihydro-4-oxoquinazolines by Gujral, Saxena, and Tiwari,[91] considerable effort was made in the study of the biological activity of this class of compounds. The derivative, 3,4-dihydro-2-methyl-4-oxo-3-o-tolylquinazoline (52) was examined extensively. It is now used clinically, and is marketed in several countries under a number of names, e.g. Methaqualone,[92,93] Revonal,[93] Metolquizolone,[94] Dilunal,[95] QZ-2,[91,96] Tuazolone,[97] and Melsedin.[98] Its hypnotic action is comparable to that of the barbiturates and its biological activity has been the subject of a number of recent publications,[91–94,96–104] and has been reviewed.[98] 2-[14]C Methaqualone was administered orally to mice and found to be absorbed rapidly and then fixed in the liver, fatty tissue, and in small concentrations in the brain. It was excreted mainly via the enterohepatic path and found in the urine as well as in faeces.[105] Methods for its detection in tissues were worked out,[106] and 3,4-dihydro-3-o-hydroxymethylphenyl-2-methyl-4-oxoquinazoline was found to be a major metabolite,[107] although some was excreted unchanged in the urine.[108] It was reported that 8.0 grams of the drug caused death to humans after 40 hours.[108]

Methaqualone was superior to sodium phenobarbitone as an anticonvulsant against Metrazol-induced seizures,[96] and of forty compounds tested (for oral anticonvulsant activity against Leptazol-induced convulsions in mice) 3-p-bromophenyl-3,4-dihydro-2-methyl-4-oxoquinazoline (53) (known as B.D.H. 1880) was the most active. It was one quarter as active as Phenytoin against Leptazol and eight times more active than Troxidone against electroshock-induced convulsions. The 4-thio derivative was less active but removal of the bromine atom in the 3-phenyl group resulted in substantial loss of activity.[109]

The oxoquinazoline structure is apparently responsible for the effect of these drugs on the nervous system, and 3,4-dihydro-4-oxo-,[110] as well as 1,2,3,4-tetrahydro-2,4-dioxo-,[110-113] 1,2,3,4-tetrahydro-4-oxo-2-thio-,[111] and 1,2,3,4-tetrahydro-4-oxoquinazoline[111] have hypnotic and hypotensive activity. The hypotensive activity of 1-alkyl-3,4-dihydro-6-methyl-3-*p*-tolylquinazolinium salts may be attributed to the formation of their 4-oxo derivatives in the body.[114] 2-[115] and 4-Hydrazino-,[116] and 2,4-dihydrazinoquinazoline[117] also have some hypotensive activity.

Low antihistamine activity was observed in 4-*N'*-alkyl-2'-dialkyl-aminoethylaminoquinazolines (54), but the activity was highly specific and the compounds had no antiacetylcholine activity.[118] Of the seventeen 1,2,3,4-tetrahydro-4-oxoquinazolines examined, 1-2'-dimethylam-inoethyl-1,2,3,4-tetrahydro-4-oxo-2-2'-pyridylquinazoline (55) showed the highest specific antihistamine activity *in vivo* and *in vitro*. It had low toxicity with almost complete absence of sedating side effects.[119]

7-Chloro-2-ethyl-1,2,3,4-tetrahydro-4-oxo-6-sulphamoylquinazo-line (56) is a very good oral non-mercurial diuretic which is now administered clinically. It is marketed under the names Quinethazone, Aquamox, and Hydramox.[120] Clinical studies showed that it caused rapid excretion of water and sodium ions. The duration of the activity was 24 hours and an optimal weekly dose of 100–150 mg generally sufficed.[121] Its diuretic potency was similar to Chlorothiazide, and administration for two days induced an average loss in weight of 2 lb in a group of 30 patients. Daily administration kept the patients in an edema-free state without significant side effects.[122] Minor changes in the 2-alkyl substituents caused a small overall effect on the diuretic activity.[123]

Attempts were made to prepare quinazolines which would be useful as growth factors. 2,4-Diamino-6-*p*-carboxyanilinomethylquinazoline (57) was very slightly active,[124] and 4-p-[l(+)-1,3-dicar-boxypropylcarbamoyl]anilinoquinazoline (58) was 0.01 to 0.1 as active as pteroylglutamic acid.[125] Baker and collaborators[126,127] synthesized the folic acid analogues 2-amino-6-p-(1,3-dicarboxypropylcarbamoyl)-anilinomethyl-3,4,5,6,7,8-hexahydro-4-oxoquinazoline (59) and 2,4-dia-mino-6-p-(1,3-dicarboxypropylcarbamoyl)aminomethyl-5,6,7,8-tetra-hydroquinazoline (60), and found that with $P.$ $cerevisiae,$ 59 had less

than half the inhibitory activity of aminopterin, whereas the more closely related compound 60 was eight times as active. In tests with $S.$ $faecalis,$ 59 was one thirtieth as active, and 60 was six times as active as aminopterin.[127] The growth inhibitory properties of 2,4-diamino-5,6-dihydroquinazolines are worthy of mention.[128]

18—q.

3-Carboxymethyl-6,8-dichloro-3,4-dihydro-2-methyl-4-oxoquinaz-
oline is of agricultural importance because of its plant-growth regulating activity. It is as potent as 2,4-dichlorophenoxyacetic acid in
the Lepidium test.[129] 2-Chloro-4-ethylamino-, 4-diethylamino-, and
2,4-bisdiethylaminoquinazoline were claimed to be plant-growth
regulators.[130]

Tricycloquinazoline

(61)

The epidermal carcinogen, tricycloquinazoline (61), received much
attention recently, and several derivatives were synthesized in order to
establish its mode of action.[131] The shape of 61 is critical because isomeric
compounds are considerably less active.[132] The molecule does not appear
to bind with epidermal proteins and phospholipids. 1-, 3-, and 4-Methyl
derivatives are carcinogenic but less active than 61, and the 3,8-dimethyl
and 3,8,13-trimethyl derivatives are weakly active, whereas the 2-
methyl derivative is inactive. Coplanarity is apparently essential because
the activity decreases in the order 3-methyl, 3-ethyl, 3-t-butyl. Partridge
and collaborators assumed that very weak π orbital binding of the
carcinogen with purine and pyrimidine pairs in DNA may occur.[133]

Several derivatives of 3,4-dihydro-4-oxoquinazoline and of 4-
aminoquinazoline were tested and found active against protozoans.[134]
Of particular interest is 6-p-amidinophenyldiazoamino-4-amino-1,2-
dimethylquinazolinium chloride hydrochloride which is active against
Trypanosoma rhodesiense in mice and is comparable with Pentam-
idine.[135] The meta-compound, 6-m-amidinophenyldiazoamino-4-amino-
1,2-dimethylquinazolinium chloride hydrochloride, is active against
Babesia canis[136] in dogs, and more active than Berenil against Babesia
rodhaini in mice.[135]

Antibacterial activity was observed in a number of amino-,[137]
guanidino-,[138] and oxoquinazolines.[139]

Antiviral activity against vaccinia virus in chick embryos,[140] and
against influenza virus, was noted in oxoquinazolines.[141]

3,4-Dihydro-2-methyl-4-thioquinazoline,[142] 4-oxo-2-thio-[143] and

2,4-dithio-1,2,3,4-tetrahydroquinazoline[142] were weakly goitrogenic. Several oxo-, thio-, chloro-, and nitroquinazolines have been incorporated into the vitamin B_{12} molecule, by replacing the 5,6-dimethylbenzimidazole moiety, and possessed cobalamine activity.[144] 3,4-Dihydro-3-hydroxy-4-oxoquinazoline was found useful in protection from radiation damage.[145]

3. References

1. Chakravarti and Chakravarti, *J. Proc. Inst. Chemists (India)*, **24**, 96 (1952); *Chem. Abstr.*, **47**, 2838 (1953).
2. Chakravarti and Chakravarti, *Sci. Cult. (Calcutta)*, **18**, 553 (1953); *Chem. Abstr.*, **48**, 5875 (1954).
3. Chatterjee and Majumdar, *Sci. Cult. (Calcutta)*, **17**, 306 (1952); *Chem. Abstr.*, **46**, 10185 (1952).
4. Chakravarti, Chakravarti, Cohen, Dasgupta, Datta, and Miller, *Tetrahedron*, **16**, 224 (1961).
5. Chakravarti, Chakravarti, and Chakravarti, *J. Chem. Soc.*, **1953**, 3337.
6. Chatterjee and Majumdar, *J. Am. Chem. Soc.*, **76**, 2459 (1954); Chakravarti, Chakravarti, and Chakravarti, *Experientia*, **9**, 333 (1953).
7. Chatterjee and Majumdar, *J. Am. Chem. Soc.*, **75**, 4365 (1953).
8. Price, *Fortschr. Chem. Org. Naturstoffe*, **13**, 330 (1956); cf. Bently, *The Chemistry of Natural Products, Vol. VII; The Alkaloids, Part II*, Interscience, 1965, Chaps. 2 and 6.
9. Pakrashi, Bhattacharyya, Johnson, and Budzikiewicz, *Tetrahedron*, **19**, 1011 (1963).
10. Sen and Ghose, *J. Indian Chem. Soc.*, **1**, 315 (1925); *Chem. Abstr.*, **19**, 2501 (1925).
11. Späth and Nikawitz, *Ber. Deut. Chem. Ges.*, **67**, 45 (1934).
12. Openshaw in *The Alkaloids* (Ed. Manske), Academic Press, 1953, Vol. III, p. 101.
13. Henry, *The Plant Alkaloids*, Churchill, 1949, p. 617.
14. Ghose, *J. Indian Chem. Soc.*, **4**, 1 (1927).
15. Hanford and Adams, *J. Am. Chem. Soc.*, **57**, 921 (1935).
16. Späth, Kuffner, and Platzer, *Ber. Deut. Chem. Ges.*, **68**, 497 (1935).
17. Morris, Hanford, and Adams, *J. Am. Chem. Soc.*, **57**, 951 (1935).
18. Späth, Kuffner, and Platzer, *Ber. Deut. Chem. Ges.*, **68**, 699 (1935).
19. Späth and Platzer, *Ber. Deut. Chem. Ges.*, **69**, 255 (1936).
20. Hooper, *Pharm. J.*, **18**, 841 (1888).
21. Späth and Kesztler, *Ber. Deut. Chem. Ges.*, **69**, 384 (1936); Rosenfeld and Kolesnikov, *Ber. Deut. Chem. Ges.*, **69**, 2022 (1936).
22. Späth, Kuffner, and Platzer, *Ber. Deut. Chem. Ges.*, **68**, 1384 (1935).
23. Schöpf and Oechler, *Ann. Chem.*, **523**, 1 (1936); see also Macholán, *Collection Czech. Chem. Commun.*, **24**, 550 (1959).
24. Leonard and Martell, Jr., *Tetrahedron Letters*, (25), 44 (1960).
25. Gröger, Johne, and Mothes, *Experientia*, **21**, 13 (1965).
26. Späth and Kesztler-Gandini, *Monatsh. Chem.*, **91**, 1150 (1960).
27. Kuffner, Lenneis, and Bauer, *Monatsh. Chem.*, **91**, 1152 (1960).

28. Southwick and Casanova, Jr., *J. Am. Chem. Soc.*, **80**, 1168 (1958).

29. Amin, Mehta, and Samarath, *Proc. First Intern. Pharmacol.*, 488 (1961).

30. Mehta, Naravane, and Desai, *J. Org. Chem.*, **28**, 445 (1963).

31. Amin and Mehta, *Nature*, **184**, 1317 (1959).

32. Cambridge, Jansen, and Jarman, *Nature*, **196**, 1217 (1962).

33. Koretskaya, *Zh. Obshch. Khim.*, **27**, 3361 (1957); *Chem. Abstr.*, **52**, 9163 (1958); Koretskaya and Utkin, *Zh. Obshch. Khim.*, **28**, 1087 (1958); *Chem. Abstr.*, **52**, 18501 (1958).

34. Linyuchev and Ban'kovskiĭ, *Tr. Vses. Nauchn.-Issled. Inst. Lekarstv. i Aromat. Rast.*, **11**, 65 (1959); *Chem. Abstr.*, **55**, 18893 (1961).

35. Lamberton and Johns, *Chem. Comm.*, **1965**, 267.

36. Späth and Platzer, *Ber. Deut. Chem. Ges.*, **68**, 2221 (1935).

37. Muñoz and Madroñero, *Chem. Ber.*, **95**, 2182 (1962).

38. Stephen and Stephen, *J. Chem. Soc.*, **1956**, 4694.

39. Fitzgerald, Johns, Lamberton, and Redcliffe, *Australian J. Chem.*, **19**, 151 (1966).

40. Mothes and Schütte, *Angew. Chem.*, **75**, 357 (1963).

41. Wiselogle, *A Survey of Antimalarial Drugs*, Edwards Ann Arbor, 1946, Vol. II, Part II.

42. Koepfli, Mead, and Brockman, Jr., *J. Am. Chem. Soc.*, **69**, 1837 (1947).

43. Chou, Fu, and Kao, *J. Am. Chem. Soc.*, **70**, 1765 (1948).

44. Kuehl, Jr., Spencer, and Folkers, *J. Am. Chem. Soc.*, **70**, 2091 (1948).

45. Koepfli, Mead, and Brockman, Jr., *J. Am. Chem. Soc.*, **71**, 1048 (1949).

46. Koepfli, Brockman, Jr., and Moffat, *J. Am. Chem. Soc.*, **72**, 3323 (1950).

47. Ablondi, Gordon, Morton, and Williams, *J. Org. Chem.*, **17**, 14 (1952).

48. Hutchings, Gordon, Ablondi, Wolf, and Williams, *J. Org. Chem.*, **17**, 19 (1952).

49. Baker, Schaub, McEvoy, and Williams, *J. Org. Chem.*, **17**, 132 (1952).

50. Baker, McEvoy, Schaub, Joseph, and Williams, *J. Org. Chem.*, **18**, 153 (1953).

51. Baker, McEvoy, Schaub, Joseph, and Williams, *J. Org. Chem.*, **18**, 178 (1953).

52. Hewitt, Wallace, Gill, and Williams, *Am. J. Trop. Med. Hyg.*, **1**, 768 (1952).

53. Baker, Schaub, Joseph, McEvoy, and Williams, *J. Org. Chem.*, **18**, 133 (1953).

54. Baker, Joseph, Schaub, McEvoy, and Williams, *J. Org. Chem.*, **18**, 138 (1953).

55. Baker, Joseph, Schaub, McEvoy, and Williams, *J. Org. Chem.*, **17**, 157 (1952).

56. Baker, Schaub, Joseph, McEvoy, and Williams, *J. Org. Chem.*, **17**, 164 (1952).

57. Openshaw in *The Alkaloids* (Ed. Manske), Academic Press, 1960, Vol. VII, p. 247.

58. Asahina, *J. Pharm. Soc. Japan*, (503), 1 (1924); *Chem. Abstr.*, **18**, 1667 (1924).

59. Asahina and Kashiwaki, *J. Pharm. Soc. Japan*, (405), 1293 (1915); *Chem. Abstr.*, **10**, 607 (1916).

60. Asahina and Ota, *J. Pharm. Soc. Japan*, (530), 293 (1926); *Chem. Abstr.*, **21**, 2134 (1927).

61. Asahina and Mayeda, *J. Pharm. Soc. Japan*, (416), 871 (1916); *Chem. Abstr.*, **11**, 332 (1917).
62. Asahina and Fujita, *J. Pharm. Soc. Japan*, (476), 863 (1921); *Chem. Abstr.*, **16**, 1584 (1922).
63. Kermack, Perkin, Jr., and Robinson, *J. Chem. Soc.*, **1921**, 1602.
64. Marion in *The Alkaloids* (Ed. Manske and Holmes), Academic Press, 1952, Vol. II, p. 402.
65. Asahina, Manske, and Robinson, *J. Chem. Soc.*, **1927**, 1708.
66. Asahina and Ohta, *Ber. Deut. Chem. Ges.*, **61**, 319, 869 (1928).
67. Schöpf and Steuer, *Ann. Chem.*, **558**, 124 (1947).
68. Chatterjee, Bose, and Ghosh, *Tetrahedron*, **7**, 257 (1959).
69. Pachter and Suld, *J. Org. Chem.*, **25**, 1680 (1960).
70. Gopinath, Govindachari, and Rao, *Tetrahedron*, **8**, 293 (1960).
71. Pachter, Raffauf, Ullyot, and Ribeiro, *J. Am. Chem. Soc.*, **82**, 5187 (1960).
72. Pachter, Mohrbacher, and Zacharias, *J. Am. Chem. Soc.*, **83**, 635 (1961).
73. Mosher, Fuhrman, Buchwald, and Fischer, *Science*, **144**, 1100 (1964); see also Narahashi, Moore, and Scott, *J. Gen. Physiol.*, **47**, 965 (1964).
74. Yokoo, *J. Chem. Soc. Japan.*, **71**, 590 (1950).
75. Goto, Kishi, Takahashi, and Hirata, *Tetrahedron*, **21**, 2059 (1965), and references cited therein.
76. Tsuda, Ikuma, Kawamura, Tachikawa, Sakai, Tamura, and Amakasu, *Chem. Pharm. Bull. (Japan)*, **12**, 1357 (1964), and references cited therein.
77. Woodward, *Pure Appl. Chem.*, **9**, 49 (1964).
78. Tsuda, Ikuma, Kawamura, Tachikawa, Baba, and Miyadera, *Chem. Pharm. Bull. (Japan)*, **10**, 247, 856, 865 (1962).
79. Goto, Kishi, and Hirata, *Bull. Chem. Soc. Japan*, **35**, 1045 (1962).
80. Tomiie, Furusaki, Kasami, Yasuoka, Miyake, Haisa, and Nitta, *Tetrahedron Letters*, **1963**, 2101.
81. Goto, Kishi, Takahashi and Hirata, *Tetrahedron Letters*, **1963**, 2105.
82. Goto, Takahashi, Kishi, Hirata, Tomiie, and Nitta, *Tetrahedron Letters*, **1963**, 2115.
83. Magidson and Lŭ-Hua, *Zh. Obshch. Khim.*, **29**, 2843 (1959).
84. Lŭ-Hua and Magidson, *Zh. Obshch. Khim.*, **29**, 3299 (1959).
85. Jain and Narang, *Res. Bull. East Punjab Univ.*, (29), 51 (1953); *Chem. Abstr.*, **49**, 1063 (1955); Bami and Dhatt, *Current Sci. (India)*, **26**, 85 (1957); Rani, Vig, Gupta, and Narang, *J. Indian Chem. Soc.*, **30**, 331 (1953).
86. Basu, Dhatt, Prakash, Bami, and Singh, *J. Sci. Ind. Res. India*, **21C**, 245 (1962).
87. Dhatt and Bami, *J. Sci. Ind. Res. India*, **18C**, 256 (1959).
88. Chapman, Gibson, and Mann, *J. Chem. Soc.*, **1947**, 890.
89. Curd, Landquist, and Rose, *J. Chem. Soc.*, **1947**, 775.
90. Falco, Goodwin, Hitchings, Rollo, and Russell, *Brit. J. Pharmacol.*, **6**, 185 (1951).
91. Gujral, Saxena, and Tiwari, *Indian J. Med. Res.*, **43**, 637 (1955); *Chem. Abstr.*, **50**, 6662 (1956).
92. Prabhu, Browne, and Zaroslinski, *Arch. Intern. Pharmacodyn.*, **148**, 228 (1964); *Chem. Abstr.*, **60**, 15014 (1964).
93. Eberhardt, Freundt, and Langbein, *Arzneimittelforsch.*, **12**, 1087 (1962); *Chem. Abstr.*, **58**, 6647 (1963); Duchastel, *Union Med. Canada*, **91**, 288 (1962); *Chem. Abstr.*, **56**, 14894 (1962).

94. Boissier and Picard, *Therapie*, **15**, 57 (1960); *Chem. Abstr.*, **57**, 6564 (1962).
95. Klosa, *J. Prakt. Chem.*, **14**, 84 (1961).
96. Gujral, Sareen, and Kohli, *Indian J. Med. Res.*, **45**, 207 (1957); *Chem. Abstr.*, **51**, 15787 (1957).
97. Swift, Dickens, and Becker, *Arch. Intern. Pharmacodyn.*, **128**, 112 (1960).
98. Chappel and Seemann, in *Progress in Medicinal Chemistry* (Ed. Ellis and West), Butterworths, 1963, Ch. 3, p. 89; see also Wheeler, in *Medicinal Chemistry* (Ed. Campaigne and Hartung), Wiley, 1963, Vol. VI, p. 1.
99. Hoffmeister, *Arch. Intern. Pharmacodyn.*, **139**, 512 (1962); *Chem. Abstr.*, **58**, 10634 (1963).
100. Bough, Gurd, Hall, and Lessel, *Nature*, **200**, 656 (1963).
101. Boissier, Dumont, and Malen, *Therapie*, **13**, 30 (1958); *Chem. Abstr.*, **53**, 15365 (1959); Becker and Hays, *Proc. Soc. Exp. Biol. Med.*, **99**, 17 (1958); *Chem. Abstr.*, **53**, 3481 (1959); Gebler, *Pharmazie*, **17**, 616 (1962); *Chem. Abstr.*, **58**, 6109 (1963); Hays and Michelson, *U.S. Pat.*, 3,051,623 (1962); *Chem. Abstr.*, **58**, 1317 (1963); Andrisano and Chiesi, *Ateneo Parmense*, **32**, 671 (1961); *Chem. Abstr.*, **58**, 3428 (1963).
102. Ottaviano, *Boll. Soc. Ital. Biol. Sper.*, **39**, 1768 (1963); Saxena and Khanna, *Indian J. Med. Res.*, **46**, 63 (1958); *Chem. Abstr.*, **52**, 9432 (1958); Wallace and Tiernan Inc., *Brit. Pat.*, 914,630 (1963); *Chem. Abstr.*, **58**, 11176 (1963).
103. Boissier and Pagny, *Med. Exp.*, **1**, 368 (1959); *Chem. Abstr.*, **54**, 21460 (1960).
104. Malhotra, Kohli, Sareen, Kishore, Amma, and Gujral, *Indian J. Med. Sci.*, **14**, 501 (1960); *Chem. Abstr.*, **54**, 25282 (1960).
105. Cohen, Picard, and Boissier, *Arch. Intern. Pharmacodyn.*, **136**, 271 (1962); *Chem. Abstr.*, **57**, 3965 (1962).
106. Akagi, Oketani, and Takada, *Chem. Pharm. Bull. (Japan)*, **11**, 62 (1963); Nakano, *Yakuzaigaku*, **22**, 267 (1962); *Chem. Abstr.*, **59**, 6199 (1963); Nagase, Kanaya, and Hoshida, *Tokyo Yakka Daigaku Kenkyu Nempo*, **12**, 117 (1963); *Chem. Abstr.*, **59**, 6199 (1963).
107. Akagi, Oketani, and Yamane, *Chem. Pharm. Bull. (Japan)*, **11**, 1216 (1963).
108. Geldmacher-Mallinckrodt, and Lautenbach, *Arch. Toxikol.*, **20**, 31 (1963); *Chem. Abstr.*, **59**, 6885 (1963).
109. Bianchi and David, *J. Pharm. Pharmacol.*, **12**, 501 (1960).
110. Pala and Uberti, *Arzneimittelforsch.*, **12**, 1204 (1962); see however, Sandberg, *Svensk. Farm. Tidskr.*, **61**, 453 (1957); *Chem. Abstr.*, **51**, 16940 (1957); and Khanna and Dhar, *J. Sci. Ind. Res. India*, **21B**, 378 (1962).
111. Toyoshima, Shimada, Hamano, and Ogo, *J. Pharm. Soc. Japan*, **85**, 502 (1965).
112. Danielsson and Skoglund, *Acta Pharm. Suecica*, **2**, 167 (1965); see also Danielsson, *Acta Pharm. Suecica*, **2**, 149 (1965).
113. Fujimori and Cobb, *J. Pharmacol. Exp. Therap.*, **148**, 151 (1965); see also Wenzel, *J. Am. Pharm. Assoc.*, **44**, 550 (1955); Hayao, Havera, Strycker, Leipzig, Kulp, and Hartzler, *J. Med. Chem.*, **8**, 807 (1965).
114. Valenti, *Biochim. Terap. Sper.*, **17**, 84 (1930); *Chem. Abstr.*, **24**, 2804 (1930).
115. Schuler and Meier, *Helv. Physiol. Pharmacol. Acta*, **13**, 106 (1955); *Chem. Abstr.*, **50**, 481 (1956).
116. Kumada, Watanabe, Yamamoto, and Zenno, *Yakugaku Kenkyo*, **30**, 635 (1958); *Chem. Abstr.*, **53**, 20554 (1959).

117. Schuler and Wyss, *Arch. Intern. Pharmacodyn.*, **128**, 431 (1960); Druey and Marxer, *J. Med. Pharm. Chem.*, **1**, 1 (1959); Werle, Schauer, and Hartung, *Klin. Wochschr.*, **33**, 562 (1955); *Chem. Abstr.*, **49**, 13516 (1955).

118. Chapman, Clarke, and Wilson, *J. Chem. Soc.*, **1963**, 2256; Graham, *Arch. Intern. Pharmacodyn.*, **123**, 419 (1960).

119. Muačević, Stötzer, and Wick, *Arzneimittelforsch.*, **15**, 613 (1965).

120. Hallesy and Benitz, *Arzneimittelforsch.*, **13**, 665 (1963); Krück, *Arzneimittelforsch*, **13**, 673 (1963); Cohen, Klarberg, and Vaughan, Jr., *J. Am. Chem. Soc.*, **82**, 2731 (1960).

121. Frank, Dentler, and Berg, *Arzneimittelforsch.*, **13**, 676 (1963).

122. Seller, Fuchs, Onesti, Swartz, Brest, and Moyer, *Clin. Pharmacol. Therap.*, **3**, 180 (1960); *Chem. Abstr.*, **56**, 14892 (1962).

123. Cohen, Klarberg, and Vaughan, Jr., *J. Am. Chem. Soc.*, **81**, 5508 (1959).

124. Oakes, Rydon, and Undheim, *J. Chem. Soc.*, **1962**, 4678.

125. Martin, Moss, and Avakian, *J. Biol. Chem.*, **167**, 737 (1947).

126. Koehler, Goodman, DeGraw, and Baker, *J. Am. Chem. Soc.*, **80**, 5779 (1958); DeGraw, Goodman, Koehler, and Baker, *J. Org. Chem.*, **24**, 1632 (1959); DeGraw, Goodman, and Baker, *J. Org. Chem.*, **26**, 1156 (1961).

127. DeGraw, Goodman, Weinstein, and Baker, *J. Org. Chem.*, **27**, 576 (1962).

128. Modest, Chatterjee, Foley, and Farber, *Acta Unio Intern. Contra Cancrum*, **20**, 112 (1964).

129. Lehr-Splawinski, *Zeszyty Nauk. Uniw. Jagiel.*, *Ser. Nauk Mat.-Przyrod.*, *Mat.*, *Fiz.*, *Chem.*, **(6)**, 53 (1959); *Chem. Abstr.*, **55**, 3602 (1961).

130. Gysin and Knüsli, *Ger. Pat.*, 1,035,398 (1958); *Chem. Abstr.*, **54**, 25543 (1960); *Brit. Pat.*, 822,069 (1959); *Chem. Abstr.*, **55**, 2005 (1961).

131. Partridge, Slorach, and Vipond, *J. Chem. Soc.*, **1964**, 3670, and references cited therein.

132. Baldwin, Cunningham, Davey, Partridge, and Vipond, *Brit. J. Cancer*, **17**, 266 (1963).

133. Baldwin, Palmer, and Partridge, *Brit. J. Cancer*, **16**, 740 (1962); Baldwin, Cunningham, Partridge, and Vipond, *Brit. J. Cancer*, **16**, 275 (1962); Baldwin, Cunningham, Dean, Partridge, Surtees, and Vipond, *Biochem. Pharmacol.*, **14**, 323 (1965), and references cited therein.

134. Saxena and Singh, *J. Sci. Ind. Res. (India)*, **19C**, 293 (1960); Kaushiva, *Ann. Biochem. Exp. Med. (Calcutta)*, Suppl. **20**, 493 (1960); *Chem. Abstr.*, **58**, 8254 (1963); Sachdev, Dhami, and Atwal, *Tetrahedron*, **14**, 304 (1961); Curd and Young, *U.S. Pat.*, 2,643,253 (1953); *Chem. Abstr.*, **49**, 384 (1955); Sen and Singh, *J. Indian Chem. Soc.*, **42**, 409 (1965).

135. Berg, *J. Chem. Soc.*, **1961**, 4041.

136. Berg and Lucas, *Nature*, **189**, 64 (1961).

137. Neipp, Kunz, and Meier, *Schweiz Z. Allgem. Pathol. Bakteriol.*, **19**, 331 (1956); *Chem. Abstr.*, **50**, 15700 (1956); Martin, Wheeler, Majewski, and Corrigan, *J. Med. Chem.*, **7**, 812 (1964); Ciba Ltd., *Brit. Pat.*, 664,262 (1952); *Chem. Abstr.*, **47**, 617 (1953); Asano and Asai, *J. Pharm. Soc. Japan*, **78**, 450 (1958); Taniyama, Yasui, Uchida, and Okuda, *J. Pharm. Soc. Japan*, **81**, 431 (1961); Hu and Liu, *Yao Hsüeh Hsüeh Pao*, **7**, 109 (1959); *Chem. Abstr.*, **54**, 759 (1960); Hunter and Nathan, *U.S. Pat.*, 2,425,326 (1947); *Chem. Abstr.*, **41**, 6673 (1947); Okabayashi and Makisumi, *Chem. Pharm. Bull. (Japan)*, **8**, 1095 (1960).

138. Brown, *J. Chem. Soc.*, **1964**, 3012; Thayer, Gravatt, Magnuson, and McKee, *Antibiot. Chemotherapy*, **2**, 463 (1952); *Chem. Abstr.*, **47**, 7099 (1953); Doub, Richardson, and Campbell, *Ger. Pat.*, 1,139,124 (1962); *Chem. Abstr.*, **58**, 9100 (1963).

139. Libermann and Boyer, *Compt. Rend.*, **227**, 377 (1948); Libermann, *U.S. Pat.*, 2,522,831 (1950); *Chem. Abstr.*, **45**, 312 (1951); Gut, Morávek, Párkányi, Prystaš, Škoda, and Šorm, *Collection Czech. Chem. Commun.*, **24**, 3154 (1959).

140. Gupta, Khan, and Agarwal, *J. Sci. Ind. Res. India*, **21C**, 189 (1962); Agarwal, Gupta, Khan, Clifford, and Chandra, *J. Sci. Ind. Res. India*, **21C**, 309 (1962); Gupta, Agarwal, and Khan, *Indian J. Exp. Biol.*, **1**, 61 (1963); *Chem. Abstr.*, **58**, 14477 (1963).

141. Weinstein, Chang, and Hudson, *Antibiot. Chemotherapy*, **7**, 443 (1957); *Chem. Abstr.*, **52**, 4834 (1958).

142. Hartmann, Portela, and Cardeza, *Rev. Soc. Argentina Biol.*, **30**, 87 (1954); *Chem. Abstr.*, **49**, 2612 (1955); see also Yale, *J. Am. Chem. Soc.*, **75**, 675 (1953); and Krumm-Heller and Fombelle, *Compt. Rend. Soc. Biol.*, **144**, 650 (1950); *Chem. Abstr.*, **45**, 1241 (1951).

143. Jensen, Kjerulf-Jensen, *Acta Pharmacol. Toxicol.*, **1**, 280 (1945); *Chem. Abstr.*, **40**, 7386 (1946).

144. Perlman and Barrett, *Can. J. Microbiol.*, **4**, 9 (1958); Perlman, *U.S. Pat.*, 2,872,443 (1959); *Chem. Abstr.*, **53**, 12321 (1959); Perlman, *U.S. Pat.*, 2,995,498 (1957); *Chem. Abstr.*, **56**, 3926 (1962); Ford and Hutner, *Can. J. Microbiol.*, **3**, 319 (1957).

145. Haley, Flesher, and Mavis, *Nature*, **195**, 1012 (1962); Haley, *Giorn. Ital. Chemioterap.*, **6–9**, 213 (1962); *Chem. Abstr.*, **58**, 12847 (1963).

Subject Index

2-Acetamido-8-acetoxy-6-acetoxy-
methylquinazoline 504
2-Acetamido-8-acetoxy-6-methyl-
quinazoline 504
2-Acetamido-7-chloro-5-phenyl-3H-1,
4-benzodiazepin-3-one, ring contraction 476
2-Acetamido-5-methoxytoluene, nitration 240
4-Acetamido-6-nitroquinazoline 334
4-Acetamido-7-nitroquinazoline 334
4-p-Acetamidophenylsulphonamido-2-
methoxyquinazoline 328
2,4-bisAcetamidoquinazoline 334
2-Acetonylidene-1,2,3,4-tetrahydro-4-
oxo-1-phenylquinazoline 109
8-Acetoxy-6-acetoxymethyl-2-N-
deuteroacetamidoquinazoline 504
8-Acetoxy-6-acetoxymethyl-2-N-
deuteroacetamido-5,7-dideutero-
quinazoline 504
8-Acetoxy-6-acetoxymethyl-5-deutero-
2-N-deuteroacetamidoquinazoline
504
8-Acetoxy-6-acetoxymethyl-7-
deutero-2-N-deuteroacetamido-
quinazoline 504
2-Acetoxy-6-acylcyclohexa-3,5-dien-1-
ones 325
2,4-bis-N-Acetylanilinoquinazolines
334
1-Acylindazoles 446
4-Alkoxy-2-anilinoquinazolines 239,
323
4-Alkoxy-2-chloroquinazolines 220,
239, 244
4-Alkoxy-2-cyanoquinazolines 239
4-Alkoxy-1,2-dihydro-1-hydroxy-
2-oxoquinazolines 446, 457,
458
4-Alkoxy-1,2-dihydro-2-oxoquinazo-
lines 238
2-Alkoxy-3,4-dihydro-4-oxoquinazo-
lines 242
4-Alkoxy-2-methylquinazolines
238
4-Alkoxy-2-phenylquinazolines 238
2-Alkoxyquinazolines 235
4-Alkoxyquinazolines 237, 238
oxidation of 446
4-Alkylamino-2-arylaminoquinazolines
331
4-Alkylamino-2-2'-thiazolylamino-
quinazolines 331
4-Alkylaminoquinazolines 328
hydrolysis of 333
2-Alkyl-3-aryl-3,4-dihydro-4-oxo-
quinazolines 85
hypnotic activity 509
4-N'-Alkyl-2'-dialkylaminoethyl-
aminoquinazolines, antihistamine
activity 510
1-Alkyl-3,4-dihydro-6-methyl-3-p-
tolylquinazolinium salts, hypotensive activity 510
Alkylquinazolines 39–49, 50–60
alkylation of 56
phthalones of 51

Alkylquinazolines, *contd.*
  physical properties 49–50
  reactivity of 2- and 4-alkyl groups
    50–54, 58–60
3-Alkylquinazolinium salts 398
2-Alkylthio-1,4-dihydro-4-oxoquin-
    azolines, 1-substituted 286
2-Alkylthio-3,4-dihydro-4-oxoquin-
    azolines, desulphurization 287
  3-substituted 286
2-Alkylthio-3,4-dihydro-4-thioquin-
    azolines 285
4-Alkylthioquinazolines 280
  hydrolysis 282
  methylation 283
  properties 282
8-Allyloxyquinazoline, Claisen re-
    arrangement 134, 245
6-*m*-Amidinophenyldiazoamino-4-
    amino-1,2-dimethylquinazo-
    linium chloride, hydrochloride,
    protozoan activity 512
6-*p*-Amidinophenyldiazoamino-4-
    amino-1,2-dimethylquinazolinium
    chloride, hydrochloride, protozoan
    activity 512
2-Aminoquinazoline 322–324, 327
  6-chloro-4-methyl- 324
  5,6-dihydroxy- 508
  hydrolysis 333
  5-hydroxy- 325
  6-hydroxy- 504
  8-hydroxy-6-hydroxymethyl- 504,
    508
  6-hydroxy-4-methyl- 324
  6-hydroxymethyl-8-methoxy- 324
  ionization 332
  5-, 6-, 7-, and 8-methoxy- 324
  8-methoxy-5-methyl- 324
  8-methoxy-6-methyl- 324
  8-methoxy-7-methyl- 324
  6-methyl- 504
  pH-rate prophile 25
2-Aminoquinazolines 322, 324
  hydrolysis 333
  properties 332
4-Aminoquinazoline 327, 328, 330
  acetylation 334
  alkylation of 6-nitro- 334

2-(2'-amino-5'-nitro)phenyl-6-nitro-
    329
  6-bromo-2-*p*-nitrophenyl- 329
  2-chloro- 330
  1,2-dihydro-2-oxo- 327
  2-hydrazino- 330
  hydrolysis of 333
  ionization 332
  ionization of 6-nitro- 332
  2-methyl- 329
  2-methylthio- 284, 328
  methylation of 6-nitro- 334
  methylation of 7-nitro- 334
  6-nitro-2-*p*-nitrophenyl- 329
  2-*p*-nitrophenyl- 329
  2-phenyl- 327, 329
  properties 332
  ultraviolet spectra 332
4-ω-Aminoalkyloxyquinazolines
    237
4-Amino-2-anilino-6-methylquinazo-
    line 330
2-Amino-4-carboxyquinazoline 327
4-Amino-2-chloroquinazoline 221
2-Amino-6-*p*-(1,3-dicarboxypropyl-
    carbamoyl)anilinomethyl-3,4,5,6,
    7,8-hexahydro-4-oxoquinazoline,
    growth activity 511
2-Amino-1,4-dihydro-1-hydroxy-4-
    oxoquinazoline 458
2-Amino-3,4-dihydro-4-oxoquinazoline
    323
  3-benzyl- 335
  3-ethyl- 335
  3-*p*-methoxyphenyl- 335
  3-methyl- 334
  methylation 334
  3-phenyl- 335
  3-propyl- 335
  rearrangement 335
  ultraviolet spectrum 333
2-Amino-3,4-dihydro-4-oxoquinazo-
    lines 322–326
  3-alkyl- 326
  3-aryl- 326
  substituted 325
  3-substituted 326
2-Amino-3,4-dihydro-4-oxoquinazo-
    line-1-oxide, reduction 327

3-Amino-3,4-dihydro-4-oxoquinazoline 337–339
2(N'-3'-amino-3',4'-dihydro-4'-oxoquinazolin-2'-ylcarbonyl-hydrazinocarbonyl)- 476
deamination of 340
2-ethoxycarbonyl- 476
2-hydrazinocarbonyl- 476
2-1'-hydroxyalkyl- 340
2,6,7-trimethyl- 338
4-2'-Aminoethylquinazolines, ionization of 332
7-Amino-6-methoxyquinazoline 361
2-Amino-5-nitrobenzonitrile, dimerization of 329
3-o-Aminophenyl-4,5-dihydro-4-phenyl-5-thio-1,2,4(1-H)triazine 337
Aminoquinazolines, antibacterial activity 512
ionization of 5-, 6-, 7-, and 8-amino- 341
syntheses of 5-, 6-, 7-, and 8-amino- 341
ultraviolet spectra of 5-, 6-, 7-, and 8-amino 341
2-Aminoquinazoline-3-oxide 451
reduction of 327, 451
2-Amino-5,6,7,8-tetrahydroquinazoline 410
dehydrogenation 327, 412
4-Anilinoquinazolines 327-328
ionization of 332
2-Anilino-4,5-benzo-4-oxo-1,3-thiazine 287
2-Anilino-7,8-benzo-4-p-chloroanilinoquinazoline 331
2-Anilino-4-benzyloxyquinazoline 243
2-Anilino-3,4-dihydro-4-oxoquinazolines 326, 335
methylation 334
3-methyl- 334
3-phenyl- 334
4-Anilino-1,2-dihydro-2-oxoquinazolines 330
2-Anilino-4-2'-hydroxyethoxyquinazoline 244
4-Anilino-2-methylthioquinazoline 284

4-Anilino-8-methyl-2-o-toluidino-quinazoline 331
4-Anilinoquinazoline 328
hydrolysis 333
Arborine 490
2-Arylamino-4-chloroquinazolines 331
4-Aryloxyquinazolines 237
Arylquinazolines 39–60
physical properties 49–50
4-Arylsulphonylquinazolines 283
4-Arylthioquinazolines 281, 283
4-Azidotetrazolo(4,5-a)quinazoline 331, 337

Bechmann rearrangement 90, 96, 97, 128
Benzo-1,3-diazine 2
7,8-Benzo-2,3-dihydro-2-hydroxy-3-1'-naphthyl-2,4-diphenylquinazoline 395
7,8-Benzo-5,6-dihydroquinazoline 413
Benzo-4,1-oxazepines,1,3-disubstituted 100
Benzoxazepines, structure 450
4,1-Benzoxazepin-2,5-diones 340
12H-Benzoxazolo(2,3-b)quinazolin-2-one 128
3,1,4-Benzoxazones 83, 84
2-o-phenyl- derivatives 85
2-substituted derivatives 97
5,6-Benzopyrimidine 2
Benzothiazin-3,1,4-thiones 279
2-Benzoyl-4-isopropylquinazoline 45
3-Benzyldecahydro-2-oxoquinazoline 413
Benzyleneamidine 2
3-Benzyl-2,3,5,6,7,8-hexahydro-2-oxoquinazoline 413
4-(1'-Benzyloxy-1'-methyl)ethyl-quinazoline-1-oxide 449
Biginelli synthesis 413
2,2'-Biquinazolinyl 40
4,4'-Biquinazolinyl 36
Bischler synthesis 13, 39–41, 70, 133, 241, 400, 480
Bromoanhydrotetrodoic lactone hydrobromide 506

2-Bromo-7-methoxytropones, reaction
with substituted guanidines 326
3-*p*-Bromophenyl-3,4-dihydro-2-
methyl-4-oxoquinazoline, anticonvulsant activity 509
1-oxide 447
4-Bromo-2-phenylquinazoline 225,
327, 473
4-Butylaminoquinazoline 328
hydrolysis 333

2-Carbamoylquinazoline 474, 475
4-methyl- 474
4-Carbamoylquinazoline 473
2,6-dimethyl- 478
6-fluoro-2-methyl- 478
2-methyl- 478
2,4-bisCarboxyanilinoquinazolines
330
3-*o*-Carboxyanilino-4,5-benzo-1,2-
thiazole 1,1-dioxide 90
4-Carboxydecahydro-2-oxoquinazoline
413
3-Carboxymethyl-6,8-dichloro-3,4-
dihydro-2-methyl-4-oxoquinazo-
line, plant growth regulating
activity 512
4-Carboxy-1,2,5,6,7,8,9,10-octahydro-
2-oxoquinazoline 413
2-Carboxyquinazoline 475
decarboxylation 477
4-phenyl- 477
4-Carboxyquinazoline 478
2-Amino- 478
2-*o*-carboxyphenyl- 478
1,2-dihydro-2-oxo- 478
2,6-dimethyl- 478
2-ethyl-6-methyl- 478
2-*o*-hydroxyphenyl- 478
2-*p*-hydroxyphenyl- 478
2-methoxy- 478
2-methyl- 478
6-methyl-2-phenyl- 478
2-*o*-nitrophenyl- 478
2-phenyl- 478
4-Carboxyquinazolines 478
decarboxylation 42, 479
esterification 479
Chapman rearrangement 101

4-Chloroalkoxy-2-chloroquinazolines
221
2-*p*-Chloroanilinoquinazoline,
4-2′-diethylaminoethylamino-
331, 335
4-ethoxy- 331
4-2′-hydroxyethylamino- 335
4-methylthio- 331
4-phenoxy- 331
2,4-bis-*p*-Chloroanilinoquinazoline
335
6-Chloro-3-*p*-chlorophenyl-2,3-
dihydro-2-hydroxy-2,4-diphenyl-
quinazoline 395
6-Chloro-3,4-dihydro-3-hydroxy-4-
oxoquinazoline 460
7-Chloro-1,3-dihydro-3-hydroxy-5-
phenyl-2*H*-1,4-benzodiazepin-2-
one, ring contraction 477, 480
6-Chloro-2,3-dihydro-3-methyl-2-
oxo-4-phenylquinazoline 72
methanol and water addition reactions 73
6-Chloro-1,2-dihydro-3-methyl-4-
phenyl-2-thioquinazoline, hydration equilibrium 274
infrared spectrum of hydrochloride
275
2-Chloro-3,4-dihydro-4-oxoquinazo-
line 222, 323, 327
3-2′-chloroethyl- 244
3-2′-chloroisopropyl- 244
3-*p*-chlorophenyl- 222
3-2′-chloropropyl- 244
3-2′-dimethylaminoethyl- 244
3-phenyl- 222
3-substituted derivatives 221
3-*o*-tolyl- 222
6-Chloro-4-(*N*-ethyl-*N*-2′-chloroethyl)
aminoquinazoline 227
intramolecular alkylation 335
6-Chloro-2-ethyl-3,4-dihydro-4-oxo-
3-*p*-pyrimidin-2′-ylsulphamoyl-
phenylquinazoline, antimalarial
activity 508
9-Chloro-1-ethyl-2,3-dihydroimidazo-
(3,2-c)quinazolinium chloride 335
2-Chloro-4-ethylquinazoline, plant
growth regulator 512

7-Chloro-2-ethyl-1,2,3,4-tetrahydro-4-
   oxo-6-sylphamoylquinazoline,
   diuretic activity 510
7-chloro-2-methylamino-5-phenyl-
   3H-1,4-benzodiazepin-4-oxide
   455
7-Chloro-5-phenyl-3,1,4-benzoxadia-
   zepin-2(1-H)-one 128
7-chloro-5-phenyl-1,3-dihydro-2H-
   1,4-benzodiazepin-2-one
   4-oxide 452
2-Chloroquinazoline 219
   4-Benzyloxy- 220, 244
   4-2'-chloroethoxy- 244
   4-p-chlorophenylthio- 281
   4-2'-chloropropoxy- 244
   4-(α-cyano-α-ethoxycarbonyl)-
      methyl- 59, 221
   4-ethoxy- 219, 221, 222, 244
   4-2'-diethylaminoethoxy- 244
   4-2'-hydroxyethoxy- 244
   4-m-hydroxyphenyl- 221
   4-3'-hydroxypropoxy- 244
   4-isopropyl- 219
   kinetics of nucleophilic substitution
      228
   metathesis 230
   4-methoxy- 219, 231
   4-methyl- 219, 322
   6-methyl-4-phenyl- 219
   4-phenoxy- 221, 323
   4-phenyl- 49, 219, 231
   4-2'-pyridyl- 48, 219, 231
   reduction 231, 399
   4-2',4'-xylyl- 219
2-Chloroquinazolines 219
   4-phenoxy- derivatives 323
4-Chloroquinazoline 222
   5,6-benzo- 224
   catalytic reduction 231
   2-o-chlorophenyl- 222
   2-1',1'-dichloroethyl- 224
   2-diethylamino- 226, 322
   2-2'-furyl- 222
   hydrolysis 229
   kinetics of nucleophilic substitution
      228
   metathesis 230
   6-methoxy- 224

2-methyl- 224
6-methyl- 224
7-methyl- 224
5-nitro- 224, 279
6-nitro- 229
7-nitro- 229
2-o-nitrophenyl- 224
2-phenethyl- 222
2-phenyl- 222
purification of 223
reaction with methanol 229
reaction with Grignard reagents 44
reduction 399
2-substituted derivatives 222
2-trichloromethyl- 224, 226
4-Chloroquinazolines, catalytic
   reduction 231
   purification 223
Chloroquinazolines, dehalogenation
   233
   for dyestuffs 234
   for surface-active compounds 234
   non-reductive dehalogenation 234
Cinnoline 233
Cobalamine activity of quinazoline derivatives 513
Covalent hydration, in benz-substituted
   quinazolines 29–32
   in quinazoline 19–27
   in 2-substituted quinazolines 28–29
   in 4-substituted quinazolines 27–28
Curtius rearrangement 123
1-Cyanoindazole 450
1-Cyano-2-isobutoxycyclohex-1-ene
   411
2-Cyano-4-isopropylquinazoline 449,
   474
   reaction with Grignard reagents 45,
      475
2-Cyanoquinazoline 474, 475
   4-benzyloxy- 474
   4-ethoxy- 474
   hydrolysis 475
   4-methoxy- 474
   4-phenoxy- 474
   4-propoxy- 474
4-Cyanoquinazoline 473–475
   hydrolysis 475
   oxidation of 3,4-dihydro- 473

4-Cyanoquinazoline, *contd.*
 2-phenyl- 473
 reaction with Grignard reagents
  44–45

Desoxyvasicine 492, 493
4-Deuteroquinazoline, mass spectrum
  19
 proton magnetic resonance spectrum
  17
 synthesis 13
2,4-Dialkoxyquinazolines 239
1,3-Dialkyl-4-oxoquinazolinium salts
  105
1,3-Dialkyl-1,2,3,4-tetrahydro-2,4-
  dioxoquinazolines 244
2,4-Diamino-6-*p*-carboxyanilino-
  methylquinazoline, growth factor
  510
2,4-Diamino-6-*p*-(1,3-dicarboxy-
  propylcarbamoyl)aminomethyl-
  5,6,7,8-tetrahydroquinazoline,
  growth factor 511
2,4-Diamino-5,6-dihydroquinazolines,
  growth inhibitory properties
  511
2,4-Diaminoquinazoline 330, 331
 benzoylation of 6-methyl- 334
 6-butyl- 332
 6,7-dimethyl- 330
 6,8-dimethyl- 330
 5-ethyl- 332
 6-ethyl- 330
 hydrolysis 333
 5-isopropyl-8-methyl- 330
 5-methyl- 332
 6-methyl- 330, 333
 properties 332
 6-propyl- 332
 5,6-tetramethylene- 332
 5,6,8-trimethyl- 332
 5,6-trimethylene- 332
 transamination 335
2,4-Dianilinoquinazolines 330, 331
 hydrolysis 330, 334
 6-methyl- 330
2,4-Diarylaminoquinazolines 331
2,4-Diarylthioquinazolines 285
1,3-Diazanaphthalene 2

2,4-Dibenzamido-6-methylquinazoline
  334
2,4-Dibenzyl-5,8-dimethylquinazoline
  44
4-*p*-[*l*(+)-1,3-dicarboxypropyl-
  carbamoyl]anilinoquinazoline,
  growth factor 511
2,4-Di-*p*-chlorophenylthioquinazoline
  281
2,4-Dichloroquinazoline 225
 metathesis 230
 reaction with Grignard reagents 45
 reduction 231
2,4-Dichloroquinazolines 225
1,2-Di-(2'-Chloroquinazolin-4'-
  yloxy)ethane 221
1,3-Dichloro-1,2,3,4-tetrahydro-2,4-
  dioxoquinazoline 226
 bleaching action 235
α-, β-, and γ-Dichroines 496
Di-3,4-dihydro-4-quinazolinyl 32
2,4-Diethoxyquinazoline 239
4-(4'-Diethylamino-1'-methyl)butyl-
  aminoquinazoline, antimalarial
  activity 509
2,4-Di-2'-diethylaminoethoxyquinazo-
  line 244
4-Diethylaminoquinazoline, hydrolysis
  333
 plant growth regulator 512
2,4-bisDiethylaminoquinazoline, as
  plant growth regulator 512
2,4-Dihydrazinoquinazoline 330,
  337
1,4-Dihydro-2-(1',4'-dihydro-1',2'-
  dimethyl-4'-oxo-2'-quinolinyl)-1-
  methyl-4-oxoquinazoline 102
3,4-Dihydro-2-(2',4'-dihydroxy-3'-
  quinolinyl)-4-oxoquinazoline 82
1,2-Dihydro-2-2-dimethyl-4-methyl-
  thioquinazoline 402
3,4-Dihydro-1,3-dimethyl-4-oxo-
  quinazolinium iodide 242, 279
3,4-Dihydro-1,3-dimethyl-4-thio-
  quinazolinium iodide 279, 281
3,4-Dihydro-1-ethyl-3-methyl-4-oxo-
  quinazolinium iodide 242
2,3-Dihydro-2-hydroxy-2,4-diphenyl-
  3-*p*-tolylquinazoline 395

2,3-Dihydro-3-hydroxy-4-methyl-2-
  oxoquinazoline 459
1,4-Dihydro-1-hydroxy-4-oxoquinazo-
  line 448, 458
  tautomerism 446, 458
3,4-Dihydro-8-hydroxy-4-oxoquinazo-
  lines, 2-, and 2,3-substituted
  derivatives 115
3,4-Dihydro-3-hydroxy-4-oxoquinazo-
  line 453, 459
  infrared spectrum 459
  3-methyl- 458
  protection from radiation damage
    513
  tautomerism 459
1,4-Dihydro-1-hydroxy-4-oxoquinazo-
  line-3-oxide 459
1,4-Dihydro-1-methyl-4-(β-methyl-
  β(3-methyl-5-oxo-1-phenyl-
  pyrazolin-4-ylidene)ethylidene)-
  quinazoline 58
3,4-Dihydro-2-methyl-4-oxo-3,3′-
  piperidinopropylquinazoline,
  hydrolysis of 110
2,3-Dihydro-3-methyl-2-oxoquinazo-
  line 72
1,4-Dihydro-1-methyl-4-oxoquinazo-
  lines 99, 243, 491
1,2-Dihydro-3-methyl-2-oxoquinazo-
  linium iodide 73
1,2-Dihydro-4-methyl-2-oxoquinazo-
  line-3-oxide 459
1,4-Dihydro-2-methyl-4-oxoquinazo-
  lines, 1-substituted derivatives
    100
3,4-Dihydro-2-methyl-4-oxoquinazo-
  line 55, 75, 81, 82, 94
  3-acetamido-7-nitro- 339
  5-acetamido-7-nitro-4-phenyl-
    hydrazono- derivative 339
  3-amino- 112
  3-aminomethyl- 114
  3-o-benzimidazol-2′-ylphenyl- 97
  3-benzoylmethyl- 106
  3-benzyl- 86, 480
  5-carboxy- 479
  7-carboxy- 54
  5-carboxy-3-phenyl- 80, 479
  chlorination 226

7-chloro-6-sulphamoyl- 98
5-cyano- 474
7-cyano- 474
6,7-dimethoxy- 240
7,8-dimethoxy- 240
6-ethoxy- 240
8-ethoxy- 240
3-ethoxycarbonylmethyl- 86
3-ethyl-5-nitro- 244
7-hydroxy- 134
3-o-hydroxymethylphenyl- 509
6-methoxy- 240
8-methoxy- 240
3-methyl- 79
6,7-methylenedioxy- 240
3-methyl-5-nitro- 104
3-methyl-8-nitro- 79
3-2′-naphthyl- 91
nitration 55
5-nitro- 84
6-nitro- 78, 80
7-nitro- 78, 105
8-nitro- 79
5-nitro-3-substituted derivatives
  84
oxidation 110
3-phenyl- 88, 92, 93
phthalone derivatives 108
3-piperidinomethyl- 114
3-o-tolyl- 98, 110
3-p-tolyl- 91
3-xanthhydryl- 106
3,4-Dihydro-3-methyl-4-oxoquinazo-
  line 87, 96, 114
  2-anilino- 336
  8-bromoacetyl- 480
  chlorination 224
  2-(3′,4′-dihydro-3′-oxoquinoxalin-
    2′-yl)methyl- 109
  2-ethoxalylmethyl- 109
  2-ethyl-5-nitro- 104
  hydrolysis of 110
  ionization 104
  7-nitro- 75, 111
  8-nitro- 104
  reduction 110
3,4-Dihydro-2-methyl-4-oxo-3-o-
  tolylquinazoline, hypnotic activity 509

3,4-Dihydro-2-methyl-4-oxo-3-*o*-
    tolylquinazoline, *contd.*
  1-oxide 447
3,4-Dihydro-2-methyl-4-oxo-3-*o*-
    tolylquinazoline 2-^{14}C 94
2-(3'-(1,2-Dihydro-1-methyl-4-
    phenylquinazolin-2-ylidene)-
    prop-1'-enyl)1-methyl-4-phenyl-
    quinazolinium iodide 58
1,2-Dihydro-3-methylquinazolinium
    salts, oxidation of 96
3,4-Dihydro-2-methyl-4-selenoquinazo-
    line 278
3,4-Dihydro-2-methyl-4-thioquinazo-
    line, goitrogenic activity 513
3,4-Dihydro-4-oxo-2,6-diphenyl-
    pyrimidine 97
1,2-Dihydro-2-oxo-5-phenyl-3*H*-
    1,4-benzodiazepin-4-oxides 456
3,4-Dihydro-4-oxo-2-phenylquinazo-
    line 75, 79, 80, 82, 85, 91, 94–98
  3-acetyl- 95
  3-aryl-7-nitro- 86
  3-benzamido- 340
  6,7-benzo- 95
  7,8-benzo- 95
  5,7-dihydroxy- 134
  3-*o*-methoxyphenyl- 89
  3-*p*-methoxyphenyl- 89
  3-methyl- 79
  3-2'-naphthyl- 79, 89
  7-nitro- 82
  3-phenyl- 79, 80, 88, 89, 91
  salts 76
  3-*m*-tolyl- 79, 89
  3-2',4'-xylyl- 89
3,4-Dihydro-4-oxo-3-3'-piperidino-
    propylquinazoline, hydrolysis of
    110
1,2-Dihydro-2-oxoquinazoline 70
  4-alkoxy- 448
  4-anilino- 329, 334
  5,6-benzo-4-methyl- 72
  1-benzoyl-6-methyl-4-phenyl- 73
  4-carboxy- 71
  covalent hydration 73
  4-ethoxy- 72
  infrared spectrum 72
  ionization 72

  4-isopropyl- 71, 447, 449
  8-methoxy- 70
  4-methyl- 70, 224
  methylation 73
  6-methyl-4-phenyl- 70
  4-2'-pyridyl- 70
  4-*p*-tolyl- 70
  ultraviolet spectrum 73
  4-2',4'-xylyl- 70
1,2-Dihydro-2-oxoquinazolines,
    methylation 73
  nomenclature 69
  syntheses 69–72
  tautomerism 73
2,3-Dihydro-2-oxoquinazolines
  3-alkyl- 398
  3-aryl- 398
1,4-Dihydro-4-oxoquinazoline, 1-
    benzyl-6-chloro- 100
  2-benzyl-1-methyl- 104, 491
  2-*p*-*N*-β-chloroethyl-*N*-methyl-
    aminostyryl-1-methyl- 107
  1-*p*-chlorophenyl- 100
  1-*p*-chlorophenyl-2-phenyl- 101
  1,2-dimethyl- 99, 102
  1,2-diphenyl- 101
  1-*p*-fluorophenyl-2-phenyl- 101
  2-1'-hydroxyethyl-1-methyl- 100
  2-hydroxymethyl-1-methyl- 100
  1-*p*-methoxyphenyl-2-phenyl- 101
  1-methyl- 100, 104, 402, 491
1,4-Dihydro-4-oxoquinazolines, prepar-
    ation of 99–102
3,4-Dihydro-4-oxoquinazoline (*mono-
    substituted*) 74, 75, 80, 83
  6-, and 7-acetamido- 341
  3-acetyl- 106
  2-alkylamino- derivatives 323–326
  alkylation 104
  3-allyl- 87, 98, 115
  2-amino- 116
  5-, 6-, 7-, and 8-amino- 340, 341
  2-*o*-aminobenzoylmethyl- 82
  2-(2'-amino-4'-hydroxy-3'-quinolyl)-
    92
  3-aminomethyl- 114
  2-*o*-aminophenyl- 97
  3-*p*-aminophenyl- 115
  2-anilino- 326, 335

3,4-Dihydro-4-oxoquinazoline (*mono-substituted*), *contd.*
2-*p*-anisidino- 335
2-arylamino- 323, 326
5,6-benzo- 95
6,7-benzo- 393
2-benzyl- 82, 94, 104, 492
6-bromo- 80
6-bromo-3-*p*-bromophenyl- 397
3-(4'-bromo-2'-methyl)phenyl- 98
3-*p*-bromophenyl- 88, 96
2-butoxy- 236
3-butyl- 87, 112
carboxy- 475, 476, 479
2-carboxyethenyl- 109
3-carboxymethyl- 492
2-carboxymethylamino- 323
3-*o*-carboxyphenyl- 87
3-*p*-carboxyphenyl- 96
chlorination 112
6-chloro- 460
2-*p*-chlorobenzyl- 82
6-chlorocarbonyl- 479
3-2'-chloroethyl- 76
3-(5'-chloro-2'-oxo)pentyl- 106
3-*p*-chlorophenyl- 96
2-*p*-chlorophenylthio- 287
chlorosulphonation 111, 480
2-cyano- 1, 116, 473
3-2'-cyanoethyl- 106
3-cyanomethyl- 86
3-cyclohexyl- 87
2-2'-diethylaminoethyl- 115
3-2'-diethylaminoethyl- 75
2-2'-diethylaminoethylamino- 323
3-(4'-diethylamino-1'-methyl)butyl- 76
3-3'-diethylaminopropyl- 112
3-3',4'-dimethoxyphenethyl- 98
2-ethoxy- 116, 235, 236
2-ethoxycarbonyl- 476
2-ethoxycarbonylmethyl- 82
3-ethoxycarbonylmethyl- 86
2-ethoxycarbonylthio- 287
2-ethyl- 74
3-ethyl- 87
2-ethylamino- 335
6-fluoro-3-*p*-fluorophenyl- 405

2-formyl- 480
2-2'-furyl- 75, 91
2-guanidino- 325
2-hydrazino- 336
hydrolysis 110
2-4'-hydroxybutyl- 99
3-2'-hydroxyethyl- 106
2-(1'-hydroxy-2'-nitro)ethyl- 480
infrared spectra 102, 103
ionization 104
3-isobutyl- 87, 98
2-isopentyl- 81
2-isopropyl- 74, 81, 94
3-isopropyl- 87
2-methoxy- 236
5-, 6-, 7-, and 8-methoxy- 240
2-methoxycarbonyl- 477
2-*o*-methoxycarbonylphenyl- 99
3-methyl- 393, 402
6-methyl- 460
7-methyl- 74
2-methylamino- 335
2-*N*-methylanilino- 323, 327
3-(6'-methyl-3'-methylmercapto-
    1',2',4'-triazin-5'-yl)- 112
5-methylsulphonyl- 287
2-methylthio- 284
5-methylthio- 287
2-morpholino- 323
nitration 111
5-, 6-, 7-, and 8-nitro- 279
7-nitro- 236
nomenclature 69
oxidation 110
2-(1'-oxo-3'-phenylimino-2'-in-
    danyl)- 108
2-phenoxy- 236
3-phenyl 88, 92, 96, 110, 112, 339, 402
5-phenylthio- 287
physical properties 102–104
2-2'-piperidinoethyl- 115
3-propargyl- 106
2-propoxy- 236
2-propyl- 94
3-propyl- 87
2-propylamino- 335
2-pyrazolyl- derivatives 336
3-3'-pyrazolylmethyl- 497

3,4-Dihydro-4-oxoquinazoline (*mono-substituted*), *contd.*
  reaction with Grignard reagents 113
  reduction 110
  2-*o*-sulphamoylphenyl- 90
  2-sulphanilamidoethyl- 115
  sulphonation 111, 112, 480
  syntheses 74–99
  tautomerism 102
  2-thiocarbamoyl- 475
  3-thioureido- 340
  3-toluene-*p*-sulphonyl- 107
  3-*m*-tolyl- 88, 92
  3-*p*-tolyl- 88, 92, 96
  2-(3′,3′,3′-trichloro-2′-hydroxy)-propyl- 109
  2-trichloromethyl- 226
  2-3′,3′,3′-trichloropropenyl- 109
  ultraviolet spectra 103, 104
  3-ureido- 340
  3-vinyl- 96
  3-xanthhydryl- 106
3,4-Dihydro-4-oxoquinazoline (*poly-substituted*), 2,3-2′-acetoxytri-methylene- 495
  3-benzyl-2-formyl- 480
  3-benzyloxy-6-nitro- 460
  6-bromo-3-*p*-bromophenyl- 76
  6-carboxy-4-*p*-carboxyphenyl- 479
  6-chloro-3-2′-diethylaminoethyl- 76
  6-chloro-3-2′-ethylaminoethyl- 227
  7-chloro-2-2′-furyl- 91
  7-chloro-8-methoxy- 240
  2-(2′-chloro-5′-nitro)phenyl-6-nitro- 115
  6-chloro-3-phenyl- 76
  2-*p*-chlorophenyl-3-phenyl- 89
  2,3-diethyl-5-nitro- 244
  6,7-dimethoxy-2-benzyl- 240
  6,7-dimethoxy-2-3′,4′-dimethoxy-benzyl- 240
  6-ethoxycarbonyl-3-*p*-ethoxy-carbonylphenyl- 479
  2-ethoxycarbonyl-3-phenyl- 476
  2-ethyl-3-phenyl- 99
  2-fluoro-3-phenyl- 222
  6-methoxy-3-*p*-methoxyphenyl- 96

  6-methoxy-7-nitro- 240
  6-methoxy-7-phenylsulphonyl- 288
  6-methoxy-7-phenylthio- 288
  2-*N*-methylanilino-3-phenyl- 334
  6,7-methylenedioxy-2-propyl- 240
  3-methyl-2-*N*-methylcarbamoyl- 476
  2-1′-naphthyl-3-phenyl- 89
  3-phenyl-2-propyl- 79
  2,3-tetramethylene- 115, 496
  2,6,8-trimethyl- 80
  2,3-trimethylene- 493
3,4-Dihydro-4-oxoquinazolines, acetylation 104
  alkylation 104, 236
  antimalarial activity of 2,3-disubstituted derivatives 508
  chemical properties 104–116
  chlorination 112
  chlorosulphonation 111, 480
  2,3-disubstituted 79, 93
  electrolytic reduction 402
  hydrolysis 110
  infrared spectra 102, 103
  ionization 104
  reaction with Grignard reagents 113
  2-substituted 96
  3-substituted 75, 96, 110
  sulphonation 480
3,4-Dihydro-4-oxoquinazoline-1-oxide 448
  2-amino- 458
  3-benzyloxy-6-nitro- 460
  deoxygenation of 3-*p*-bromophenyl- 449
  deoxygenation of 3-phenyl- 449
  deoxygenation of 3-*o*-tolyl- 449
  3-hydroxy- 459
  3-hydroxy-6-methyl- 460
  3-methyl- 458
  methylation 458
  oxidation 457
  tautomerism 458
3,4-Dihydro-4-oxo-3-quinazolin-2′-ylquinazoline 231
3,4-Dihydro-4-oxo-3-quinazolin-4′-ylquinazoline 231

3,4-Dihydro-4-oxo-2-styrylquinazo-
    lines 107
  quaternary salts 108
  reduction of 108
3,4-Dihydro-4-oxo-3-4'-sulphamoyl-
    phenylquinazolines 86
1,2-Dihydroquinazoline, 3-allyl-
    salts 391
  4-amino-2,2-dimethyl- 393, 402
  2,2-dimethyl-4-methylthio- 281
  4-methoxy- 394
  3-methyl- salts 391
  4-phenoxy- 394
  2,3-trimethylene- picrate 392
1,2-Dihydroquinazolines 391–392,
    402–405
  ultraviolet spectra of 2-substituted-
    3-methylquinazolinium salts
    392
  use in analytical study 392
2,3-Dihydroquinazolines 395
1,4-Dihydroquinazoline 394
  basicity 403
  1-benzyl- 394
  1,2-dimethyl- 394
  1-methyl- 394
  1-methyl-2-o-nitrophenyl- 394
  1-methyl-2-phenyl- 394
  physical properties of 1-substituted
    403
  ultraviolet spectra 403
3,4-Dihydroquinazoline 295, 298
  3-aryl-4-hydroxy-4-substituted 400
  7,8-benzo-2,4-diphenyl-4-hydroxy-
    3-1'-naphthyl- 400
  2-benzyl- 400
  2-bromo-4-phenyl- 222
  3-p-bromophenyl- 402
  2-3'-bromopropyl- 493
  2-bromo-4-2',4'-xylyl- 222
  4-t-butyl- 404
  2-2'-carboxyethyl- 405
  2-o-carboxyphenyl- 405
  6-chloro-3-p-chlorophenyl- 405
  6-chloro-3-p-chlorophenyl-4-
    hydroxy-2,4-diphenyl- 400
  2-o-chlorobenzyl- 400
  2-p-chlorobenzyl- 400
  3-p-chlorophenyl- 402

2,3-dimethyl- 403
6,8-dimethyl-2,4-diphenyl-4-
    hydroxy-3-2',4'-xylyl- 400
1,6-dimethyl-3-p-tolyl- iodide 403
6-ethoxy-3-p-ethoxyphenyl- 96
4-ethoxy-2-ethylthio-3-phenyl- 274
2-ethyl- 400
4-ethyl- 399
6-fluoro-3-p-fluorophenyl- 405
2-guanidino- 396
4-hydrazono-3-phenyl- 339
4-hydroxy-2,4-diphenyl- 395
6-hydroxy-2,3-2'-hydroxytri-
    methylene- 495
4-hydroxy-3-methyl- 21, 405
2,3-2'-hydroxytrimethylene- 492
2-methoxymethyl- 400
2-p-methoxyphenyl- 400
2-methyl- 394, 400, 403
3-methyl- 282, 403, 405
4-, and 8-methyl- 399
6-methyl-2,4-diphenyl-4-hydroxy-
    3-p-tolyl- 400
4-methylimino-2-methylthio-3-
    phenyl- 336
6-methyl-2-methylthio-3-p-tolyl-
    402
2-methyl-6-nitro-3-p-nitrophenyl-
    405
6-methyl-4-phenyl- 399
6-methyl-3-p-tolyl- 396, 398
2-1'-naphthyl- 400
6-nitro-3-p-nitrophenyl- 401
2-o-nitrophenyl- 400
2-m-nitrophenyl- 400
2-phenyl- 399, 400
3-phenyl- 402
4-phenyl- 49, 399
2-propyl- 400
4-isopropyl- 399
2,3-tetramethylene- 496
2,3-trimethylene- 400
3,4-Dihydroquinazolines 395-400,
    402–405
  acetylation 404
  methylation 403
  nitrosation 404
  oxidation 41, 404
  reduction 401

3,4-Dihydroquinazolines, *contd.*
  3-substituted 41, 403–405
  4-substituted 41, 398
  ultraviolet spectra 403
5,6-Dihydroquinazolines 413
1,2-Dihydroquinazoline-3-oxide 456,
    457
  4-methyl-2-nitromethyl- 456
  2,2,4-trimethyl- 456, 457
5,6-Dihydroquinazo(4,3-b)quinazol-8-
    one 116
2,3-Dihydrothiazolo(2,3-b)quinazolin-
    5-ones 288
1,2-Dihydro-2-thioquinazoline 270
  alkylation 271
  4-amino- 327, 328
  4-amino-6-chloro- 328
  4-anilino- 335
  covalent hydration 271
  ionization 271
  1-methyl- 270
  4-methyl- 270
  4-phenyl- 222
  tautomerism 271
  ultraviolet spectra 271
  4-2′,4′-xylyl- 222
2,3-Dihydro-2-thioquinazoline,
    3-alkyl- derivatives 398
  3-aryl- derivatives 398
  3-aryl-6,7-methylenedioxy- 273
  6-bromo- derivatives 273
  mercury salts 274
  3-methyl- 270
  3-phenyl- 272
  silver salts 271
  3-substituted derivatives 271
1,4-Dihydro-4-thioquinazoline,
    1,2-diphenyl- 278
  1-ethyl- 278, 280
  1-p-fluorophenyl-2-phenyl- 278
  1-methyl- 278–280, 282, 283
3,4-Dihydro-4-thioquinazoline 277
  2-benzyl-3-methyl- 278
  3-o-(m-, and p-)-bromophenyl-2-
    methyl- 278
  6-chloro-2-methyl- 278
  3-p-chlorophenyl-2-methyl- 278
  3-2′-dibutylaminoethyl- 278
  3-2′-diethylaminoethyl- 278

3-3′-diethylaminopropyl- 278
3-2′-dipropylaminoethyl- 278
2-ethyl- 277
3-p-fluorophenyl-2-methyl- 278
2-isopropyl- 277
2-methyl- 277, 278
3-methyl- 278
2-methyl-6-nitro- 278
2-methyl-3-o-tolyl- 278
2-phenyl- 278
2-propyl- 277
tautomerism 282
3,4-Dihydro-4-thioquinazolines,
    3-amino- 339
  desulphurization 282, 400
  3-hydroxy- 458
  infrared spectra of 3-substituted
    derivatives 282
  3-methyl- 280
  oxidation 282
  2-phenyl- 279
  2-, 3-, and 2,3-substituted derivatives
    279
1,2-Dihydro-2,2,4-trimethylquinoline
    (acetone anil) 324
1,2-Dihydro-3-vinylquinazolinium
    salts, oxidation 96
2,3-Dihydroxyindole 459
4-(1′,3′-Dihydroxy-2′-methyl)propyl-
    aminoquinazoline, hydrolysis
    333
2,4-Dimethoxy-2-3′,4′-dimethoxy-
    benzylquinazoline 241
2,4-Di-2′-methoxyethoxyquinazoline
    243
2,4-Dimethoxy-5-methoxycarbonyl-
    quinazoline 131
6,7-Dimethoxy-2-methylquinazoline
    240
6,7-Dimethoxy-2-3′,4′-methylene-
    dioxybenzylquinazoline 241
6,7-Dimethoxy-2-phenylquinazoline
    240, 241
2,4-Dimethoxyquinazoline 239, 243
2,4-Dimethylaminoquinazoline 330
1-2′-Dimethylaminoethyl-1,2,3,4-
    tetrahydro-4-oxo-2-2′pyridyl-
    quinazoline, antihistamine activity
    510

7-(3'-Dimethylamino-1'-hydroxy)-
propyl-2,4-dimethylquinazoline
55
4-Dimethylamino-2-methyl-6-nitro-
quinazoline 328
2-p-Dimethylaminostyryl-1-methyl-
4-phenylquinazolinium iodide 58
4,4'-Dimethyl-2,2'-biquinazolinyl 40
2,2'-Dimethyl-4,4'-biquinazolinyl 36
2(2'-(4,5-Dimethylimidazol-2-yl)azo-
phenyl)-8-hydroxy-4,5,7-tri-
methylquinazoline, reagent for
lithium 135
2,8-Dimethyl-5,11-6H,12H-methano-
dibenzo(b,f)(1,5)diazocine 406
1,2-Dimethyl-4-phenylquinazolinium
iodide 56, 57, 114
2,4-Dimethylquinazoline 52, 55
6-acetyl- 480
7-acetyl- 53, 480
8-acetyl- 480
7-3'-dimethylaminopropionyl- 53
8-methoxy- 241
ultraviolet spectrum 20
2,6-Dimethylquinazoline 42, 54
oxidation 54
nitration 55
4,5-Dimethylquinazolines 40
1,4-Dimethylquinazolinium iodide
56, 58
2,4-Dimethylthioquinazoline 283,
284, 328, 331
Dimroth rearrangement 335
2,4-Diphenoxyquinazoline 239
4-Diphenylamino-2-phenylquinazoline
330
4,4'-Diphenyl-2,2'-biquinazolinyl 40
2,4-Diphenylquinazoline 43
5,6-benzo- 43
6-chloro- 44
5,7-dimethyl- 44
6,8-dimethyl- 41
6-methyl- 41, 44
6-nitro- 400
2,4-Dithioquinazolines 284
alkylation of 3-substituted-1,2,3,4-
tetrahydro- 285
3-aryl-1,2,3,4-tetrahydro- 284
nomenclature 270

3-phenyl-1,2,3,4-tetrahydro- 284
1,2,3,4-tetrahydro- 284

4-(Estra-1',3',5'-trien-17'-on-3'-yl)-
oxyquinazoline 244
2-Ethoxycarbonyl-3,1,4-benzoxazone
476
4-Ethoxyquinazoline 230
2-anilino- 243
2-ethyl-5-nitro- 105, 243
2-methoxy- 239
2-methyl- 243
2-methyl-5-nitro- 105
7-nitro- 236
2-phenoxy- 239
2-trichloromethyl- 237
4-Ethylamino-2-methyl-6-nitroquina-
zoline 328
1-Ethyl-4-(3'(1-ethyl-1,4-dihydro-
quinazolin-4-ylidene)prop-1'-
enyl)quinazolinium iodide 58
2-Ethyl-6-methylquinazoline 42
1-Ethyl-4-methylthioquinazolinium
iodide 280
1-Ethyl-4-methylquinazolinium
toluene-p-sulphonate 58
Ethyl 3,4,5,6-tetrahydroanthranilate
411
1-Ethyl-1,2,3,5-tetrahydro-5-oxo-
imidazo(2,1-b)quinazoline 244
4-Ethylthio-1-methylquinazolinium
iodide 280
7-Ethylthioquinazoline 227
Evodiamine 500, 501
hydrate 500

Febrifugine 496
antimalarial activity 500
d-isomer 499
d,l-isomer 497, 498
d,l-pseudo-isomer 498
5-, 6-, and 7-Fluoroquinazoline 237
metathesis 227
2-2'-Furyl-4-phenoxyquinazolines 237

Grimmel, Guenther, and Morgan's synthesis 93-94, 338
Guanidinoquinazolines, antibacterial
activity 512

2-Guanidinoquinazolines   324
2-Guanidino-4,6,7-trimethylquinazo-
   line hydrochlorides   325
Glycorine   491
Glycosmicine   491
Glycosmine   492
Glycosminine   491, 492

Halogenoquinazolines   219, 222, 226,
   227
   benz-substituted   226
1,2,3,4,5,6-Hexahydrobenzo(b)(1,5)-
   diazocine   407
1,4,5,6,7,8-Hexahydro-1,2-diphenyl-4-
   thioquinazoline   412
3,4,5,6,7,8-Hexahydro-4-oxoquinazo-
   lines, 2-substituted   410
3,4,5,6,7,8-Hexahydroquinazolines
   413
Hofmann rearrangement   123
Hortiacine   502
Hortiamine   503
   hydrochloride   502
Houben-Hoesch synthesis   43
4-Hydrazinoquinazoline   330, 455
   4-N'-benzoyl-   336, 337
   4-N'-toluene-p-sulphonyl-   336
Hydroxyevodiamine   502
Hydroxyquinazolines   133–134
   ionization   135
   Mannich reactions   135
   metal complexes   134
5-Hydroxyquinazoline   133
   6,8-dimethyl-   133
   6,8-dimethyl-2-phenyl-   134
   2,4,6,8-tetramethyl-   134
   2,6,8-trimethyl-   134
8-Hydroxyquinazoline   133
   alkylation   135
   7-allyl-   134
   2,4-dimethyl-   133
   4-methyl-   133
   4-methyl-2-phenyl-   133
   4-propyl-   133
   4,5,7-trimethyl-2-o-nitrobenzamido-
      133, 135
4-Hydroxyquinazoline-1,3-dioxide
   459, 460
   tautomers   459

2-o-Hydroxystyryl-1-methyl-4-
   phenylquinazolinium iodide   58
Hydroxyvasicine   495

β-Iminoisatins, oxidation to 3-substi-
   tuted-1,2,3,4-tetrahydro-2,4-
   dioxoquinazolines   125
2-β-Indol-3'-ylethenyl-1-methyl-4-
   phenylquinazolinium iodide   58
Isatoic anhydrides   87
Isofebrifugine   496, 499
Isohortiamine   503

Legal's colour reaction   13
Lossen rearrangement   123

Mannich reactions   52, 114, 480
Methaqualone 2-^{14}C   509
6-Methoxy-4,7-diphenylthioquinazo-
   line   288
2-Methoxyquinazoline   236
4-Methoxyquinazoline   104, 327, 451
   7,8-benzo-2-methyl-   238
   hydrochloride   229
   2-methylthio-   284
   2-phenoxy-   239
   2-trichloromethyl-   237
   ultraviolet spectrum   103
8-Methoxyquinazoline   240, 242
   2-benzyl-   240
   2-p-bromophenyl-   240
   2-o-chlorophenyl-   240
   2-2',4'-dichlorophenyl-   240
   2-methyl-   240
   4-methyl-   241
   4-methyl-2-phenyl-   241
   2-phenyl-   240
   2-propyl-   240
   4-propyl-   241
   2-p-tolyl-   240
5-Methoxy-4-nitroanthranilic acid
   240
6-Methoxy-7-nitroquinazoline   240
4-Methylamino-2-methyl-6-nitro-
   quinazoline   328
6-Methyl-2,4-di-p-toluidinoquinazoline
   331
7-Methyl-2,4-di-m-toluidinoquinazo-
   line   331

8-Methyl-2,4-di-*o*-toluidinoquinazoline 331

O-Methyl-*O'*,*O''*-isopropylidenetetrodo-
toxin hydrochloride hydrate   507

1-Methyl-4-(1'-methylbenzothia-
zolidin-2'-ylidenemethyl)quina-
zolinium toluene-*p*-sulphonate   56

1-Methyl-4-methylthioquinazolinium
iodide   56, 279, 280
hydrolysis of   283

2-Methyl-4-phenoxyquinazolines   238

6-Methyl-2-phenylquinazoline   42
oxidation of   54

2-Methylquinazoline   39, 42, 48, 49
oxidation   54
ultraviolet spectrum   20

4-Methylquinazoline   40, 42, 46
5,6-benzo- *hydrochloride*   325
covalent hydration   27, 28
2-carbamoyl-   42
2-cyanamino-   324
2-dimethylamino-   322
2-Methyl-   55
2-methylamino-   322
2-phenyl-   53
2-(1',2',3',4'-tetrahydro-6'-methoxy-
1'-quinolyl)-   324
ultraviolet spectra   20

2-Methyl-4-tribromomethylquinazo-
line   54

3-Methyl-5*H*-thiazolo(2,3-b)quinazo-
line   290

6,7-Methylenedioxyquinazoline   241
methylation   242

6,7-Methylenedioxy-2-3',4'-methylene-
dioxybenzylquinazoline   241

6,7-Methylenedioxy-2-3',4'-methylene-
dioxyphenylquinazoline   241

6-Methylquinazo(4,3-b)quinazol-8-one
116

2-Methylthioquinazoline   271
ionization   271
4-methyl-   271

4-Methylthio-2-phenylquinazoline 281

4-Methylthioquinazoline   280

4-Methylthio-2-trichloromethyl-
quinazoline   281

1-Morpholinocyclohex-1-ene   411

3-(6'-Morpholino-2'-oxo)hexyl-3,4-
dihydro-4-oxoquinazoline, antimalarial activity   508

4-Morpholinoquinazoline   428
hydrolysis   333

1-Morpholino-2-thiocarbamoylcyclo-
hex-1-ene   411

Naphthyridine   233

Neimentowski's synthesis   74, 240,
479, 480
mechanism   76–77

6-Nitro-4-anilino-1-methylquinazo-
linium toluene-*p*-sulphonate   334

7-Nitro-4-anilino-1-methylquinazo-
linium toluene-*p*-sulphonate   334

4-Nitroisoquinoline   27

7-Nitro-4-pentyloxyquinazoline   236

6-Nitro-4-phenoxyquinazoline,
hydrolysis   242

7-Nitro-4-phenoxyquinazoline,
hydrolysis   242

Nortetrodoic acid   507

1,2,3,4,5,6,7,8-Octhydro-2-oxoquina-
zoline, 3-benzyl-   413
4-*o*-chlorophenyl-   413

1,2,3,4,5,6,7,8-Octahydro-2,4-dioxo-
quinazoline   391

1,2,3,4,5,6,7,8-Octahydro-2,4-dithio-
quinazoline, 1,3-di-*p*-methoxy-
phenyl-   409
1,3-diphenyl-   409
1,3-di-*m*-tolyl-   409
1,3-di-*p*-tolyl-   409

1,2,3,4,5,6,7,8-Octahydro-2-oxo-4-
thioquinazolines, 1,3-substituted
411

1,2,3,4,5,6,7,8-Octahydro-4-oxo-2-
thioquinazoline, 3-*o*-chlorophenyl-
411
3-*p*-methoxyphenyl-   411
3-phenyl-   411
3-*p*-tolyl-   411

7-Oxobenzo(d)quinazo(3,2-b)thiazole
5,5-dioxide   90

Oxoquinazolines, antibacterial
activity   512
antiviral activity   512
incorporation in vitamin B_{12} 513

Palladium-charcoal catalyst, prepara-
    tion 232
Phenmiazine 2
4-Phenoxyquinazoline 45
    hydrolysis 242
    reduction 393
4-Phenoxyquinazolines 237
2-Phenyl-4-2'-phenyliminophenethyl-
    quinazoline 54
4-Phenylquinazoline 39–42, 45, 234
    2-acetoxymethyl-6-chloro- 450
    2-acetylcarbamoyl-6-chloro- 476
    2-carboxy- 54
    2-carboxy-6-chloro- 476, 477
    6-chloro-2-dimethylamino- 455
    6-chloro-2-ethoxycarbonyl- 476
    6-chloro-2-formyl- 480
    6-chloro-2-methyliminomethyl-
        449
    2-hydrazino- 322
2-(δ-4'-Phenylquinazolin-2'-yl)buta-
    dienyl-4-phenylquinazoline
    1,1'-bismethiodide 58
4-Phenylthioquinazoline, reduction
    394
3-Phenyl-1,2,4-triazolo(4,5-c)quin-
    azoline 337
2-Phenyl-4-trichloromethylquinazo-
    line 226
    hydrolysis 59
    reduction 49
Perhydro-2,4-dioxoquinazoline, trans
    3-benzoyloxy- 414
    trans 3-hydroxy- 414
    11-hydroxy- 414
    trans 3-phenylsulphonyloxy- 414
Phthalazine 233
Phosphorus pentasulphide, purification
    of 278
3-(7'-Piperidino-2'-oxo)heptyl-3,4-
    dihydro-4-oxoquinazoline, anti-
    malarial activity 508
4-Piperidinoquinazoline, hydrolysis
    333
2-Pyrimidin-2'-ylquinazolines 324

Quinazoline 11–36
    2-acetamido- 334
    4-acetonylmethyl- 47

4-acetoxy- 106
    addition reactions 35
    alkylation 35
    basic centre in 35
    4-1'-benzoylethyl- 47
    4-(1'-benzoyloxy-1'-methyl)ethyl-
        449
    2-benzyl- 54
    4-benzyl- 44, 45
    4-butan-2'-onyl- 47
    4-butoxy- 243
    4-(1'-carbamoyl-1'-methyl)ethyl-
        449, 474
    4-4'-carboxybutyl- 47
    2-2'-carboxyethenyl- 51
    4-5'-carboxypentyl- 47
    catalytic reduction 402
    charge densities 14
    chemical shifts and coupling con-
        stants 18
    covalent hydration 19–32
    2-α-cyanobenzyl- 46
    2-(α-cyano-α-ethoxycarbonyl)-
        methyl- 46
    4-(α-cyano-α-ethoxycarbonyl)-
        methyl- 46
    2-cyanomethyl- 58
    4-cyano- 328, 455
    4-cyclohexan-2'-onyl- 47
    4-cyclopentan-2'-onyl- 47
    4-(α,α-diethoxycarbonyl)methyl-
        45, 46, 59
    4-(α,α-diethoxycarbonyl)propyl- 46
    4-3'-diethylaminopropyl- 283
    2-ethoxalylmethyl- 54, 58
    4-ethoxycarbonylmethyl- 46
    2-ethoxy- 243
    4-ethyl- 45, 47
    4-(2'-hydroxy-2'-p-nitrophenyl)-
        ethyl- 52
    hydrolysis 33
    5-, 6-, 7-, and 8-hydroxy- 133
    infrared spectra 15
    ionization constants 23
    ionization potential 14
    2-isopropoxy- 243
    2-isopropyl- 54
    4-isopropyl- 44, 45, 47
    mass spectrum 18

Quinazoline, *contd.*
  7-methoxy- 241
  4-(3'-methylbutan-2'-onyl)- 47
  5-, 6-, and 8-methyl- 42
  7-methyl- 42, 47
  nitration 34
  4-nitromethyl- 46
  4-*p*-nitrostyryl- 51
  oxidation of 33
  4-pentyloxy- 243
  2-phenoxy- 236, 323
  2-phenyl- 42, 49
  4-phenyl- 39, 40, 41, 42, 45, 234
  phosphorescence, phosphorescence-
      polarization, and absorption-
      polarization spectra of 15
  physical properties 13–33
  polarography 32
  4-1'-propionylethyl- 47
  2-propyl- 54
  4-propyl- 46
  proton magnetic resonance spectra
      16, 22, 23
  4-2'-pyridyl- 48, 231
  reactions of 33–36
  reduction of 34
  4-sulpho- 455
  synthesis of 11–13
  2-(3',3',3'-trichloro-2'-hydroxy)-
      propyl- 51
  ultraviolet spectra 14, 19, 21
Quinazolines, biological activity 9,
    508–513
  cyanine dyes 58
  dual character of 3–4
  infrared spectra 15–16
  oxidation 8
  primary syntheses 4–6
  polarography 32–33
  reactions of 6-7
  reduction of 8
  rearrangements in 8
  secondary syntheses 6
  tautomerism 7–8
Quinazoline-1-oxide 446
  4-alkoxy- 447
  4-benzyloxy- 446, 448
  2-chloromethyl-6-chloro-4-phenyl-
      447, 449

  2,4-dihydroxy- 446
  4-ethoxy- 446
  4-hydrazino- 449
  4-hydroxy- 446
  4-isopropyl- 447–449
  4-isopropyl-2-phenyl- 449
  4-methoxy- 446, 448, 449
  4-methoxy-2-phenyl- 449
  2-methyl-6-chloro-4-phenyl- 447
  4-phenoxy- 446
  4-propoxy- 446
Quinazoline-3-oxide 446, 451
  4-amino- 451
  4-aryl-2-chloromethyl- 452
  basicity 453
  7-chloro- 452
  6-chloro-2-chloromethyl-4-phenyl-
      2-^{14}C 452, 455
  6-chloro-2-methyl-4-phenyl- 450
  2-chloromethyl-4-phenyl- 456
  covalent hydration 452
  2,4-dihydroxy- 446
  4,7-dimethyl- 452
  6,8-dimethyl-2-methylaminomethyl-
      4-phenyl- 456
  4-hydroxy- 446
  5-, 6-, 7-, and 8-methoxy- 452
  7-methoxy-4-methyl- 452
  8-methoxy-4-methyl- 452
  7-methyl- 452
  oxidation 453
  proton magnetic resonance spectrum
      453, 454
  structure of hydrated cation 453
Quinazoline-3-oxides 450, 455
  covalent hydration in 454
  fluorescence spectra 452
  infrared spectra 452
  ionization constants 454
  ultraviolet spectra 452
2-Quinazolin-2'-ylcarbonylcarbamoyl-
    quinoxaline 474
2,4-Quinazolinyl diethers 239
  thermal rearrangement 244
  transalkylation 239
Quinazolinyl ethers 241
  metathesis 243
  rearrangements in 243
  transalkylation 243

2-Quinazolinyl ethers 235
  hydrolysis 242
4-Quinazolinyl ethers 236
  hydrolysis 242
  thermal rearrangement 244

Reduced quinazolines 391
  ionization constants 404
Reidel's synthesis 48, 133, 226, 241
Reissert reaction 448, 449, 455
Ring-chain tautomerism 22, 35
Rhetsine 501
Rhetsinine 502
Rutaecarpine 500, 501

Seconortetrodioic acid 507
Sen and Ray's synthesis 94–95, 240
Spheroidin 503

Tables, use of 9–10
Tarichatoxin 503
2,4,6,8-Tetrachloroquinazoline 226
2,3,4,5-Tetrahydro-1H-benzo(e)(1,4)-
  diazepine 408
5,6,11,12-Tetrahydro-2,8-dimethyl-
  5,11-endomethylenephenhomia-
  zine 406
5,6,11,12-Tetrahydro-2,8-dimethyl-
  phenhomiazine 406
1,2,3,4-Tetrahydro-2,4-dioxoquinazo-
  line 491
  6-acetoxy- 460
  alkylation 130
  3-amino- 338–340
  3-amino-1-methyl- 339
  5-, 6-, 7-, and 8-amino- 340, 341
  6,7-benzo- 119
  7,8-benzo-3-1'-naphthyl- 126
  3-benzoyl- 119
  1-benzyl- 119
  3-benzyl- 122
  3-benzyloxy- 459
  3-benzyloxy-6-nitro- 460
  6-bromo- 119, 120
  3-m-bromophenyl- 119
  3-butyl- 122
  3-t-butyl- 122
  7-t-butyl- 119
  1-carbamoylmethyl- 119

  5-carboxy- 120, 131, 479
  7-carboxy- 479
  8-carboxy- 119, 479
  3-o-carboxyphenyl- 118–121
  1- and 3-chloro- 133
  6-chloro- 460
  7-chloro- 120
  5-chlorocarbonyl- 479
  6-chloro-3-p-chlorophenyl- 126
  7-chloro-3-m-chlorophenyl- 126
  8-chloro-3-o-chlorophenyl- 126
  6-chloro-3-phenyl- 128
  3-cyclohexyl- 122
  6,8-dibromo- 119, 121, 132
  6,8-dibromo-3-ethyl- 122
  1,3-dichloro- 133
  6,8-dichloro- 119, 125, 226
  6,8-dichloro-3-ethyl- 122
  5,8-dichloro-3-2′,5′-dichlorophenyl-
    126
  1,3-bis-2′-diethylaminoethyl- 244
  6,8-diiodo- 119
  6,8-diiodo-3-ethyl- 122
  6,7-dimethoxy- 120
  1,3-dimethyl- 120, 128
  6-dimethylamino- 341
  6,8-dimethyl-3-2′,4′-xylyl- 126
  6,8-dinitro- 132
  1-ethyl- 120
  3-ethyl- 122
  hydrolysis of 130
  1-hydroxy- 457
  3-hydroxy- 459
  6-hydroxy- 120, 226, 459
  7-hydroxy- 120
  1-hydroxy-2-o-hydroxyphenyl- 458
  3-o-hydroxyphenyl- 128
  3-isopropyl- 122
  5-, 6-, 7-, and 8-methoxy- 120
  5-methoxycarbonyl- 131
  5-methoxycarbonyl-1,3-dimethyl-
    131
  1-methyl- 119, 120, 491
  3-methyl- 117, 118, 120, 122, 225,
    287
  6-methyl- 119
  7-methyl- 119, 120, 122, 132, 133,
    479
  8-methyl- 120

1,2,3,4-Tetrahydro-2,4-dioxoquinazo-
line, *contd.*
1-methyl-3-phenyl- 121, 128
1-methyl-3-*p*-tolyl- 121
6-methyl-3-*p*-tolyl- 126
7-methyl-3-*m*-tolyl- 126
8-methyl-3-*o*-tolyl- 126
nitration 132
6-nitro- 120, 132, 284
7-nitro- 119, 120, 128
8-nitro- 119, 132
1-phenyl- 119, 127
3-phenyl- 119, 121, 123, 125, 126
3-phenylsulphonamido- 339
3-phenylsulphonyloxy- 459
3-propyl- 122
3-2'-pyridylcarbonylamino- 339
3-3'-pyridylcarbonylamino- 339
3-*p*-sulphamoylphenyl- 121
tautomerism 129
3-toluene-*p*-sulphonyloxy- 459
3-*p*-tolyl- 119, 121
7-trifluoromethyl- 119
1-2',4',6'-trinitrophenyl- 119
1,2,3,4-Tetrahydro-2,4-dioxoquinazo-
lines, 3-amino- 338
3-aryl- 126, 127
colour reaction of nitro- 129
complexes with phenols 129
hydrolysis 130
infrared spectra 130
ionization 129
mass spectra 130
physical properties 128–130
salts of halogeno- 129
synthesis of 116–128
sulpho- 480
1,2,3,4-Tetrahydro-2,4-dithioquinazo-
line 284
6-amino- 283, 284
6-chloro- 283, 328
goitrogenic activity 513
1,2,3,4-Tetrahydro-4-hydroxy-2-
hydroxyiminoquinazolines, 3-
substituted derivatives 274
1,2,3,4-Tetrahydro-4-imino-3-phenyl-
2-thioquinazoline 328
hydrolysis 286
rearrangement 328, 335

1,2,3,4,-Tetrahydro-3-methyl-4-
methylene-2-thioquinazoline 277
1,2,3,4-Tetrahydro-2-oxoquinazoline
396
3-allyl-4-carboxy-4-hydroxy- 289
3-allyl-4-hydroxy- 289
3-aryl-4-carboxy-4-hydroxy- 478
4-carboxy-4-hydroxy-3-phenyl-
274
6-chloro-3-methyl-4-phenyl- 73
1,6-dimethyl- 396
4-ethoxy-derivatives 398
oxidation of 127
1,2,3,4-Tetrahydro-4-oxoquinazoline
392, 393
2-*o*-aminophenyl- 394
6,7-benzo- 393
3-benzoylamino-2-methyl- 392
2-benzyl-1-methyl- 490, 491
1,3-dihydroxymethyl- 392
2,2-dimethyl- 403
3-methyl- 391, 393
1-methyl-3-phenyl- 394
1-methyl-3-phenyl-2-phenylimino-
334
2,3-tetramethylene- 496
1,2,3,4-Tetrahydro-4-oxoquinazolines,
antihistamine activity 510
oxidation of 2- and 3-substituted-
96
2-substituted sulpho- 480
ultraviolet spectra 403
1,2,3,4-Tetrahydro-4-oxo-2-thio-
quinazoline 284, 285
1-allyl- 285, 287
3-allyl- 289
1-β-chloroallyl- 291
1-chlorophenacyl- 291
goitrogenic activity 513
1-2'-hydroxyethyl- 285
3-2'-hydroxyethyl- 286, 290
1-methyl-3-phenyl- 394
1-phenacyl- 285, 291
3-phenyl- 286, 287
3-*p*-tolyl- 287
1,2,3,4-Tetrahydro-4-oxo-2-thio-
quinazolines 285
alkylation 286
3-alkyl- 285

1,2,3,4-Tetrahydro-4-oxo-2-thio-
    quinazolines, *contd.*
3-aryl-   285, 286
chlorination   287
desulphurization of 3-substituted
    287
oxidation   287
1,2,3,4-Tetrahydroquinazoline   400
6-bromo-3-*p*-bromophenyl-1-
    hydroxymethyl-   410
6-chloro-3-*p*-chlorophenyl-1-
    hydroxymethyl-   410
1,3-dimethylene-   408
1,3-dimethylene-3-phenyl-   408
6-ethoxy-3-*p*-ethoxyphenyl-   405
2-hydroxy-2-methyl-6-nitro-3-*p*-
    nitrophenyl-   405
2-hydroxy-6-nitro-3-*p*-nitrophenyl-
    401
4-hydroxy-3-phenyl-   402
1-hydroxymethyl-3-phenyl-   407
ionization   405
6-methoxy-3-*p*-methoxyphenyl-
    405
1- and 3- methyl-   402
6-methyl-3-*p*-tolyl-   396, 398, 401,
    405, 406
2-methyl-1,3-trimethylene-   408
oxidation   405
3-phenyl-   96, 402
2-phenyl-1,3-trimethylene-   408
picrates   405
properties   402–405
salts   405
2-substituted 1,6-dimethyl-3-*p*-
    tolyl-   403
2,3-tetramethylene-   496
1,3-trimethylene-   408
ultraviolet spectrum   408
5,6,7,8-Tetrahydroquinazolines   410,
    411
2-amino-   411
dehydrogenation   412
2,4-diamino-   410, 411
4-ethoxycarbonyl-   411
infrared spectra   412
2-methyl-   49, 411
4-methyl-   410
2-phenyl-   49, 410

polarography   412
preparation   409
properties   412
2-substituted   410
ultraviolet spectra   412
1,2,3,4-Tetrahydro-2-thioquinazoline,
    3-allyl-   276
3-allyl-4-carboxy-4-hydroxy-   273
3-allyl-4-hydroxy-4-phenyl-   273
3-benzyl-   276
1-benzyl-3-phenyl-   276
3-*t*-butyl-   276
4-carboxy-4-hydroxy-3-phenyl-
    272
4-carboxy-4-hydroxy-3-*o*-tolyl-
    273
3-cyclohexyl-   276
6-chloro-3-methyl-4-phenyl-   276
4-ethoxy- derivatives   398
4-ethoxy-6,7-methylenedioxy-3-
    phenyl-   274
4-ethoxy-3-phenyl-   272
3-ethyl-   276
4-hydroxy-3-1′-naphthyl-4-phenyl-
    273
4-hydroxy-3-2′-naphthyl-4-phenyl-
    273
4-hydroxy-3-phenyl-   272
3-isobutyl-   276
3-isopropyl-   276
mercury salts   274
3-methyl-   276
3-methyl-4-hydroxy-4-phenyl-   273
6-methyl-3-phenyl-   276
6-methyl-4-phenyl-   276
6-methyl-3-*o*-tolyl-   276
6-methyl-3-*p*-tolyl-   276
3-1′-naphthyl-   276
3-2′-naphthyl-   276
3- and 4-phenyl-   276
3-propyl-   276
silver salts   274
3-*o*-tolyl-   276
3-*p*-tolyl-   276
4-2′,4′-xylyl-   276
1,2,3,4-Tetrahydro-2-thioquinazolines,
    3-aryl-4-carboxy-4-hydroxy-   478
bromination   277
methylation   277

1,2,3,4-Tetrahydro-2-thioquinazolines,
  contd.
  physical properties 277
  reduction 277
  thermochromic change in 3-aryl-4-
    alkoxy(or hydroxy)- 273
1,2,3,4-Tetrahydro-4-thioquinazolines
    281
  2,2-dimethyl- 281, 393, 402
  2-methyl- 281
5,6-Tetramethylene-2-phenyl-4-thio-
    (1,3)oxazines 411
Tetrazolo(4,5-a)quinazolin-5-one 327
Tetrodoic acid hydrobromide 507
Tetrodonic acid 507
Tetrodotoxin 503
  acetylation 505
  hemilactal system 508
3H-1,3-Thiazino(3,2-a)quinazolin-6-
    ones 292
Thiazoloquinazolines 288
11H-Thiazolo(3,2-c)quinazolines 288
  2,3-dihydro- 292
Thiazolo(2,3-b)quinazolin-5-ones 288,
    290
  2-alkyl- 288
  bromination of 3-phenyl- 290
  2,3-dihydro- 290, 291
  nitration of 3-phenyl- 290
Thiazolo(3,2-a)quinazolin-5-ones 288,
    291
  2-p-chlorophenyl- 291
  2,3-dihydro- 291
  2-phenyl- 291
9,10-Thiopegen-10,4-one 288
10,11-Thiopegen-9,4-one 288
4,11-Thiopegene 288
2-Thioquinazolines, nomenclature
    270

physical properties 274
  tautomerism 271
4-Thioquinazolines 282
  infrared spectra 282
  ionization constants 282
  nomenclature 270
  tautomerism 282
Thiosemicarbazidoquinazolines, hydro-
    lytic cleavage of 337
4-N'-Toluene-p-sulphonylhydrazino-
    quinazoline hydrochlorides for use
    in general synthesis 235
  for use in synthesis of alkylquinazo-
    lines 42
  mechanism of alkaline decomposi-
    tion 11
Triazanaphthalene 233
2,4,6-Trichloroquinazoline 226, 460
Tricycloquinazoline, carcinogenic
    activity 512
Trifluoromethylquinazolines 42, 235
2-, and 4-Trihalogenoquinazolines
    227
2,2,4-Triphenyl-3,1,4(H)-benzoxazine
    114
Tröger's base 396, 406
  alkylation 407
  ionization 407
  nomenclature 406
  optical resolution 407
  racemization 407
  reactions 406
  stereochemistry 407
  ultraviolet spectrum 407

Vasicine 492–495
Vasicinone 495
Vat dyes, from sulphamoyl derivatives
  of 2,4-dichloroquinazolines 481